I, Amber Brown

Paula Danziger

I, AMBER BROWN

Illustrated by Tony Ross

PUFFIN BOOKS

PUFFIN BOOKS
Published by the Penguin Group
Penguin Young Readers Group, 345 Hudson Street, New York, New York 10014, U.S.A.
Penguin Group (Canada), 90 Eglinton Avenue East, Suite 700, Toronto, Ontario, Canada M4P 2Y3
(a division of Pearson Penguin Canada Inc.)
Penguin Books Ltd, 80 Strand, London WC2R 0RL, England
Penguin Ireland, 25 St Stephen's Green, Dublin 2, Ireland (a division of Penguin Books Ltd)
Penguin Group (Australia), 250 Camberwell Road, Camberwell, Victoria 3124, Australia
(a division of Pearson Australia Group Pty Ltd)
Penguin Books India Pvt Ltd, 11 Community Centre,
Panchsheel Park, New Delhi - 110 017, India
Penguin Group (NZ), 67 Apollo Drive, Rosedale, North Shore 0632, New Zealand
(a division of Pearson New Zealand Ltd)
Penguin Books (South Africa) (Pty) Ltd, 24 Sturdee Avenue,
Rosebank, Johannesburg 2196, South Africa
Registered Offices: Penguin Books Ltd, 80 Strand, London WC2R 0RL, England
First published in the United States of America by G. P. Putnam's Sons,
a division of Penguin Young Readers Group, 1997
Published by Puffin Books, a division of Penguin Young Readers Group, 2009

1 3 5 7 9 10 8 6 4 2

THE LIBRARY OF CONGRESS HAS CATALOGED THE
G. P. PUTNAM'S SONS EDITION AS FOLLOWS:
Danziger, Paula, dates.
I, Amber Brown / by Paula Danziger,
Illustrated by Tony Ross.
p. cm.
Summary: Because her divorced parents share joint
custody of her, nine-year-old Amber suffers from lack of self-esteem and feels
that she is a piece of jointly-owned property.

ISBN: 978-0-399-23180-3 (hc)
Special Markets ISBN 978-0-14-241891-8
[1. Self-esteem —Fiction. 2. Divorce—Fiction 3. Parent and Child—Fiction]
I. Ross, Tony, ill. II. Title. PZ7.D2394Iaam 1999
[Fic]—dc21 98-52884 CIP AC ISBN 0399231803

Printed in the United States of America

Chapter One

. . . Only fourteen more days until Christmas.

. . . Only twelve more days until Christmas vacation.

. . . Only a few more minutes before I, Amber Brown, collapse from shopping exhaustion.

I, Amber Brown, am too pooped to pop.

"Too pooped to pop" is what I, Amber Brown, say when I am absolutely exhausted.

And I am totally exhausted . . . . but not quite ready to quit because I have to find a few more presents.

I, Amber Brown, am not only running out of energy . . . . . I am running out of money.

It's a good thing that I will be making some of my presents, but there is still one more that I need to find and buy.

"Amber, this bookstore, as much as I love bookstores, has got to be the last place we go today. I am shopped out. I am wiped out. I am just not used to this," Max, my mom's fiancé and my future stepdad, says.

I can tell that he is also too pooped to pop.

I smile at him. "Christmas shopping is *almost* done."

". . . . . And your Hanukkah shopping too." Max grins back.

I, Amber Brown, am used to Christmas shopping . . . now with Max in our lives, I'm going to be getting used to Hanukkah shopping too.

Hanukkah . . . that really added to my list

. . . eight days of giving presents to Max . . . . and he's going to give me eight days of presents too.

I, Amber Brown, could get used to this . . . . *will* get used to this because Max and Mom have decided that we will celebrate all of our holidays . . . . actually, I say celebrate . . . they say honor . . . . either way it's a good deal, the way I see it.

Max's presents are already hidden in my closet. I got those when I went out shopping with Mom the other day.

Now I've been getting presents for my mom and for some other people.

I got Christmas presents for my mom . . . and some Hanukkah ones too.

Max is going to bring a menorah over to our house . . . and every night that he's visiting and it's Hanukkah, we're going to light the candles.

"Ouch," Max says, as he drops a package on his foot. "Now my feet are really aching."

"You only dropped it on one foot so stop complaining," I tease him. "Anyway, it's not like it's bowling balls. It's the soccer ball for Justin and the basketball for his little brother, Danny."

"It's going to be fun to wrap those presents." Max laughs.

"Garbage bags," I say. "Medium-sized green garbage bags tied with red ribbon and giant red bows . . . that's how I'm going to do it. They're boys . . . and boys don't care about how a present is wrapped. I could wrap it in toilet paper, and they wouldn't care."

Max makes a face. "Well, that's a generalization if I ever heard one. If I said something like that about girls . . . . you and your mom would nail me."

I bite my lip. "Ooops, sorry, Max. . . . . I guess I better ask you something. Does this mean that you care about how your presents are wrapped . . . . because if you do, this means I'm going to have to take the toilet paper off them and wrap them up again."

There's a funny look on his face like he's not sure what to say.

I decide to take him out of his misery and tell him the truth.

After all, I've almost shopped him to death, he's got a damaged foot, and he's not used to holiday shopping with a fourth-grade girl.

So I say, "It's a joke, Max. . . . I wrapped your presents normally."

Max smiles. "Amber, I would love the presents wrapped any way because they came from you."

"I was just joking though. I'm just a jokester sometimes," I say, and then look over at a special table that says GIFTS FOR YOUR TEACHER.

Max pretends to frown about my being a jokester.

Over the loud speaker is the sound of Christmas music.

It's "Santa Claus Is Coming to Town."

I start to sing. . . . "You better watch out. . . . You better not pout. . . . Santa Claus is coming to town."

Max joins in and sings along with me.

He actually sings in tune.

Some people are looking at us and smiling.

Some are laughing.

Some join in.

After the song is finished, Max grins at me. "You know, Amber . . . I think that this is going to be the best holiday of my life . . . . spending time with you and Sarah."

I grin back. Now that I'm getting used to the fact that Mom and Max are going to get married, and that my Mom and Dad aren't going to get back together again, I grin at Max a lot.

It's like he's been a part of my life for a long time, not just since I got back from visiting England last summer with my Aunt

Pam . . . the trip when I didn't get to go to Paris to see my dad because I got the chicken pox.

Then I think about my dad. I remember Christmases from when he and my mom were still married. Some of them were happy.

I'm glad that this is going to be the best Christmas of Max's life . . . . for me, it's going to be a little weird. With Dad just back from living in Paris, I'm worried that there are going to be some problems for me, just like there were at Thanksgiving. I know the deal is that I spend Christmas with my mom, but I also know that I'm going to be able to spend some time over the rest of the vacation with my dad. But since my dad doesn't have his own place yet, I'll be able to live at home and just visit with Dad . . . . unless he takes me into New York City like he did at Thanksgiving.

I, Amber Brown, am going to have to get used to all of this. Even though my parents haven't lived together for a long time, this is just the beginning of their joint custody deal . . . . and sometimes the stuff that's happening does not make me happy.

Max repeats, "This will be the best holiday of my life. . . . . And I want it to be very special for you too. . . . Our first Hanukkah-Christmas together."

I say, "Thanks," and then I look over at the table.

There are a gazillion books there . . . and teacher mugs . . . and stationery . . . and bookmarks. . . . . And then I see it . . . the perfect, perfect book for Mrs. Holt. It's a guide to the twelve months of the year . . . holidays, special occasions, fun class projects.

I, Amber Brown, love this book, and I just know that Mrs. Holt is going to LOVE this book too.

"I hope that no one else gives this to her," I say to Max. "And I hope that she loans it to me."

Max puts down all of his packages and looks at the book with me. "This is a great choice . . . . there are activities . . . and recipes. This is terrific."

I hug the book to me. "I just love facts like this."

"Would you like a copy of this book for yourself?" Max asks.

"Even though I'm not a teacher? Oh yes, it's so much fun. And each day we see each other, I'll tell you the fact of the day."

"Then I'll get it for you," Max says.

"Thank you. Thank you. Thank you." I smile at him again. "Is this going to be for a Christmas present or for a Hanukkah present? Because Hanukkah is sooner."

"It's for today . . . . December 11," he says.

I look in the book. "On December 11, 1918, the first U.S. monument to an insect was dedicated in Alabama. It was to the boll weevil."

"Well," Max says, "that's definitely a day to celebrate."

When I, Amber Brown, get home, I'm going to immediately write to Justin, who moved to Alabama . . . and tell him this fact. It will definitely drive him buggy.

Justin Daniels. . . . This is going to be the first Christmas that he and I aren't going to spend part of the day together.

This holiday is definitely going to be a time of firsts . . . . the first time that Max will be part of it, the first time that Justin and his family won't be part of it, and the first time in two years that my father will be around for Christmas . . . and he won't be part of it.

That's definitely a lot of parts! And I just hope that those parts won't be a whole lot of trouble. . . . . . 'Tis the season to be jolly . . . . I just hope that everyone keeps remembering that.

Chapter Two

"Deck the halls with poison ivy," I, Amber Brown, sing off-tune.

"Fa, la, la, la, la, la, la, la, la." My mom also sings off-tune.

Aunt Pam, my mom's sister, says that none of us can carry a tune in a bucket.

Actually, I have never seen anyone carry a tune in a bucket.

"We fish you a Merry Christmas . . . we fish you a Merry Christmas." My mom holds up a charm with a fish on it.

Maybe with that fish, even though we

can't carry a tune in a bucket, we can carry a tuna in a bucket.

I, Amber Brown, love to pun.

I also love to make presents for my friends for the holidays.

B . . . R . . . A . . . N . . . D . . . I

I pick out the beads to go between the letters . . . . and the charms to go on the bracelet . . . . a little dog charm that looks like her dog (except that there is no slobber coming out of the charm dog's mouth) . . . . a nail polish bottle charm, to remind her of the time we painted our nails . . . and the dog's nails too . . .

For my Aunt Pam, I make a name bracelet with the letters P . . . A . . . M . . . E . . . L . . . A. She'd have to have a miniature wrist if I only wrote P . . . A . . . M. I put charms on it . . . a book, because she teaches English, a Big Ben building because she loves England, and a bunch of ant charms

. . . because, after all, she is an aunt. . . .

For Brenda, my Ambersitter, I also make a name bracelet. I add cooking charms—a pot, a pan, and teeny-tiny spatula. (I picked those charms as a joke because Brenda is the weirdest, if not the worstest, cook ever.) I also add a pair of scissors because Brenda always cuts her hair strangely . . . so strangely that my mom once made Brenda promise that she would NEVER cut my hair . . . . or pierce any part of my body. . . . I am glad that mom said that about my hair but I REALLY wish that she would let me get my ears pierced . . . but she says I can't, not until I'm twelve.

I finish working on the alphabet and charm bracelets and start working on the Scrabble jewelry. (For months, mom and I have been going to garage, house, and rummage sales, buying up all of the old Scrabble games that we could find. Now we are ready to use the tiles.)

I pick up an "O" and then an "H" tile. They're for my teacher, Olivia Holt. If she wears them one way, so that the "O" is on her right ear . . . she'll spell out "OH". . . . if she wears the "H" on her right ear, she'll spell out HO . . . which is very Christmas . . . especially if you say it several times.

Then, I make a pair for Aunt Pam . . . but the tiles aren't "A" and "P." They are "P" and "T" (for Thompson).

I'm almost done.

I look over at my mom, who is making sure that all the rhinestones are sticking on the picture frame that I made for my Grandma Brown, my dad's mom.

I haven't seen Grandma Brown, who lives in Florida, since before my Dad left for Paris.

It makes me sad, but maybe now that my Dad is back, we can go visit her sometime.

I take a plain picture frame and start putting rhinestones and pearls on it. When it's all finished, I'll put one of my pictures in it. (And I'll put rhinestones on the picture.)

My mom says, "This is fun . . . and it saves money."

I nod. With what I borrowed from my mom, I don't think that I'll be getting any allowance again until the middle of March. If I weren't making some of the presents, I doubt that I would be getting an allowance again until August.

I start working on one of Max's presents.

It's a salt and pepper shaker set that I found at the 99 Cent store, and I am putting lots of rhinestones on it.

I think that it will make Max smile.

I show my mother. "Isn't this the perfect gift for a bowling coach? I know that I won't strike out with this item."

First, my mom groans at my pun . . . and maybe even the thought of rhinestone bowling-ball-and-pin salt and pepper shakers, and then says, "He'll be so grateful that you could spare the time to make this for him."

I work on Max's gift.

I know that it's sort of tacky, but it's fun.

On the bowling pin, I glue on rhinestones in the shape of a strike, X.

On the bowling ball, I start to make a rhinestone slash,/, like a spare.

My mom looks at it and says, "When I look at those shakers, I think about how they are going to be back here when Max and I get married, and we all live together."

I close my eyes for a minute while I think about what she's said.

I know that they are engaged.

I know that they are going to get married.

I just have trouble thinking about all of us living together.

While my eyes are closed, disaster strikes!

"Oooops," I say, opening my eyes.

The glue has escaped from the sides of the tube and is on my hand.

My fingers are glued together. So are the bowling ball and the tube of glue . . . . all attached to my left hand.

This is not good.

In fact, it's pretty bad.

I go to wipe my eyes with my left hand but my mother grabs it, quickly.

"Don't touch your eyes," she warns.

I don't.

Her hand, which is holding mine, is now stuck to my hand, to the bowling ball and to the tube of glue.

"This is a very sticky situation," I say.

"Not funny," she says, and then starts laughing.

I start laughing too.

"I wonder if this is what people mean when they talk about mother-daughter bonding."

She shakes her head.

I think about mothers and daughters . . . . and then I think about fathers.

"Mom," I say. "Dad's going to be here to pick me up for dinner soon. Maybe we'll all have to go to dinner together."

Sometimes, even though I, Amber Brown, know that it's not a good idea . . . I still think about my parents getting back together.

The only way that I think that will happen is if I glue them together.

"Dinner together???!!!!" My mom shakes her head. "Don't even think about it. . . . THAT would be a *very* sticky situation. No, the less that I see of your father, the better."

I, Amber Brown, hate when my mom says things like that. It makes me feel really bad.

I used to think that my mom was practically perfect, but ever since she found out that my dad was moving back, she's been a little weird . . . . and sometimes she says mean things about him.

I hate when she does that.

"Nail polish remover. That's what we need," my mom says.

"I'll go get it," I volunteer and stand up.

My mother's hand moves when I do.

I realize that if I'm going to get the nail polish remover, it's going to be a mother-daughter activity.

I also realize that I have to go to the bathroom, which is not a mother-daughter activity, not at my age.

This is definitely going to become embarrassing if my mother and I remain this attached.

We go up the steps, hands glued together, to her makeup drawer.

Nail polish remover. . . .

It works.

I rush to the bathroom.

My mom goes downstairs. "Hurry up. Your father will be here any minute, and I really don't want him to be here any longer than he has to be."

While I'm upstairs, the phone rings.

I rush to get it.

It's for me.

It's Brandi, who says, "Bulletin. Bulletin. Bulletin. Do I have a bulletin for you!!!! It's so amazing. And you've just got to convince your mom to let you do it too. Guess. You've got to guess what it is."

I, Amber Brown, have no idea.

Chapter Three

Brandi is soooooooooo excited. "You've got three guesses."

I don't know where to start. "You're going to Disneyland."

"No. Two more." She giggles.

"You're getting married to Fredric Allen," I say.

"Noooooooooooooooooo. Gross," she says. "I'm just going to have to tell you."

I, Amber Brown, knew that would make her tell me. Fredric Allen is the kid in our class who picks his nose, and sometimes even eats it. He also forgot to zip up his fly on the day the class pictures were taken.

"I'm going to get my ears pierced. My parents said that I could do it as a Christmas present . . . . and guess what? Kelly's parents said that she could get hers done too."

My stomach feels sick.

I want to cry.

Two of my friends are getting their ears pierced and I have to wait 'til I'm twelve.

That's over two years from now. It's not fair.

Brandi says, "Kelly and I are going to go over to the mall and get them done today. Amber, you've got to convince your mom to let you get them done now . . . . with us. Just tell her that our moms said yes."

I don't say anything for a minute.

Brandi says, "Do you think my mom should talk to your mom?"

I shake my head and then realize that Brandi can't see that on the phone. "No. My mom said I have to wait and anyway, my dad's picking me up soon."

"That's not fair." Brandi says. "Maybe your dad could take you."

"I have to ask my mom," I say. "Maybe I can get her to change her mind."

Just because my mom had to wait until she was seventeen to get her ears pierced doesn't mean that I have to wait until I'm twelve.

"Can't you beg her? Explain that *everyone* is getting pierced ears . . . or already has them," Brandi says. "Oh, please. It'll be so cool if we could all go to the mall today and get it done."

My head is really beginning to ache. There's no way that my mom is going to say yes . . . . and it seems that Brandi Colwin, one of my best friends in the whole entire world, and Kelly Green, the new kid in our class and our new friend, have already made plans to do something that they know that I'm not going to be able to do.

I was so happy until I got this call.

I wish that my dad had gotten here and taken me away before the phone call came.

I sigh. "I'll try. Gotta go. If I don't call you back in ten minutes you'll know that my mom won't let me do it."

"I'll cross my fingers . . . . and my toes." Brandi says. "It will be *totally* wonderful if you can do this too."

Hanging up, I rush into my bedroom and change into a top that doesn't have glue on it, and then I hurry downstairs, rubbing at a piece of glue that's still stuck to the top of my hand.

I go into the kitchen where my mom is cleaning up the stuff that I was making.

"Thanks for doing that," I say and start putting things away too. "Mom. I have something to ask you . . . . and please don't say no."

"What?" She gives me a suspicious look.

I speak very quickly. "Brandi and Kelly are getting their ears pierced today . . . . and they want me to go with them . . . . and get mine done too. Oh, please . . . . oh please . . . . . oh pretty please with sugar on top."

"No." She shakes her head. "I told you that you have to wait until you are twelve to get that done. . . . I want you to wait. . . . I need to see that you will be responsible enough to keep your ears from getting infected. Amber, you are not organized. You don't keep your room clean . . . .

and even if I do change my mind, it won't be until I've seen a great many reports about how well you are doing in school. I want you to show that you are being responsible."

"I promise," I say. "I promise to be good. I am being responsible now. My grades are really good lately. And I promise that I will keep my room organized and clean."

"After you have done all of that, I will think about it . . . . but not until then."

"Mom," I beg.

She shakes her head. "Case closed."

That's it.

I know my mother.

She's not going to let me do it.

I am so unhappy.

I start to cry . . . but that doesn't do any good.

My mom just keeps organizing things.

I look at the clock.

It's ten minutes after four.

It's past the time that I told Brandi that I would call if my mom said yes.

The doorbell rings.

It's my dad.

Too late to call Brandi. I bet that she and Kelly are already on the way to the mall.

He's not going to be very happy to see me this upset.

I take a deep breath, wipe my tears, and go answer the door.

"Honey, what's wrong?" he asks.

"I'll tell you later," I say.

My mother comes into the living room.

Her voice is soooo cold when she speaks. "Philip. Just make sure that Amber isn't out too late. She has homework to do."

He nods and then he looks at me. "You're wearing the sweatshirt we got in New York."

It's the one that my dad bought for me at Thanksgiving and on it, the writing says, "JUST BE GLAD YOU'RE NOT THE TURKEY."

When I brought it home, my mom looked at it and asked, "Did your dad get one for himself that says, 'I AM THE TURKEY'?"

I give my dad a great big kiss hello, and then I give mom a great big kiss goodbye.

She sort of wipes at her check.

That really hurts.

She's never wiped off my kisses before.

It's not as if I have dog germs or something.

I bite my lip.

I, Amber Brown, am a little confused . . . and a lot sad . . . and then I figure it out.

Maybe she's not happy with me because I want to get my ears pierced, but I think it's because I don't think my mom likes it when my dad kisses me and then I immediately kiss her.

"Let's go." My dad puts his arm around me.

My mom walks us to the door and then before I leave, she leans over and gives me a great big kiss.

I give her a great big kiss back, which she doesn't wipe off her cheek.

"Make sure that she's not out too late," my mom repeats. "Tomorrow's a school day."

My dad says, "Sarah. This is my time with Amber. Joint custody, remember."

Joint custody. . . . I'm beginning to hate

those two words. I'm beginning to feel like I'm not me anymore . . . . that I'm just a part of them . . . like joint custody means each of them gets one leg, one arm . . . . or that each of them owns all of me part of the time . . . and I, Amber Brown, don't like that.

Once, when I got my hair cut too short, I told my mom how upset I was that they weren't getting along . . . . and I thought that things were going to change.

But they haven't, a lot.

My parents are so cold to each other.

It wasn't always like this.

I even remember seeing them kiss when I was younger.

Kissing.

I know that I'll have to be careful from now on.

If one parent kisses me, I can't immediately kiss the other one because it will be like they're kissing each other, sort of.

It's Divorced Parents Cooties, or something.

There should be a rulebook for kids of divorced parents with every little thing listed that we have to remember.

I, Amber Brown, think that there should also be a rulebook for parents . . . and the first rule should be that there shouldn't have to be a rulebook for their kids.

"Amber," my dad says as we get into the car, "you're with me now. Tell me why you were crying."

Chapter Four

We just sit in Dad's car for awhile.

I, Amber Brown, have to think about what I am going to do, what I'm going to tell my Dad.

I am so angry at my mom right now.

She won't let me get my ears pierced.

She's so mean when my dad is around.

She's not acting like the Mom I've always known.

But if I say all of that to my dad, then he's going to act all proud that he's the best parent . . . and he does stuff too that drives me nuts.

I take a deep breath. "I'm just upset because Brandi called, and she and Kelly are going to the mall to get their ears pierced and I couldn't go . . ."

My dad interrupts. "Is that because you had to go with me?"

All of a sudden, a light flashes inside my head.

Well, not a light . . . . . an idea . . . . . and I'm not sure that this is a good idea . . . . but I, Amber Brown, am going to go for it. I, Amber Brown, am getting tired of the way that they are both acting. I'm tired of being in the middle . . . . and I want to do something for ME.

I sniffle and nod.

And then I sniffle again. "That's one of the reasons. But don't feel bad, Daddy, because I can get them pierced some time in the future."

I don't mention that the time in the future, according to my mom, is a little over two and a half years away.

My dad sits for a minute, thinking. "Honey, I don't want you to feel bad because we have plans and you can't do that with your friends."

"It's okay," I say, "even though they are probably on their way to the mall right now, I don't feel bad . . . not that bad anyway."

My dad turns the key in the ignition and says, "Well . . . you don't have to be upset, my wonderful daughter. I will take you to the mall . . . . and you can meet up with your friends and get your ears pierced."

"Oh, Daddy." I pat him on his hand. "Thank you soooooo much. You are so wonderful . . . . the best dad in the entire world."

"As your Aunt Pam says, wagons ho," my dad says, as he pulls the car out of the parking space.

I, Amber Brown, wonder about that.

Aunt Pam is my mom's sister, and now

that my parents are divorced, is my dad supposed to be quoting my mom's sister, his ex-sister-in-law?

I, Amber Brown, am also wondering about what I've done. . . . I haven't actually lied to my dad . . . but I haven't told him the whole truth. . . . . But I really, really want to get my ears pierced . . . . and he doesn't say no . . . . and I'm his daughter too . . . . so that means that I should be able to get at least one of my ears pierced . . . . and my mom should only get half as mad because with joint custody, they share me and they each think that they own me. . . . . So really I'll have only pierced one ear that she has custody of . . .

"Vrrrrrrrrooooooooooooooooooom," my dad says as we drive.

That's something he used to say when I was little.

He turns his head to me and smiles.

"Vrrrrrrroooooooooooooooooom," I say and then sing, "Off we go into the wild blue yonder."

It's part of a song that my dad used to sing to me when I was little . . . . when he used to lift me up over his head, and I'd pretend that I was an airplane.

We both sing it together.

It's something that is ours . . . . to remember and to do now.

We finish singing.

My dad asks, "When we get to the mall,

where should I park? Where are you all going to get your ears pierced?"

I bite my lip.

I, Amber Brown, never found out where Brandi and Kelly are going.

I close my eyes and try to figure out how to handle this.

Maybe I should tell him the truth now.

If I do, I'll probably be the only fourth-grade girl in the world who doesn't have pierced ears.

If I don't, I'll have pierced ears and one angry mom . . . and probably one angry dad . . . . but in this case, one plus one equals two . . . . two pierced ears.

I, Amber Brown, decide to go for it. "They're getting them done at Jamison's Jewelry Store . . . . but because they didn't think I could go, they may have already gotten them done. . . . If they're not there, do you think I should wait?"

I hope that he says the word that I want to hear.

Instead, as he parks the car, he says, "Amber, are they really getting their ears pierced?"

"I promise," I say and wait for him to ask what Mom thinks.

He doesn't ask.

He nods. "Then you can get yours done. I trust you."

Something tells me that I am going to feel really bad about what I am going to do, but I would feel worse if my ears don't get pierced.

I, Amber Brown, am going to get my ears pierced.

I'm very excited . . . . . and very nervous . . . and not just because my ears are going to get pierced.

Chapter Five

"Amber," my dad says as we come out of the jewelry store, "it's a shame that your friends weren't there when we got there."

I nod. "A real shame."

I don't tell my dad that I was glad that they weren't there.

They might have said something like, "Oh, it's great that your mom gave in."

Then I never would have gotten my ears pierced.

My dad looks very pleased with himself. "I'm so glad that I'm back and can be more of a part of your daily life. It was such a mistake for me to move to Paris."

"I hated it when you left, Daddy. Please don't do anything like that again," I say, touching my new gold earrings.

He shakes his head. "It really was a mistake . . . . one of a long line of them I made at that time."

"What do you mean?" I ask.

He shakes his head again and then changes the subject. "For Christmas, would you like me to get you some more earrings for when you can take those out, when the holes are all better?"

I nod.

Something tells me that my mom is not going to be buying me earrings for Christmas.

Mom . . . , I wonder what she's going to do.

She's definitely not going to be a happy camper.

But Dad said I could get it done.

I didn't even have to ask him.

He just said I could.

Something tells me that this is the worst thing that I, Amber Brown, have ever done in my whole entire life.

But they deserve it, treating me like I have no right to do what I want . . . it's all got to be what they want and need . . . .

joint custody. . . . Well, I have ear custody . . . and I've just done what I want and need.

I feel really scared because my dad feels so good about what he's done, and I know that he's not going to feel so good when my mom finds out.

And I, Amber Brown, am not so sure that I feel good about what I've just done.

I'm getting a headache, and I don't think it's from the ear piercing.

My dad says, "Amber, I have a surprise for you."

"What?" I ask.

"If I tell you, it won't be a surprise. Hurry up. We have to be somewhere by six o'clock."

As we leave the mall, my stomach starts to growl and I say, "Dad, where are we going for dinner tonight? Fast food? Or slow food?"

Slow food is what my dad and I call going to a regular restaurant.

Since my dad has moved back, we eat out all of the time.

That's because he's staying with his friends the Donaldsons until he finds an apartment, but we don't go there to eat because he says that he doesn't want to be an "inconvenience."

"Where we are eating is part of the surprise," he says.

Oh no . . . a food surprise . . . the last time he said that, he took me to a Japanese restaurant and we ate sushi. Raw fish. At first, I felt like I was eating something that had once been a pet in a fishbowl, but then I got used to some of it and actually liked some of it . . . . except for something called uni that made me want to puke. And the octopus and the squid were gross, very gross . . . and not just because it felt like they belonged in *The Little Mermaid* movie.

So when my dad says "food surprise," I,

Amber Brown, get a little nervous.

I, Amber Brown, am also hungry.

And I am also curious.

I touch my new earrings and wish that my father would tell me what's going on.

I wish that my father would feed me.

At home, it's so easy.

I get hungry . . . . . I go into the kitchen and get something.

With my dad, it's different.

We have to go somewhere to get something unless it's just a snack that we can eat in his car.

It's kind of weird.

We've left the mall, and we're not heading to any place where I know that there is a restaurant.

We're going down a regular street, not far from my street.

It's not even the street where the Donaldsons live.

My dad parks in front of a house.

"We're home," he says.

I, Amber Brown, am not only very hungry.

I am very confused.

Chapter Six

"Home sweet home," my father says.

I look at him.

Then I try to look at the house.

It's dark outside, but I can see that it's a real house.

There are lights on upstairs.

I look at my father. "Whose home sweet home?"

My dad says, "Ours . . . . well, ours and the Marshall family. I decided not to rent an apartment in an apartment building . . . and I didn't want to rent a whole big house. So, when a buddy of mine at work mentioned that his tenant had moved out, I asked to see the place. I liked what I saw and rented it yesterday. Actually, there are two places to live in the house. We've got the basement and first floor. The Marshalls live on the top two floors. Come on. Let's go in. I want you to see it. And then we're going to have dinner with Steve and his kids."

I continue to sit in the car.

My dad comes over to my door, opens it and pretends to be the chauffeur.

I continue to sit in the car.

"Amber, honey. Get out. They're all waiting to have dinner with us," he says.

I continue to sit in the car and stare out the front window.

I don't even look at him.

I have so many feelings inside, I feel like I'm going to explode.

I'm confused . . . . . . upset . . . . angry . . . . jealous . . . . . sad . . . . and I don't know what to say.

It serves him right that I tricked him into helping me get my ears pierced.

I continue to sit in the car, looking out the window, and the tears start to come out of my eyes and down my face.

I really don't want to cry.

"Amber." He kneels down by the open car door. "Come on. It's cold out here . . . . and I don't understand what's the matter. I don't have a clue."

That's my dad . . . Clueless . . . Clueless Dad . . . . Clueless Dad Brown.

I, Amber Brown, am so angry at him.

"Amber," he says again. "Look at me. Tell me what's wrong. Why are you crying? I really hate it when you cry."

I look at him, but don't say anything for a minute.

He looks back. "Amber. Please. I want this to be a wonderful time. It's my new home . . . . our new home. . . . You're really going to love it."

My nose starts to run, just a little.

I sniffle.

I sniffle again and then I say, "You promised."

"I promised?" he asks.

"You promised that I would go with you to help you pick out the apartment that you were going to rent . . . that I would be part of the deciding . . . . and now you've gone and decided without me."

He leans against the car . . . . . and says nothing.

I continue. "And now I find out that it's a HOUSE with other people living in it. Steve and his kids . . . is there a Mrs. Steve?. . . . What if I don't like these kids? What if they don't like me?"

"They'll love you, honey. Everyone loves you," my father says.

"Not everyone," I say, thinking of one of the kids in my class who I can't get along with. "Please don't tell me that one of the kids is Hannah Burton."

"No Hannah Burton in the house." My father shakes his head. "Honey, there's no one from your class in the house. Two of them go to your school. One of them goes to high school. Their last name is Marshall. Steve Marshall and his kids. . . . There's Polly, Dylan, and Savannah. Steve and his wife are separated . . . and the kids live with their father."

Savannah. I think I know her.

She's a third grader, in Mr. Cohen's class.

And I think I know who Dylan is.

He's one of the sixth graders . . . one of those kids who thinks that they own the whole school because they are the oldest kids there.

He once called me "Squirt."

I don't know Polly.

And I don't want to leave the car.

And there's something else that is bothering me . . . bothering me big time.

I want my dad to say that he's sorry that he broke a promise to me.

"Honey," my Dad says. "It'll be just fine. I promise."

How can I trust him?

"Mr. Brown. Amber," someone yells out. I look over to see Savannah Marshall coming toward us.

It would serve my dad right if I asked to go home right now . . . back to my mom's and my home, where I can depend on certain things . . . where I'm used to certain things.

But with my newly pierced ears, I'm not sure that I want to go home yet.

I look over at my dad's sad face and then at Savannah's smiling face.

My stomach starts to growl.

I sniffle again.

I can't let a third grader see me cry.

I, Amber Brown, have to make a decision.

And I'm not sure what it is.

Chapter Seven

Savannah looks in the car and stares at me.

Then she looks at my father.

Then she looks at me again. "Are you okay?"

I sniffle.

I'm glad that it's getting dark so that she can't see how red and puffy my eyes are and that my face looks splotchy.

Inside my brain, I try to convince my eyes not to be all red and puffy and for my face to look non-splotchy.

Just in case that doesn't work, I say, "Allergies. I have allergies."

"To what?" She looks concerned.

I want to say "To Clueless Dads," but instead I say, "To lots of things. . . . But don't worry. I'll be okay."

My dad stands up and holds out his hand to help me get out of the car.

I think about it for a minute and make my decision.

"No thanks," I say. "I can do it myself."

My dad puts his hand back down.

I get out of the car.

I, Amber Brown, will go inside.

He's already rented it.

There's nothing I can do about that.

If I hate it, I'll never come back again.

Savannah smiles at me, and together we start walking to the house.

I am not paying any attention to my father who is walking with us.

"You're in Mr. Cohen's class," I sort of say, sort of ask.

She nods and keeps smiling.

"Lucky," I say. "He's a great teacher."

"I know," Savannah says.

My dad is walking next to me, but I'm not even looking at him, not even talking to him.

We get to the front door and go in.

There are steps straight ahead.

To the left of the steps farther back, there's a door.

My dad touches my shoulder. "Amber,

honey . . . that's where we are going to live."

I turn to Savannah and say, "I already live on Chestnut Street."

She says, "This is Elm Street . . . . so you are going to live in two places that are named after trees."

I, Amber Brown, will have two houses . . . . . on two streets named after trees.

I wonder if that means that I will be living in treehouses.

That makes me smile until I start to think about how much my life is changing.

All of a sudden, this seems very real to me.

I, Amber Brown, will finally have two houses . . . . . one where I live with my mom . . . . one where I live with my dad . . . joint custody.

It's weird.

When my dad had an apartment in our town for a short time after he and Mom broke up and then he moved to Paris, I always felt like I was just visiting there.

Now he expects me to have a home with him, not just at my mom's and my place.

Part of me likes the idea.

Part of me is not so sure.

"Want me to show this place to you?" Savannah says. "I can pretend that I'm the real estate lady, and you can be the customer."

For a minute, I think about how much fun it would be to pretend.

I, Amber Brown, love to pretend.

But this time it isn't pretend.

It's for real.

My dad says, "Savannah, thank you. But I really want to show the place to Amber myself. And I would like a few minutes alone to speak with her. So would you please go upstairs now and tell your dad that we'll be up for dinner in about ten or fifteen minutes?"

Savannah looks disappointed.

I'm a little disappointed too.

It's always fun to find other people who like to play, even if they are a little younger.

Savannah goes upstairs.

I look at my dad, not smiling . . . . waiting for him to say something.

He does. "Amber. I'm sorry."

Finally.

I continue to look at him.

He continues. "I should have let you see this first. I'm sorry that I broke my promise. It just seemed like such a good idea. It's a great place . . . and Jim has become a friend, and he has nice kids. They are a good family . . . and sometimes . . . sometimes, Amber, I feel very lonely. I've just gotten back from Paris. You're with your mom most of the time. I work all day, stay late at the office because I don't want to get in the Donaldsons' way. I suppose that I should have gotten a hotel room until I found a place, but that felt really lonely."

Twice my dad has said that he's lonely.

I, Amber Brown, feel sad for him.

He's my dad.

I don't want him to feel lonely.

I give him a big hug.

He hugs me back.

Then he gives me a kiss on the forehead. "I love you so much."

"Me too," I say.

"Am I forgiven?" he asks.

I nod.

I hope that he's going to forgive me for what I've done, getting my ears pierced.

Then I think of the other promise that he made that I really hope that he has not broken.

"Dad," I say, "it's okay as long as I still get to help pick out the furniture."

"It's a deal." He crosses his heart.

Now I, Amber Brown, am ready to see the house.

Chapter Eight

"The doorway to our home," my dad says, opening it. "There's also an entrance to our apartment from the back. This room will be the living room."

It's one big empty room.

"It will also be the dining area." He points to one side of the room, "if we don't feel like eating in the kitchen."

I nod.

There's not much to say.

It's one big empty room.

"Honey, look." My Dad walks over to the

windows at the back of the room. "Doesn't this look great?"

I join him and look out the window.

There's a really nice backyard, with trees and swings and a treehouse . . . there really is a treehouse on Elm Street.

"We can use the backyard and share it with the Marshalls," he says.

I, Amber Brown, think about how Savannah and I can play in the treehouse . . . and how my friends, Brandi and Kelly, can come over and play in it too.

I can't wait to write to Justin and tell him that he's not the only one with a treehouse, that I now have one too.

Then I remember. . . . I'm not sure yet that this is going to be one of my houses.

My dad puts his arm around my shoulder and says, "Let's look at the rest of this place."

The kitchen.

It's a kitchen. . . . Since I'm not much of a cook, kitchens aren't that important to me . . . . except as a place to eat and talk.

"I hope that you don't mind," my dad says. "I went out and bought some pots and pans . . . dishes, silverware, supplies."

I go over to the refrigerator and look inside. "And some food."

He nods. "I didn't think you would mind if I did that without you."

I shake my head. "That's fine."

I pick up the peanut butter jar. "Dad. This

is creamy peanut butter. I, Amber Brown, like chunky peanut butter."

He grins. "Then . . . . . I, Philip Brown, will get chunky peanut butter for my daughter, Amber Brown . . . . or is your name now I, Amber Brown????"

I giggle.

He says, "Well, . . . I, Amber Brown . . . . why do you like referring to yourself that way?"

I, Amber Brown, think about it.

I answer: "It makes me strong to say my name that way. Like I belong to myself . . . and am not just Amber Brown, your daughter, mom's daughter, Mrs. Holt's student. . . . I am I, AMBER BROWN. . . . You don't have to call me that . . . I just have to know that's who I am . . . and I want other people to know that's who I am."

He whistles. "For someone who is only nine, you are very sure of that."

I nod.

I am.

Divorce can do that to a kid.

Just living can do that to a kid.

I look around the room. "Okay . . . so now, where's my bedroom? If I decide to live here part time, where will I sleep? Do I, Amber Brown, have a room?"

"Yes. You, Amber Brown, do have a room. It's downstairs . . . but first I want to show you this floor."

There's not much left to show . . . a bathroom . . . . and a room with a sleeping bag in it.

"This is my bedroom," he says. "Tomorrow, I'm going to Ikea to buy some furniture. We'll talk to your mom about your taking the day off from school. It'll be so much fun. . . . . A Dad and Daughter Shop Day . . . . and it's important that we go tomorrow. The timing is very important. If we order the furniture tomorrow, it can be delivered in a few days and then a company can come over and assemble it all in one day. That way the house will be ready by Christmas . . . . our almost-instant home. I have the catalog for you to look at, to make some preliminary decisions and then we'll make the final ones at the store."

No school . . . . shopping with my dad . . . . I, Amber Brown, will like that.

He hands me a catalog.

Before I can look at it, he says, "Let me show you the downstairs. That's where your room is."

Great, I think. Downstairs in my house with Mom is the basement where we keep the washer and dryer. It's not really finished, and it's a little creepy, with cobwebs.

So in this house, he's putting me down in the basement to live like some creature in a horror book, where the monster lives in the dungeon.

He'll probably throw down scraps of bread with chunky peanut butter for me to live on.

I follow him downstairs.

This basement looks terrific.

"This will be the recreation room. We'll put the TV in here . . . . and the computer . . . and a place to do jigsaw puzzles. . . . Remember when you were little . . . how we always used to do them," my dad says.

I remember.

I was a little kid then.

We used to do Sesame Street puzzles, and ones with Mickey Mouse and Goofy.

I hope that my dad doesn't want to do those anymore.

I'm too old to do a Goofy puzzle or goofy puzzles.

I gave all my old puzzles away a long time ago to Justin's little brother, Danny.

My dad holds up a box. "I've already bought one. We can work on it every time you come to visit."

I make a face and think. . . . Please not a little kid puzzle.

I know that my dad's been away for awhile, but he can't think that I'm still that little.

I walk over to look at the puzzle, hoping that he didn't buy a Barney puzzle. I, Amber Brown, have never liked that purple dinosaur, even though purple is my favorite color.

"See." My dad looks so proud of himself.

I see.

I smile.

It's a terrific 3-D puzzle.

It looks like a big clock, with stars and moons and rainbows on it . . . and it's not only a puzzle . . . . it IS a real clock, one that has stuff in the box that will make the clock run. It's sooooooo fun!

"When we finish it, we can hang it on the wall." My dad points to a spot. "Right here . . . . or is there some other place that you think it should go?"

I smile again. "It'll be perfect there."

He looks very happy. “Now for your room.”

He walks to the back and opens a door. “Ta dum.”

It’s the bathroom.

“My room?” I ask. “Am I supposed to sleep in the tub?”

“Oops,” he says. “Wrong door. I’m still not sure of where everything is. This all happened so quickly.”

He goes over to the next door. “Ta dum.”

I look inside.

It’s a really big room . . . . about twice the size of my bedroom at my mom’s. . . . . And there’s a loft bed already in it.

A loft bed is just so great. It’s like a tree-house in your own room . . . . like a giant bunk bed with no lower bunk.

I rush inside and look up at the loft bed.

“This was here already,” Dad says. “Do you want this or a regular bed?”

I put my foot up on the first rung of the ladder by the side of the loft bed. "Are you kidding? I want this. It's sooooooooooo great."

Very quickly, I go up the ladder.

There's enough room up here for a double mattress . . . . for a whole lot of stuffed animals . . . and for me.

The ceiling is so high that I can sit up straight on the bed and still have space left over.

My father climbs up the ladder, sits down and hits his head on the ceiling.

I look up at the ceiling over the loft bed area. . . . There are fluorescent stars and moons and planets on it.

I just know that they are going to glow in the dark.

"I love this," I say.

"Then we'll live here," my dad says. "That's okay with you . . . . yes??"

I nod. "When I'm staying with you, this is great. But don't forget. . . . I'm still living with Mom too."

He nods, and then we hug each other.

"What," I ask "would you have done if I had said no?"

He shakes his head. "I don't know. I honestly don't know. I'm just glad that you didn't say no."

I look at him. "Dad. Promise me that from now on when you make a promise, you will keep it."

He nods. "I'll do my best."

That makes me a little nervous.

I really wish that he had just said, "Yes. I promise."

Saying "I'll do my best" leaves him a lot of chances to make more mistakes.

I'm not sure that I like that in a parent.

But I think about what he's done. . . . He's found a place that's nice, with a room for me that I love. . . . . And it was really nice of him to remember that we used to put puzzles together. . . . And we're going to be able to shop together for things for the house.

I, Amber Brown, am going to give this a chance.

I only hope that it turns out all right.

Chapter Nine

"Now for something else that is really exciting," my dad says, taking me to the third floor. "You're going to meet the Marshalls."

He knocks at the door.

In about a second and a half, the door is opened.

Savannah is jumping up and down. "Finally."

Behind her is Dylan, who is standing there with a french fry up his nose.

Behind Dylan is a grown-up who, dad-like, takes the french fry out of Dylan's nose and then comes up to me.

"Welcome, Amber." He reaches out to shake my hand. "I'm Steve Marshall."

First, I make sure that he's not using the hand that has the french fry in it.

He's not . . . . so I shake his hand.

"Welcome, Amber." A teenage girl comes up to me. "Hi, I'm Polly."

She's wearing black tights and a very large black T-shirt and lots of jewelry.

Behind her, someone yells, "SURPRISE!"

It's Brenda, my Ambersitter, the best sitter in the whole wide world . . . if you don't count the fact that she is also one of the world's worst cooks.

For other people, Brenda just baby-sits. For me she Ambersits.

Today Brenda's hair is spiky and pink and glitters with orange and purple.

She definitely has gone crazy with cans of glitter spray.

We rush up to each other. "What are you doing here?" I give her a hug.

"Polly is my best friend." She hugs back.

Polly. She's talked about Polly. I just didn't put it all together that Polly Marshall is the Polly who is Brenda's best friend. In fact, this whole thing is happening so quickly that I'm having trouble putting lots of stuff together.

She looks at me.

Then she looks at me again.

"Amber. When did you get your ears pierced?" she asks.

I almost forgot. "Today."

She looks at me and then she looks at my dad, who is talking to Mr. Marshall.

Brenda leans over and whispers, "Does your mom know about this? Did you get her permission?"

Biting my lip, I shake my head no.

Brenda kind of makes a gulping sound and softly says, "Wow."

"Okay," Mr. Marshall says, "you've already met Savannah . . . and this is my son, Dylan . . . . who seems to think it's funny to adorn himself with french fries."

I smile at Savannah . . . and look at Dylan, who now has french fries in his ears.

His father takes them out of Dylan's ears. "If you do that one more time, I'm going to make you eat the french fries that you have stuck in your ears and nose. Now stop doing that."

Dylan smiles. "No nose. No ears."

"And not any other parts of your body either," his dad says.

"Darn," Dylan says.

I, Amber Brown, don't want to think about where else Dylan was thinking of sticking those french fries.

"Okay, everyone," Mr. Marshall says, "it's time to eat. Amber, I hope that you like hot dogs and beans and hamburgers."

"Yum," I say.

It's kind of a party, only it's one where I only know three people well . . . . my dad and Brenda and me.

The table is already set.

I am very hungry.

We all sit down and eat.

I prepare one of my favorite meals . . . . hot dog in a roll with beans on top of that, and then mustard and ketchup on top of that, and potato chips with ridges on top of that.

Then I put some french fries on the side.

Yum.

The Marshalls are definitely not a quiet family.

I, Amber Brown, am used to meals with just my mom . . . . or now, sometimes with my mom and Max.

They are definitely not this noisy.

Here, everyone is joking around, teasing each other.

At my house, we joke and tease too, but it's not this loud.

One of the reasons that it is so noisy is that Dylan is having races with hot dogs in hot dog rolls. "Okay, sports fans . . . . which one will be the winner??? Will it be the one wearing the coat of yellow (the mustard) or will it be the one wearing the red coat. (No, he's not British . . . he's wearing catsup.) It's the yellow one in the lead. . . . . But can he cut the mustard?? Wow!!! Look!!! The one in red is not far behind . . . . and he's get-

ting closer . . . . closer . . . . now he's pulling in front. Boy, does that hot dog know how to catsup."

Dylan keeps laughing at his own jokes.

His dad laughs at them too.

My mom would never let Dylan do that at the table.

Thinking that makes me think about what else my mom would not allow. . . . . . . And I've just done it.

I get very nervous if I think about what's

going to happen when my mom finds out.

I look back at Dylan.

He's put more french fries up his nose, crossed his eyes at me and opened his mouth, which is filled with chewed up hamburger.

Something tells me that he and Justin would really have gotten along.

If Dylan thinks he's going to gross me out by doing things like that, he's not. When we were little, Justin and I used to put cheerios up our noses . . . and sometimes Justin would even add milk to his. So, if Dylan thinks that he's going to gross me out, I'm going to have to tell him about the chewing gum ball that Justin and I once made.

So what Dylan is doing with his french fries is just small potatoes to me.

His dad finally makes him stop, but I bet that Dylan is not going to stay stopped for long.

Brenda sits next to me.

That makes me feel good.

When I woke up today, I had one kind of life . . . . and now, BAM, without any warning, I've got a different kind of life . . . so it's good that Brenda is here. I know her. She doesn't change . . . . except for her hair color . . . and that's not such a big deal.

She's so excited that my dad is renting the downstairs. "And, Amber, sometimes when your dad goes out at night, I can Ambersit for you here, and we can all hang out and have a good time."

I look at my dad, who nods.

I wonder where he's going to be going out when I come here . . . and who he is going to be going out with.

Brenda continues. "And if you want and if there is time, we can go through the Ikea catalog and help you pick out things for your room . . . so that when you go shopping, you'll already have an idea of what you want."

Everything is happening so quickly.

I ask, "Brenda, how long have you known about this?"

She says, "Two days. Polly called me when your dad decided to rent the place . . . . and then yesterday after your dad went shopping, he came over here and Polly and I were doing our science project. We all started talking. We offered to help you with your room if you want."

I nod.

Dylan starts pretending that he's going to

squirt catsup at Savannah, who starts yelling.

While Mr. Marshall gives Dylan one more chance before he has to leave the table, Brenda leans over to me and whispers, "I couldn't tell you when I found out. They made me promise. Your dad wanted to be the one to tell you."

I nod and bite my lip.

"Are you okay with all of this?" she whispers.

I shrug. "I think so. I don't know."

My dad is looking over at us, and I just know that he is trying to listen so I just sit there.

Brenda smiles at me. "Amber. It's going to be so much fun. Don't worry. You're really lucky. . . . You have a great home with your mom, and now you're going to have a great home with your dad."

I, Amber Brown, hope that's true.

My father leans over and says, "Amber. Don't forget what they said at the jewelry store. You've got to put some of that ointment on your ears so that they don't get infected."

Brenda says, "I'll help her with that, Mr. Brown. If you will all excuse us for a few minutes, I'll put the ointment on so that we don't forget."

Once Brenda and I go into the bathroom so that I can privately put the ointment on my earlobes, she says, "Amber, I thought your mom told you that you couldn't have your ears pierced until you were twelve."

I try my reasoning out on her. "But my dad said that it was okay . . . and anyway it's my body, not anyone else's."

She shakes her head. "No go."

"But you have a lot of holes on your ears," I say.

"I also have a mother who gave me permission. . . . She has said that I am not to get my tongue pierced, though . . . . but I don't want to do that anyway."

"Ugh," I say.

My earlobes hurt enough.

I, Amber Brown, can not imagine what it would be like to have a pierced tongue . . . . and I'm not going to find out.

That's not something that my mother will even have to tell me not to do.

"Amber Brown," Brenda the Ambersitter says, "I don't want to be around when you have to tell your mother that you've gotten your ears pierced."

Actually, I, Amber Brown, don't want to be around then either.

Chapter Ten

"This has been a great day," my dad says, as we park in a space in front of Mom's and my house.

"Yes," I say, touching my ears.

Part of me wishes that I hadn't gotten them pierced today because I know that this day is not going to stay a great day.

"Wait 'til your mom sees your ears." My dad smiles at me.

"Wait 'til my mom sees my ears," I say, in a very quiet voice.

"Dad," I say. "Let's just sit out in the car

for a few minutes. I want to spend a little more time with you."

My dad grins.

He is sooooooooo happy that I want to spend more time with him.

And I do . . . . . and this would all be soooooo much easier if I didn't have to deal with my pierced ears and my mother.

I, Amber Brown, have wanted pierced ears for a long time and always have imagined what a happy day it would be when I finally got them.

My dad talks to me about how much fun it will be to furniture shop, how he wants to do it tomorrow. "I hope that your mother says that it's okay for you to take the day off from school. I really want to have the furniture all done by Christmas. Our house will feel so much more like a home if it is all filled with furniture."

I just nod.

My dad looks at his watch. "Honey, let's

go in now. I promised your mom that we would be back early so that you could check your homework. We don't want to do anything that will make her angry."

Too late for that, I think.

We get out of the car and walk to the door.

My dad rings the bell.

"We can just go in," I say.

My dad shakes his head. "You can just go in. . . . I can't. This is your mom's and your house . . . and I don't live here anymore, so I ring the bell."

There's so much to figure out, to work out.

My dad is trying very hard to do it all right.

I, Amber Brown, am feeling guilty for making it not all right.

"Dad," I say. "I can go in by myself. You can call Mom later."

I figure that way she'll get angry at me

first and then calm down a little by the time she talks to him.

The door opens.

It's too late.

"Sarah. Would you mind if I came in? There's something that I would like to ask you."

"Okay," she says. "Come in."

She walks into the living room, and we all sit down.

I jump up again. "I'll go upstairs and check over my homework."

"Good idea," my mom says.

I rush to go out the door and up to my room.

"Amber. Wait," my dad calls out. "Before you go, show your mom what we had done today."

I just stand there.

I look at my dad.

I look at my mom.

I cover my ears.

"Amber," my mother says softly, "show me what you did today."

"Mom," I say.

"Amber," she says.

"Amber," my dad says. "What's going on? Show your mom your new earrings."

My mom jumps up, comes over to where I am standing and says, "Amber. Take your hands away from your ears . . . and let me see what you have done."

I take my hands away from my ears.

She looks at my newly pierced ears.

"How could you???" she yells. "I told you that you would have to wait until you are twelve."

I start to cry.

She turns to my dad and yells. "And how dare you?? How dare you go against something that I have made a rule about!"

My dad says, "But I didn't know."

He looks at me.

He looks angry and sad and hurt.

"Sarah," he says. "I had no idea."

"I bet you didn't," she says, angrily.

"I didn't." Now my dad sounds angry. "Do you think that I would have done this if I knew that you had said no? We would have talked about it first if I had any idea."

"Well, you should have checked with me," she says.

"You're not the only rule maker in this family." My dad folds his arms in front of him.

"And you are not a part of this family." My mother makes a terrible face at him.

I, Amber Brown, feel sick to my stomach.

This was such a great day until now.

And now the ungreat part is just starting.

"I may not be a part of your family . . . BUT I am still a part of Amber's family . . . and I have some rights here," my dad says. "She's my daughter too."

"And where have you been when I've had to make all the decisions? You've been in Paris . . . . and now you waltz back here and expect to be able to do just what you want . . . when you want to. Philip. . . ." My mom takes a deep breath and tries to calm down. "How could you do something like this? After I told Amber today that she would have to wait."

"I told you . . . . I didn't know that," he says, looking at me.

My stomach is hurting a lot, and I don't think it's because of my hot dog meal.

I look at my dad.

I look at my mom.

I start to yell. "I'm sick of this. You each

think you own me. Daddy, you come back from Paris and now there's all this fighting about what I can do and when. Mom says one thing. You say the other. I feel like I have no say. I don't even know who I, Amber Brown, am anymore. . . . I feel like it's all up to each of you . . . and that sometimes it's not even about me . . . . it's just another way for you two to fight."

I stamp my foot.

I've never acted like this.

I am so mad that I stamp my foot again. "There . . . . that's one stamp for each of you . . . so that neither of you feel left out . . . so that neither of you feel like I'm not angry at both of you."

"Amber," my dad says. "I don't get it. We've had a great time today . . . and it's not my fault that you didn't tell me that your mom said you shouldn't get your ears pierced. If anyone here should be angry . . . it should be me . . . . and your mother. You haven't been fair to either of us."

I stamp my feet again. "Oh, okay . . . . . so NOW I see. . . . . You can both be angry but I can't . . . . it's the two of you . . . . not me. Well, I'm sick of it."

I start to cry again.

My mom looks at me. I want her to come over and hug me.

But she doesn't.

I really want my mom to hug me.

But she doesn't.

And my dad isn't hugging me either.

I, Amber Brown, feel just awful.

My mom says, "Amber. I want you to go upstairs for now, to your room. I want you to think about what you've done. And while you are doing that, your father and I are going to talk. We'll call you down after we've talked. Now go to your room right now."

"But," I start.

"Right now," she says, folding her arms in front of her.

I go to my room right now.

And I don't think I ever want to leave it again.

Chapter Eleven

I can't even look at my spelling list.

I can't even think about checking my homework.

My parents are downstairs.

I hope that they don't yell at each other.

I hope that they don't do something awful.

I hope that they don't yell at me.

I hope that this all turns out okay.

I hope that they still love me.

I pick up a mirror and look at my stupid earrings.

Why did I do something so dumb?

Why?

I think about the reasons why.

I wanted pierced ears.

I like jewelry.

All of my friends were getting their ears pierced, and I would be the only doofus without pierced ears.

Well . . . . I know not the *only* one . . . . but all my good friends (except Justin).

My mom is angry at my dad.

My dad is angry at my mom.

They are both angry at me.

I look at the earrings in the mirror.

They are pretty little gold balls . . . . just the kind that I always wanted as my starter set.

Now they'll probably tarnish, turn black, infect my earlobes, and then an infection will spread throughout my entire body.

And then I'll die . . . . and my parents will be so sorry.

I bite my lip.

Maybe they won't be so sorry.

If I'm not around, they will never have to see each other again.

I know that they'd both like that.

Well, my mom would like that.

Sometimes I think my dad still cares about my mom and wishes that they hadn't broken up . . . but now they are fighting again so who knows?

If I'm not around, my mom and Max can get married and start all over again . . . . have other kids, ones who don't want their ears pierced.

If I'm not around, my dad can live anywhere in the world that he wants to live . . . . so he won't have to stay in a place just to have joint custody.

Maybe they'll have joint custody of my grave.

I'll write out a will and leave each of them one of my earrings.

I get a note pad and pen and lie down on my bed.

My stuffed toy gorilla is sitting next to me.

"What should I leave to you?" I ask him.

He says nothing.

He is really a stuffed animal so I realize that I can't leave him anything, I will have to leave him to someone.

Brandi will get him . . . . and I'll leave the dolphin, Sushi, to Kelly.

Justin will regain custody of our chewing gum ball.

I hope that every once in a while, he will chew a piece of gum, add it to the ball, and think of me.

"Amber," my mother says, and then knocks on my door.

"Come in," I say.

She walks in the door and looks at me. "I'm glad to see that you are doing your homework."

"I'm writing my will," I say.

She looks surprised, and then she starts to smile.

I can tell that she is trying not to laugh.

I don't think it's funny, my writing my will.

"You can finish that after you come downstairs and talk with me and your father," she says.

I get up off my bed.

I just want my mom to hug me, and she isn't doing that.

We go downstairs.

My parents have been drinking coffee.

They seem very calm.

I sit down.

They both look at me.

For a minute, none of us say anything.

They both keep looking at me.

My mom speaks first. "Amber. Do you know what you have done that is wrong?"

I sigh.

I wish that they would tell me what I did rather than making me guess . . . . or tell them.

"Yes," I say. "I asked your permission to do something and you said no . . . and then I did it anyway."

She nods. "And?"

"And I'm sorry." I say.

"That's good," she says. "And . . . ."

Now, I, Amber Brown, am lost.

I've told her what I did.

I said I was sorry.

"And . . . ." both of my parents say at the same time.

Usually when two people say the same

thing at the same time, I yell "pinkies" and the two people have to link pinkies.

This time I don't think it is a good time.

Probably if I yelled "Thumbs down" that would be something that they would do . . . . to me.

"And . . . ." I say, and then pause. "You've got to help me with this, please."

My mom shakes her head but my dad

speaks. "And you got me involved in it. You never told me that your mom said no."

"But I didn't lie," I say.

"But you didn't tell the truth," my mom says.

My dad nods.

This is sooooooooooo hard.

I wish that there was something that I could do.

All of this talking is making me very nervous.

I just want to get to the end of this conversation to find out what is going to happen to me, to my earrings, to my going shopping, to their ever loving me again.

We talk . . . . . . about what I did . . . . . how from now on, my mom and dad are going to talk things out, let each other know what's happening, what they feel . . . . they also say that they will talk to me about what I feel . . . . and that there will be times of disagreement, but we'll all try to work it out.

I have to promise not to "play one parent against the other."

"Can I go shopping with Dad tomorrow?" I ask.

"No," they both say at exactly the same time.

It's another "link pinkies" moment . . . . only I wish that they had both said yes.

I've wanted my parents to agree on stuff for a long time.

Now I'm not so sure that I like it.

My mom says, "Your father has explained to me why it is so important to get the furniture now. So after we're done talking about all of this, you and your father will be able to look at the catalogs and pick things out that way. But you can NOT take the day off."

My dad nods.

"So that's my punishment?" I ask.

"Part of it . . . although even if you weren't being punished, I don't think that I would have allowed you to miss school. . . . I don't think Mrs. Holt would have given permission. As for the rest of your punishment, we're still working that out . . . . we're not totally sure of what we are going to do, what you will have to do."

"May I keep the earrings?" I ask.

My mom sighs. "I have to think about that. There are so many choices. At the moment I am thinking that you will have to take them out tonight and let the holes close up, but I'm not sure."

At the moment, I, Amber Brown, am thinking that I don't like what my mom is thinking.

I am hoping that I can get her to change her mind.

I look over at my dad and make a kind of begging face.

He shakes his head. "This is a decision that your mother and I have to make together."

He looks at my mom and frowns. "And it's one that we haven't been able to reach agreement on."

She looks at him and frowns back.

I have one very annoyed mom, and I don't think that I'm the only one that she is annoyed with.

I think that my dad is also annoyed.

. . . . And I don't think that this is just about me.

I'm afraid that my parents are going to start fighting with each other.

The doorbell rings.

Saved by the bell.

Chapter Twelve

This has turned into the longest day of my life.

Most days, there's just normal every day things happening.

Today, more things have happened than usually happens in a week: wake up . . . . . make presents . . . . uncrazyglue myself . . . . . . go out with my dad, get my ears pierced, see my new house and meet a whole bunch of new people who are now going to be part of my life . . . . and then it's back home with mom finding out about my ears . . . . going to my room . . . . . making a will . . . then there's this big scene with my parents . . . . and now the doorbell rings.

I, Amber Brown, am not sure that more can happen on this day.

I rush to the door.

"I'm home," the voice says.

It's Max.

This is not really his home.

He doesn't stay here . . . but he likes to say that to practice for when he and Mom will be married and he will be living here.

I hope that my dad doesn't hear Max say, "I'm home."

I open the door.

He's carrying a huge box of things for our bowling team's Christmas party. There is a Pinster Piñata that I helped him make when Mom and I went over to his house one day. There is a battery-run bowling Santa . . . and the pins are his elves. I painted the pins to look like elves. And there are candies and cookies and little awards for each person on the team.

Max is the best coach in the world.

"So what happened on this day of December 12?" Max asks.

I remember what I read this morning. "On this day in 1901, some guy named Macaroni sent the first radio signal across the Atlantic Ocean. It went from Cornwall, England, to Newfoundland, Canada."

Max smiles. "Marconi. Not Macaroni. . . . . Unless he had a pasta life."

Max laughs at his own joke, which I, Amber Brown, don't get.

"Where's our Sarah?" he asks.

"They went into the kitchen," I say. "She and Dad are talking."

He walks into the kitchen.

When Mom sees Max, she jumps up and gives him a kiss.

Then Max says hello to my dad.

My dad says hello back.

Neither of them is smiling.

I take a deep breath and wonder what's going to happen next.

Mom says, "Honey."

All three of us say "Yes."

My dad, Max, and me.

"Max." My mom kisses his cheek. "Amber and Philip are going to be in the kitchen for awhile, picking out some things for Philip's new house."

Max nods.

Mom continues. "So let's go into the living room and talk about the team's Christmas party. Let's let Philip and Amber do their selecting."

"Okay." Max goes over to the refrigerator, opens the door, and pulls out a can of root beer for himself and a can of seltzer for my mom. "Can I interest either of you in something to drink?"

My dad shakes his head no.

I ask for and get some orange juice.

My dad watches as they leave the room.

Then he opens the catalog and says, "On your mark . . . . . . get set . . . . . . shop. We have a house that we want to turn into a home."

And we shop.

Chapter Thirteen

"*Barukh atah Adonai, Eloheynu melekh ha-olam, asher kid'shanu be-mitzvotav ve-tzivanu le-hadlik ner shel Hanukkah.*" Max recites the blessing in Hebrew as he lights the candles on the menorah.

I, Amber Brown, read the English translation. "Praised are You, O Lord, Our God, King of the Universe, who sanctified us with His commandments and commanded us to kindle the Hanukkah lights."

"It's time to play with the dreidel," Max says.

Mom, Max, and I spin the dreidel and I, Amber Brown, win a lot of candy money.

Then we give each other presents.

I, Amber Brown, tell Max to open his first even though I really want to open mine first. I really want him to like his present.

Actually, I really love opening presents so Max lets me unwrap his, and then he looks at the bowling salt and pepper shakers.

"Just what I needed!" He gives me a hug.

"Even though you already have salt and pepper shakers at your house?" I ask.

He nods. "I really need these. My house has been wanting things that are made for me by a child whom I love."

"And who loves you," I say softly.

We give each other a hug.

I look over at my mom.

She's starting to cry, just a little.

But she's smiling a lot.

"Are you crying because you know that in about six months these salt and pepper shakers will be living with us? I know that they are not your favorite items," I tease her.

She wipes at her tears and keeps on smiling. "No. I'm just happy. You know that."

"Open your present." I hand it to her. "It's from Max and me."

She starts to unwrap the present and then hands it to me. "You can unwrap it if you want."

I want.

I do love unwrapping presents, even if they are not for me, even if I am giving them to the other person and know exactly what's in it.

I hand it back to my mom. "We worked on this the night you had to work late, and Max came over to keep me company."

It's a photo album, covered in velvet and filled with pictures of me, of Max, and of my mom, Max, and me all together.

My mom looks at it and her eyes start to tear again.

"Cry baby," I say.

"My baby," she says, hugging me.

"I'm not a baby anymore," I remind her.

"You'll always be my baby," she says.

"Mom," I say.

She hugs me again and then Max says, "Now for your present."

He picks it up and brings it over to me. It looks heavy the way he's carrying it.

I reach for it.

"Let's put it on the table," Max says. "It'll be safer that way."

I, Amber Brown, have no idea what it is.

It's a kind of big box, one that Max had hidden in a small suitcase.

It's the first time that I've seen it.

Maybe it's the computer game thing that I asked for.

I want to shake it, but he's said to be careful so I am.

I just tip it a little.

It's very heavy.

I rip off the wrapping and open the box.

Inside the present is wrapped in a green garbage bag, like the ones that I used to wrap Justin and Danny's presents.

It's a ball.

It's a bowling ball.

It's a pink glitter bowling ball.

And my name is engraved on it . . . .

I turn it around. "There are no holes."

Max laughs. "It's a new way of bowling."

I look at him.

"Joke," he says. "We'll take it over to the sports shop and they'll drill holes in it that will be perfect for your fingers."

I hug the bowling ball.

"It's got to have a name," I say.

We start to think of names for the bowling ball. Split. Spare. Rover. Spot. Turkey. The Pink Comet. Destructo. The Avenger. Dropsy. The Ballamatic.

Finally, I think of one that I like. "It's called B.B., short for bowling ball . . . . so it will always be my B.B."

"And you will always be my baby," my mom says.

I cross my eyes at her.

"Max, thank you so much," I say. "Could I borrow that suitcase to keep B.B. in?"

He nods and smiles. "Okay . . . but something tells me that tomorrow when we light the candles there just might be something to keep that in."

"A bowling ball bag?" I ask. "Is it a pink glitter one?"

Max shrugs. "You'll see tomorrow."

"Oh no." I remember. "Tomorrow I'm going to be with my dad."

Actually, I, Amber Brown, have been looking forward to going over to my dad's house and seeing all of the things that we picked out.

This is my weekend with Dad, our time to be together before Christmas.

This will be my first time to stay over in my dad's and my house.

But I also want to be together with Mom and Max, and not just because of my bowling bag present.

I really like celebrating Hanukkah with Max . . . . and not just because of the presents.

Mom and Max and me. Dad and me.

I can't be in both places at the same time.

This is not easy.

And it's really just beginning.

It's going to be like this for the rest of my kid life.

I, Amber Brown, think about this.

I will probably have to be split like this forever.

Even when I am a grown-up.

I will always have to make choices.

Yikes! Double yikes.

It's weird.

In some ways, my life is better since my parents got divorced.

In some ways, it's harder.

But this is my life, and I've got to try to make it work out.

"Never mind," my mom says. "When you come back on Sunday, it will still be Hanukkah . . . . and we'll celebrate it then."

"And you will get your purple glitter bowling bag then," Max says, and then covers his mouth. "Ooops."

"Not very good at keeping secrets, are we???!!!!" my mom says, putting her arm around his waist.

He shakes his head and grins.

I think about my pink glitter bowling ball and my purple glitter bowling bag.

I may not be the best bowler in the league, but I will certainly be the most colorful.

And I, Amber Brown, love being colorful.

Chapter Fourteen

"Wow!" I say. "Dad, my room looks terrific."

He grins. "It does, doesn't it? It was amazing. One day the furniture was delivered . . . and the next day, four guys arrived from the company I called and in a few hours they assembled everything."

I look around my room.

There are two bureaus, a wardrobe closet, a desk, and a chair.

"Hooks are on the wall. The rug is on the floor. Curtains are hung." My dad points things out. "I did all of that. I also hung the shower curtain in your bathroom and put away all of the linens and the kitchen stuff."

"Wow," I say again. "You did all of that."

He grins. "Well, most of it. Mrs. Garfield, who cleans the Marshalls' house, helped me. She'll be working for us too."

"That means I won't have to make my bed?" I ask.

"No," he answers. "She'll be here only one day a week. You make your own bed, except for the day that she's working here."

"Shucks," I say.

My dad sits down on the office chair. "Amber, how are we going to work out your clothes? Do you want to bring some of them over here? That way you won't have to carry a suitcase to school on afternoons that you will be coming over to my house after you've been staying at your mother's."

I, Amber Brown, haven't thought about that. "I don't know. I'll talk to Mom."

He nods. "Okay . . . . and as for Christmas, I will give you a gift certificate to a department store, and you and your mom can go shopping for clothes for you."

I wonder if Mom will want to shop for stuff that will be staying in my Dad's house.

I just don't know.

I guess that my dad doesn't either because he says, "I can have Brenda Ambersit one day and take you shopping."

"Great," I say.

"Actually, I'm not so sure that's a good idea," he says.

"But it's your idea," I remind him.

"You won't end up dressing like Brenda?" He shakes his head. "She's a very nice person, but she has very strange taste."

"You mean like the things she's wearing today?" I say, remembering what she looked like when we came into the house and saw Polly and Brenda heading out the door.

Brenda had on a black skirt with a pink poodle on it over her leggings . . . . and she was wearing a black T-shirt that says "Retro lives."

I, Amber Brown, have no idea who Retro is or where he, she, or it lives, but I thought that Brenda looked really great. I especially loved her pink high top sneakers and her lacy black and pink socks.

"I liked what Polly was wearing," I say, remembering Polly's black leggings and long turquoise sweater. "Maybe Brenda and Polly and I can go shopping together."

I wonder how I, Amber Brown, would look dressed up like Brenda, but don't tell my father that.

"Great idea," my dad says. "After Christmas, I'll send the three of you shopping . . . . and I'll treat everyone to lunch."

"Great." I think of all of the things that I can get.

There are some definite pluses to being a shared custody kid, even though this whole thing still makes me a little nervous.

"Amber. Mr. Brown," Savannah yells down from upstairs. "Is it okay if I come downstairs?"

"Yes," my dad and I yell at the same time.

"Pinkies," I say to my dad, holding up my pinky.

We link pinkies.

My dad starts to laugh. "Amber, the other day at work, my boss and I said the same thing at the same time and I yelled 'Link Pinkies.' I was very embarrassed."

I giggle. "What did your boss say? Did he think you are weird?"

My dad continues to laugh. "Actually, he

has a six-year-old daughter who makes him do it everytime they say something at the same time. So, he just linked pinkies."

Savannah and Dylan come running into the room.

They are really laughing.

They are holding something behind their backs.

"Guess," Dylan yells. "You've got to guess what we have."

I hate this game right now.

I like to HAVE someone else have to guess, but I don't like it when I have to be the guesser.

"You'll never guess." Dylan is jumping up and down.

Even more than having to guess, I hate being told that I'll never guess.

Finally, Dylan pulls something out from behind his back.

It's a lollipop, attached to the back half of a rubber rat.

Savannah has one that is a lollipop, attached to the back half of a rubber frog.

Gross. Really gross.

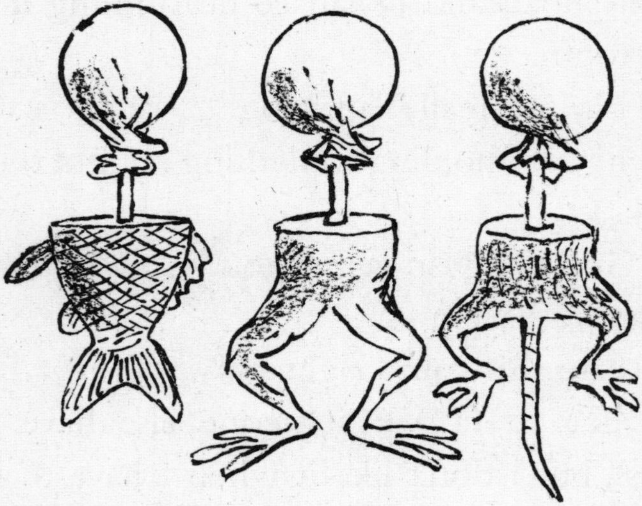

I have to get one!

"Merry Christmas early," Savannah says, handing me a badly wrapped present. "Since you aren't going to be here until after Christmas, we're giving this to you early."

It's a lollipop, with the back half of a rubber fish on it.

I really like it.

"Thank you," I say.

We all put the lollipops in our mouths and look like we have a fish, a frog, and a rat coming out of our mouths.

It's truly disgusting . . . and I really, really like it.

Something tells me that I'm really going have fun living in the same house with the Marshalls.

Chapter Fifteen

Dear Amber,

Surprise . . . . a Christmas card from your old friend, Justin Daniels. (Remember me??????) Mom said I should write to you. (You know that I hate to write. I wish that you still lived next door . . . . even though the boys around here *really* tease if a boy is friends with a girl . . . but we would be friends anyway . . . you're still the same . . . you don't do anything dumb like collect Barbie dolls or Beanie Babies, do you????)

The package from you and your mom just arrived at our house . . . . but mom said that we can't open it until Christmas . . . . but even wrapped, Danny and I have figured out what you sent us. (We've been bouncing the wrapped presents from you around . . . . the bows came off but it still looks good.) Anyway, we hope that we are right about what's in there . . . . and that it is unbreakable . . . . or my mom is going to be really mad at us.

Only two more days until Christmas. . . . I can't wait.

Well, Merry Christmas and Happy New Year.

Justin

P.S. My parents said that as one of my Christmas presents, I'm going to get a gift certificate to go away to camp this summer. Why don't you ask your parents if you can go too?

Chapter Sixteen

Dear Justin,

Finally, FINALLY, a letter from you!

I am soooooooo glad.

Actually, your Christmas card arrived right after Christmas. (Do you still turn your homework assignments in late??????)

A late Merry Christmas and an almost Happy New Year to you! (And Happy Hanukkah to you even though you don't celebrate it

. . . . . . I do now . . . . . . and actually I think it's great to know about everyone's holidays . . . . next year I'm going to learn all about Kwanza.)

There is so much to tell you . . . . but I'm getting ready to return to my mom's and my house. (I'm at my dad's and my house right now.)

I live in two houses now . . . . . it's not always easy.

Sometimes I want to wear something, and it's at the other house.

Sometimes I want to finish reading a book, and it's at the other house.

Sometimes when I'm with my dad, I get homesick for my mom.

Sometimes when I'm with my mom, I get homesick for my dad.

. . . . And when I'm at one house and not the other, I wonder what

I'm missing at the house that I am not at.

Phew.

But I am definitely glad that my dad has moved back.

He's really sorry that he left, but we've talked about that . . . and I understand it a little better. (I wish that I didn't have to think about things like my parents' breakup and how they felt afterwards and why they did the things they do . . . . but I do, especially with my father.) Sometimes all of this makes me feel more grown-up than I want to be . . . but what the heck!

At my dad's house, there is a family that lives upstairs.

I think that you would really like the boy, Dylan . . . . . he's a couple of years older than us . . . . but he's funny a lot of the time. (When he's not being a pain.) Yesterday, he put half of a plastic rat under my pillow so that when I went to bed and pulled back the covers, there it was. (My screaming scared everyone in the house . . . . everyone but Dylan, that is!!!!!!!) He's a real trickster . . . and a pain, sometimes . . . . but I think that the two of you would really get along.

Guess what!?!? My ears are pierced!!! I did it without my mom's permission . . . I know, Bad Amber! You thought that my ears would have to be closed up . . . . . . or, even worse, kept open, OR that I could only wear Barney or Barbie earrings. BUT that didn't happen. I had to repay my dad for the piercing, pay if they got infected (they haven't), and I can only use the starter pair until I am twelve. I know . . . you, Justin Daniels, are saying, "Girl stuff. Piercing your ears. Yuck!" But it is important to me.

There's lots more going on . . . . but I know that you don't like to talk seriously, so I talk to Brandi and Kelly about a lot of stuff . . . and now I can also talk to Brenda, my Ambersitter . . . . and to Polly and Savannah, the other two kids who live upstairs.

I know that you hate when I say things that sound "mushy," but I still miss you lots . . . . and I think it's a great idea for both of us to go to the same camp this summer. I'm going to BEG my parents to let me go.

So, I hope that you have a Happy

New Year . . . that lots of good and interesting things happen. (And when is your new baby brother or sister going to be born????)

I wish you a Happy New Year . . . And I wish me one, too.

Love,

Amber

Rave Reviews for Harry S. P

♥ "...(differs) from the others in its natu... of outdoors activities and unusual offbeat adventures...mention of transportation challenges and unusual accommodations leads the visitor away from well-worn paths."

—*The Bookwatch*

♥ "..this extensive, up-to-date guide for Costa Rica is a welcome sight. Selected accommodations and restaurants span the scale from luxury to low budget, while the author's respectful, ecologically aware perspective contributes a progressive view of the sights and scenes encompassed in mountains and lowlands, rain forests, and beaches."

— *American Library Association Booklist*

♥ "Pariser's book may be the best-balanced, most comprehensive guide of the entire Tico bunch. .This is the one to take with you on your next trip around Costa Rica."

— Lan Sluder, *Great Expedition*

♥ "..straighforward, easy to use...valuable practical tips...beautiful color photos..."

— Gypsy Cole, *The Tico Times* (a Costa Rican English-language weekly)

♥ "This book will be one you'll want in your library and to carry with you on your next trip to Costa Rica.... The...references are excellent and good reading. If you want to expand your knowledge about Costa Rica..then buy a copy of this book and READ it! You'll enjoy the light writing style."

— Shirley Miller, *Costa Rica Outlook*

♥ "Thank you for traveling with me though Costa Rica. ...I feel like we are friends, since you recently accompanied me for two weeks of bliss."

— D. H., Springfield, IL

♥ "...a great deal of practical information..."

— *The Bergen Record*

♥ "...the definitive book to read...well-written and well-researched...you are shown the best jungle hikes, the best jungle hikes, the best beaches with top offshore diving and snorkeling locations, white water rivers suitable for rafting/kayaking (with recommended outfitters), tips for bird watching, and mucn more... I recommend that you buy this book."

— *Travel Books Review*

♥ "Your material about Tortuguero National Park is solid... I even learned a thing or two..."

— Daryl Loth, CEO, Tortuguero Safaris

♥ "Lovely, absolutely lovely..very well researched and fair!"

— Joelle, Webmistress, www.Cahuita.com

This book is dedicated to **Dai Qing**, *a courageous journalist who continues to battle for the future of China's environment. For more information on her see* http://www.catch22.com/~vudu/daiqing.html

Cover set in Sabon. Text set in Trump Medieval and Avenir. Maps set in Avenir. Design by Harry S. Pariser. Cover photo by Fred Aspinall; used courtesy of his son John. Mouse opossum and rainforest bat, courtesy of Sergio Miranda. All other photos by Harry S. Pariser. Cover design by Eric Gauvin Design (egauvin@pacbell.net) in collaboration with Harry S. Pariser. Photos and maps are available for license: contact the publisher.

Explore Costa Rica

Harry S. Pariser

manatee press
San Francisco

www.savethemanatee.com

Manatee Press
P. O. Box 225001
San Francisco, CA 94122-5001
(415) 665-4829
fax 810-314-0685
single-copy orders *only*: 800-729-6423
www.savethemanatee.com
editorial@savethemanatee.com

ISBN 1-893643-50-6

Other Books by Harry S. Pariser

Explore Belize ISBN 1-55650-785-2

Explore the Dominican Republic ISBN 1-55650-814-X

Explore Barbados *(June 2000)* ISBN 1-893643-51-4

Handheld computer versions (Palm OS and Windows CE) of Explore Costa Rica are available at **www.peanutpress.com**. Adobe Acrobat (PDF) versions available at **www.fatbrain.com**. For more information visit your private site at www.savethemanatee.com/innersoul ***login:*** manati ***password*** bluesea. ***Free updates available here!***

About the Author

Mr. Pariser is a writer, artist, photographer, and graphic designer. Born and raised in southwestern Pennsylvania, he is a graduate of the College of Communications of Boston University.

Mr. Pariser's first two books *Guide to Jamaica* and *Guide to Puerto Rico and the Virgin Islands* were published in 1986 and 1987 and were among the first titles ever published by the then-fledgling Moon Publications. Harry first became involved in publishing when, for his first book, he sojourned at Moon's Chico "office" a small house and helped layout the books. At that time, he worked on a Tandy TRS-80, a clunky DOS computer which used 5.25-inch floppy disks. Text was formatted in a giant typesetter; output and photos and illustrations were shot individually and then pasted up. Maps were made on special paper and hand drawn with technical pen and used labels which were pasted on. Today, all of this is done with computers!

Mr. Pariser has lived in Japan: in Kyoto, in the historical city of Kanazawa (facing the Japan Sea), and in Kagoshima, a city at the southern tip of Kyushu across the bay from an active volcano.He has traveled extensively in Europe, Africa, Asia, Central America, and the Caribbean. His articles and photographs have appeared in *The Japan Times, Costa Rica Outlook, Belize First, Caribbean Travel & Life, the San Jose Mercury News, San Francisco Frontlines, Atevo.com, Yack.com,* among others.

His books include *Adventure Guide to Costa Rica*, Explore Belize, *Explore the Dominican Republic, Adventure Guide to the Virgin Islands, Adventure Guide to Puerto Rico, Jamaica: A Visitor's Guide*, and *Adventure Guide to Barbados*.

Mr. Pariser studied printmaking in Japan and San Francisco; batik design in Malaysia and Indonesia; and Spanish, Chinese Painting, Pagemaker, Filemaker Pro, Quark, Internet Journalism, Newspaper Pagination, Illustrator, Typography, and Photoshop at City College in San Francisco. He speaks Japanese, Indonesian, and Spanish.

Besides spending considerable time getting computers and programs to do what he needs them to do, his pursuits include painting, cooking, backpacking and hiking, photography, and listening to music — especially jazz, salsa, calypso, and African pop. His other interests range from politics to anthropology to linguistics to cinema, theater, and literature. He built his first website in 1994. He lives in the Inner Sunet area of San Francisco where he is active in preserving the neighborhood character. Mr. Pariser received the Society of American Travel Writer's Lowell Thomas Award 1995 Best Guidebook Award (Silver) for his *Adventure Guide to Barbados*. He is a member of the National Writers Union (www.nwu.org) and www.guidebookwriters.com.

Reader's Response Form

Explore Costa Rica

I found your book rewarding because ______________________________
____
____

Your book could be improved by ________________________________
____

The best places I stayed in were (explain why) ____________________
____
____
____

I found the best food at______________________________________
____

Some good and bad experiences I had were_________________________
____

Will you return to Costa Rica?_______.

If not, why not? ____
____
____

If so, where do you plan to go? ________________________________
____
____

I purchased this book at _______________________________________

I learned about this book from __________________________________

I also own (*circle*) the Palm Pilot version of this book and the ematter.com version (PDF) of this book.

Please include any other comments on a separate sheet and mail completed form to Manatee Press or fax to 650-573-9670. Or e-mail comments to **editorial@savethemanatee.com**.

A note on prices

Establishments for which no prices are listed are classified as follows: **low budget** (less than $20 d), **inexpensive** ($20-30 d), **moderate** ($31-50 d), **expensive** ($51-90 d), **luxury** ($90-120), and **ultra-luxury** (over $120 d). All prices are high-season and do not include taxes and meals unless specified otherwise. Always confirm prices and ask about surcharges for credit cards.

Acknowledgements

Thanks go out to William Thomas Douglas, Sergio Miranda, Eduardo and Sergio Miranda, Greg and Brian Chavez, Amso Bien, Howard K. Solomon, Michael S. Kaye, Terry Pratt, Amos Bien, Barbara MacGregor, Marco Montoya (Grano de Oro), Daryl Loth (photo and Tortuguero Revisions), Joelle, Richard Krug, Milton and Diana Lieberman, Rocio Lopez and to many others. Special thanks go out to my instructors at City College San Francisco's graphic design, journalism, and photography departments: Margaret Hock, John Seckman, Lorraine Leber, George Shirk, Sharron Evans, Eric Sinclair, Suzanne Korey, Andrea Schwartz, and Kathy Walkup. Matthew Shambrom was very helpful with my page setup in Quark. In addition to helping with the cover, Eric Gauvin was also of tremendous assistance with technical questions. Sarge Holtzman, Jack Handler, and Frank Free answered many legal questions. Thanks to Joyce Huber, Arthur Koch, Ron and Pam Lippert, Meg White, Anna Conti and David Sumner, Ida, Ricky Weisbroth, Grant Rauscher, Shane Hill, Janet Byron, and Cate Corcoran, for their support. Pat Bliss answered many questions. Howard Karel and Aaron Silverman provided useful suggestions. Fred Adler was also of great assistance. Special thanks go to Debbie Dachner and Natalie Sáenz of JGR & Associates who do such a truly exceptional job on behalf of the ICT. A final thank you goes out to my mother who always worries about me.

Table of Contents

Introduction

Practicalities

Travel Section

Puntarenas to Panama 357

Abbreviations

N	North	C	*Calle* or *colones*
S	South	OW	one way
E	East	RT	round trip
W	West	ha	hectare(s)
pd	per day	L	left
pp	per person	R	right
s	single	km	kilometer(s)
db	double	mi.	mile(s)
t	triple	ICT	C. R. Tourism Institute

free web updates

www.savethemanatee.com

Explore Costa Rica: Fast Facts: A-Z

Accommodation — Every type of hotel in every price range is available as are some campgrounds. The nicest hotels and lodges tend to be small, intimate affairs.

Area Code — To dial Costa Rica from outside the country dial 1-506 and the number. Omit the area code when dialing within Costa Rica.

Art and artists — There are a number of fine artists and craftspeople in Costa Rica. The best places to visit studios are in the Monteverde and Escazú areas.

Business Hours — Generally from 8-noon and 1-5 or 2-5. Many close on Sun. as do restaurants. Banks are generally open Mon. to Fri. from 9-3.

Camping —There are few organized campsites. Tent-supplied "gourmet" camping is an up-and-coming phenomenon.

Clothes —Informal is the rule. You won't need much if any in the way of warm clothing.

Car rental — Cars may be rented at the airport, in San José, and in select location such as Liberia (Guanacaste) and Quepos (Manuel Antonio).

Credit Cards — Generally accepted. However may be subject to a surcharge by hotels.

Currency—The Costa Rican *colón* is divided into 100 *centavos*. You will get around US$1=C300 , more or less. Cash is better than traveler's checks in terms of rates, but the difference is small.

Departure tax — US$18

Driving — Driving is on the opposite side as in the US. Valid drivers licenses are required. A credit card is required to rent a vehicle.

Electricity —110 Volts AC

Internet —Public access is very limited. There are one or two commercial businesses in San José, along with one in the outlying suburb of San Pedro, and some hotels will allow you to send and receive e-mail messages.

Language — Spanish is the offical language. English is widely spoken at touristic spots, but Spanish is important for getting around. There are a large number of schools which teach Spanish.

Laundry — Laundromats are scarce. Most hotels will do laundry for a fee. Save by bringing some detergent and washing a few small items yourself.

Liquor Laws —Alcohol is available from any store. Dry laws are in effect for two days during Easter and two days before and after a presidential election.

Mail — Expect it to take at least a week to the States. Rates are cheap.

Maps —Good maps are hard to find. Obtain the ITMB map before arriving.

Marriage — Possible to do it here. Costa Ricans often live "common law," thus depriving divorce lawyers of income.

Newspapers —*The Miami Herald* (US$1.25) is available daily in tourist centers. The weekly tabloid *The Tico Times* is the only local English-language read.

Pets —Leave them at home if at all possible. Otherwise, you will require proof of rabies and distemper vaccinations.

Radio/TV —Many tourist hotels have satellite TV or cable. There are over a hundred AM and FM radio stations, but reception can be poor in the hinterlands.

Restrooms/toilets — Called servicios or sanatarios. "Caballeros "means men and "Damas "means women.

Ruins — Nothing outstanding. The most interesting archaeological site is at Guayabo National Monument. The Jade and Gold museums in San José have outstanding collections of artifacts. If in the area, the unusual stone spheres near Palmar Sur are worthy of a visit.

Taxes — Government tax of 3% is added to accommodation. VAT tax (15%) is added to meals, tours, and other items. Smaller establishments are not required to charge, and this latter tax may be modified in 1998.

Taxis — Metered in San José. Make sure that the night meter (20% addtional) is not turned on during the day. Rides in rural areas tend to be extortionate.

Telephones — Service is good. Internal calls are inexpensive. Phone cards are available and may be used at phones marked "chip." Pay phones are scarce. Dial 116 to reach an international operator. For calling card and collect calls reach AT&T at 0-800-011-4114, MCI at 0-800-012-2222, Sprint at 0-800-013-0213, and Canada Bell at 0-800-015-1162. To call Costa Rica from the US dial 1, then 506, then the local number.

Theft — Don't walk around San José at night with valuables. Never leave anything of value in a vehicle, not even for a moment! Pickpockets frequent buses.

Time— Costa Rica operates on Central Standard Time (six hours behind GMT, Greenwich mean time).

Tipping — A 10% service charge is generally already added to restaurant bills so added tipping is not necessary. Bellhops receive around 200 *colónes* per bag. Taxi drivers are not tipped. Many hotels leave envelopes in the room with which to tip maids. Guides are often tipped.

Visas — With a few exceptions, you will not need a visa. Entry permits are valid for 30 days.

Water — Generally safe to drink. The more cautious may prefer to stick to bottled water. If you are staying at a lodge, ask at the front desk about the safety of the water.

Costa Rica encompasses an area half the size of Ireland and slightly larger than Bhutan. It brings together pronounced geographical extremes — ranging from spectacular beaches to majestic volcanoes, to swampy lowlands with swarms of birds, to highlands which turn frigid at night. In addition to traditional Tico hospitality, Costa Rica offers hiking and water sports, casinos and discos, and other attractions. Its wealth of wildlife which makes it a paradise for naturalists and birdwatchers.

The Land

Geography

Covering 19,653 sq. mi. (50,900 sq km), an area a bit smaller than West Virginia, Costa Rica lies on a NW-SE axis between Nicaragua to the N and Panama to the S. Costa Rica extends 288 mi. (464 km) N to S and 170 mi. (274 km) E to W, and no part of the country is more than 300 mi. (200 km) from the sea. A series of cordilleras (mountain ranges), ridges, and valleys traverse the nation's length. Its unoffical border with Nicaragua, accepted provisionally by both sides, extends for 186 mi. (300 km) along the N. its S border with Panama covers 226 mi. (363 km). This border was definitively delineated only in 1941 after a century-long dispute.

MOUNTAINS: The nation has four principal mountain ranges. The Cordillera Volcanía de Guanacaste lies in the far NW; to the S rises the lower and smaller Cordillera de Tilarán. Farther S still are the Cordillera Central followed by the Cordillera de Talamanca. Although the last is of non-volcanic origin, the latter two sets of ranges contain several volcanoes.

The Big Picture

The Central American isthmus is the only region in the world which is both interoceanic and intercontinental. Bordered by Mexico to the N and Colombia to the S, the region geogaphically comprises seven nations: Belize, Guatemala, El Salvador, Honduras, Nicaragua, Costa Rica, and Panama. All of the nations except Belize are former members of the Spanish Empire, although some contain large indigenous populations, and they share a similar cultural base which includes the Spanish language and the Catholic religion. Despite their surface similarities, each has evolved its own national character, making union unlikely. To the region's N lies Mexico, and to its S lies the continent of South America, to which the region connects at Columbia.

VOLCANOES: Costa Rica's volcanoes — Poás, Irazú, Rincón de la Vieja, Arenal, Tenorio, Turrialba, and Barua — are perhaps the most spectacular geographic features. Around C you're certain to notice volcanic sand, which is either black or light grey. While the light-colored sand is from obsidian, the black sand comes from pumice.

The term **volcano** (volcán in Spanish) derives from Vulcano, an active volcanic island off the N tip of Sicily, which was believed to be the entrance to the nether world and the domain of Vulcan, the Roman deity who forged armor as well as Jupiter's thunderbolts. Universally, volcanoes have similarly been linked with hell, gods, and demons.

Magma is molten rock generated through the melting of rocks in the crust and upper mantle, the thin outer shell of the Earth; it is less dense than solid rock. Its buoyancy causes it to rise to the surface as well as the hill or mountain which results as the magma cools and

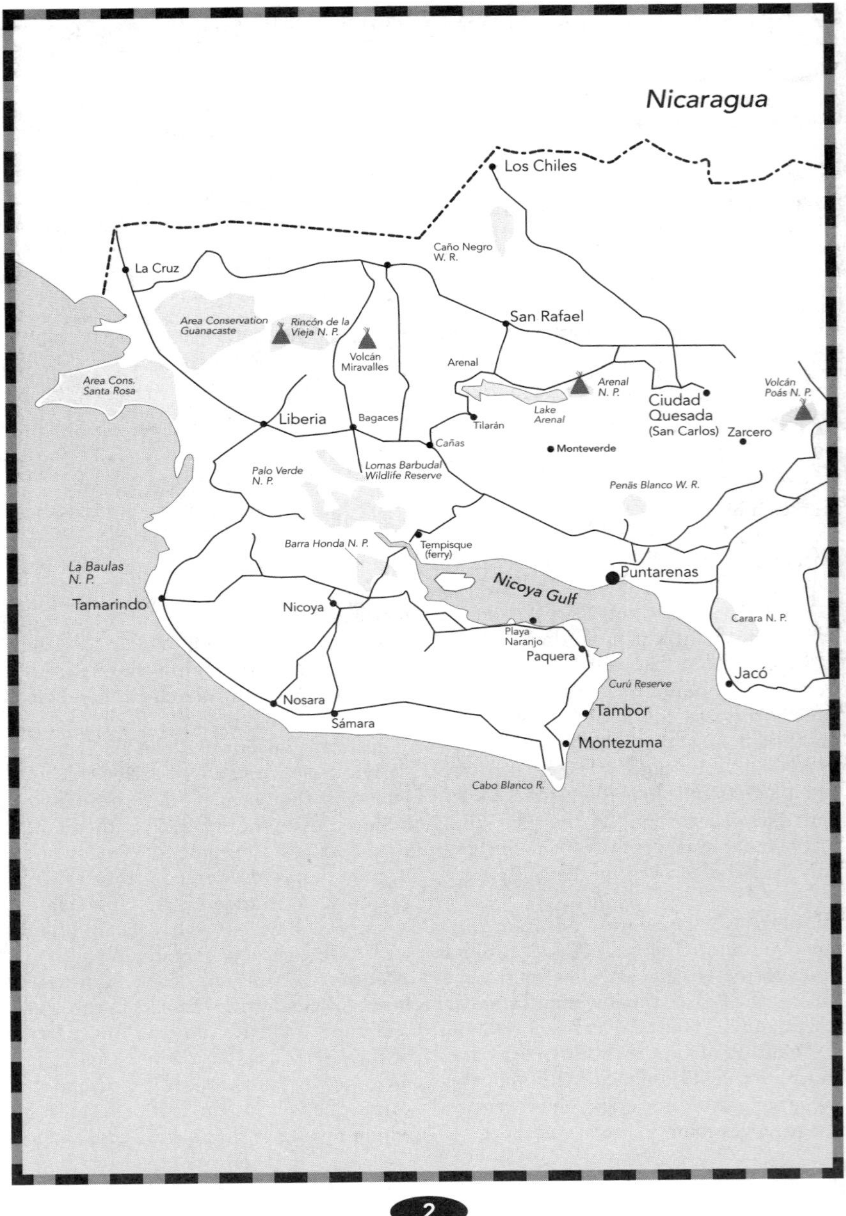

Nicaragua
Los Chiles
Caño Negro
W. R.
La Cruz
San Rafael
Area Conservation
Guanacaste
Rincón de la
Vieja N. P.
Volcán
Miravalles
Arenal
Arenal
N. P.
Volcán
Poás N. P.
Area Cons.
Santa Rosa
Ciudad
Quesada
(San Carlos)
Zarcero
Lake
Arenal
Liberia
Bagaces
Tilarán
Cañas
Monteverde
Palo Verde
N. P.
Lomas Barbudal
Wildlife Reserve
Penãs Blanco W. R.
Barra Honda N. P.
Tempisque
(ferry)
La Baulas
N. P.
Puntarenas
Nicoya Gulf
Tamarindo
Nicoya
Carara N. P.
Playa
Naranjo
Paquera
Jacó
Curú Reserve
Nosara
Tambor
Sámara
Montezuma
Cabo Blanco R.

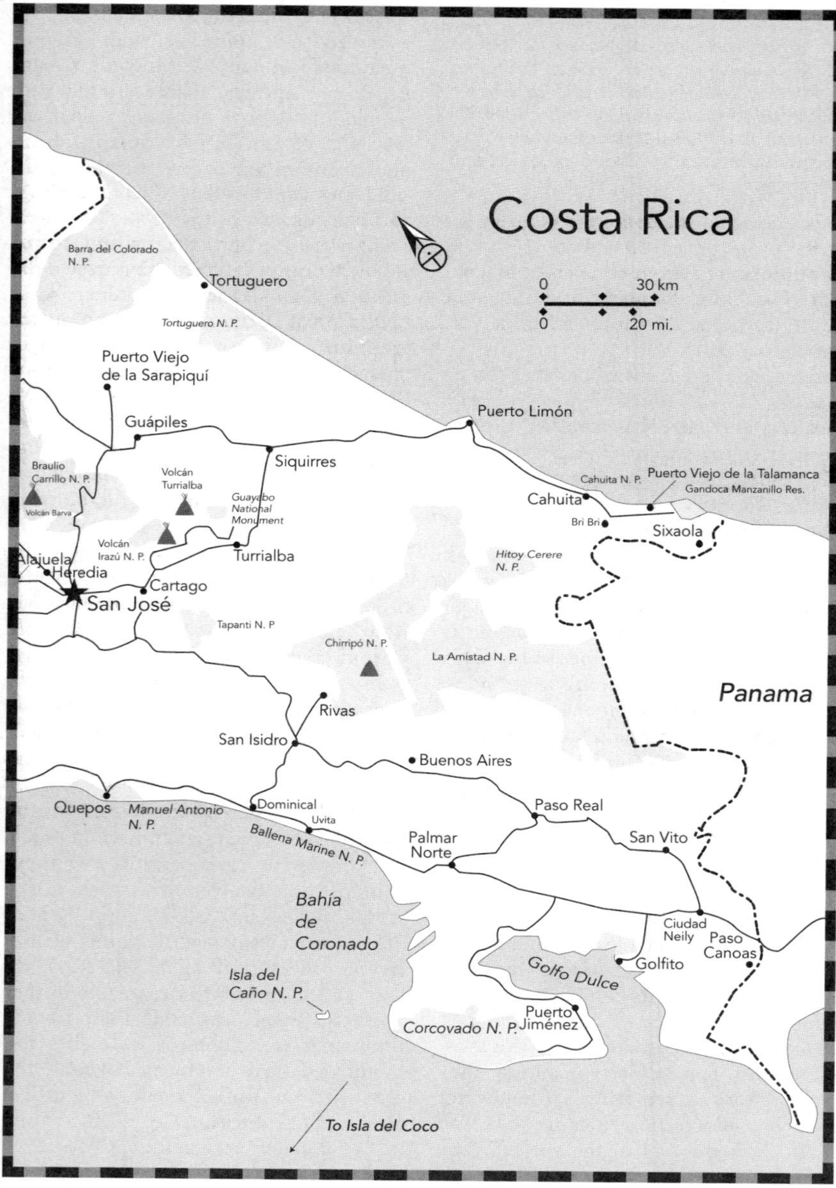
Costa Rica
0
30 km
0
20 mi.
Barra del Colorado N. P.
Tortuguero
Tortuguero N. P.
Puerto Viejo de la Sarapiquí
Guápiles
Puerto Limón
Siquirres
Braulio Carrillo N. P.
Volcán Barva
Volcán Turrialba
Guayabo National Monument
Volcán Irazú N. P.
Turrialba
Alajuela
Heredia
Cartago
San José
Cahuita N. P.
Puerto Viejo de la Talamanca
Gandoca Manzanillo Res.
Cahuita
Bri Bri
Sixaola
Hitoy Cerere N. P.
Tapanti N. P
Chirripó N. P.
La Amistad N. P.
Panama
Rivas
San Isidro
Buenos Aires
Quepos
Manuel Antonio N. P.
Dominical
Uvita
Ballena Marine N. P.
Paso Real
Palmar Norte
San Vito
Bahía de Coronado
Ciudad Neily
Paso Canoas
Golfito
Golfo Dulce
Isla del Caño N. P.
Puerto Jiménez
Corcovado N. P.
To Isla del Coco

i Volcanologists can contact the Escuela Centroamericana de Geología, Universidad de Costa Rica, Apdo. 35 UCR, San José; the Observatorio Vulcanólogico y Sismológico de Costa Rica, Escuela de Ciencias Geográficas, Universidad Nacional, Heredia; and the Instituto Costarricense de Electricidad, Apdo. 10032, San José.

accumulates. The three types of magma (rhyolitic or granitic, basaltic, and andesitic) produce the majority of volcanic rock.

Although there are various types of volcanoes, Costa Rica's major volcanic peaks are all ***strato-volcanoes*** or composite volcanoes — so called because they build up through eruptions stemming from a vent and comprise interbedded cinder, ash, and lava in varying proportions. Generally conical, irregular shapes result from landsides, streams carving eroded paths, major explosions, and a shift of position of the summit's vent. The remnants of lava flows can be seen draping their sides. Volcanoes are classifed as "active," "extinct" and "dormant," but whether a given peak is dormant or extinct is often difficult to ascertain. The most active peak in Costa Rica is Arenal which last erupted in 1998.

When magma reaches the earth's surface, it is known as ***lava***. Commonly seen at the top of active volcanoes, as well as in Rincón de la Vieja, ***fumaroles*** (from the Latin word fumus, meaning "smoke") are vents which emit gases and vapors.

Hot springs are undoubtedly the most delightful feature of volcanoes; they stem from circulating groundwater which contacts hot volcanic rock and then finds its way to the surface. The water's mineral contents give it the characteristic smell as well as its medicinal properties. Most of Costa Rica's hot springs center around the Arenal and Rincón de la Vieja areas to the NW of San José. Similarly, mud pools contain a mix of water, volcanic mud, and minerals that is kept bubbling through volcanic heat.

Eruptions are both the up and down side of volcanoes. While they cause devastation, they also lay down fertile soil. Lightning is a frequent companion of eruptions, and they are almost always preceded by earthquakes. Tsunamis, like the one that devastated the SW coast of Nicaragua in Aug. 1992, are seismic sea waves traveling at a speed of 500 mph (800 kph) and generated by movements of the earth's crusts or by underwater volcanic explosions.

RIVERS: Innumerable rivers and streams originate in the interior highlands and flow either to the Pacific or the Caribbean. Sadly, many have become polluted and others are slated for damming in order to generate electricity. There are also pollution problems: On Nov. 14, 1991, the owner of Rios Tropicales and his brother kayaked along the Río Torres which runs through metropolitan San José. In order to dramatize the pollution, they equipped themselves with wet suits, gloves, and gas masks.

The most famous whitewater rafting river is the Reventazón. The Río San Juan collects water from streams in the northern lowlands and then flows through Nicaragua until it reaches its mouth, a delta region formed in conjunction with the Río Colorado, which lies almost entirely within Costa Rica. (This is a popular excursion). The Río

Tortuguero flows directly to the Tortuguero waterway which parallels the Caribbean coast, stretching from the mouth of the Río Colorado to a point just N of Limón. The rivers that empty into the Pacific are mostly fewer, shorter, and steeper.

VALLEYS: Nestled in the Central Highlands and situated in a temperate area 3,280-4,920 ft. (1-1,500 m) in elevation, the Meseta Central, comprises the major part of the Valle Centra; it consists of two basins separated by low hills. Taken together, these encompass an area of nearly 3,861 sq. mi. (10,000 sq. km). As well as being rainier and more humid than its San José neighbor to the W, the Cartago Basin, to the E, is smaller and higher (4,920 ft., 1,500 m). Situated between the Cordillera de Talamanca and the mountains bordering the Pacific, the low-lying Valle de General lies to the S. Settlement began here only in the 1920s.

> ?!¿ Although smaller than most US states and Canadian provinces, Costa Rica is larger than Holland, Denmark, Belgium, and Switzerland.

COASTAL TERRAINS: Marked by steep cliffs and and numerous narrow beaches, the Pacific coast stretches 631 mi. (1,016 km) and contains three peninsulas: Buriya, Osa, and Nicoya. Although it is not entirely continuous—being separated in stretches by low-lying coastal mountains — a narrow alluvial coastal plain extends from the Peninsula de Osa in the S up to the port of Puntarenas where it widens, merging with the Valle de Tempisque. The Palmer lowland complex to the SW includes rainforests. Widest along the Nicaraguan border, the swampy, heavily forested Caribbean lowland comprises about 20% of the land area.

Climate

Costa Rica possesses an especially delightful climate in its highland areas. Its mild, subtropical weather varies little throughout the year: Most of the variation in temperatures comes from differences in elevation. The E and SE coasts cool down delightfully at night during the winter.

RAINFALL: Rain, which generally consists of short showers, is most likely to occur from July through the end of November; the driest months are February and March. Although the average rainfall is about 150-200 inches (3,807-5,076 mm), annual precipitation totals actually vary from 59 in. (1,500 mm) in the NW to 197 in. (5,000 mm) in the S.

Although no area is drought-stricken, there is a considerable variety in both rainfall and the length of the dry and wet seasons. Winds prevail from the N during the winter and early spring months and come in from the SE during the rest of the year. Receiving the heaviest rainfall, the Caribbean coast has no dry season, and its mean annual total exceeds 2,000 mm (79 in.) everywhere. During

> **i** Check the inside front page of the daily *La Nación* for the national weather forecast.
> For information about weather while in Costa Rica, call the National Meterological Institute which gives forecasts in Spanish. (☎ 222-5616, then dial "2" and then"1.")
> Cable Tica subscribers can tune into the Spanish-version of the Weather Channel.
> *On the Internet visit:*
> **www.imn.ac.cr/prono/prono.htm**
> **weather.yahoo.com/regional/Costa_Rica.htm**

the rainy season along the drier NW coast, rain falls in late afternoon or evening.

Temporary rainstorms of short duration which cover a small area are known as ***aguaceros***; less intense storms, more widely distributed and of longer duration are known as ***temporales***. Temporales del Atlantico and temporales de Pacifico are the two types. Both are the result of laterally moving air masses reaching mountains, rising, and cooling. More and more as a result of widespread deforestation, temporales result in flooding. March showers are known as *"aquacero de los cafetaleros"* (the coffee grower's shower), and the mid-Dec. rains are known as *"las lagrimas de Mary"* (Mary's tears).

Between Nov. and Jan, ***nortes*** — cold polar air fronts channeled southward between North American mountain ranges — reach Costa Rica, one of the few places in the world where polar air travels so close to the equator. When they blow inland from the Pacific Ocean these winds bring fine weather to the Pacific coast where this type of breeze is known as ***papagayo***.

Seasons and Zones

What residents of the Northern temperate zones know as "summer and "winter" are reversed for the Costa Ricans. As arriving Spaniards acclimatized, they associated their Mediterranean regimen of hot, dry summers and cool, wet winters with their new abode, disregarding the difference in time of year. Thus, while ***verano*** (summer) refers to the dry season between Dec. and May, ***invierno*** (winter) refers to the wet season which, running from May through Nov., corresponds with the Northern Hemispheric summer and fall. In some years the Pacific coast has a third period, veranillo (little summer)—a short dry season which sometimes emerges during July and August.

CLIMATE ZONES: Costa Rica has three distinct climates. The ***tierra caliente*** (torrid zone) encompasses the two coastal plains which rise up to 1500 ft. (450 m) with a corresponding temperature range of 85°-90°F (29.4°-32.2°C); the ***tierra templada*** contains the Meseta Central as well as other regions from 1,500-5,000 ft. (450-1500 m) with temperatures of 75°-80°F (23.9°-26.7°C); the ***tierra fria*** (frigid zone) includes areas over 5,000 ft. (1,524 m) with temperatures ranging from 41°-59° F (5°-15°C).

On lower slopes and intermontane depressions, mean annual temperatures range from 52°-78°F (12°-24°C). Up in the higher regions of the Cordillera de Talamanca and the Cordillera Central, the annual average is less than 52°F (12°C), and the temperature may reach 32°F (0°C) on occasion. Variation in temperatures is greatest during the dry season when the nights are cool in the highlands.

Earthquakes

Other than crazy drivers, the major environmental hazards to which Costa Rica is subject are volcanic eruptions and earthquakes.

Positioned atop a number of faults, Costa Rica is second only to Guatemala in Central America as a center of seismic activity. But Costa Rica has not experienced quakes as catastrophic as those affecting Nicaragua in 1972, Guatemala in 1976, and El Salvador in 1986. If you should experience tremors during your visit, just remember that they have been going on for millions of years and will continue until the planet's final demise. If a major tremor should occur, don't rush outside. Get to a doorway, an inside corner wall or crawl under a desk or table for protection.

PAST EARTHQUAKES: Most of Cartago was destroyed by a volcanic eruption in 1910; it was also devastated by others in 1620 and 1841. Limón was heavily damaged in 1935 and again, to a lesser extent, on April 22, 1991. Three of the most recent earthquakes were in 1973 in Tilarán and two in 1983 when an April quake based off the tip of Osa Peninsula left one dead and 500 homeless, and a second quake in July, based 60 km S of San José, left 3,000 homeless, two dead, and 13 seriously injured. A quake, measuring 5.5 on the Richter scale, struck on Mar. 25, 1990, causing landslides on the San Juan-Atlantic Coast Highway and causing extensive damage in Puntarenas. A series of frequent, smaller tremors followed during the ensuing months. Mostly causing damage along the east coast, the latest quake was in on April 22, 1991. It registered 7.1 on the Richter scale.

Flora and Fauna

Straddling an area from 8° to 11° N of the equator, Costa Rica has an unusual variety of ecosystems. Its high, rugged, and youthful cordilleras contain a complex ecological mosaic, as do its plains, rivers, and coasts—an ecological diversity paralleled in Central America only by Guatemala.

As defined by LR. Holdridge, there are 12 life zones in Costa Rica, based on seasonal distribution and variation of rainfall and temperature. There are four major zones (tropical dry, moist, wet, and rainforest) each of which is further subdivided into premontane and lower montane divisions. There's also the tropical subalpine rain ***páramo*** (flat, barren cold plain), which constitutes only a small area in Costa Rica.

NATURE WATCHING: The land is very much alive, and nature abounds outside of crowded, polluted San José. Many species are nocturnal, but tend to gather in early evening or morning at water holes. If you're visiting on your own, don't be disappointed if you fail to see many animals; the dense underbrush frequently makes viewing difficult. Many of the smaller animals are strictly nocturnal, and others are wary of humans. However, some animals are highly visible. These include the active monkeys, peccaries, and coatis.

Plant Life and Tropical Forests

Costa Rica has a phantasmogorical variety of flora. There are over 800 species of ferns, 1,200 species of orchids, and 2,000 varieties of trees. To appreciate what still exists and in order to understand today's problems, it's necessary to examine the past.

> Develop a sense of the forest's "musicality," responding to it as you would to a complex interplay of musical instruments. Only by attuning yourself to its rhythms, can you truly experience the rainforest's wonders.

ECOLOGICAL HISTORY: Arriving Spaniards found a covering of virgin forest, most of which was rainforest largely made up of broadleaf evergreens. Deciduous forests abounded in the NW; mangrove forests lined the coasts. A dense growth of palms stretched along the Caribbean coast from Puerto Limón N to the Nicaraguan bor-

Cattle ranching has devastated the rainforest. A trip up to rainforest lodge Rara Avis (on which this shot was taken) illustrates the effects.

der. Although the indigenous people had practiced slash-and-burn cultivation, they were so comparatively few in number that they had little impact. During the 19th C., much land was stripped of its primeval growth in the Meseta Central to be used for agriculture and, along the Caribbean coast, for bananas. Due to the dearth of sawmills and the lack of transportation, nearly all of the timber was either burned or left to rot on the ground — a process that virtually exterminated a number of species. By the 1940s only scattered stands of timber remained in the Meseta Central. However, it was estimated that 78% of Costa Rica was still covered by largely virgin growth forest as of 1942.

The opening of the Costa Rican segment of the Interamerican Highway opened up the valley area of the Río General along with other areas for cultivation. The expansion of agriculture in general and cattle ranching in particular also took its toll. Between 1950 and 1960, an estimated 108,000 acres (44,000 ha) were cut annually, a figure that increased to more than 148,000 acres (60,000 ha) during the 1961-67 period.

As during the homesteading era in the US, the forests were viewed simply as impediments to economic progress. Also, by cutting down the trees, the campesino obtained squatter's rights because he had "improved" the acreage. According to government figures, as of 1977 some 12,000 sq. mi. (20,000 sq. km) — about 39% of the total land area — was wooded.

Despite the protection afforded by the government, the remaining forests are threatened by the estimated 100-200,000 ***precarista*** (squatter) families and by the estimated 200,000 refugees in the country to whom forest reserves and private forested tracts represent idle land waiting to be claimed. In their eyes, although farmland is easier to squat initially, forested land appears a better long-term bet.

A study of satellite photos taken in 1983 showed only 17% of the country was still covered by virgin forest. Ironically, owing to the nature of its soil composition and topography, more than half of the land is judged unsuitable for growing permanent crops or for anything other than trees. Although the nation contains a dozen ecological zones and from 8-12,000 species of plants, its forests are still falling at a rate nine times faster than Brazil's.

Rainforest Ecosystems

Rainforests contain the planet's most complex ecosystem, and rainforests have a richer animal and plant life than any other type of forest. Unlike other areas in which living organisms face conflicts in the face of a hostile climate, in the rainforest organisms struggle for survival primarily against each other. Each being—whether plant, animal, insect, or microbe—has been able to develop its niche. and because there are so many species, numerous examples of specialized niches can be found.

Rainforests occur in regions without major seasonal variation (although rainfall does vary during the year) and where more than 70 in. (1,800 mm) of rain fall annually. When seen from the air, the canopy appears uneven because there are trees of varied species and stages of development.

VARIETIES: There is no single "true rainforest," and forest botanists have varying

How Old Are the Rainforests?

The rainforests were once believed to have been stable environments for 60 million years or more. However, thinking on this point has shifted owing to research conducted from the 1970s onward.

As the northern temperate zone underwent radical shifts in temperature during glacial and interglacial periods (with a resulting movement of ice sheets and shifts in vegetation and fauna), the tropics also underwent equally radical alterations known as pluvials (wet, warm periods) and interpluvials (dry, cold periods). As the glaciers would descend, the tropics would enter an interpluvial. Much of the Amazon had dry, scrub vegetation as recently as 6,000 years ago.

How old are the nation's ecosystems? *Quite young!* The land mass was not even in place in Central America—along with the connections to Columbia and Mexico—until about three million years ago. This region is believed to have had its origins in the "Galapagos Hot Spot," an active area of sea-floor spreading which drifted slowly until reaching its present position. This same process had happened previously, and the mass continued on through the Caribbean—forming Cuba and the Antilles as it went.

The rainforests, therefore, should not be viewed as timeless, stable relics but rather as dynamic, changing ecosystems whose vegetation shifts as climates change and new species colonize new areas as they become available and accessible to seeds. Rainforests are diverse because most times of the year are reasonably suitable for plant growth and animal activity.

In contrast, the temperate zone not only has a winter—which weeds out species through the environmental stresses it poses—but the northern hemisphere was also largely convered with glaciers (or affected by ice sheets) until relatively recently. Consequently vegetation is still recolonizing habitats there; recent studies of fossil pollen indicate that forest composition has undergone stiking changes in the past 5,000 years. This is another reason why the tropics boast more species. Also, as many species have had their origins here, the number of species dwindles as you leave the area.

— *from information supplied by Drs. Diana and Milton Lieberman*

Costa Rican Flora: A to Z in Spanish
Aguacate —avocado
Almendro —wild almond
Cacao silvestre — wild cocoa
Caña de Indio — Indian cane
Caoba —mahogany
Carambola—star fruit
Ceiba — kapok
Chaperno — dogwood
Cocobolo — rosewood
Cocotero — coconut palm
Fruta dorada — golden nutmeg
Guanacaste —ear tree
Guanábana — soursop
Guarumo — trumpet tree
Guatusa — paca palm
Guayabo — guava
Guácimo — bastard cedar
Higuerón — wild strangler fig
Icacos — sea grape
Lirio de Agua — water hyacinth
Mangle — mangrove
Manzanillo — machineel
Mapola — hibiscus
Naranja — orange
Níspero — chicle tree
Palma real — royal palm
Palma de sombrero — hat palm
Panamá Panama — wood
Papayo de monte — wild papaya
Pochote — spiny cedar
Toronja — grapefruit

definitions of the term. It may be argued that there are some 30 types including such categories as semi-deciduous forests, tropical evergreen alluvial forests, and evergreen lowland forests—each of which can be further subdivided into three or four more categories. Equatorial evergreen rainforests comprise two thirds of the total. As one moves away from the equator on either side the forests develop marked wet and dry seasons.

CLOUD FORESTS: Cloud forest is another name for montane rainforest which is characterized by heavy rainfall and persistent condensation due to the upward deflection of moisture-laden air currents by mountains. Trees here are typically short and gnarled. Costa Rica's most famous cloud forest is at Monteverde in the NW. The so-called elfin woodland or forest is so named because of its stunted, moss-covered trees.

TROPICAL DRY FORESTS: Rainforests without as much rain, the tropical dry forests, once covered Pacific coastal lowlands stretching from Panama to Mexico, covering an area the size of France. Today, they have shrunk to a mere two percent of the total area and only part of this is under protection; surviving sections are found in Guanacaste and Santa Rosa conservation areas among other locations.

LAYERS: Life in the rainforest is stratified in vertical layers. The **upper canopy** contains animals which are mainly herbivorous and, in Costa Rica, have prehensile tails. They rarely descend to earth. Typically more than a hundred feet (30 m) in height , these canopy trees generally lack the girth associated with tall trees of the temperate forest, perhaps because there are fewer strong winds to combat and each tree must compete with the others for sunlight.

The **next lower layer** is filled with small trees, lianas, and epiphytes. Some of the plants are parasitic, others use trees solely for support purposes.

The **ground surface layer** is littered with branches, twigs, and foliage. Most animals here live on insects and fruit; others are carnivorous. Contrary to popular opinion the ground cover is thick only where sunlight filters through sufficiently to allow such vegetation; secondary forest growth is generally much more impenetrable than old growth forest.

What You Can Do to Save the Forests

- ***Start at home*** Much of North America's old growth forest is under threat from the timber industry. It is unrealistic to expect nations like Indonesia, Brazil, and Costa Rica to save their forests if the US and Canada cut theirs down. In particular, the government-subsidized rape of the US National Forests and the destruction of British Columbia's old growth must be halted.
- ***Visit the rainforests*** Showing an interest in the rainforest reinforces pride in the forests and instills a sense of value in local people. When you return, tell your friends and relatives about what you've seen.
- ***Boycott tropical products*** Don't purchase imported tropical birds, snakes, or animal hides. Avoid buying products made of teak, mahogany, or other tropical woods unless you are positive that the furniture comes from tree farms and not from virgin rainforest. Encourage retailers to question the source of their products.
- ***Organize*** If you live in a major city such as New York, there is likely to be an environmental organization for whom you can volunteer. If there is not, start your own! For maximum effectiveness, coordinate your efforts with groups operating in tropical nations.
- ***Educate yourself*** The most important hope for the human race is education. Read as much as you can, see as much as you can, and write to your political leaders and to newspapers to inform people what you have seen.

The extensive root system of the trees and associated fungi (*mycorrhizae*) form a thick mat which holds thin topsoils in place when it rains. If these are cut, the soil will wash away; the steeper the slope, the faster the rate of runoff. As most of the nutrients are regenerated via the ecosystem, the land soon deteriorates after cutting. As the sun beats down on the soil, sometimes baking it hard as a sidewalk, the crucial fungal mat and other organic life die off. It may take hundreds—if not thousands—of years to replace important nutrients through weathering, rainfall, or volcanic eruption, and such forests may never recover.

INTERACTIONS: As the name implies, rainforests receive ample rain, which promotes a rich variety of vegetation. Animals and insects, in turn, must adapt to that variety. Lowland rainforests receive at least 100 in. (2,540 mm) of rain. Although some rainforests receive almost no rain during certain parts of the year, they are generally cloaked in clouds from which they draw moisture. The high level of plant-animal interaction—taking forms such as predation, parasitism, hyperparasitism, symbiosis, and mutualism—is believed by many biologists to be one major factor promoting diversity. The interactions are innumerable and highly complex: strangler figs steal sunlight from canopy trees; wasps may pollinate figs; bats and birds transport seeds and pollinate flowers. When a species of bird, for example, becomes rare or extinct, it may have an effect on a tree which depends heavily upon it to distribute its seeds. There is no such thing as self-sufficiency in a rainforest; all life is interdependent.

BIODIVERSITY: Those who are unfamiliar with the rainforest tend to undervalue it. Tropical deforestation is one of the great tragedies of our time. We are far from cataloging all the species inhabiting the rainforests, and when the forests are cut down, many species can be lost forever.

More than 70% of the plants known to produce compounds with anticancerous properties are tropical, and there may be many cures waiting to be found. One survey of Costa Rican plants found that 15% had potential as anti-cancer agents. Cures for malaria and dysentery have been found in the forests. Louis XIV was cured of amoebic dysentery by ipecac, a South American plant that remains the most effective cure. Cortisone and diosgenin, the active agents in birth control pills, were developed from Guatemalan and Mexican wild yams.

These are some of the 3,000 plants that tribal peoples use worldwide as contraceptives. Continued research could yield yet other methods of birth control. Not all rainforest products are medicinal. Rice, corn, and most spices — including vanilla, the unripe fermented stick-like fruits of the Central American Orchid, *vanilla fragrans*—are also medicinal. Other products native people have extracted from the rainforest include latex, resins, starch, sugar, thatch, dyes, and fatty oils. The rainforest also acts as a genetic pool, and when disease strikes a monoculture such as bananas, it's possible to hybridize it with rainforest varieties to see if this produces an immunity to pests or fungus.

GREENERY AND GREENHOUSE: Biodiversity is only one of many reasons to preserve the forest. They also act as watersheds, and cutting can result in flooding and erosion as well as increased aridity. Much rain is produced through the transpiration of trees, which helps keep the air saturated with moisture.

Although it is commonly believed that rainforests produce much of the earth's oxygen, in fact there is an equilibrium between the amount mature forests consume through the decay of organic matter and the amount they produce via photosynthesis. However, many scientists believe that widespread burning of tropical forests releases large amounts of carbon dioxide into the atmosphere.

The amount of carbon dioxide in the atmosphere has risen by 15% in the past century (with about half of this occurring since 1958), and forest clearance may account for half of that gain. As carbon dioxide, along with other atmospheric elements, traps heat that would otherwise escape into space, temperatures may rise. Rainfall patterns would change and ocean levels would rise as the polar ice packs melt. In many areas, deforestation has already had an adverse effect on the environment. Although many uncertainties remain about the "greenhouse effect," one certainty is that by the time the effects are apparent they will be irreversible.

FATE OF THE FORESTS: Just a few thousand years ago, a belt of rainforests, covering some five billion acres (14% of the planet's surface) stretched around the equator. Wherever there was sufficient rainfall and high enough temperatures there was rainforest. Over half the total area has now been destroyed, much of it in the past few hundred years with the rate accelerating after the end of WWII. Squatters and logging continue to cause deforestation throughout the region. At current rates, much of the remaining forest will vanish by the end of the century. One reason for the expansion into the forests is the need for arable land in areas where land ownership is concentrated in a few hands and most peasants are landless. For example, in El Salvador fewer than 2,000 families control 40% of the land. Cattle ranching, logging, mining, and industry are other reasons to cut the forests. Forests do not recover easily.

Trees and Tropical Vegetation

The hallmark of the rainforest is diversity, and trees are no exception to that rule. While temperate forests contain only an average of four species per acre, tropical forests may have from 20 to 86. Rainforest trees often have shallow root systems and they may be physically supported by basal buttressing or stilt roots. These root systems are bound together in mutual beneficial relationships with the lowly fungi.

If you look carefully, you can spot a link between the white threads of fungi, decomposing a leaf or fruit, with a rootlet of a tree. Fungi are able to recycle 20 times as much potassium and phosphorus to a tree as it will lose in the rains. The rainforest's high humidity and relatively uniform temperatures allows fungi to flourish.

Perhaps in a largely unsuccessful evolutionary attempt by nature to combat strangler vines and other plants, the trees are generally smooth barked.

CHARACTERISTICS: When viewed from the side, **tree buttresses** appear triangular When viewed in cross section buttresses may resemble an irregular 2-, 5- or occasionally up to 10-armed star. They function much like the guy ropes on a tent: hitting them with the blunt side of a machete will produce a "bong" showing that they are under tension. There are three types of buttresses: **plank** (resembling giant wedges, **flying** (of the stilt-root type), and **serpentine** (often looped or undulating from side to side, these extend for some distance from the tree). Many trees have buttresses of more than one type.

Exploring the Canopy

In recent years, biologist Don Perry's exploits, along with a number of television specials, have focused attention on the canopy — a realm of the earth heretofore restricted to our arboreal relatives and other creatures. It's now possible for mere mortals to ascend to the canopy layer. Methods include being hoisted up and down in a harness, having yourself hoisted up and rappelling yourself down, or cruising by the canopy in a glorified ski lift. Fees are typically high, both because material and labor costs are expensive and promoters hope to turn a buck. If you're heading up in the canopy, prepare yourself for the fact that you may not see a whole lot of wildlife.

Both the Rainforest Aerial Tram as well as many of the nation's various platforms are described in the travel section. Some of the platforms are designed to be used by serious researchers. All involve the use of ropes and are not for the timid or agoraphobic. The Rainforest Aerial Tram offers a much safer and more comfortable experience. It is modeled on a device that Don Perry used to explore the canopy with and is only one of a number of designs in use.

Another type of device, the construction crane, has been used together with a gondola to explore the rainforest canopy in Panama and in Venezuela. In 1995, a US$1 million, 260-ft. (80-m) version was completed near the scenic Columbia River Gorge in Carson, WA. The crane was originally slated to be erected in the Olympic peninsula but was stymied by protesting locals who feared research might lead to more prohibitions on logging.

Another device — described in the marvelous book *The High Frontier* by Mark Moffett — is a colorful dirigible balloon which has been used in Cameroun to explore the canopy.

Heliconias

Famous worldwide as an ornamental, the heliconia (platanillo), lends an infusion of bizarre color and shape to the tropical landscape. The name of these medium to large erect herbs comes from Helicon, a mountain in southern Greece which was believed to have been the home of the muses. They are a member of the order known as the Zingiberales, and there are thought to be around 200-250 species. Relatives within this category include the banana, the birds-of-paradise, the gingers, and the prayer plants.

The family name *Zingiberales* comes from the Sanskrit word *sringavera* which means "horn shaped" in reference to the rhizomes. Each erect shoot has a stem and leaves which are frequently (although not always) topped by an infloresence with yellow or red bracts. Each infloresence may produce up to 50 hermaphroditic flowers. Leaves are composed of stalk and blade and resemble banana leaves. Flowers produce a blue colored fruit which has three seeds. The heliconia is represented in Costa Rica by some 30 species; as it thrives in secondary forests, heliconias are very common and is cultivated at places such as Costa Flores near Guapiles.

In Costa Rica you're most likely to find heliconias near rivers and along roads; they thrive in light gaps. Most are found in the tropical lowlands or in middle-elevation or cloud forest habitats. Lured by the bright colored flowers and bracts, hummingbirds, arrive to pollinate the blooms. The birds spread pollen as they fly from flower to flower in search of nectar.

A special characteristic of rainforest trees are the **drip-tip** leaves which are elongated at the end by an inch. This allows them to shed water after a shower more quickly and resume assimilating and transpiring. An additional advantage is that the quick passage of water may act to deter the growth of mosses and lichen.

The calabash fruit is an example of "cauliflory" or flowering from the trunk

Another feature of tropical trees is **cauliflory** or flowering from the trunk. Southeast Asian examples of fruit produced in this fashion are jackfruit and durian. Neotropical examples include cacao and calabash.

VARIETIES: The tropical dry forest contains more than 30 species of hardwood. Found only in the NW, two of the three species of **caoba** (mahogany) are indigenous. Attempts to grow the hardwood commercially have been stymied by the mahogany shootborer which thrives in mahogany groves.

Another giant which thrives in Guanacaste, the evergreen **cenízero's** English name (raintree) derives from the aphids who, residing in its branches, extract large quantities of sap, drain it of nitrogen-rich compounds, then defecate diligently.

Used for furniture, walls, beams, and counters, the ***pilón*** or ***zapatero*** tree is large, with serpentine buttresses.

Termite-resistant and heavy, the ***manú*** (Manwood) tree, now virtually extinct in unprotected forests, was commonly used for dock construction, posts, beams, and large columns.

Another favorite is the ***Ira Roosa*** which is primarily used to build furniture or do interiors. Growing up to 40 m (128 ft.) in height, the ***fruta dorada*** (Wild Nutmeg) abounds in moist forests.

One of the largest trees, the deciduous and corpulent ***calyptrogyne*** or "dove-tail" tree has a well-formed straight and smooth trunk.

Commonly seen on coffee plantations, the ***poro*** tree's function is not only to shade coffee but also to fix nitrogen into the soil; its prunings provide feed for ani-

INBio and the Preservation of Biodiversity

Created in 1989 and dedicated to the preservation of biodiversity, INBio is among the most dynamic of Costa Rica's foundations. The institute's highy ambitious long-term goal is to catalog every species of life in the nation. INBio employs some 40 parataxonimists who have collected some 2.5 million specimens.

The signing of a revolutionary agreement with Merck has cast a spotlight on this organization. It signed a two-year pact with Merck in 1991 in which INBio was intended to supply the drug company with samples in exchange for funds and training. Merck contracted to pay a royalty on any drugs developed, and any revenues will be split between INBio and the Ministry of Natural Resources.

This agreement incited controversy because some accused the organization of selling the nation's resources too cheaply as well as not having the right, as a private party, to negotiate on behalf of the entire nation. However, despite the controversy, INBio has signed cooperative agreements with Kenya, Indonesia, and the Philippines, and its contract with Merck was renewed.

A second agreement has been signed with the Intergraph Corporation, another Fortune 500 company, who agreed to donate some $750,000 worth of equipment and software in exchange for publicity. The organization is intent on screening its own samples.

InBio is also working on a number of projects which are aimed at discovering projects of agiculture, industrial, or pharmaceutical value. For example, INBio is prospecting for insect species in Guanacaste in the hope of discovering significant chemicals in insects, and a second project involves research on how a certain tropical dry forest tree kills nematodes, pests which also destroy bananas. It's funded by the National Banana Corporation along with a British biotech company.

Their extensive collection is open to visitors, and their new InBio Parque (detailed under Santo Domingo de Heredia in the travel section) presents a unique way to explore biodiversit

www.inbio.ac.cr

Common Misperceptions About Rainforests

- Rainforests are not "the lungs of the planet." Mature trees produce asmuch oxygen as they consume. The danger in destroying rainforests lies with the effects on rainfall, flooding, and global warming resulting from increasing amounts of carbondioxide being released into the atmosphere.
- Rainforests are not bursting at the seams with colorful plants, wild orchids, andanimals. The overwhelming color is green; flowers are few; and the animal you're most likely to see is the ant.
- Rainforests are not a renewable resource. It is impossible to cut trees without destroying other plants and affecting the environment.
- Rainforests are not merely a source of wood. There are other values associated with them which must be considered.
- Once damaged, rainforest does not simply grow back as it once was. It may take centuries for the complex ecosystem to regenerate. Reforestation cannot restore the environment.
- Despite its rich appearance, rainforest soil may not be fertile. Most of the nutrients are contained in the biomass.
- There is no need to "manage" a rainforest. They've been doing just fine for eons on their own. Everything in the rainforest is recycled, and anything removed has an effect.
- "Selective" cutting has detrimental consequences because it affects the surrounding soil quality and weakens the forest as the strongest specimens are removed. No way has yet been found to exploit a rainforest so that all species may be preserved.
- One "endangered" species cannot be effectively protected without safeguarding its ecosystem as well. Botanical gardens or seed banks cannot save important species. These are too numerous in quantity, seeds have too short a lifespan, and the species depend upon animals for their lifecycle equilibrium.
- Any reduction in consumption of tropical hardwoods will not preserve rainforests. The only effective method is to protect the forests in reserves and parks. The forests are falling at too fast a rate for any other methods to be effective.

mals as well as firewood. The ***jícaro*** (Calabash) tree is easily identifiable by its hanging, balloon-like gourds.

FORBIDDEN FRUIT: Small, with a short trunk and numerous branches, the **manchineel *(manzanillo*)** grows near the sea. Its elliptical-shaped leaves possess a strange bright green sheen. The machineel secretes an acid which may be deadly. Biting into this innocuous-looking yet highly poisonous fruit, said to be the original apple in the Garden of Eden, will cause your mouth to burn and your tongue to swell up. In fact, all parts of this tree are potentially deadly. Cattle, standing under the tree after a torrential tropical downpour, have been said to lose their hides as drops fall from leaves. Other tales tell of people going blind after a leaf touched an eye.

If you should spot one of these trees —which are particularly prevalent along Manuel Antonio's beaches — stay well away!

EPIPHYTES: The luxuriant verdancy commonly associated with rainforests depends upon these hangers on. Taken from the Greek words meaning "upon plants," **epiphytes** are essential to the romantic and exotic image of the "jungle." Although they may be found in temperate and drier tropical forests as well, the combination of rain and warmth unique to the rainforest help them flourish here.

Treetop life has many advantages. Birds and bats arrive to pollinate and deposit nutrient-rich dung, and it is more likely that their seeds will be dispersed by the wind. Water may be harder to come by and evaporation is a problem, so many bromeliads have evolved tanks to hold up to two gallons (eight liters) of water as well as other adaptations. Don't make the mistake of thinking that these plants are parasitic. Although they are perhaps unwelcome guests, most do not feed on their hosts. Generally, they arrive in the form of tiny dustlike seeds. These establish themselves on moss or lichen which serves as a starter. All told there are 247 species of epiphytes found in Costa Rica.

Latin for "upon plants," epiphytes, contrary to popular opinion, are not parasites. They also host a number of creatures.

An epiphytic, tree-dwelling cactus, the ***pitahaya silvestre*** thrives in the NW. Its flowers, some 11.8 in. (30 cm) long and weighing up to 100 g (four oz.), are among the world's largest. Opening only at night, they release a potent, moth-attracting, jasmine-like fragrance which may be sniffed as far as 1,000 ft. (100 m) downwind.

Tiny epiphytes residing on leaf surfaces, **epiphylls** (algae, liverworts, lichens, and mosses) are generally found on lower plants.

Named after Swedish botanist Olaf Bromel, **bromeliads** are ground-dwelling epiphytes, the most famous of which is the ***piña*** (pineapple). One of the species of bromeliad typically found in Guanacaste, ***Piñuelas*** are equipped with large (100-140 cm, 39-55 in.), skinny, and jagged, aloe vera-like leaves.

?!? Orchids were named by Dioscorides, a Greek physician who, noting the similarity of the tubers of one species he was examining to male genitals, named the species "orches."

ORCHIDS: Costa Rica's extraordinary natural wealth includes 1,200 varieties of ***orquídaes*** (orchids), the grandest collection in all of Central America; the ***guaria morada***, a commonly seen orchid, is the national flower. Although they grow all over the country, orchids are most diverse in the 2,625-6,562 ft. (800-2,000 m) humid forests.

Not all orchids are epiphytic and the ones that are generally possess thicker leaves and keep their *stomata* — tiny pores on their leaves which absorb carbon dioxide — shut during the day, utilizing a metabolic process to store the carbon dioxide for the next day's use.

Nearly all orchids are pollinated by

insects or hummingbirds, and it is believed that many may only be pollinated by a single specific one. Certain orchid blooms even bear an amazing resemblance to certain bees or wasps.

Although prized for their aesthetic value, orchids command little economic importance. They were once thought to have medicinal properties, but these claims have largely proven false and not a single species is currently used in modern medicine. Their only valuable product is vanilla, an extract obtained from the cured unripened pods of various species belonging to the genus *Vanilla*.

VINES AND COMPANY: Woody (vines, lianas, and bush ropes) and herbaceous climbers are rainforest landmarks and give it its tropical quality. Using trees as trellises, vines crawl up from the ground to reach the light. Scramblers grow in gaps in the rainforest.

LIANAS: Over 90% of liana species are found in the tropics where they commonly grow as long as 230 ft. (70 m) and as wide as six in. (15 cm) or more. Lianas use a combination of twining around the tree and tendrils or hooks to secure themselves. As with vines, they drop their shaded understory leaves as they reach maturity. The longest lianas are rattans — one of the rainforest's harvestable products — which may grow to more than 500 ft. in length. In order to guard against damage done by kinking as trees sway, lianas have evolved bends, coils, and twists.

One of the most remarkable of these is the ***uña de gato*** (cat-claw bignone) which, in its juvenile form, grows leaves and tendrils bearing a remarkable, almost haunting resemblance to cat claws. It appears almost as if the plant could walk!

In addition to closing the canopy, thus stabilizing the microclimate, lianas also offer protection to animals such as sloths. By sleeping in a mass of lianas, sloths tie in to a tensile network of vines that will alert them to the presence of an arboreal predator.

STRANGLER FIGS: Beginning life as epiphytes, some species of *Ficus* (fig) and *Clusia* (non-fig species) send down woody, clasping roots that wind themselves around the trunk as they reach for the earth. As the roots grow in size, they meld and develop into a trunk which surrounds the tree. These "strangler figs" most likely kill the tree not through strangulation but by robbing it of canopy space. They can grow in the ruins of buildings as well.

Known locally as ***matapalos*** or "tree killers," strangler figs are often the only trees left in an otherwise cleared tract of forest. There is little incentive to use their poor quality wood, and their spreading branches provide shade. The holes, cracks and turns in its trunk host geckos, anoles, ants, stingless bees, scorpions, and other life—each inhabiting its ecological niche. Bats, birds, and other fruit eaters flock around the trees, attracting ornithologists in the process. Even peccaries and other ground dwellers arrive to share in the bounty that falls to the ground. These creatures all help distribute its seeds when they defecate.

UNIQUE NATIVES: The ***pejibaye palm*** is well known for its fruit and edible palm heart.

Found mainly in dry forest environments, ***Indio desnudo*** ("naked Indian") utilizes chloroplasts under its orange bark in order to continue to synthesize during the months from Nov. to May when it is leafless.

Noted for its eye-catching "plank" root buttresses, the ***ceiba*** or kapok tree has

Barú Falls, near the Pacific coast town of Dominical, are a great place to swim.

Boiling mud pots are an attraction at Rincón de la Vieja National Park in the northwest.

The aerial approach to Tortuguero National Park

A Spider Monkey flies through the air in search of fruit.

A Mouse Opossum

White faced Monkey

Anhinga

Anhinga in flight

Brown Pelican

Green Macaw at Laguna del Lagarto
Immature Tiger Heron (right)

La Paz Falls are found by the road on the way to Sarapiquí.

Heliconia's name comes from Helicon, a mountain in southern Greece which was believed to have been the home of the muses.

The owl butterfly's "eye" serves to deter predators and is a classic example of biological mimicry.

conical spines on its trunk. The silky quality of the fibers surrounding the seed in its fruit have given it the English name of silk cotton tree.

The ***Guanacaste*** receives its English name (ear fruit) from the unique shape of its fruits. Although it gives the province of Guanacaste its name, these trees may well be extinct in the area within the next 100 years as they require an enclosed, noncompetitive tropical forest in order to thrive.

The ***roble*** or ***encino*** (Oak) is distinguished by a hard-covered dark bark and acorns which may take two growing seasons to mature. Another variety is the ***roble encino***,an evergreen which thrives in upland dry forest.

While some palms have adapted to brackish tidal swamps and dune swales, the ***coco*** (coconut palm) is the only one that makes these areas its sole habitat. It may have originated in the Indian Ocean. While those on the Pacific coast are related to Asian varieties, the ones on the Caribbean side are of the Jamaican tall variety found in West Africa and in the W Indian Ocean.

Producing a resin that, when fossilized, is the source for amber, the ***guapinol*** (stinking toe) tree bears large, toe-shaped pods.

A cousin of the tree which produces the Brazil nut, the ***jícaro*** (Monkey Pot) bears large woody fruits which hang upside down. Upon ripening the lid drops off, revealing 20-50 seeds which are favored by hungry bats.

Lightest of the commercial woods, ***balsa*** is native to humid subtropical and tropical areas; Spanish for "raft," it has had a variety of uses through the centuries. The latest is to deter supertankers from building up static charges owing to wave action which can result in explosions.

Large, symmetrical, strong, and stout, the ***jabillo's'*** English name (sandbox tree) comes from its fruit; the ribbed peel, when de-seeded and flattened, was used to sprinkle sand used for blotting ink spilt on parchment.

OTHERS: Tree ferns make a major impression on the imagination of most visitors; they abound in the high-rainfall forests. In Costa Rica, they are labeled ***rabo de mica*** ("monkey tail") ferns in reference to their uncurling young fronds. Often called "living fossils," ***zamia*** (cycads) superficially resemble small palms and have conelike flowers which emerge from the base of their fronds.

A free-floating aquatic perennial, the ***jacinto de agua*** (water hyacinth) has spread during this century from its South American homeland to become one of the most troublesome and widespread aquatic weeds. Members of the three species present can be seen everywhere from Carara to Tortuguero.

The red spots on the underside of the green leaves belonging to the ***sangre de Cristo***, ("blood of Christ") plant resemble stained glass windows.

Of African origin, ***jarágua*** is the commonest cultivated pasture grass, and it is especially abundant in Guanacaste where, owing to its remarkable regenerative abilities after a fire, it has been supplanting other indigenous grasses. They are more adept than the native varieties in converting croplands into pastures.

Rendered distinctive through its large (up to two m, 6.5 ft.) leaves, the ***sombrilla de pobre*** ("poor person's umbrella") is common in verdant, elevated areas; locals cut them down for use as umbrellas.

By producing nectar both deep in their flowers (for bees and hummingbirds) and also at nectaries on petals, stems, and leaves (for aggressive ants and wasps),

passion flowers provide themselves with both pollination and protection.

Unforgettable residents of the rainforest, ***labios ardientes*** ("ardent lips") or (hooker's lips) lend a bit of local color to the rainforest landscape.

MANGROVES: Mangrove (***mangle***) forests are found along the coasts; these water-rooted trees serve as a marine marine community around its roots—organisms which, in turn, attract a variety of other sealife. Some species live out their lives in the shelter of the mangroves, and many fish use it as a shelter or feeding ground; lobsters use the mangrove environs as a nursery for their young. Above the water level, they shelter seabirds and are important nesting sites. Their organic detritus, exported to the reef by the tides, is consumed by its inhabitants, providing the base of an extensive food web.

Mangroves also dampen high waves and winds generated by tropical storms. By trapping silt in their roots and catching leaves and other debris which decompose to form soil, the red mangroves act as land builders and stave off erosion. Eventually, the red mangroves kill themselves off by building up too much soil, and the black and white mangroves take over.

In the meanwhile, the red mangroves have sent out progeny in the form of floating seedlings — bottom-heavy youngsters that grow on the tree until reaching six. in to a foot in length. If they drop in shallow water, the seeds touch bottom and implant themselves. In deeper water they stay afloat and cross a shoal drag until they lodge.

Named for their light-colored bark, the **white mangroves** are highly salt-tolerant. If growing in a swampy area, they produce *pneumatophores*, root system extensions which grow vertically to a height that allows them to stay above the water during flooding or tides and that carry on gaseous exchange.

Producing a useful wood, the **black mangrove** also generates pneumatophores. Smaller than the others, the **buttonwood** is not a true mangrove but is found on the coasts where no other varieties occur.

Animal Life

The Animal Kingdom's wonderful diversity compliments that of the plants. Many of the indigenous species are in danger of extinction, largely from loss of their traditional habitats through deforestation. Sea turtles, though, are threatened by overhunting and beach development. The panoply of species includes manatees, ocelots, sloths, deer, coatimundis, coyotes, jaguars, marguays, peccaries, tapirs, plus squirrel, capuchin, and spider monkeys. Unlike their temperate counterparts, rainforest animals are relatively difficult to spot. You need to keep still, have a keen eye, and — best of all — have a local friend or guide along.

DOMESTICATED ANIMALS: Today's barnyard animals — cows, pigs, horses, donkeys, goats, and chickens—come from a lineage stretching back to the 1560-70s when the *conquistadores* brought them in from Nicaragua. There are also a fine but few examples of the Paso Fino and Andalusian (a special favorite) breeds, and a herd of water buffalo which was imported from Trinidad in 1975 and resides near Limón.

Mammals

PRIMATES: New World monkeys differ from their Old World and ape cousins in many respects. Their noses have wide-apart, sideward-pointing nostrils as opposed to close-set, downward-pointing ones, they are primarily arboreal, and show a greater variation in color patterns. Also, all of the New World monkey species live in trees, and each species has a distinct method of moving through branches.

Actually sounding more like a "growler" than a howler, the sounds of the mantled **howler monkey** (*mono congo*) reverberate up to several km away. The unusual sound results from a special bone in its throat which acts as an amplifier. There are numerous local explanations as to why howlers roar. Some say it is when rain is approaching or when other animals are feeding. Actually, they react to loud noises and to rain; their roaring is more frequent during midday. The cacophonous howling begins with an accelerating series of low-pitched grunts by the male which change to a series of long, deep roars; the females join the fun with higher-pitched roars. Another unique characteristic of the howler is its prehensile tail which features a dermatoglyph or fingerprint.

The hands of spider monkeys resemble suspensory hooks. Their long fingers are permanently curved in order to minimize effort while swinging from branch to branch, and their thumbs are nearly vestigal.

The capuchin monkey is the monkey you are most likely to see. One starred in a film, made in Costa Rica, about a plague in Africa!

Living in groups of up to 20 led by a senior male, the group dines on flowers, fruits, and tender leaves. Entirely black, except for its sides, which have a pale fringed mantle, the howler's robust shoulders contrast with its comparatively diminutive hindquarters.

You might see a **black-handed spider monkey** (***mono araña***) moving rapidly through the trees. Spiders have a very complex language and live in bands of about 20, which frequently subdivide into smaller groupings.

You will quickly identify the **white-throated capuchin (*mono cara blanca*)** by white shoulders, upper chest, and face. Its name comes from the resemblance of its head and shoulder covering to a monk's hood. Both extremely curious and agile, this noisy forager lives in groups of five to 15; its varied diet includes birds, fruits, insects, tender leaves, eggs, and honey. Its vocabulary includes barks, screams, yips, and whistles.

The **Central American squirrel monkey** (***mono tití, mono ardilla***) dwells only in

Costa Rican Wildlife: A to Z In Spanish

Ardilla — squirrel	**Pájaro** — **bird**
Ave—bird	**Pelicano** — pelican
Baula—leatherback turtl**e**	**Perezoso** — sloth
Buchón—pelican	**Perica** — three-toed sloth
Cabra de monte — brocket dear	**Perro de agua** — river otter
Caimán — caiman	**Pizote** — coati
Cariblanco — white-lipped peccary	**Puerco espín** — porcupine
Caucel — margay	**Puma** — cougar, mountain lion
Chiza — squirrel	**Quioro** — chestnut-mandibled toucan
Cocodrilo — crocodile	**Rana** — frog
Colibrí— hummingbird	**Saíno** — collared peccary
Culebra — snake	**Sapo** — toad
Cuzuco—armadillo	**Serafín**—silky anteater
Danta — tapir	**Serpiente**—snake
Gallito de agua — northern jacana	**Taltusa** — gopher
Garcilla bueyara — cattle egret, heron	**Tepezcuintle** — paca
Gavilán — roadside hawk	**Terciopelo** — fer-de-lance
Gaviota — gull	**Tigre**—jaguar
Guatusa — agouti	**Tigrillo** — tiger cat
Hormiguero—antbird	**Tijereta del mar**—magnificent frigatebird
Lapa — scarlet macaw	**Tijo**—smooth- or groove-billed ani
León breñero—jaguarundi	**Tolomuco** — tayra
Loro—**parrot**	**Tortuga** — turtle
Manigordo—ocelot	**Tortuga blanca** — green turtle
Mapachín—raccoon	**Tortuga bocado** — snapping turtle
Mariposa — butterfly	**Tortuga cabezona** — loggerhead turtle
Martilla — kinkajou	**Tortuga carey** — hawksbill turtle
Martín pescador — kingfisher	**Tortuga jicóte** — mud turtle
Mono araña — spider monkey	**Tortuga negra** — Pacific green turtle
Mono ardilla, mono tití — squirrel monkey	**Tortuga verde** — green turtle
Mono cara blanca — Capuchin monkey	**Tortuga** — turtle
Mono congo — howler monkey	**Venado coliblanco** — white-tailed deer
Murciélago — bat	**Zompopas** — farmer ants
Nutria — river otter	**Zorro hediondo** — skunk
Oso hormiguero—lesser anteater, tamandua	**Zorro** — opossum
Paloma—pigeon or dove	**© Harry S. Pariser**

the country's SW corner. Thought to have been introduced by man because of its miniscule geographical range, it resides in lowland rainforest in small groups. It is identified by its black-capped head, olive green shoulders and hips, and orange-gold hands, feet, back, and lower legs.

RACCOON FAMILY: Omnivorous, solitary, nocturnal, crafty, and clean the northern ***mapache*** (raccoon) will dine on anything from frogs and fish to fruit and vegetables. Its cousin is the mischievous and sociable White-nosed ***pizote*** (**coati**) Nimble, omnivorous, and solitary in old age, the hunts at dawn and dusk—resting in treetops or in hollow trunks the rest of the

The coati is a close cousin of the raccoon.

time. The term coati-mundi refers only to solitary coatis (adult males over two years old).

Mainly nocturnal, the gregarious ***martilla*** (**kinkajou**) dines on small animals, birds, eggs, and honey. It has short and wooly fur, large soulful eyes, and small ears. Its long prehensile tail is used to anchor itself as it moves from tree to tree. During the day, it naps in a tree hollow.

Smaller and lacking the prehensile tail, the ***olingo*** (**pale-faced kinkajou**) is a close relative. Actively agile, it journeys high in the rainforest canopy.

A third related species is the ***cacomistle***, a nocturnal and solitary tawny-brown creature which barks and has a tail longer than its head and body.

WEASEL FAMILY: With attractive fur that is short and thick but soft, the **Long-tailed weasel**'s (***comadreja's***) slim frame allows it to slither into the burrows of mice. It also feeds on rabbits, birds, and reptiles. A nervous, nocturnal, and solitary creature, it is hard to catch more than a glimpse of one.

The **grison** or **huron** (***grisón***) resembles a large weasel with extremely short legs and tail and a long neck and back.

Perhaps the nation's least popular mammal, the **striped hog-nosed skunk** (***zorro hediondo***) is probably better left unseen and unsmelled. Although it is not a true rainforest creature, it is sometimes found there.

The **southern river otter** (***nutria, perro de agua***) eats fish, shrimp, and turtles. An excellent swimmer, This creature, while graceful under water, waddles awkwardly on land.

The **tayra** (***tolumuco***) resembles a lanky mink with a long-haired tail; it feeds on grubs, bird nests, fruit, eggs, fruit, and chicken and goat meat; it resides in an underground burrow.

CAT FAMILY: The cat's physique suits its killer lifestyle. Its teeth are designed for killing and meat eating, and its excellent sight and hearing, strong shoulders, and sharp claws come in handy while going after game. It is the principal predator in rainforests worldwide.

Some are territorial, most are solitary, and all prey on anything that comes their way—from large insects to small mammals. The best time to see one is after nightfall when they take to trails and their bright eyeshine makes them visible. Should you come across a den with kittens, leave them alone. They have not been abandoned: the mother has gone off to search for food.

The **jaguar** (***tigre***) is this hemisphere's largest cat. This graceful, nocturnal and diurnal "king of the tropical rainforest" it may reach six ft. (two m) in length and three ft. (one m) in height at shoulder level. It dines on peccaries, deer, monkeys, sloths, and even fish. As the only large, spotted cat in the Americas, the jaguar is easily identifiable. You might hear one roar at night—a series of hoarse, deep grunts. Although an encounter is unlikely, if you should see one, walk toward it and shout and clap your hands. If you run, it may pursue, and you'll regret it!

The **puma** ranks second in size. Slightly smaller than a jaguar, it has an unspotted tan or dark brown hide, a leaner, more low-slung frame, and a longer, thicker tail. It is the only large, uniformly colored cat. It is sometimes called a cougar or mountain lion. Although pumas may tag along behind humans out of curiousity, few attacks on have ever been documented.

The **ocelot** (***manigordo***) resembles a miniaturized jaguar Unlike a jaguar, it has stripes, not spots, on its neck. It feeds on anything from rabbits to insects. An ocelot captures its game on the ground and may be encountered walking on man-made trails at night.

A smaller version of the ocelot, the **tiger cat** (***tigrillo***) has a combination of spots and stripes. Ranging between 33 and 51 inches (85 and 130 cm), it may weigh up to 22 lbs (10 kg). Rarely sighted, it survives in the Tortuguero, Santa Rosa, and Corcovado national parks, the Reserva Forestal Río Macho, and on the lower slopes of the Cordillera Talamanca.

More solitary and nocturnal than the ocelot, the **margay** (***caucel, tigrillo***) is the size of a large house cat. and weighs 6-10 lbs (3-22kg). The margay has a somewhat bushy tail which runs well over half the extended length of its head and black-spotted body. Once widespread and now endangered more by habitat loss than by hunting, this majestic and magnificent feline abounds now only in Corcovado and Santa Rosa. It may easily be confused with ocelots. Also known locally as a *caucel*, the **oncilla** has the shape of a a slender house cat. Some are black.

With unspotted blackish-brown or chestnut-to-red fur, the **jaguarundi** (***león breñero***) has a small flattened head, long sleek body, short legs — all of which make it appear to be a cross between a cat and a weasel.

MARSUPIALS: The three species of opossum (***zorro***) found here are four-eyed, woody, and regular. Arboreal, it is a nocturnal omnivore. The **wooly mouse** and **slaty slender mouse opossums** (***zorra, zorricí***) are also found here.

Five-toed, **opossums** have short legs, long tails, large and delicate ears. Their first hindfoot toe functions as an opposable "thumb" which is used to clutch thin branches for climbing.

Born only eight days after fertilization, opossum infants follow a trail of their mother's saliva from the cloaca to her pouch where they secure themselves to their mother's nipples for the next 60 days. These malodorous creatures—which feed on small animals and fruits—enjoy rolling in fresh dung; when handled, they are aggressive, defecating and squirting evil-smelling urine with a twist of their tail.

EDENTATAS: Indigenous to the Americas, the name of this order—which includes anteaters, sloths, and armadillos—refers to the few teeth found in the latter two and their complete absence in the anteaters. They represent the last remnant of an order that evolved during the period when South America was an isolated island continent. Sloths and anteaters are both arboreal, soft furred creatures.

Residing in the highest tree tops and living off plants and leaves, are the distantly-related, brown-throated **three-toed sloth** (***perezoso de tres dedos***) and the rarer **two-toed sloth** (***perezoso de dos dedos***). Their Spanish name (***perezoso***) means "lazy," which perfectly fits their somnolent attitude, slow movements, and ability to hang upside down for long periods without moving.

A sloth differs from other edentates in that it has well-developed crushing teeth and a digestive tract akin to a grazing ruminant (cud chewer). It uses its many-chambered stomach to digest leaves through bacterial fermentation. Long-limbed and clawed creatures, sloths are camouflaged by the blue-green and green single-cell algae which grow on microscopic grooves and notches on its fur. Some species of moths feed on this algae. Cecropia (***guarumo***) trees are a particular favorite of sloths and often provide the best view.

Sloths descend once a week or so to defecate, carefully digging a hole with their stubby tails and burying their feces; one explanation for their descent (which exposes them to predators) is that the decomposition of their feces at the tree's base might provide them with a higher quality food supply.

Apparently practicing a form of recycling, sloth pellets may return to the tree half the nutrients that the beast has taken. As sloths generally feed on only 15 to 40 trees in the period of a few months and have a single tree they return to frequently, this seems to be an intelligent investment. But this is not the only way they contribute to the ecosystem. Beetles, moths, and mites live on sloths and deposit their eggs in the sloth's dung.

With a prehensile tail and a long retractile tongue, the strictly nocturnal **silky anteater** (***cebita, tapacara, serafin de planar***) breaks open ant and termite nests to feed. The best way to find one is to gaze into clumps of lianas up to 10 m (33 ft.) above the jungle floor for something resembling a golden tennis ball, which is in reality a sleeping anteater.

Another species is the banded or **lesser anteater** (***oso jaceta, oso hormiguero***), distinguished by the black V-shaped mark across its back, resembling a vest worn backwards.

The **northern tamandua** (***oso mielero***) is black vested and nocturnal. During the day, you will see them accompanied by a dense halo of flies and mosquitoes, which they brush away with a forepaw.

The **giant anteater** (***oso caballo***) is a large shaggy creature that ambles about on its knuckles.

Mainly insectivorous and nocturnal, **armadillos** are protected by banded and bony plates separated by soft skin which permits the creature to bend. Resembling a trotting windup toy, an armadillo may run right into you. Their burrows can be recognized by the smooth, dome-shaped roof. Each litter conceived in the burrow is a set of four identical quadruplets hatched from a single egg.

The **nine-banded long-nosed armadillo** (***cusuco***) eats beetles, ants, termites, fungi, berries, slugs, centipedes, millipedes, and other such exotic cuisine. Chiefly nocturnal, it is the most commonly seen variety.

The rare northern **naked-tail armadillo** (***armado de zopilote***) walks about on the tips of its foreclaws. You might catch a glimpse of its naked tail disappearing under a log.

TAPIRS: Tapirs are members of the genus Perisodactyles, a family which includes horses and the African and Asian rhinoceroses, is characterized by two unmatched or unequal hoof-covered toes.

The **Baird's tapir** (***danto, danta, macho de monte***) is one of the Americas' largest mammals. The rainforest's largest terrestrial mammal, it weighs as much as 550 lbs. (250 kg) and may grow six ft. (two m) long and up to three ft. (one m) high. Dining on seeds, leaves, twigs, and fruit, the tapir devotes 90% of its waking time to foraging for food because the microorganisms that live in its stomach and digest its plant material through fermentation are not very efficient. Its excellent hearing and sense of smell compensate for this ungainly creature's poor eyesight.

Solitary, nocturnal, and marsh-dwelling, it bolts when frightened — flattening everything in its wake! Despite the fact that they are the mammalian equivalent of the all-terrain vehicle, tapirs are shy creatures and difficult to see. However, hunters can easily locate them through dogs and calls, and their meat is considered a delicacy.

PECCARIES AND DEER: These are the two families of *Artiocactyla* (even-toed hoofed animals) found in the rainforest.

Resembling a gigantic pig, the **collared peccary** (***saino, javelino, chancho de monte***) lives in a group of two to 15. The group members recognize each other via their pungent, musky body odor which is reminiscent of chicken soup or cheese. A peccary may be identified by a faint but nevertheless distinct collar of pale yellow hairs running from its lower cheek down to the top of its shoulder. They are most often found at salt licks or mud wallows.

Another species is the ***cariblanco*** (white-lipped peccary). Generally black in the rainforest environs, it may also be brownish or red. There's always at least a sprinkling of white hair on its jaws and body and some are even snow white. Feeding in large herds on fruits, palm nuts, and the like, white-lipped peccaries cover a large area daily and leave the ground churned and pocked in their wake. The noise coming from large groups (tooth clacking, screaming, bellowing) has given them a greatly exaggerated reputation for aggressiveness. They generally retreat in the face of humans although one might rumble past you without seeing you.

The **white-tailed deer** (***venado, venado colo blanco***) was almost exterminated during the 1940s when the harvest of 10,000-40,000 animals was used for leather goods manufacture and for dog food. They are identical to but smaller than the white-tailed deer found in the US. Not rainforest animals, they are generally found out in the open. Male deer have antlers which are shed and regrown annually.

Another variety is the **red brocket deer** or ***cabra de monte***. Its tapered shape is ideal for pushing through rainforest. Diurnal and solitary, it feeds on fallen fruits, flowers, and on other vegetation.

MANATEES: The **manatee** or sea cow (***manatí***), has been sighted in Tortuguero and off of Gandoca on rare occasions. Once ranging from S America up to N Carolina, their numbers have dwindled dramatically. It moves along the ocean floor (at a maximum pace of six mph) searching for food, surfacing every four or five minutes to breathe. Surprisingly, the creature was thought to be the model for the legend of the mermaid — perhaps because of the mother's habit of sheltering her offspring with her flipper as the infant feeds.

Weighing 400-1,300 lbs. (181-590 kg), this pudgy creature is covered with finely

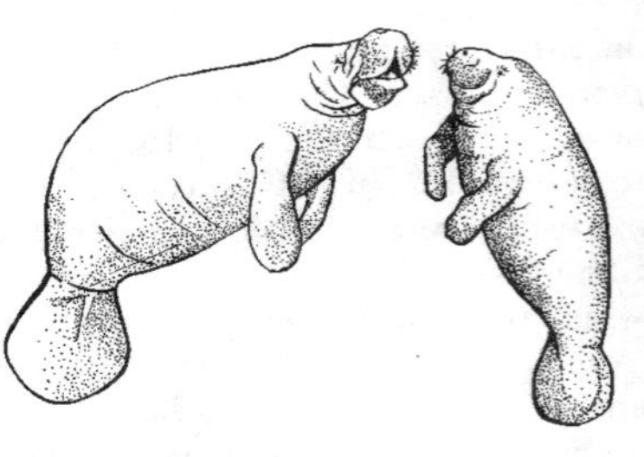

Manatees at play
© Joyce Huber. Used by permission.

wrinkled grey or brown skin decorated with barnacles and algae; it may reach 12 ft. (4 m) in length. Although to you they may appear ugly with their small eyes, thick lips, bristly muzzles, and wrinkled necks, they are affectionate, kissing each other and sometimes swimming flipper-to-flipper. Dwelling in lagoons and in brackish water, they may consume as much as 100 lbs. of aquatic vegetables per day. Strictly vegetarian, their only enemy is man who has hunted them for the hide, oil, and meat.The manatee's nearest living relative is the elephant).

RODENTS: The rodents' trademark is their sharp and versatile front incisors. Supported by several different complex systems of jaw and muscle structures, these teeth may be used to slice, dig, pry, and cut. Some rodents can even fell trees and kill animals.

These differences permit them to be separated into three groups: squirrel-like (*Sciuromorpha*), cavy-like (*Caviomorpha*), and mouse-like (*Myomorpha*). By far the most diverse order of mammals, there are some 1,750 species worldwide — a number which nearly equals the 2,300 other species of mammals.

Omnivorous, squirrels are common in the rainforest. They feed on palm nuts as well as fruits, insects, fungi, and even leaves, bark, and flowers. The **red-tailed squirrel** (***ardilla roja. ardilla chisa***) is widespread in some parts and may commonly be observed scurrying up a tree. Other species include the variegated squirrel, Deppe's squirrel, Richmond's squirrel, the Central American dwarf squirrel, and the montane squirrel.

Long-legged hoofed creatures with bristle-like hair and strong jaws, the cavy-like rodents all have four toes on their front feet. Living near rivers and active during the day, the edgy brown-colored Central American **agouti** (***guatusa***) dines on tender shoots, fruits, and seeds. Diurnal and largely solitary, they are frequently seen in protected areas, especially in late afternoon. Newborn young stay apart in their own burrow; mama calls them out for nursing and care.

Its cousin, the nocturnal and largely solitary **paca** (***tepezcuintle***) is larger and twice as heavy, has horizontal rows of cream-colored spots along its flanks, and a piglike body. The paca resides in a burrow.

A clumsy vegetarian, the skinny prehensile-tailed **porcupine** (***puercospín***) is covered with short, strong, and rigid quills. Its barb-tipped spines detach readily, and work their way inward in the flesh of an attacker. It forages at night for fruits and seeds.

Rothschild's Porcupine is entirely spiney and mostly black. The spines of the Mexican hairy porcupine are largely covered with dark fur. Another common rodent is the **gopher** (***taltusa***). There are also a number of rats and mice.

RABBITS: Dwelling in thickets and forests, **cottontail rabbits** (***conejos***) eat grass and tree bark; they may have up to five litters per year. The only other species found is the Brazilian which is smaller, reddish, and has only a small tail.

BATS: Bats are the most important animals, in terms of sheer number of species, in most New World tropical rainforests. The only mammals which fly, bats have wings made of amazingly elastic skin which contracts rather than folds when the wings are closed. Emitting largely-ultrasonic high-frequency sounds through their nose or mouth, bats plot their route by calibrating distances to solid objects based on returning echoes.

In addition to consuming huge quantities of insects, bats benefit the environment through pollination of many important plants and by seed dispersal. Costa Rica has over 100 bat species, as compared to only 40 in the US. Some feed on nectar, others on frogs, others on fish, and still others on sleeping birds and on lizards. Contrary to popular belief, bats will not become tangled in your hair nor will they bite except in self-defense.

Hiding out in caves — their harems guarded by a single male—the **short-tailed fruit bat** (***murciélago***) flies out at night. It resides in the rainforest understory and is an important seed disperser.

The infamous **vampire bat** (***vampiro***) also lives in Costa Rica. Stealthily landing on a horse or cow, it makes an incision, a process which may take up to 20 min., and, exuding an anticoagulant, quietly proceeds to lap up the blood. It may run and hop with agility on all fours, using its thickened thumb as a foot. Its feces contain a fungus which causes histoplasmosis, a dehabilitating disease.

The **fishing** or **bulldog bat** (***murciélago pescador***) skims water as it flies and feeds on insects and fish which it grasps with its enormous feet.

Nectar-feeding or **long-tongued bats** are important pollinators, often attracted by plants with large flowers which open at night. Other species include the Jamaican fruit bat, the lesser short-tailed fruit bat, the black myotis, the sac-wing bat, and the false vampire.

Reptiles and Amphibians

Reptiles and amphibians thrive in the rainforest, but they also blend in very well. Although many species of lizards and frogs are found, there are only 26 species of salamanders—mostly found in montane rainforests. Snakes are definitely around, but they are secretive, mostly nocturnal, and tend to be small.

TURTLES: There are a large variety. Smaller turtles include the ***tortuga bocado*** or **snapping turtle** and the semiaquatic ***tortuga jicóte*** or **mud turtle**.

Medium-sized with a total length of about a meter and weighing 165-440 lbs. (75-200 kg), the large-finned, herbiverous ***tortuga blanca*** or ***tortuga verde*** (**green turtle**) lays eggs every two to three years, storming the beaches in massive groups termed ***barricadas***. Dining only on marine plants like turtle grass, the turtle has a short rounded head and occurs on both coasts.

One of the smallest sea turtles at 35 in. (90 cm) or less, the ***tortuga carey*** (**hawksbill**) has a spindle-shaped shell and weighs around 220 lbs. (100 kg). Because of its tortoise shell—a brown translucent layer of corneous gelatin that covers it and peels off the shell when processed—it has been pursued and slaughtered throughout the world. It eats largely mollusks, sponges, and seaweed. Worldwide demand for its shell, worth a fortune in Japan, appears to have condemned it to extinction.

The short-finned ***tortuga cabezona*** (**loggerhead turtle**) is rarely longer than 4 ft. (1.20 m). The loggerhead's narrow and bird-jawed large head is twice the size of the green turtle's. It feeds on sea urchins, jellyfish, starfish, and crabs. Loggerheads are threatened with extinction by coastal development, egg gathering, and from hunting by raccoons.

Black, with very narrow fins, the ***baula*** (**leatherback**) gets its name from the black leathery hide which covers its back in lieu of a shell. It may reach up to seven feet (two meters) in length and weigh up to 1,500 lbs. (700 kg).

The leatherback's chief predator has always been the poacher. Costa Rican poachers traditionally have lain in wait for the turtles. Flipping the latest arrival on her back, they would stab it with long knives, slicing down to the lower shell which was torn off. After extracting the calipee, used to make turtle soup, a poacher would run off to the next turtle—leaving his helpless victim flailing with her intestines exposed. Arriving the next morning, vultures circled the still-living turtle and then descended to feast on her entrails. Although poaching has diminished, dogs also pose a threat: they love to dig up eggs.

The ***lora, carpintera*** **(Pacific ridley)** is the most abundant yet least understood of the sea turtles. It is endangered by its nesting habits. Although restrictions have been put in force since this date, the Mexicans slaughtered over a million for use in the leather industry in 1968 alone. And, as beachside development continues worldwide, their future survival appears uncertain.

A final species is the ***tortuga negra*** (**Pacific green turtle**)which, like the green, hawksbill, and leatherback, are found on both coasts; the ridley is found only on the Pacific side. While the loggerhead is found mainly on the Caribbean, it is also occasionally seen on the Pacific.

NESTING SITES AND TIMES: Green turtles generally nest at Tortuguero and Barra de Matina during early July into Oct., peaking in August. Leatherbacks nest from Feb. to July, peaking in April and May, at Barra de Matina and from Oct. to March at Playa Grande. They also nest at Nancite and Playa Naranjo. Pacific ridleys arrive in barricadas of up to 120,000 to lay eggs on Playa Nancite and in Ostional along the Pacific side during 4-8 day periods from July to Dec. Pacific greens nest at Nancite and Playa Naranjo; hawksbills nest on both coasts all year 'round, but they can be seen most easily at Tortuguero from July to Oct. For information on egglaying, see the description in the Tortuguero section.

Leaf frogs spend their days sleeping on a leaf with in their colorful legs tucked in. Scientists believe that their brightly-colored legs, which are exposed when the frog decides to jump, startles predators and allows an extra time margin in which to escape.

FROGS AND TOADS: The glands of the marine toad (*bufo marinus*) contain toxins. This predominately nocturnal toad exercises control over its paratoid gland, and it can direct its poison in a fine spray, one that can prove fatal to dogs and cats if they pick it up in their mouths. If you carry it around, it will be likely to defend itself by urinating. An equal-opportunity eater, it will snack on anything from wasps to dog and cat food set out for pets.

Second only in size to marine toads, the aggressive **smoky frog** (***rana tenero***) grows to at least 6 in. (160 mm) and has been known to eat snakes up to 20 in. (500 mm) long.

Resembling an amorphous blob of jelly, the **burrowing toad** (***sapo borracho***) dries up completely while underground; when disturbed, it excretes a sticky white substance which causes an acute allergic reaction in some humans.

The small **glass frog** (***rana de vidrio***) is so translucent that it barely casts a shadow. It has green veins and a visible red vein leading to its heart.

Smooth-skinned and lacking warts, the **poisonous true toad** (***sapo***) dwells in mid-elevation wet forests.

The gaudy **leaf frog** (***rano calzonudo***), is Central America's most colorful. It is readily identifiable by its bright, leaf-green dorsum, creamy-white throat and belly, orange hands and feet, dark blue side markings, and blood-red irises.

The **tink frog** (***martillito***) is named after its sharp call, incredibly powerful given the fact that it is less than an inch (25 mm) long. It exercises remarkable agility and can run like a mouse on its stubby legs.

> ?!? The poison dart frog's name refers to Western Colombia's Chocó tribesmen who extracted an alkaloid-based poison from the skin glands which they used on the tips of their blowgun darts.

POISON DART FROGS: *Dendrobatids* are the genus of poison dart frogs (***ranita roja, ranita venerosa***) which are aspomatic—possessing a warning coloration which advertises their toxicity. Their natural danskins, coming in bright red and blue decorator colors, broadcast a message geared chiefly toward predatory birds. Many other frogs also have these "flash" colors, primary coloring on their undersides and groins which are flashed in the view of predators, causing confusion. The frogs are harmless to handle as long as your skin is unbroken; putting them in your mouth is not recommended.

MATING PRACTICES: Male frogs perch in mushrooms, calling out for a mate. After a female arrives, he scouts for the proper site. When she lags behind, he calls and waits. The female rubs the male's head and chin with her head. Facing back to back, she lays a few eggs which the male fertilizes and guards for a two-week period, after which the female returns.

Taking one of the newly hatched tadpoles on her back, the female deposits it in a suitably isolated pool of water (which is often the leaf axil of a bromeliad). She may have to climb up a tree in order to do this. As the water lacks nutrients, the female returns later repeatedly to lay unfertilized eggs which the embryo feeds on. In order to prevent a damselfly larva from decimating her brood, each tadpole is deposited in a different location. When she approaches a bromeliad which is already occupied, the tadpole makes its presence known by aiming its head towards the center, holding itself rigid, and rapidly vibrating its tail.

LIZARDS: The **basilisk** or "Jesus Christ lizard" (*Basiliscus basiliscus*) is so named because while fleeing predators or pursuing prey it may dart across the surface of a stream, balancing itself with its tail. Resembling miniature sailfin dinosaurs, you'll undoubtedly see these lowland dwellers scurrying across your path.

The territorial, primarily vegetarian ***garobo*** or ***iguana negra*** (**ctenosaur**) occurs in the drier lowlands. The **iguana** is distinguished from its cousin by a large scale on the side of the head slightly below and behind the rear angle of the lower jaw, green coloration, and a longer tail.

There are also a wide variety of **anoles**, small sit-and-wait predators that North Americans mistakenly call chameleons. Other lizards include the **skink** and the **spiny lizard**.

There are two species of crocodilians: the occasionally cannibalistic **caimán**, which grows up to eight ft. (2.5 m), inhabiting lowland swamps and slow-moving streams; and the larger, coastal dwelling **crocodile (*crocodilia*)**.

?!¿ To tell the difference between a caimán and a crocodile you must look at the brow, snout and back. While the caimán's brow slopes down to the base of its snout, the crocodile is flat-headed. The caimán has a shorter and wider snout than the crocodile. Finally, the crocodile's back is spiky and ridged, unlike the caimán's.

A caíman lurks in a Tortuguero waterway.

SNAKES: Despite what one might expect, there is actually a much greater chance of your dying crossing the street in San José than from receiving a poisonous snakebite here.

Of the 162 species, 22 are poisonous. The most infamous is the ***terciopelo* (fer-de-lance, "velvet snake")** which is colored olive green to dark brown with yellow, V-shaped markings along the sides. Reaching lengths up to seven feet or more, this lowland-dwelling snake

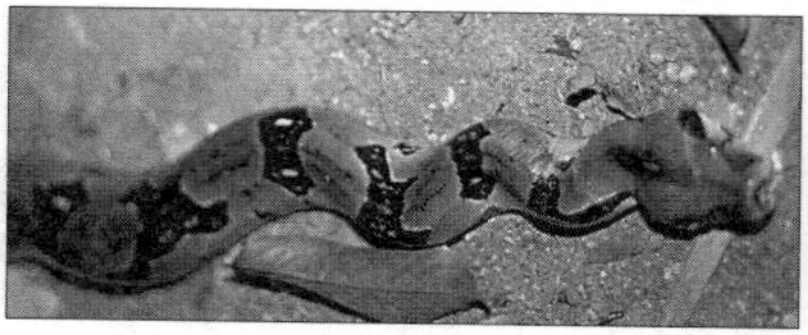

A boa in Corcovado. Snakes do not attack: They will defend themselves if cornered. Otherwise, they will attempt to flee.

dines on mammals, especially opossums, with an occasional bird thrown in for variety. If you leave it alone, it won't bother you. Its natural foe is the snake-feeding which is immune to its venom.

Another, similar variety, but stockier and more aggressive, is the ***mano de piedra*** ("stone fist," hognose viper, *Bothreicheis nasutus*).

The small (20 in., 50 cm), ***bocaracá*** (**eyelash vipe**r) is quite poisonous. It has low excresences resembling horns above its eyes. Strictly arboreal, it tends to thrive in the tropical lowlands.

Another arboroeal poisonous snake is the **víbora de árbol** or **arboicola** which is found between 4,260-8,200 ft. (1,300-2,500 m.).

The deadliest snake is the rare **cascabel muda** ("silent rattler") which may reach up to six ft. (two m). There's also the ***cascabel*** **(tropical rattler)** which has been known to bite cows on their tongues as they graze. It's found only in Guanacaste.

Another serpent to watch out for is ***la coral*** (the **coral snake**), which does not bother humans unless handled. It comes in a number of species: one colored red, yellow and black and others which are variously striped black and red, black and orange, or black and white.

The harmless ***sabanera*** (grassnake) has a dull brown color and a distinctive red or orange underbelly. There's also the***bejuquilla*** ("little vine"), a vine snake living in arid areas.

A climber par excellence, the large, non-venomous ***boa*** (**boa constrictor**) devours everything from lizards to dogs. After striking its prey, the boa coils around it. After the prey's death, it locates its head and swallows it whole.

The most frightening snake is the ***culebra del mar*** (**pelagic sea snake**), for which there is no serum available; it's found from 1-20 km offshore along the Pacific coast from California to Chile. Fortunately, only ten people have been bit by it during the past decade.

Birds

Costa Rica's geographical location as a land bridge between two continents makes it a meeting ground for a huge variety of American birds. A full tenth of the world's flighted species visit or permanently reside here.

There are over 850 species of birds, more than in all of North America N of Mexico. This population includes brightly colored wild parakeets, an assortment of trogons and macaws, hummingbirds, pelicans, antshrikes, swallows, wrens, thrushes, warblers, ovenbirds, cuckoos, hawks, swifts, owls, egrets, and others.

WHERE TO FIND BIRDS: One of the reasons birdwatchers flock to Costa Rica is the number and variety of its species. Even if you aren't a diehard, be to bring binoculars. Everyone has a favorite spot. It may be around your hotel or at a nature preserve. The parks and reserves—public or private—are sure bets. One of Costa Rica's great outdoor aviaries is the area surrounding the mouth of the Río Tempisque inside the Palo Verde National Park.

AVIFAUNA ZONES: The first includes the province of Guanacaste. Northern birds predominate here. Santa Rosa and Palo Verde both are outstanding birding spots as are other parks and reserves in the region. Many migratory birds are found in Palo Verde's Tempisque river basin. The cloud forests in the highlands contain a large number of endemic species as well as Andean or southern varieties. The southern Pacific area boasts Corcovado, one of the best all-around places to see birds. The Caribbean coast also provides fine birding in its lowlands. Many South American species are found here.

> Birdwatchers will want to pick up a copy of *The Birds of Costa Rica* by F. Gary Stiles and Alexander Skutch, the most authoritative guide available. Buy it before you arrive. It is very expensive in Costa Rica. Another useful book is the ***Site Guide*** by Dennis W. Rogers. which provides checklists and directions to birding sites.

SEASONAL MIGRANTS: There is a remarkable influx of long-distance migrants from North America. Warblers predominate—both in their numbers and in the variety of different species that appear. Other species include thrushes, vireos, tanagers, cuckoos, kingfishers, raptors, swallows, and flycatchers. Birds first start arriving along the Caribbean coast in August; their numbers swell throughout the country in September and October.

Prominent winter residents include the small yellow-throated vireo, the scarlet-rumped tanager (***sargento***), the red-winged blackbird (***tordo sargento***), the sanderling, and the Tennessee warbler. Others are not true migrants but tropical birds that go N to breed, spending more than half the year in Costa Rica. Birds that migrate in spectacular flocks include Swainson's hawks, turkey vultures, and barn, bank, and cliff swallows.

BIRDS WITH CHARACTER: First arriving in the New World from Africa around 1877, the **cattle egret** (***garcilla bueyara***) follows cattle and eats insects disturbed as they move about.

Thriving in deforested territory, the sedentary **roadside hawk** (***gavilán***) abounds in Guanacaste, preying on lizards, snakes, rodents, and large insects.

The enormous ***rey de zopilote*** (**king vulture**) has creamy white and black on its wings, and a red and orange head.

Found in the waters near Puntarenas, the nearly jet-black **magnificent frigate bird** (***tijereta de mar, zopilote de mar***) swoops ominously overhead, occasionally veering down to the water to make a capture.

Dark colored **antbirds** (***hormigueros***) are best seen if you are on a solitary excursion into one of the primary forests.

Related to the oriole and the grackle, the omnivorous ***oropendola*** is mostly black with yellow outer tail feathers. The female constructs her sagging saclike nests on the ends of tree branches. The make an unforgettable sight!

"Motmot, motmot" is the cry of the blue-crowned **motmot** (***pajaro bobo***) which numbers among the most beautiful of the nation's birds.

The **chestnut-mandibled toucan** (***dios tede***) is the largest in Central America. One of the forest's largest fruit eaters, its piercing call and brown and yellow bill are its trademarks.

The **orange-chinned parakeet** (***perico)*** is bright green with an orange patch just below its bill.

The **three-wattled bellbird** (***pajaro campana, campanero tricarunculado***) has a metallic call much like a bell. The male is chestnut with white chest, neck, and head; it has three wattles. The female is olive-green and has fine yellow stripes on her upper chest and on the sides of her head. Her bill is also black but lacks the wattles.

COWBIRDS: There are two varieties of cowbirds in Costa Rica : **giant** (***vaquero grande***) and **bronzed (*vaquero ojirrojo*)**. Members of the oriole family, these birds are celebrated for their breeding practices which some biologists have regarded with moral indignation. Either too lazy or too enlightened to build nests and nurture offspring, cowbirds indulge in a practice known as brood parasitism. After locating a suitable nest, the female sneaks in and deposits her egg among those of the builder.

Whereas giant cowbirds chiefly choose the nests of *oropendolas* and *caciques* to victimize, the bronzed seek out sparrow, finches, and other nests. Baby giants hatch a week earlier than their nestmates and develop more quickly so they are able to dominate the others.

Working in Panama, researcher Neal Smith discovered that the birds exhibit two types of behavior. In one, a cowbird sneaks around an nest and stealthily lays an egg or two. The eggs resemble oropendola eggs, but, should the female oropendola suspect something is up, she will not hesitate to roll the egg out of the nest.

In other cases, the cowbird brazenly lays up to five eggs, which do not resemble oropendola eggs, in the presence of the female oropendola. In these instances, the aggressive cowbird hatchlings protect the nest from botflies by swiftly swallowing the flies and their larva as well. In nests where the cowbirds practice their usual behavior, Smith noted that the nest was protected from the botflies through the proximity of a bee or wasp nest.

Along with the Resplendant Quetzal, the Scarlet Macaw is one of Costa Rica;s most unforgettable birds. It remains largely in the Osa Peninsula and in Carara reserve.

THE SCARLET MACAW: This spectacularly plumaged parrot is one of the nation's most beautiful birds. It resides on the Pacific side, and about the only reliable places to see macaws are in the Corcovado and Carara national parks. Its bright red-orange plumage has touches of yellow and blue and does not vary with age or between sexes. You are likely to see it flying overhead and sounding off raucously.

Scarlet macaws (***lapas***) apparently mate for life which is one reason they are in danger of extinction. Another is their black market value—up to US$500 per bird. A third is habitat destruction: they generally nest in large trees. Since 1992, it's been illegal to import macaws to the US.

You'll commonly see macaws in fruit trees where they may be found pecking through the pulp of fruits and cracking open the seeds, the contents of which they devour. They may also consume the pulp, as well as some leaves and flowers, but the seeds are their bread and butter.

The birds can perform gymnastics in pursuit of their daily fruit which would be the envy of any olympic acrobatics team member. For example, they may reach over sideways on one foot to pluck a fruit or they may hang upside down. The bird's four-taloned feet — two of which face forward and two backwards — enable it to accomplish these feats. Another tool which the bird puts to effective use is its remarkable hooked beak which may be used for climbing. Macaws have also been known to consume riverbank clay which may serve to counter the effects of poisonous seeds which are high in alkaloids and tannins.

The birds generally mate in Dec.; the female lays two eggs. During the month-long incubation, her partner brings her delicacies which he has previously swallowed and stored in a throat pouch. Regurgitating, he feeds his mate, and both feed the chicks this way. Chicks fledge at three to four months. Male and female are distinguishable only during breeding and nesting. You may commonly see them preening each other. Macaws may live for as long as 45 years.

A related species, the **green macaw** (***buffon***) is found on the Caribbean coast but rarely seen. It dines on the fruit of the wild almond (*Dipteryx panamesis*), a tree species which is also endangered owing to poaching and habitat loss. If no effective actions are taken, it is likely that the species may disappear from Costa Rica in ten years. Once a common sight along the Caribbean coast, its range is now restricted to the area between San Carlos and Sarapiquí.

THE QUETZAL: Living in the cool cloud forests of Monteverde, Braulio Carrillo, and Chirripó among other places, the **Resplendant Quetzal** (pronounced "ketZAL") is the nation's most famous animal, *period*! Costa Rica is the easiest place to see a quetzal, and the place to find them is in damp, epiphyte-laden mountain forests between 4,000 and 10,000 ft. (1,200 to 3,000 m), particularly along edges and canopies.

The bird usually keeps the highest profile during breeding season between March and June when macaws nest in high hollows of decaying tree trunks. Because they subsist on fruit and insects, the easiest place to spot them is around fruiting trees. Males and females take turns sitting on the pale blue eggs which are laid directly atop the sawdustlike material that covers the floor of the hole. They are readily identifiable by their red underbelly, iridescent green back, and trailing green plumes. The short yellow bill is ideal for drilling in soft, dead wood.

Usually found alone or in pairs, they sound with a sharp cackling "*perwicka*" when disturbed or taking off. The male sounds a strikingly melodious or whining "*keow kowee keow k'loo keow k'loo keeloo.*" It also cries "*very good, very good*" in rising display flight. In flight, the quetzal resembles a woodpecker—flying in short, undulating dips and rises, plumes rolling brashly to its rear. The tail length of the male ranges from 14 in. (36 cm) to 25 in. (64 cm). Only the male of the species grows a long tail. The plainer female sports barred tail feathers and only a touch of red.

The Aztecs borrowed the bird's image for Quetzacóatl, their feathered serpent god, and its name is derived from *quetzalli*, an early Aztec word for its tail feathers, which also means "precious" or "beautiful." Native American kings and priests used the bird's feathers for adornment. Decreed sacred, males were caught, plucked, and released. Unfortunately, quetzals by the thousands were slaughtered for export to Europe during the mid-19th C., and the carnage continues to this day.

The Guatemalans named the quetzal their national bird in the mistaken belief that it could not live in captivity. The first part of its scientific name, *Pharomarchrus mocinno*, derives from the Greek words for "long mantle" and the second immortalizes the 19th C. naturalist who helped bring the first scientific specimens to Europe. Nine other species of trogons, the group to which the quetzal belongs, also reside in Costa Rica.

HUMMINGBIRDS: Bold and strikingly beautiful, the fiery-throated hummingbird (***colibrí garganta de fuego***) hovers above flowers. Colored a glossy green, it has iridescent patterning which is only visible from above and at close range. Its dull-colored relative is the long-tailed hermit (***ermitaño colilargo***).

Hummingbirds are attracted to colorful flowers and, should you wear bright red, you may find yourself a target! Despite what you might think, these enchanting creatures are nourished not by nectar but by insects. They are thought to use the low-nutrient nectar, which has a high sugar content, for an energy boost. The flowers which have evolved to cater to this addiction are often tubular and suspended away from their branches in order to allow the birds space to probe with their long tongues.

LONG-TAILED MANAKINS: Commonly found in the forests of the NW, these chickadee-sized birds are noted both for their size and behavior. Blue-black in color, males have azure backs and scarlet crowns and legs. Two slender plumes fork from their tails. The females are greenish-colored, with short tails. Perhaps because they dine mainly on abundantly available fruit, manakins have evolved their own eccentric mating behavior.

Males partner with each other in a dynamic singing duo. One tweets *"to-de-lo"* and the other responds with a noisy, less melodic reply. The two birds dance in tandem in a kind of cartwheel with rotating positions. While the birds are going at it, a female may be attracted. The dominant male mates with her and then resumes dancing with his partner.

GREAT CURRASOW: An unforgettable resident of the forest, the 36-inch (91-cm) great currasow is black, with a long tail, a curly erectile crest and a bright yellow knob at the base of its bill. The smaller female lacks this knob and is grey colored. The bird spends its days scratching the ground in search of fallen fruit and small animals. If frightened, it generally runs away, emitting a high-pitched yip like a dog. Endangered, it is now most easily spotted in Santa Rosa, Rincón de la Vieja, and in Corcovado.

OTHER BIRDS: Other indigenous species of note include the Muscovy duck, a variety of woodpeckers, the rufous-naped hen, the turkey vulture and its relatives, the green kingfisher, the boat-billed heron, the bananaquit, the groove-billed ani, the five species of tinamou, the brown jay, the white-collared swift, the rufous-tailed jacamar, the laughing falcon, the mangrove swallow, the jacana, the ochre-bellied flycatcher, the white-fronted nunbird, the pauraque, the tropical screech owl, the spotted barbtail, the great-tailed grackle, western and spotted sandpipers, variable seedeater, ruddy-tailed and common-tody flycatchers, the barred antshrike, the tropical kingbird, the wrenthrush, and the rufous-colored sparrow.

Insects

Insect life is both varied and abundant In the 89,000 acres (36,000 ha) of Corcovado National Park, there are at least 220 species of butterflies. In mountainous Chirippó, only 70 km away, there are 30 species, with less than 5% overlap. There are more cicada species than found E of the Mississippi River in the US. There may be as many as 20 million or more different species in tropical rainforests worldwide. A study by Terry Erwin of the Smithsonian estimated that

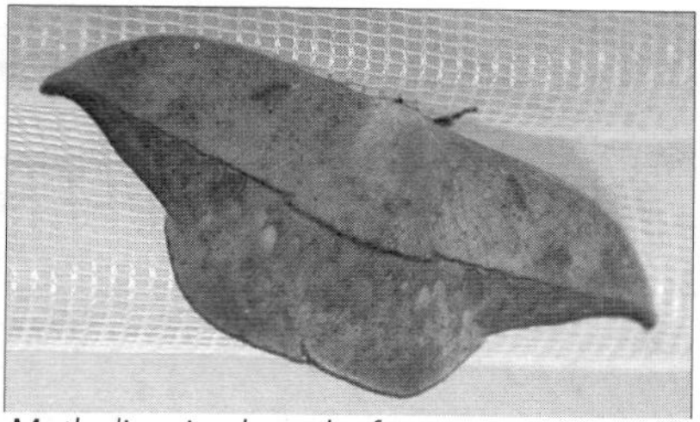

Moth disguised as a leaf.

each tree supports 405 unique insect species.

Lest you be tempted to view insects as uninteresting, remember that they have been around for at least 400 million years and butterflies are believed to have evolved around 200 million years ago during the Triassic. Tropical forests have evolved in tandem with insects, and some of the most fascinating interactions involve flora and insects. Many are masters of disguise and blend in with their surroundings. Katydids take on the colors of moss and lichens; caterpillars craftily masquerade as bird droppings; moths masterfully imitate dead leaves. Take time out to watch the bugs!

> Be sure to check out Philip J. de Vries' fine guide, *Butterflies of Costa Rica.*

BUTTERFLIES: All told there are 1,239 species, but few are unusual or spectacular. Possibly the world's most beautiful butterfly, the **morpho** (***celeste común***) is common in forests from sea level to 4,500 ft. (1,400 m). The most colorful of the two forms found, which has almost completely iridescent blue upper wings, is most plentiful on the Caribbean coast.

The **cream owl butterfly *(buhito pardo*)** has two glaring eyes on its underside. Suggestions are that these serve: as mimicry to suggest a vertebrate and ward off attacks, as mimicry of a large, distasteful tree frog that hangs out on the sides of trees, or as target spots for predators which allow the butterfly to escape relatively unscathed.

Other butterfly species of note include the common calico, the zebra, the Saturnias, skippers,*hecale, orión,* giant swallowtail, and the orange-barred sulfur.

LIFESTYLE: As they have no jaws, butterflies must take all nutrients in liquid form. They feed on water with mineral salts found in the earth, nectar, juice from decaying fruit, juices from carrion, honeydew secretions from aphids, and other such delicacies. While you may find them warming up in the sun or drinking water at mud banks, they rest on the undersides of leaves to protect themselves during rainstorms.

MEMORABLE VIEWING: The pencil-thin **helicopter damselfly** (*gallito azul*) beats each of its four wings independently, resembling a slow motion windmill. Its wing movement renders it invisible to spiders, upon whom it launches a single attack burst, snipping and capturing the succulent abdomen as the rest falls.

The pit-making **ant lion** (***gallito azul***) is actually the larval form of a beautiful insect similar to a damselfly. It spends its childhood digging a pit, heaping up loosened particles on its head and tossing them clear. Then burying itself—only its

> ?!? Costa Rica has just under four percent of the world's species in .0001% of the world's surface area. Some 86,000 species have been identified (6% of the worldwide total), and it is estimated that 420,000 remain undiscovered. Some 71,000 species of insects have been identified and 845 species of fungi.

jaws project—it awaits its prey. Any captured game has its contents sucked out and empty skin tossed out of the pit. After it has stored up enough food to support its next incarnation, it enters a cocoon, reemerging as a sexually mature adult.

A pretty good handful, the male **rhinoceros (elephant) beetle** (***cornizuelo***) sports a long upward-curved horn, but the females are hornless; they are endangered by habitat destruction.

The most conspicuous moth larva found in Guanacaste, the **frangipani sphinx** appears to mimic the coral snake, both with its bright yellow coloring and red orange head and in the way it thrashes back and forth when touched; it also bites viciously!

The ***machaca*** (**peanut-head bug, lantern fly**) is one of Latin America's best known insects. Its enormous hind wing eye spots and lizard-shaped head are probably designed to confuse predators, and its color harmonizes perfectly with the large branches and logs on which it rests. If pestered a will release a fetid skunklike spray or drum its grotesque head against a tree trunk. A popular Latin American folk saying maintains that if a young girl is stung by a *machaca*, she must have sex with her boyfriend within 24 hours or die. In many parts of latin America, locals are terrified of this harmless insect.

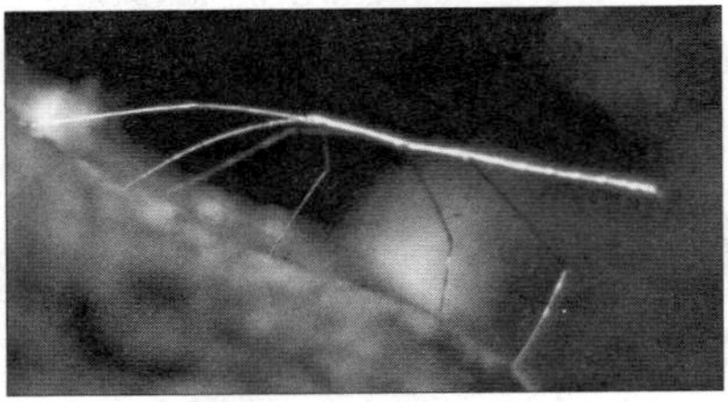

A walking stick lolls in the sun next to a waterfall in Corcovado.

Other intriguing bugs include the **tarantula**, **paper wasp**, the local version of the **praying mantis**, and the **Guanacaste stick insect** (***palito andando***).

ANTS: One resident of the rainforest you'll undoubtedly encounter is the ant. If you sit down, you may well have some unpleasant bites to contend with. Shake a bush and ants will scurry out. In many tracts, they may outweigh all of the vertebrates present.

A large black ant you may see along the trail but should be watched out for, the **bullet ant** (***hormiga bala***) has a nasty sting.

Commonly seen marching along a forest trail holding aloft cut pieces of leaves and flowers, **leaf-cutting** or **farmer ants** (***zompopas***) cut leaves into shreds, and carry them off to their nests where they then clear the leaves of unwanted fungal spores, chew the plant material, mix it with a combination of saliva and excrement, in order to cultivate a spongy, breadlike fungus (***Rhozites gongylophora***) on which they dine. This fungus no longer produces sexual spores and has come to rely solely upon the ants for propogation.

Ranking among the largest and most complex societies in the world, each colony may have a million members and each member has a role to play. The smallest tend to the eggs and larvae, larger ones forage, and the even larger soldiers defend the nest. Watch them as they meet, stroke antennae, and exchange chemical cues.

Joined in a symbiotic relationship with the acacia tree, the **acacia-ant** (***hormiga de cornizuelo***) wards off herbivores while the tree supplies the ants with nectar, protein and and protection in return. The ants produce an alarm pheromone which can be detected some six ft. (two m) downwind. You can easily recognize acacia trees by their hollow swollen horns, resembling those of cattle.

Another example of mutualism is found between the ***Azteca*** or ***cecropia* ants** and their namesake plant. In order to ward off herbivores, the cecropia attracts the ants which it provides with specialized food called *Beltian bodies*. These are budlike leaflet tips which the ants harvest and use to nourish their larvae which are raised inside the tree's thorns. In return, the ants defend the tree. Although stingless, they bite with their tough jaws and secrete caustic chemicals which they rub into bites.

Semi-nomadic **army ants** may travel in packs of up to 20 million members foraging along a 20-foot-wide front. They bring back bits of twigs, lichen, leaves and other insects to feed their queen; the detritus also feeds the roots of nearby plants. Activities of the army ants help a number of species—from birds to flies to milllipedes—in their feeding.

The rarely seen red-colored **trapdoor ant** thrusts her abdomen forward, injecting venom with her stinger.

TERMITES: Resembling gigantic wasp nests and found on trees, dark brown or black termite nests are a frequent feature of the forested landscape. Made of "carton," wood chewed up by workers and cemented with fecal "glue," the nest has a single reproductive king and queen commanding hordes of up to 100,000 attending workers and soldiers. Camouflaging itself with bits and pieces of termite nest, the **assassin bug** (***reduvio***) preys at the entrance. Termites digest raw cellulose, a substance low in nutritional value, with the aid of protozoa dwelling in their guts.

MILLIPEDES: With 20 body segments, the forest-floor **millipede** (***milpies***) is readily identifiable both by its movements and its dull whitish- yellow color. Its ability to curl up in a spiral and expel violently a solution of hydrogen cyanide and benzaldehyde as far as 30 cm (12 in.) discourages predators.

In copulation, the males (65-90 mm, 26-35 in. long) have a habit of "riding" the larger females (70-100 mm, 28-39 in. long) for periods up to five days or longer. Unescorted females are rare in millipedal society, but bachelor millipedes may remain sexually unfulfilled for long periods. Since copulation generally occurs within the first few hours, it is thought that the natural selective purpose of this "riding" behavior is to discourage the females from mating again.

As the sperm is utilized only after ovoposition and a female will mate with

Termites' nest. In death as in life, termites contribute to the rainforest ecosystem. Their defecated roughage is a feast for fungi, which also grow on their carcasses.

many others if left alone, rivalry among sperm would result. If faced with a sexual competitor, the male will flex the rear of his body in order to force a female's head and rear over her genital openings, thus barring access.

Their relative, the **scorpion** (***alacrán, escorpión***) stings only in self defense; they are active at night when they prey on insects and spiders.

FLIES: Biting flies can be a problem in season, and the most loathesome insect of all is the **botfly** (*Dermatobia hominis*) whose larvae mature inside flesh. An egg-laden female botfly captures a night-flying female mosquito and glues her eggs on to it. When the mosquito is released and bites a victim, the host's body heat triggers an egg to hatch, and it falls off and burrows in.

Secreting an antibiotic into its burrow which staves off competing bacteria and fungi, the larva secures itself with two anal hooks; its spiracle pokes out of the tiny hole, and a small mound forms which will grow to the size of a goose egg before the mature larva falls out.

Should you be unfortunate enough to fall prey to a larva—an extremely unlikely occurrence for the average visitor—you have three cures available. One is to use the acrid white sap of the ***matatorsalo*** (bot killer) which kills the larva but leaves its corpse intact. Another is to apply a piece of soft, raw meat to the top of the airhole. As the maggot must breathe, it burrows upward into the meat. A third is to apply a generous helping of Elmer's glue or cement to the hole; cover this with a circular patch of adhesive tape; seal this tape with a final application of glue. Squeeze out the dead larva the next morning.

The only other alternative is to leave it to grow to maturity, giving you an opportunity to experience the transmogrification of part of yourself into another creature. It only hurts when the maggot squirms and if you swim, presumably because you are cutting off its air supply. Whatever you do, don't try to pull it out because it will burst. Part of its body will remain inside and cause an infection.

Horseflies are an annoyance during May at 1,800-4,800 ft. (600-1,600 m), and another biting fly is the hardy but hunchbacked **black fly** (***mosca de café***).

OTHER NUISANCES: Coming in a number of species, the **mosquito** (***zancudo***) needs no introduction, nor does the giant **cockroach** (***cucaracha***). Finally, although they should not be a problem for visitors, Africanized "killer" bees are proving a menace; since their arrival in 1983, they have attacked more than 500 people, resulting in nine deaths.

Sealife

ECHINODERMATA: The name for this large division of the animal kingdom combines the Greek words for *echinos* (hedgehog) and *derma* (skin). Its members include sea urchins, sea cucumbers, and starfish. All have in common the fact that they all move with the help of tube feet or spines.

Known by the scientific name *Astrospecten*, **starfish** (***estrella de mar***) are five-footed carnivorous inhabitants which use their modified "tube-feet" to burrow into the sea.

Sluggish **sea cucumbers** ingest large quantities of sand, extract the organic matter, and excrete the rest. Crustaceans and fish reside in the larger ones.

By all means avoid trampling on that armed knight of the underwater sand dunes, the **sea urchin**! Consisting of a semi-circular calacareous (calcium carbonate) shell, the sea urchin is protected by its brown, jointed barbs. It uses its mouth, protected on its underside, to graze by scraping algae from rocks. Surprisingly to those uninitiated in its lore, sea urchins are considered a gastronomic delicacy in many countries. The ancient Greeks believed they had aphrodisiacal and other properties beneficial to health. They are prized by the French and fetch four times the price of oysters in Paris. The Spanish consume them raw, boiled, in *gratinés*, or in soups. In Barbados they are called "sea eggs," and the Japanese eat them as sushi.

Sea urchins hide underneath corals, and wounds often occur when you lose your footing and scrape against one. Should a sea urchin spine breaks off inside your finger or toe, don't try to remove it: it's impossible! You might try the cure people use in New Guinea. With a blunt object mash up the spine under your skin so that it will be absorbed naturally. Then dip your finger in urine; the ammonia helps to trigger the process of disintegration. Needless to say, preventing yourself from contact is best.

SPONGES: Found in the ocean depths, reddish or brown sponges are among the simplest forms of multicellular life and have been around for more than a half billion years. They pump large amounts of water between their internal filters and extract plankton. There are numerous sizes, shapes, and colors, but they all may be recognized by their large, distinctive excurrent openings. Unlike other animals, they exhibit no reaction when disturbed.

CNIDARIANS: The members of this phylum—hydroids, anemones, corals, and jellyfish—are distingushed by their simple structure: a cup-shaped body terminating in a combination mouth-anus which, in turn, is encircled by tentacles. While hydroids and corals (covered later in this section) are colonial, jellyfish and anemones are individual. This phylum's name comes from another identifying characteristic: nematocysts, stinging capsules primarily used for defense and capturing prey.

Growing in skeletal colonies resembling ferns or feathers, **hydroids** ("water form" in Greek) spend their youth as solitary medusas before settling down in old age. Some will sting. The most famous hydroid is undoubtedly the floating Portugese Man-Of-War; its stinging tentacles can be extended or retracted; wordwide, there have been reports of trailing tentacles reaching 50 feet! It belongs to the family of siphonophores, free-floating hydroid colonies which control their depth by means of a gas-filled float.

The true **jellyfish** are identifiable by their domes which vary in shape. Nematocysts reside in both the feeding tube and in their tentacles.

Also known as sea wasps, **box jellies** may be identifed by their cuboidal dome from each corner of which a single tentacle extends. Many of them can sting rather fiercely; keep well away. If you should get stung by any of the above, get out of the water and peel off any tentacles. Avoid rubbing the injured area. Wash the area with alcohol and apply meat tenderizer for five to ten minutes. The jellyfish season is Aug. to Oct.

Solitary bottom-dwellers, **sea anemones** are polyps which lack a skeleton and use their tentacles to stun prey and force them to their mouth. They often protect shrimp and crabs who, immune to their sting, reside right by them. Their tentacles may retract for protection when disturbed. One type of anemones live in tubes which are buried in the murky muck or sand. Their tentacles only come out to play at night.

CRUSTACEANS: The **ghost crab** (*Ocypode*) abounds on the beaches, tunneling down beneath the sand and emerging to feed at night. It can survive for 48 hours without contacting water. However, it must return to the sea to moisten its gill chambers as well as to lay eggs, which hatch into plankton larvae.

The **hermit crab** carries a discarded mollusc shell in order to protect its vulnerable abdomen. As it grows, it must find a larger home, and you may see two struggling over the same shell.

The Coral Reef Ecosystem

The coral reef is one of the least appreciated of the world's innumerable wonders. This is in part because little has been known about it until recent decades. A coral reef is the only geological feature fashioned by living creatures, and it is a delicate environment. Many of the world's reefs—which took millions of years to form—have already suffered adverse effects from human activities. One of the greatest opportunities the tropics offer is to explore this wondrous environment, one which in many ways goes beyond the limits of the wildest fantasy conjured up in a science fiction novel.

Corals produce the calcium carbonate (limestone) responsible for the buildup of offlying cays and islets as well as most sand on the beaches. Bearing the brunt of waves, they also conserve the shoreline.

Although reefs began forming milleniums ago, they are in a constant state of flux. Seemingly solid, they actually depend upon a delicate ecological balance to survive. Deforestation, dredging, temperature change, an increase or decrease in salinity, silt, or sewage discharge may kill them.

Because temperature ranges must remain between 68° and 95° F, they are only found in the tropics and—because they require light to grow—only in shallow water. They are also intolerant of fresh water, so reefs can not survive where rivers empty into the sea.

THE CORAL POLYP: While corals are actually animals, botanists view them as being mostly plant, and geologists dub them "honorary" rocks. Acting more like plants than animals, corals survive through photosynthesis: the algae inside the coral polyps do the work while the polyps themselves secrete calcium carbonate and stick together for protection from waves and boring sponges. Bearing a close structural resemblance to its relative the anemone, a polyp feeds at night by using the ring or rings of tentacles surrounding its mouth to capture prey (such as plankton) with nematocysts, small stinging darts.

The coral polyps appear to be able to survive in such packed surroundings through their symbiotic relationship with the algae present in their tissues. Coral polyps exhale carbon dioxide and the algae consume it, producing needed oxygen. Although only half of the world's coral species possess this symbiotic relationship with these single-celled captive species of dinoflagellates (*Gymnodinium microdriaticum*), these "hermatypic" corals, as they are called, are the ones that build the reef. The nutritional benefits gained from their relationship with the algae enable them to grow a larger skeleton and to do so more rapidly than would otherwise be possible.

Save the Dolphins!

Over the course of the past three decades or so more than 6.5 million dolphins have been killed through activities associated with tuna fishing. The dolphin are often found near the yellowfin tuna which swim below them. Regrettably, Costa Rica does not afford protection for these dolphins. Dolphin-safe practices have not been instituted, and Costa Rica is not a member of any international institution regulating marine species conservation. The latest threat to these splendid creatures comes from a Spaniard who is attempting to establish a Sea-World type of enterprise along the Guanacaste coast.

APROCA (☎ 255-3365; Apdo. 1863-1002) is one organization working to save the dolphins.

Polyps have the ability to regulate the density of these cells in their tissues and can expel some of them in a spew of mucus should they multiply too quickly. Looking at coral, the brownish colored algal cells show through transparent tissues. When you see a coral garden through your mask, you are actually viewing a field of captive single-celled algae.

A vital, though invisible, component of the reef ecosystem is bacteria, microorganisms which decompose and recycle all matter on which everything from worms to coral polyps feed. Inhabitants of the reef range from crabs to barnacles to sea squirts to multicolored tropical fish.

Remarkably, the polyps themselves are consumed by only a small percentage of the reef's inabitants. They often contain high levels of toxic substances and are also thought to sting fish and other animals that attempt to consume them. Corals also retract their polyps during daylight hours when the fish can see them. Reefs originate as the polyps develop, and the calcium secretions form a base as they grow. One polyp can have a 1,000-year lifespan.

CORAL TYPES: Corals may be divided into three groups. The **hard** or **stony corals** (such as staghorn, brain, star, or rose) secrete a limey skeleton. The horny corals (for example sea plumes, sea whips, sea fans, and gorgonians) have a supporting skeleton-like structure known as a **gorgonin** (after the head of Medusa). The shapes of these corals result from the fashion in which the polyps and their connecting tissues excrete calcium carbonate; there are over a thousand different patterns—one specific to each species. Each also has its own method of budding. Found in the Caribbean, giant elk-horn corals may contain over a million polyps and live for several hundred years or longer.

The last category consists of the **soft corals**. While these too are colonies of polyps, their skeletons are composed of soft organic material, and their polyps always have eight tentacles instead of the six or multiples of six found in the stony corals. Unlike the hard corals, soft corals disintegrate after death and do not add to the reef's stony structure. Instead of depositing limestone crystals, they excrete a jelly-like matrix which is imbued with *spicules* (diminutive spikes) of stony material; the jelly-like substance gives these corals their flexibility. Sea fans and sea whips exhibit similar patterns.

There are also false corals. The precious **black coral** is a type of soft coral. Prized by jewelers because its branches may be cleaned and polished to high gloss ebony-black, it resembles bushes of fine grey-black twigs.

COMPETITION: To the snorkeler, the reef appears to be a peaceful haven. The

Snorkeling Tips

- You can snorkel and swim for longer periods with confidence if you wear a tee-shirt while in the water.
- Be sure to make sure that your mask fits before snorkeling. To do this, put the mask on your face, suck your breath in, and inhale through your nose. While you continue to inhale, the mask should stay on you. Try another shape if this does not work.
- Moustaches, a stand of hair, or suntan lotion may spoil your fit. Moustache wearers should use a bit of vaseline or lip balm to improve the seal.
- The strap is to prevent the mask from falling off, not to tighten the seal; it should be set up high for comfort.
- Before submerging you should spit into your mask, coat the lens with your finger, and then rinse; this should have an anti fogging effect. Avoid exhaling through your nose: this may cause fog as well as release moisture.
- Snorkel only on the outer side of the reef on on low-wind or calm days, bring your own equipment or at least a mask you feel comfortable with (especially if you require a prescription mask)
- If you're using a kayak, it's a good idea to tie a line to it and carry it around when snorkeling.

reality is that, because the reef is a comparatively benign environment, the fiercest competition has developed here. Although the coral appears static to the onlooker, they are continually competing with each other for space. Some have developed sweeper tentacles which have an especially high concentration of stinging cells. Reaching out to a competing coral, they stick it and execute it. Other species dispatch digestive filaments which eat their prey. Soft corals appear to leach out toxic chemicals called terpines which kill nearby organisms. Because predation is such a problem, two-thirds of reef species are toxic. Others hide in stony outcrops or have formed protective relationships with other organisms. The banded clown fish, for example, lives among sea anemones whose stingers protect it. The cleaner fish protect themselves from the larger fish by setting up stations at which they pick parasites off their carnivorous customers. The sabre-toothed blenny is a false cleaner fish. It mimics the coloration and shape of the feeder fish, approaches, then takes a chunk out of the larger fish and runs off!

CORAL LOVE AFFAIRS: Not prone to celibacy or sexual prudery, coral polyps reproduce sexually and asexually through budding, and a polyp joins together with thousands and even millions of its neighbors to form a coral. (In a few cases, only one polyp forms a single coral). During sexual reproduction polyps release millions of their spermatozoa into the water. Many species are dimorphic—with both male and female polyps. Some species have internal, others external, fertilization. As larvae develop, their "mother" expels them and they float off to form a new coral.

EXPLORING REEFS: Coral reefs are extremely fragile environments. Much damage has been done to reefs worldwide through the carelessness of humans. Despite their size, reefs grow very slowly, and it can take decades or even hundreds of years to repair the effects of a few moments.

COSTA RICAN REEFS: Endangered by runoff from banana plantations, the nation's largest coral reef is found off

Cahuita on the Atlantic coast and is a national park. It suffered major damage during an earthquake and has also been hurt by pesticide runoff from the banana plantations. Much smaller ones are found off the Pacific coast and in the Gandoca-Manzanillo Reserve, also facing the Caribbean.

UNDERWATER FLORA: Most of the plants you see underwater are algae, primitive plants that can survive only underwater because they do not have the mechanisms to prevent themselves from drying out. Lacking roots, algae draw their minerals and water directly from the sea.

Another type of algae, calcareous red algae, are very important for reef formation. Resembling rounded stones, they are 95% rock and only 5% living tissue. Plants returned to live in the sea, sea grasses are found in relatively shallow water in sandy and muddy bays and flats; they have roots and small flowers. One species, dubbed "turtle grass," provides food for turtles. In addition, seagrasses help to stabilize the sea floor, maintain water clarity by trapping fine sediments from upland soil erosion, stave off beach erosion, and provide living space for numerous fish, crustaceans, and shellfish.

History

THE START: The area now known as the nation of Costa Rica was, before the Spaniards' arrival, a sparsely settled chunk of the extended isthmus linking two enormous continents—a region where the northern Mesoamerican cultures met the southern Andean cultures.

Arriving in the 16th C., Spaniards estimated there to be 25,000 indigenous people, divided into five major tribal groups. Residing in the Península de Nicoya, the Mayan Chorotegas accounted for approximately half the total number. They had arrived from Chiapas, Mexico around the 13th C. The warlike, nomadic Caribs roamed the Caribbean coast. Dwelling in fortified villages comprised of enormous cone-shaped huts, which could contain up to several hundred people, the fierce Boricua lived in the Talamanca region along the Pacific. Their dialect belonged to the Chibchan language group, common throughout Central America and the Andes. Little is known about the group thought to be the oldest indigenous tribe, the matrilineal Corobicis. Grouped into two small, widely separated settlements, the agriculturally-oriented, Aztec-influenced Nahuas have been credited with the introduction of cacao into the region.

> "The most appropriate activity would be a day of national mourning." – Alonso Porras, Principal, Ninfa Cabezas School, quoted in *The Tico Times* on the subject of Columbus Day celebrations.

COLUMBUS INTRUDES: During his fourth and final voyage of 1502, Christopher Columbus anchored at the present-day port of Puerto Limón. He bartered for the gold disks the Caribs wore as pendants. His brother Bartolomé remained behind to explore, only to flee when his party was attacked. Every attempt to conquer the isthmus in the early 1500s, from the very first one by Diego de Nicuesa, ended in failure, with *conquistadores* retreating in the face of hunger, disease, and armed resistance. Unlike the Mayan and Aztec regions, here there was no single Native American empire to conquer: each tribe had to be fought anew. The Native Americans would burn their crops rather than allow the invaders to take them. And the would-be conquerers expended a great deal of their time and energy contending with one another. Between 1511 and 1517, many Native Americans were seized and shipped off to slavery in Cuba; many others fell victim to smallpox. Anthropologists estimate their numbers at 400,000; many of them dropped dead of the newly introduced communicable diseases without even so much as seeing one of the intruders.

THE FIRST CONQUESTS: The first successful expedition was led by Gil González Dávila who traded with the Peninsula de Nicoya's Chorotegas while his compadre Diego de Aguero — at least according to the official version—baptized thousands. This settlement ended when Gonzalez Davila was arrested in Panama by Pedrarias Davila, the Governor of Veragua, for trespassing on his jurisdiction. Likewise, a small settlement by Francisco Fernando de Cordova in 1524 ended under threats from Pedrarias.

Appointed by the family of Christopher Columbus who had died in 1506, an expedition in 1534 by Felipe Gutierrez ended in disaster, with some of its members resorting to cannibalism. In 1540 Hernan Sánchez de Badajoz founded the settlement of Badajoz at the mouth of the Río Sixaola. He was driven out by Rodrigo de Contreras, the new governor of Nicaragua. Contreras, in turn, was routed by the Native Americans who rebelled at his cruelty. Other conquistadors followed but none enjoyed success.

EARLY COLONIZATION: In 1539 Costa Rica was separated from Veragua and was organized as a in 1542. In 1561 Juan de Cavallon established the first settlement at Garcimuñoz at a point on the Río Cirueas on the Pacific side. Disheartened at the lack of gold in the area, Cavallon deserted the colony in 1562 and was replaced by Juan Vasquez de Coronado who moved the settlement into the Meseta Central in 1564. From the new town of Cartago, Coronado explored the area, surveying Costa Rica's boundaries.

Lost at sea during a return visit to Spain, Coronado was replaced by Perafín de Ribera in 1568. That same year Costa Rica was subsumed in the newly-established kingdom of Guatemala. Ribera fought against the indigenous people of the Talamanca region from 1570-72, a costly campaign which again produced no gold. At the time of his departure in 1573, two small settlements had sprung up: Cartago and Aranuez.

EARLY SOCIETY: Decimated by introduced diseases, intertribal warfare, and by conquest, the Native Americans declined in number. Many starved to death after they had been driven from their land. By 1569, their numbers in Nicoya had declined to 3,300. Others, such as many of the Chorotega tribe, intermarried with the Spaniards, producing a mestizo population that viewed itself as Spanish, not Native American.
Other Native Americans, such as the Changuenes, were captured by the Zambos Mosquitos (descendants of unions between Miskito Native Americans and shipwrecked African slaves) and sold to Jamaica by them in conspiracy with English pirates. Other than in such areas as isolated Talamanca, the Native Americans died out.

Black slaves were also integrated through intermarriage. Increasingly viewed as a backwater — its lack of gold exposed — few found the colony attractive. The census of 1700 counted 20,000 inhabitants, includng 2,500 Spaniards. Owing to the area's limited natural resources, *hidalgos* (gentry) and *plebeyos* (commoners) alike were impoverished.

The system of *repartimientos* (allotments), under which Native Americans were forced into labor on estates was enforced throughout the Americas; in other Central American nations it resulted in sharp class divisions with a subservient Native American and *mestizo* class at the bottom. In the case of Costa Rica, although 20,000 Indians were pressed into servitude, the system was a failure, and the captives either died or were assimilated. In lieu of the plantation-style estates which developed elsewhere in Latin America, small family-run farms emerged.

Well into the 18th C., the economy continued to be based on subsistence agriculture and barter transactions. Money had become so scarce that *cacao* beans were designated the official currency in 1709. The Talamanca highlands remained unvanquished, and in the early 17th C., the *zambos* (bandits of Native American-Black heritage) along with the Miskito Native Americans continually raided the Matina Valley in the Meseta Central. In order to halt the raids, a tribute was paid to the Miskito King from 1779-1841.

Pirates also plagued the colony, resulting in closure of all of the ports and the collapse of exports. The pirate Henry Morgan and his brigands were turned back in 1666 from their attempt to sack Cartago by an outnumbered band of colonial militia—an episode seen as divine intervention by the Virgin of Ujarrás, the saint whose image they had carried into battle.

Things began to improve under the administration of Diego de la Haya Fernández (1718-27). Under his tenure, the port of Caldera was reopened, the Matina valley was fortified against Miskitos, and cacao plantations were developed. He oversaw the rebuilding of Cartago on a grander scale after it was destroyed by a volcanic eruption in 1723.

Lacking a resident bishop, the Catholic Church here was not as strong as in other nations. However, the church encouraged farmers to settle near parishes, and, in this fashion, Heredia (as Cubujuquí in 1706), Alajuela (as Villa Hermosa in 1782), and San José (as Villaneuva de la Boca del Monte in 1736) were founded.

INDEPENDENCE: In September 1821, the captain general of Guatemala proclaimed the independence of the Central American provinces without consulting Costa Rica. After meeting, the municipal councils of the four major towns (Cartago, San José, Heredia, and Alajuela) formed a junta to draft a provisional constitution. In May of 1822, the newly-crowned Emperor of Mexico, Augustin de Iturbide, declared his authority over the Central American provinces. While, out of the four main settlements, Cartago and Heredia favored union with Mexico, San José and Alajuela favored either independence or union with the rest of Central America.

Civil war erupted as Mexican supporters from Cartago and Heredia marched on San José, only to be defeated at Ochomongo. In March 1823, a provincial congress in Cartago declared independence from Spain and applied for union with Colombia, in an attempt to forestall an attack from Mexico. After Iturbide was overthrown around the same time, however, opinion shifted, and the Costa Rican Congress voted in August 1823 to join the newly formed United Provinces of Central America (commonly referred to as the Central American Federation) which included Guatemala, Honduras, Nicaragua, and El Salvador. The first Jefe Supremo of the Free State of Costa Rica served from 1824-33.

In 1824, the inhabitants of Guanacaste seceded from Nicaragua and elected to join Costa Rica. The unstable federation collapsed, and Costa Ricans thereafter were wary of attempts to unite Central America, believing themselves to have little in common with their neighbors in the region.

CIVIL WAR: In the early 1830s, geopolitical conflict erupted over the decision of where to base the capital. Heretofore, each of the four major cities had operated administratively as city states rather than as parts of the same nation. Under the Law of Movement enacted in 1834 under José Rafael de Gallegos, the capital was to be rotated from town to town every four years. This failed to resolve the conflict and, after the new head of state Braulio Carrillo Colina established the capital at San José, the three rival towns formed the League of Cities under Nicolas Ulloa to oppose Carrillo.

Crushing the revolt decisively that October, Carrillo went on to largely disregard the constitution. Defeated in an 1838 reelection bid, he seized dictatorial power. In 1841 he gave squatters title to government-owned agricultural land, abolished the constitution, and declared himself dictator for life. Carrillo was driven out of power by an alliance between one of his generals, Vincente Villasor, and Honduran Central American Federation proponent Morazán. Shortly after their accession to power, these two also fell into disfavor and were executed.

THE FIRST PRESIDENT: In 1847 José María Castro Madriz, a 29-year-old editor and publisher, was named the nation's first president by the Congress. His wife, Doña Pacifica, designed the national flag. Declaring Costa Rica an independent republic the next year, he instituted a headstrong program of reforms — including constitutional changes and replacement of the army with a national guard — which resulted in his replacement by more conservative coffee baron Juan Rafael Mora Porras. Mora Porras encouraged the cultivation of coffee for export, an idea in harmony with the liberal laissez faire capitalism espoused in Europe at the time. Politics during this era consisted of rivalries between families. Suffrage was restricted by property and literacy qualifications to a small minority.

WAR WITH WILLIAM WALKER: In 1855 Tennesseean William Walker was deployed by Nicaraguan liberals at the head of a group of European and American mercenaries and given the mission of overthrowing the conservative government. Instead of handing power over to the liberals as had been originally agreed upon contractually, Walker installed himself as dictator and reintroduced slavery. Prodded on by business competitors of Cornelius Vanderbilt, he nationalized Vanderbilt's transport firm which carried gold seekers bound for California across Nicaragua. Vanderbilt retaliated by encouraging Mora Porras to declare war in Feb. 1856.

Walker invaded Guanacaste, but in April the Costa Ricans attacked Rivas across the border. Drummer boy Juan Santamaría set fire to the town, driving out Walker's forces and setting himself up as Costa Rica's first and only national hero. Walker was decisively defeated by a coalition of Costa Rica and other Central American forces during the second battle of Rivas in April 1857. This war has been credited with giving the new nation's people their first sense of national unity. A border conflict with Nicaragua came on the heels of the war's finale. Under the Cañas-Juarez treaty of April 1858, Costa Rica's title to Guanacaste was confirmed, and, while Nicaragua's right to the Río San Juan was acknowledged, Costa Rica was granted navigation rights.

THE MONTEALEGRES: After the war, Mora Porras was replaced by coffee baron José María Montealegre after a military coup. A new constitution—providing for limited suffrage as well as indirect election of the president via the Congress, was promulgated in 1859. Although "elections" continued, the army elite and the Montealegre family wielded the real power. In 1870, their chosen president, Jiménez Zamora, was ousted in the aftermath of a coup led by populist General Tomás Guardia Gutiérrez. His new constitution of 1871 was destined to last until 1949, and Guardia was formally elected in 1872.

Although the constitution specified a one term limit for presidential office holders, Guardia dismissed the new president in 1876 and ruled with an iron fist straight through from 1877 until his death in 1882. Although his avowed aim was to break the hold of the coffee barons—by redistributing land and imposing heavy taxes—what he in fact achieved was to replace this elite with another composed of his family and friends. Guardia encouraged public education, improved urban sanitation, abolished capital punishment, and provided trade incentives, but his foremost achievement was the laying of a railway line from the Caribbean coast to the Meseta Central. The line cost US$8 million and 4,000 lives. All of this development came at an additional cost, however, and the nation was saddled with a massive debt, which still had repercussions 40 years later.

POST-GUARDIA: Guardia was succeeded in office by his brother-in-law, army commmander Fernández Oreamuno. After his death in 1885, power passed to Bernardo Soto Alfaro, who created the nation's first free, compulsory public school system. Soto stepped down in 1889 and ushered in a new era when the first election with an unrestricted press, free debates, and an honest tally was subsequently held.

The election of José Joaquin Rodriguez Zeledón marked the first peaceful transition from those in power to the opposition. It also brought in members of the "Generation of '89," the young liberals who were to govern the nation and control its political life for all but a brief period over the next half century. Although he came from a long liberal lineage, Rodriguez revealed himself to be yet another despot. Refusing to work together with the Congress, he dismissed it in 1892.

That same year saw the formation of the Partido Union Catolica. The nation's first genuine political party, the PUC was organized by German-born bishop Bernard August Thiel. Although the party was organized in reaction to the severe governmental curbs on the church's power (that had begun under Guardia and had continued to grow), it focused on criticizing the nation's economic inequities.

INTO THE 1900s: While Rodriguez picked Rafael Yglesias Castro to succeed him, the PUC fronted José Gregorio Trejos Gutierrez in the 1894 elections. Although Trejos Gutierrez won a plurality in spite of governmental fraud, the Congress chose Yglesias, and a revolt in the countryside ended in the PUC's dissolution.

Another in what was fast becoming a long line of authoritarian presidents, Yglesias arranged to have the constitution amended so that he might succeed himself in 1898. Ascensión Esquivel Ibarra, a compromise candidate agreeable to both the government and opposition, was selected in 1902. Esquivel was instrumental in fostering new democratic reforms and advancements in education, policies continued by his successor Cleto González Viquez. González was elected in 1906 in a five-way race. Although he had received the highest number of votes, his election was secured only after Esquivel had exiled the three candidates with the lowest count!

Ricardo Jiménez Oreamuno, who succeeded him in 1910, successfully pushed for a constitutional amendment, ratified in 1913, which established direct presidential election and, although the numbers still remained small, expanded voter franchise. Despite these improvements, the politics of still prevailed, and parties remained dormant until election time when they awakened from hibernation to support their "liberal" candidate. By this time Costa Rica's population had tripled (to 360,000) since 1860. A large number of immigrants had arrived from Spain, Germany, and Italy, and a new rural elite, comprising small farmers, were making their presence felt in local government.

THE TINOCO DICTATORSHIP: Alfredo Gonzales Flores, picked as a compromise candidate by the Congress in 1914 followed Oreamuno. He faced a severe economic crisis brought on largely by falling coffee prices and the closure of the European markets due to the onset of WWI. Gonzales Flores attempted — through higher export levies on coffee and by proposing increased taxation of the upper classes—to prevent capital flight to the US, moves which lost him the elite's support.

His cuts in government expenditures and civil service salaries proved unpopular among local politicians. And governmental corruption lost him his popular backing. His government was overthrown in a Jan. 1917 military coup led by his own secretary of war, General Federico Tinoco Granados.

Tinoco, too, soon lost his own widespread support. Woodrow Wilson had announced a policy of nonrecognition for governments which had not been democratically elected—a policy which curtailed trade with the US. In Aug. 1919, Tinoco handed over command to his vice president Juan Batista Quiros Segura.

The American Government, however, was still insistent on new elections. The US positioned the cruiser *USS Denver* off the coast, thus forcing Quiros's resignation. A former vice president under Gonzales Flores assumed command until Juan Acosta Garcia, who had been Gonzales Flores' foreign minister, was elected in 1920.

Meanwhile, in 1916 Costa Rica had filed suit in the Central American

Court, protesting the perpetual rights granted the US to build a trans-isthmian canal through Nicaragua. The canal would use a portion of the hotly contested Río San Juan. Although the court ruled against Nicaragua and the US in 1918, the defendants ignored the decision, and the discredited court subsequently disbanded. The southern border with Panama had been disputed since the days that nation was part of Colombia. A conflict in 1921 between the two nations was settled only after US intervention.

"DEMOCRACY" RESTORED: In 1919 Julio Acosta Garcia was elected, taking office the following year. For the next three four-year terms, the presidency alternated between "liberal" past presidents Jiménez Oreamuno (Don Ricardo) and Gonzalez Viquez (Don Cleto). Despite the lack of any substantive differences between candidates in the 20s and 30s, campaigns were hotly contested, with frequent charges on both sides of voter manipulation and fraud. Secret ballots and yet wider suffrage was introduced during the 20s.

Jiménez Oreamuno, under pressure from discontented laborers, pioneered minimum wage legislation, underwrote the establishment of a government-owned insurance monopoly offering low cost coverage, and purchased untilled acreage from the United Fruit Company—out of which plots were distributed to landless farmers.

Over the course of time, the efficacy of the educational system had produced political awareness which gave rise to social dissent. During the 1930s, workers organized themselves, farmers became increasingly vocal, and the educated urban upper middle class complained about deficiencies in health care, housing, and transportation. Discontent focused on the prevailing system of liberal elite rule, concentrated in the hands of only a few families, and on its symbiotic relationship with a bureaucracy selected by patronage.

Returning from theological studies in Europe in 1912, Jorge Volio Jiménez published a journal propounding "social Christianity" rooted in recent Catholic thought. Mercurial, often demagogic and enigmatic, Volio was politician, priest, scholar, and soldier—possibly the most original thinker and theorist of his era. Founding the Partido Reformista, he entered the 1923 election on a platform calling for union legalization, taxes on the ruling class, and other broad social reforms. Coming in third, he became second vice president in the Jiménez Oreamuno administration, a position which compromised him in the eyes of his supporters, marking the end of his party. When he was implicated in a coup attempt, President Oreamuno explained that he had suffered a mental breakdown and shipped him off to Europe for an extended treatment. Volio continued to fight with his church superiors and was eventually defrocked.

THE LEFT EMERGES: Organized by 19-year-old student Manuel Mora Valverde in 1929, Bloque Obreros y Campesinos (Workers and Peasants Bloc) fielded candidates in the 1932 election. By the late 1930s, the BOC had gained control over important sectors of the labor movement, including Spanish-speaking banana plantation laborers. The party organized a 1934 strike which shut down the nation's banana production and forced United Fruit to equalize wages paid to Jamaican and Costa Rican workers.

León Cortés Castro, the PRN candidate,

followed Jiménez Oreamuno in power in 1936. Like Oreamuno, Cortés intervened in order to stabilize prices and to encourage the growth of the banana industry, approving an extension of the Pacific railway. Suspected of being a Nazi sympathizer because of his ties to rich German expatriates, Cortés appointed a native German immigration official to prevent entry by Jews. He cracked down hard on the left, and his political opponents' civil rights were frequently curtailed.

In order to challenge Cortés in the 1940 election, Jiménez Oreamuno formed the Alianza Democratica (Democratic Alliance) which included the BOC, but he was forced to resign as its leader after obstructive pressure from Cortés. Cortés handpicked physician Rafael Angel Calderón Guardia to represent him until he could legally run for office again. Facing only token opposition, he won by a landslide.

THE CALDERÓN ERA: Surprisingly to Cortés, Calderón proved to be independent. Relying on patronage and for his support, the new president was the first to stress social and economic reforms as a priority. A staunch Catholic, he sought with the Catholic church. A paternalistic elitist, he dictated reforms from above, reforms which made others in his social stratum view him as a traitor to his class. In 1941 Cortés broke with Calderón to form the Partido Demócrata.

While the PD opposed Calderón's proposed reforms, other critics charged that government inefficiency and corruption, rather than constitutional restrictions, stood in the way of their implementation. Other harsh critics were the Acción Demócrata, an organization formed by Francisco Orlich Bolmarcich and Alberto Marten, and the Centro para el Estudio de Problemas Nacionales (CEPN), which produced critiques and studies.

On Dec. 8, 1941, Costa Rica declared war against Japan. This was largely a symbolic gesture as the nation had neither men nor other resources to offer. After the United Fruit Company's merchant vessel the *S. S. San Pablo* was torpedoed by a German submarine killing 27 and, consequently, seriously hampering exports, Calderón enacted an alien property act which enabled him to seize the property and assets of wealthy resident German and Italian families. Encouraged by the CEPN, largely unknown landowner José Figueres Ferrer purchased airtime, using it to make a speech highly critical of governmental policy. Figueres was later arrested and sent into exile.

A series of 15 constitutional amendments, known collectively as the Social Guarantees, passed in 1943, These gave the Congress wider authority, paving the way for the administration's agenda of interventionist legislation. The bills enacted encompassed passage of social security legislation which included health insurance, a law allowing squatters title to land, and a comprehensive labor code—one which guaranteed some types of workers a minimum wage, ensured job security, mandated collective bargaining, and legalized strikes.

Calderón, together with the church under the leadership of Archbishop Sanabria, permitted the communists participation in the civil service, police, and government in exchange for their support. The POC changed its name to the Partido Vanguardia Popular and included other leftist organizations, and Sanabria allowed Catholics to join the PVP. At the same time he encouraged Father Benjamin

Nuñez Vargas to form the Confederacion Costarricense de Trabajo Rerum Novarum (Costa Rican Confederation of Labor Rerum Novarum), a Catholic-run labor union which would compete with the other, communist-led ones.

In order to back Teodoro Picado Michalski, Calderón's handpicked successor, the PRN and PVP formed the Bloque de la Victoria (Victory Block). Anti communist conservative Picado accepted the PVP's participation as necessary in order to defeat Cortés. In what was a record turnout of 137,000 voters, Picado defeated Cortés two-to-one in the Feb. 1944 election and also scored a similar victory in the legislature.

THE PICADO ADMINISTRATION: The Partido Social Democrata, PSD, was formed several months later, merging the Acción Democrata with the CEPN. This left-of-center, anti-communist party's platform advocated systematic progressive reform based on the prewar European social democratic party model. Decrying both present and past corruption and election manipulation, the PSD sought a complete overhaul for the system.

Returning from exile in May 1944, Figueres joined the party leadership but, in spite of its staunch middle class backing, it remained a marginal force. After Cortés' sudden death in 1946, Figueres joined the PD. His hopes were dashed, however, when he was defeated in his bid for leadership by conservative businessman Fernando Castro Cervantes. He then went on to form a splinter party with Cortés' son. Reviving the party name Partido Unión Nacional (PUN) and backed by business interests who feared Calderón's return to power, venerated conservative newspaper editor Otilio Ulate Blanco entered the 1948 election as the party's standard bearer.

In the meanwhile, the violence that had scared the 1944 election campaign had continued to escalate. Demonstrations, strikes, and coup attempts plagued the Picado administration, leaving it increasingly dependent on the communist-controlled worker's militia to provide security. Governmental opponents were periodically abducted and questioned without regard for their civil rights. Some were forced into exile.

In 1946, after troops fired into a crowd protesting irregularities in off-year congressional elections, killing two and wounding several, Picado disavowed all responsibility. The Huelga de Brazo Caídos (Strike of the Fallen Arms)—which brought the nation to a virtual standstill for two weeks—was staged by merchants and managers in major cities. The communist militia attempted to break the strike by breaking into shops and distributing merchandise. However, Picado was forced to capitulate, signing an agreement to place controls on the security forces and pledging that the next election would be fair.

While in exile, Figueres had plotted to overthrow the Calderón government, forming the Caribbean Legion which was supported by Guatemala and Cuba. From Lucha Sin Fin (Struggle without End), his farmhouse base located S of Cartago, Figueres continued to build his militia. Negotiating in Guatemala with other exile groups in 1947, he signed the Pact of the Caribbean in which he pledged to use Costa Rica as a base for liberating other countries struggling under dictatorships—including Honduras, the Dominican Republic, Venezuela, and Nicaragua—if they helped him to overthrow the Picado/Calderón regime.

Supported by both the PRN and the

PVP, Calderón still commanded working class backing when he ran again in 1948. He also had the bureaucracy and the government apparatus to support him. Castro Cervantes and the PD opted to support Ulate. The reformist PSD also threw in its support. All denounced the violations of civil liberties and the governmental inefficiency which hallmarked the regime. Despite Picado's pledge, the security forces disrupted meetings and attempted to intimidate voters.

With 100,000 votes counted on Feb. 8, preliminary results showed that Ulate had won by a 10,000 vote margin. Both parties claimed that election irregularities had adversely affected balloting. After examination, the election commission upheld the results by two to one. Maintaining that the one dissenting member had invalidated its decision, the Picado administration insisted that the president be selected by the Calderón-controlled current legislature, which voted 28 to 18 for annulment—a move which left it open for them to name Calderón as the new president. Ulate was arrested and released the next day, an indication that the government was committed to holding on to power by whatever means necessary.

Over the next two weeks Archbishop Sanabria attempted to mediate as Figueres assembled a 600-man volunteer army at La Lucha. The rebels were up against a small army and police force, the PRN-armed *calderonistas*, and the communist-run 3,000-man militia. Shortly after capturing an airfield and blocking the Interamerican Highway, Figueres was forced to retreat into the nearby mountains, leaving forces behind to cover the airfield. Capturing Puerto Limón and Cartago, Figueres forced the government's fall.

On April 19th, Picado and his lieutenant, Nuñez, signed a pact allowing for the government's conditional surrender at the Mexican Embassy in San José. Amnesty was granted to all those fighting on the government side. No one would be responsible for property that had been damaged or lost during the conflict, and the PVP as well as the communist-controlled labor union were guaranteed continued legality. Finally, it was agreed that the Social Guarantees would not be repealed. Calderón and Picado were exiled to Nicaragua and 74-year-old Santos León Herrera, who had been completing his third term as vice president, was appointed caretaker president.

Known as the "War of National Liberation," this short-lived but brutal and divisive civil war left bitter aftereffects. More than 2,000 died—mostly on the government side—and many more were wounded. Intervention by Nicaragua, which sent troops in to Guanacaste to buttress the government, was insufficient and arrived too late.

THE ULATE-FIGUERES ERA: Cognizant of the difficult realities facing the nation, Figueres and president-elect Ulate suppressed their differences of opinion for the common good. They both agreed to give power to an interim government for an 18-month period in which a constituent assembly would be elected and would prepare a new constitution. On May 8 Figueres became the president of the Junta Fundadora de la Segunda Republica (Founding Junta of the Second Republic) whose members were Marten, Orlich, and Nuñez.

During the first 18 months the junta passed 834 decree-laws, many of which violated the suspended constitution as well as the cease fire agreements. One of the more notable of these was the law granting suffrage to women. Meanwhile, hundreds of *calderonistas* remained across the border in Nicaragua. The exposure of a counter-revolutionary plot as well as a large weapons cache enabled Figueres to renege on his pact with the former government. The PVP was outlawed, the communist-run unions banned, critics were purged from governmental posts and teaching positions, and over 200 communists were arrested. The Court of Immediate Sanctions, a special tribunal, was set up in order to retroactively punish alleged crimes committed during the previous administration and during the civil war. Operating outside of the regular court system, no appeals were permitted.

Astutely, Figueres abolished the army — a force not loyal to him — in Dec. 1948, replacing it with a 1,500-man Guardia Civil. His Caribbean Legion, however, continued to operate independently.

At the beginning of that same month Costa Rica had ratified the Interamerican Treaty of Reciprocal Assistance (Rio Treaty), a mutual defense pact between Central American nations in which the US served as guarantor. On Dec. 10, a week after its ratification, 800 well-equipped *calderonistas* poured in from Nicaragua. When the envisioned general revolution failed to materialize, the insurgents pulled back. While the OAS harshly criticized Nicaragua for its support of the invasion, it also rebuked Costa Rica for permitting Nicaraguan exiles to train on its territory and advised that the Caribbean Legion be disbanded. In April 1949 the minister of public security, Colónel Edgar Cardona Quirós, attempted a coup which garnered no support.

The youthful PSD activists, who were in charge of drawing up proposals for the new constitution, had their radical recommendations largely rejected by the mostly-PUN constituted assembly. The body even omitted the term "Second Republic" from the constitution's final version. The 1949 constitution, Costa Rica's eighth since 1825, established separation of powers and embodied the substance of the Social Guarantees. The function of the Figueres-devised Tribuno Supremo de Eleciones (TSE) was to supervise elections.

On Nov. 8, 1949 Ulate and the Legislative Assembly took power. Most of Figueres's changes were left intact by the Ulate government. The high price of coffee and the reopening of the banana plantations brought revenues in, and the external debt left by the junta was reduced by US$30 million during the first two years. The World Bank financed construction of a new airport as well as the purchase of agricultural and industrial equipment. The US aided in financing the building of a dam and power plant on the Río Reventazón.

In late 1951 Figueres formed the Partido Liberación Nacional and announced his candidacy for the July 1953 election. Incorporating the PSD, the broader-based social democratic PLN identified itself with the Figueres-led victory and the as yet unfulfilled promise of a Second Republic. Its platform stressed that institutional reform and modernization were prerequisites to substantive social reform. This could be achieved through improved efficiency, applying advanced technology, and long-term planning. Despite the party's pro-American stance, it advocated monitoring and regulation of foreign companies and investment.

Although Figueres designed the party as a permanent organization—one which would operate independently of any specific individual, it came to revolve, nevertheless, around "Don Pepe," as Figueres was known to his followers.

FIGUERES'S SECOND TERM: In the 1954 elections the PUN candidate withdrew, and both the PUN and the PD united behind the candidacy of conservative businessman Fernando Castro Cervantes. Figueres's promises to end poverty and improve the standard of living for all classes contrasted sharply with Castro Cervantes, who put forward no program other than opposition to Figueres. Figueres was elected by a two-to-one margin in July. His controversial administration renegotiated its contract with United Fruit, doubled income taxes imposed on the wealthy, financed agricultural development and food processing projects with revenue generated by the governmental alcohol monopoly, and hiked import duties in order to shelter fledgling industries. Critics charged that these expansive, expensive policies increased inflation, indebtedness, and economic instability. In pushing through his legislative agenda, Figueres had faced bitter opposition in the Legislative Assembly from both the PLN and the conservative opposition.

No love was lost either between Nicaragua's dictator Somoza Garcia and Figueres. Both men hated each other's guts and actively plotted one another's demise. After captured members of a coup attempt revealed that they were Costa Rican trained, Somoza Garcia challenged Figueres to a duel. Figueres responded by advising him to "grow up." Figueres also sheltered opponents of dictators ruling in the Dominican Republic and Venezuela.

INSURGENTS INVADE: On Jan. 11, 1955, several hundred — well armed and equipped—poured across the border from Nicaragua. Moving swiftly, this self-proclaimed "Authentic Anti-Communist Revolutionary Army" captured Quesada, lying about 50 km NW of San José, and took over sections of Guanacaste. One of their aircraft strafed San José. Two days later an OAS fact-finding mission decided that, despite Nicaragua's denials, the forces had come from Nicaragua, and Nicaragua was told to capture the insurgents operating from its territory. Fulfilling the terms of the Río treaty, the US sold Costa Rica four fighter aircraft for US$1, a move which served to deter any additional air attacks. Somoza Garcia, protesting the shipment, claimed that the US was "putting dangerous toys in the hands of a lunatic." Quesada was retaken on Jan. 21, and the two nations agreed on a demilitarized zone. The OAS-recommended formal treaty of friendship remained unsigned until Dec. 1956, three months after Somoza Garcia's assassination.

ECHANDI'S ADMINISTRATION: In the 1958 election Ulate was still ineligible to run again under the constitution so Echandi was again selected as the PUN's candidate. The PLN's choice was Francisco Orlich Bolmarich. A close friend of Figueres, he had served as party leader in the Legislative Assembly. Late in 1956, after a disagreement on financial policy, Figueres's finance minister, Jorge Rossi Chavarria, broke away—along with many of the party's moderates—to form the Partido Independente. Rossi split the PLN vote, ensuring Echandi's victory. The PLN now held 20 seats in the Legislative Assembly as opposed to the PR's 11, the PUN's 10, and the PI's three. The PR's strong showing was evidence that Calderón's support base, even after a decade in exile, was still considerable. Lacking a majority in the legislature, free enterprise advocate Echandi was unable to alter Figueres's basic programs and policies. After coffee prices plummeted in 1957, Echandi was forced to borrow money abroad, and the national debt mounted up further.

THE 1960S: Two former presidents, Ulate for the PUN and a newly-returned Calderón heading the PR slate, contended in the 1962 election. But a healed PLN, with Francisco Orlich Bolmarich again its candidate, won half the vote. Calderón ran a distant second, Ulate a poor third, and a pro-Cuban Marxist party candidate received less than 3,000 votes.

Although the administration expropriated unused United Fruit Company land as well as large individually owned estates for redistribution to landless farmers, support waned as the economy plummeted headlong into a recession. Striking banana plantation workers blamed Orlich for the industry's decline.

Irazú's untimely March 1963 eruption, which coincided with US President Kennedy's visit, devastated the vital agricultural region surrounding San José. And the right wing assaulted the cancerous growth in the public sector which, according to some estimates, consumed half of the GNP.

Despite their past roles as opponents in the civil war, Ulate and Calderón swallowed their differences and, together with former president Echandi, formed the conservative Unificacion Nacional, and, for the 1966 presidential election, threw their support behind anti-PLN candidate Trejos Fernandez, a little-known university professor. Figueres, although now constitutionally eligible once more, deigned not to run, and the PLN selected the party's aggressive left wing leader Daniel Oduber Quiros, who had challenged Orlich for the nomination four years earlier.

Trejos's "neo-liberal" candidacy promised an administration attentive to the needs of the private sector. His influential backers propagated fears that another PLN victory would lead to a one party state. Backing given Oduber by the communist Alianza Socialista Popular, an organization which had been determined to be constitutionally ineligible to field its own candidate, did him more harm than good. In the end, Trejos won 222,800 votes to Oduber's 218,000. Introducing a sales and import tax, Trejos worked to slash public sector expenditures. His grant of a strip mining concession to ALCOA aroused ire.

FIGUERES RETURNS: Representing himself as a candidate of the "democratic left," Figueres handily triumphed over Echandi in the 1970 presidential contest, harvesting 55% of the vote. His second administration concerned itself with improving and extending past PLN-initiated programs rather than breaking new ground. Attempts were made to diversify the economy in order to loosen its dependence on bananas and coffee. Just before his inauguration in April 1970, student and non-student demonstrators stormed the legislature buildings in order to protest approval of ALCOA's strip mining concession. This and other subsequent disturbances were blamed on communist agitation.

Figueres was tainted by his association with Robert Vesco. When Vesco—who had invested heavily in the country and applied for citizenship—was indicted in the US, a Costa Rican judge refused to issue extradition papers, claiming that its extradition treaty with the US failed to cover the charges against him. Allegations uncovered in the US linked Figueres with this white collar criminal, claiming that Vesco had showered him with campaign contributions, personal gifts, and investment capital for one of his businesses.

THE MID '70S: In 1974 Oduber broke with the nation's informal each term/different party tradition by securing 42% of the vote in a field of eight candidates. During the campaign, the issue of alleged communist subversion had been so intense that the election tribunal banned the use of the words "Marxist" and "communist" from the campaign. Oduber called for nationalization, higher taxes, land redistribution, and strengthening of the public sector in order to increase employment and raise the standard of living. After the party's proscription had been lifted by a constitutional amendment, Mora Valverde revived the PVP.

Oduber reopened trade with Cuba and reestablished diplomatic relations, broken under the Orlich administration in 1962. After the tax on banana exports was raised by more than a third in May 1975, Oduber had to threaten the multinational fruit companies with expropriation in order to force them to pay the tax. He encouraged export-oriented agricultural production at the expense of local industries which produced goods for local consumption. In mid-1976, a party crisis appeared when Figueres pressed for a constitutional amendment that would allow the president to succeed himself. To add to the tense atmosphere, electrical workers struck, and a plot to overthrow the government was unveiled.

As Oduber's administration reached its finale, Figueres withdrew from party activities, the economy continued to worsen, and the Sandinista struggle against dictator Anastasio Somoza Debayle in neighboring Nicaragua threatened to suck Costa Rica in. In the 1978 election, Figueres decided not to campaign for Monge, the PLN's candidate. The greater part of the opposition, composed of right-of-center groups, organized the Unidad Opositora (Unity Opposition) which fielded businessman and former PLN-member Rodrigo Carazo Odio. Taking a firm anti-communist line, Carazo pledged to recall the Costa Rican ambassador in Moscow. He also promised to expel Robert Vesco. As head of his own party in 1974, Carazo had won only 10% of the vote. But this time he took 49% of the vote in the five-candidate race to Monge's 42%. Unidad secured 27 seats in the Legislative Assembly, the PLN took 25, and the Pueblo Unido, a leftist coalition, won three.

THE TURBULENT 1980S: Relations with Nicaragua had deteriorated throughout the end of the 70s, culminating with Costa Rica's breaking relations in November 1978, and calling for its expulsion from the OAS. Costa Rica actively supported the Sandinistas in their struggle, serving as a conduit for supplies and arms—a very profitable business—to the 5,000 Costa Rican-based troops under Eden Pastora Gomez. After Somoza fled in July 1979, Costa Rica recognized Nicaragua's provisional junta.

Banana plantation workers struck again in 1979 and in 1980. In March of 1981, three USMC American Embassy guards were wounded when Costa Ricans attacked their vehicles. A San José shootout with terrorists in June left three Civil Guardsmen dead. A public rally in San José, called to protest the government's perceived lack of effectiveness in dealing with violence, turned violent itself when guardsmen, attempting to intervene when the crowd called for Carazo's resignation, were stoned. Relations with Cuba were again severed that May.

As Unidad fought within itself and the PLN refused to cooperate, Carazo was forced to govern again and again by presidential decree. By the end of his term, the nation's foreign debt climbed to a staggering US$3 billion, up from US$800 million, and foreign reserves were depleted. Its per capita indebtedness was calculated to be the world's highest, and unemployment rose to 14%.

In September 1981, the government officially suspended payments on its external debt payments and, in November, it halted bond repayments and requested debt payment rescheduling. This move, along with other violations of a pact reached earlier in the year with the IMF, caused the fund to suspend the release of scheduled loan funds and close down its Costa Rican office.

MONGE'S TENURE: Distancing itself from the now battered and beleaguered Carazo, Unidad nominated 33-year-old Rafael Angel Calderón Fournier, son of a former president. In Feb. 1982, the PLN's Monge won 53% of the vote against Calderón Fournier's 33%. The remaining 10% was distributed among the other candidates including former president Echandi Jiménez. The PLN increased its seats to 33 in the Assembly, a comfortable majority.

Doctors struck in April 1982 for 42 days after the government refused them a US$40 increase in their base pay. At Del Monte's Banana Development Company, 3,000 workers struck, demanding an increase; their wages averaged US$.67 per hour! Six strikers were wounded after Rural Guards fired at them.

Monge had run on a "*volvamos a la tierra* " or a "Return to the Land" slate, and he continued and even increased agricultural subsidies. Monge also announced a "100-Day Plan" which was designed to deal with the weakening *colón*, enormous public deficit, rising inflation, and a decline in confidence by foreign investors. Under his administration, although the economy's decline was stabilized—with marked reductions in inflation and unemployment, the nation's economic problems remained severe.

In 1983, teachers, telephone workers, and petroleum workers struck, and, in Sept. 1983 thousands marched through the streets of San José in reaffirmation of the nation's neutrality. On Sept. 28, the CIA instigated a confrontation at the Peñas Blancas border crossing, using anti-Sandinista guerillas belonging to ARDE, Eden Pastora's Democratic Revolutionary Alliance.

The foreign debt climbed to US$3.8 billion by 1984, exceeding the US$3.1 billion GDP, and a more than threefold increase since 1981 when the debt stood at US$1.1 billion. Between 1979 and 1984, the GNP per capita declined 13%, the official unemployment rate increased 69.5%, the *colón* was devalued by 550%, and both imports and exports declined. With intraregional commerce cut off and depressed agricultural export prices, the economy was in trouble. Monge also brought back the army in the camouflaged form of the paramilitary Organizacion Para Emergencias Nacionales (OPEN). In May 1984, 20-30,000 people marched through San José, demanding that Monge uphold the nation's policy of neutrality after the nation received US$4.6 million in military aid that year. In an attempt to counteract this drift to the right, which was necessitated by the nation's dependence upon the US, Monge left for Europe on a "Truth Mission" in June and July; although promises of US$375 million in aid from Europe were announced, only a trickle of that amount ever came in, and US aid continued to exercise a dominant influence. Also that year a new labor law replaced the nation's trade union movement with a system of worker-employer cooperatives.

THE 1986 ELECTIONS: In a break with two traditions—one in which parties customarily alternate terms and the other of not electing a candidate on his first try, PLN candidate Oscar Arias Sanchez won over PUSC candidate Rafael Angel Calderón Fournier. Holder of a doctorate in economics from the University of Essex, Arias came from a wealthy family. The PLN also retained a slim legislative majority with 29 of the 57 seats.

After the US Army Corp of Engineers arrived to begin public works projects involving bridge construction on the Pacific highway, President-elect Arias, while supporting the plan, made this controversial statement: "If I were President Reagan I would give the US$100 million (in contra aid) to aid the economies of Costa Rica, El Salvador, and Honduras instead." Just before the election he dedicated the last of the 80,000 homes promised under his National Housing Program.

THE 1990 ELECTIONS: Successful at last after three tries at the presidency, lawyer Rafael Angel Calderón defeated by a 51.3% to 47.2% margin economist and conservative PLN leader Dr. Carlos Manuel Castillo, whose party was plagued by political infighting during the campaign. As there were few substantive differences between the two candidates—both living in glass houses which the other had the stones to break, the campaign was a ho-hum affair with the issue of corruption lying dormant.

In the Liberation primary, Castillo triumphed over the younger Rolando Araya after US$750,000 in alleged drug money was found wrapped with Araya campaign stickers and after top Araya aide Ricardo Alem was charged with attempting to launder money. (Araya was later cleared of the charges, and—amidst much hoopla—Alem was apprehended in Miami in 1995.) The resignation of Liberation deputy Leonel Villalobos was also demanded after he allegedly performed improper favors for naturalized Costa Rican Fernando Melo who was accused of links to drug traffickers.

After denying it at first, Castillo was forced to admit that he had received a US$2,364 donation from Melo in 1985, thus throwing his credibility and morality into doubt. To top this all off, his close friend and former boss, ex-president Daniel Oduber admitted receiving a one million *colón* contribution from US citizen James Lionel Casey who is wanted for drug charges in the States. On the other hand, Calderón denied an accusation that he had received cash donations of US$500,000 in 1985 from Panama's General Noriega.

CALDERÓN DAYS: With a background that includes a two-year stint as head of the Costa Rican Association for the

Defense of Democracy and Liberty (an organization closely linked to the US Republican Party) and a personal friendship with George Bush, whose mastermind consultant Roger Ailes contributed to his campaign, there is no mistaking Calderón's right wing orientation. Despite his father's reputation and his nickname of "Junior," he is definitely no friend of the left. Called by his detractors a *caballo con ropa* (a "horse with clothes"), Calderón swiftly moved to raise prices on clothing, housing, fuels, power, water, and telephones. Calderón's administration was marred by an incident in which a drug raid by the Green Beret-trained section of the elite Immediate Action Unit led to the accidental death of a 12-year-old. Despite the trauma it caused, the unit was not dissolved despite early assurances it would be, and the boy's killer was dealt with more leniently than the average petty thief.

Calderón had promised to cut the fiscal deficit from 30 million *colones* to 20 million; the deficit rose. In addition to promising to cut public sector spending, he also promised to increase employment, jail all pickpockets, provide small farmers with credit, construct thousands of new homes, repair the roads, and cut taxes! Some houses have been built, but spending has grown, and the other goals remain unaccomplished.

1992 AND 1993 EVENTS: On Feb. 21, members of the Commando Cobra, a 12-member Guardia Rural patrol, brutally murdered two unarmed men carrying sacks of marijuana. They are also charged with raping two young Indian women. One of the most noteworthy incidents of 1992 was the two-week takeover of the Nicaraguan Embassy in March by José Manuel Urbina, a former Contra and nationalized Costa Rican. Seizing the embassy on March 8, his group took 21 hostages and demanded both money and political change in Nicaragua but settled for US$250,000 in ransom money and tickets to the Dominican Republic.

In 1993, a group calling itself the "Death Commando" took over the Supreme Court on April 26. Among the 23 taken hostage were 18 Supreme Court justices. They demanded the release of four prisoners held in Costa Rica on drug trafficking charges, passage to an unspecified country, and US$20 million in ransom. Although the terrorists were initially thought to be Columbian, it turned out that the ringleaders were Gilberto and Guillermo Fallas, a pair of Tico brothers who had worked for the Judicial Police and the Ministry of Public Security. Their motivation was Guillermo's perceived need for a liver transplant. The ransom was reduced to US$8 million and then a comparatively paltry US$150,000, and the promised passage to Guatemala. They disarmed before boarding the airplane and were apprehended.

THE 1994 CAMPAIGN: The Liberación candidate was José María Figueres, the son of the former president. A 1976 *Washington Post* article, which resurfaced during the campaign, quoted CIA reports which name "a relative of President Figueres" as a member of a death squad which "executed at least one narcotics trafficker in early 1973 and has sworn to kill more."

Although the case — involving the murder of a Mexican drug dealer — was declared closed by a judge in 1976, the 1991 book, *El Caso Chemise*, has revived the controversy, alleging that Figueres, who was working for the narcotics police at the time, murdered the alleged marijuana dealer while he was in his custody. To get the nomination, Figueres defeated Margarita Penón de Arias, wife of former president Arias, who had never held political office. Although Figueres was also linked to a gold mining investment fraud led by US white collar criminals, he still triumphed over the PUSC's Miguel Angel Rodriguez.

THE FIGUERES PRESIDENCY: Figueres proved to be the most unpopular president in the past two decades. His policies provoked controversy because they were so far afield of what was anticipated from a Liberación president. Government-owned utilities rate hikes during 1994 hit the poor hard, and prices were raised on other essentials as well. In May 1994 riot police fired M-16 rifles at a crowd of some 200 striking banana workers at the Geest plantation complex in the Sarapiquí area. The workers had been blocking road access in protest of a wage cut and the dismissal of workers who had joined the union.

On Sept. 14, 1994, the president asked the Congress to shut down operations of the bankrupt Banco Anglo Costarricense. Founded in 1863, the bank was the nation's oldest but had suffered losses of US$102 million in previous months as a result of unauthorized venture in Venezuelan foreign debt bonds along with massive (and illegal) overdrafts and uncollectible loans. Massive fraud was uncovered at the INS, the national insurance company, and the national public deficit climbed to 267 billion *colones* (0r around US$1.5 billion).

In Oct. 1994, the Anti-Drug Police arrested a US citizen with six kilos of heroin in her baggage; this was the largest bust (worth US$2 million on the street) in Costa Rican history. Tropical storm Gordon ravaged the Pacific coast and the Meseta Central in Nov. 1994; the storm forced 1,500 to evacuate and left 600 homeless and caused some US$15 million in damages.

In Oct. 1995, he forged a pact with opponent Calderón and his Unity Party. In order to relieve the public debt, Figueres had to pass an increase in the sales tax (from 10% to 15%) as well as other taxes, and government sector jobs had to

Costa Rica is a multicultural society as this mural on the Caribbean coast attests.

be cut back. A teachers' strike began on July 17, 1995. On Jufly 26, tens of thousands of teachers and employees of government agencies slated for closing marched on the Casa Presidencial in Zapote and called for curtailment of the reform plans as well as the overhaul of teachers' pension plans. Violence erupted that evening when 50 out of some 50,000 demonstrators started hurling rocks. Teachers agreed to return to work on Aug. 21 in return for the offer of a chance for a fresh evaluation of their case before Congress.

Inflation for 1995 was 22.56%, up from 19.68% the year before. US President William Jefferson Clinton visited the nation in May 1997.

THE 1998 ELECTIONS: José Miguel Corrales was the PLN's candidate for the third time. He was defeated by Miguel Angel Rodríguez of the PUSC. Rodriguez holds economics and law degrees from the University of Costa Rica and a doctorate in economics from the University of California at Berkeley. He has promised to sell some of the state institutions in order to reduce internal government debt. Pro-business, Rodríguez believes in free trade, and low interest rates and low inflation. He intends to promote tourism as well as special health and housing subsidies for low-income Ticos. Sometimes criticized for his personality, he responded by saying that "I didn't enter a friendliness contest, or to become a pageant queen."

In Sept. 1998, Rodriguez stirred up more controversy after he defended a controversial new development at Playa Tambor by a multinational hotel firm allegedly guilty of environmental destruction in the past. "Who hasn't destroyed a little bit of nature to build the foundations of a house?," Rodriguez queried.

Hurricane Mitch battered the nation's Pacific coast in Oct. 1998. It left six dead and 2,600 homeless.

In Jan. 1999, President Rodríguez announced that the 155% raise (to US$22,000 per month) the previous would be rolled back. The President subseqeuently renounced the pay rise. However, he still earns 30% more than previously.

In April 1999, Rodriguez criticized the opposition for its efforts to block the 'liberalization' of electricity providers which, opponents of maintained, might lead to privatization of the ICE, the electricity company. "To achieve their anti-patriotic and irresponsible aims, they have resorted to everything.... To lies, demagoguery, and filibusterism." (A reference to American William Walker who invaded in 1856 with a gang of "filibusters").

That May a crowd of some 4,000 protested agains the privatization of major state institutions, the high cost of living, and new education policies regarding grading for high school graduation test.

In May it was disclosed that the Social Security System (Caja) had ourchesed US$5 million worth of shares in an unregulated trust fund at the behest of Banco Popular. The bank failed to make good on the loans, claiming that the trust fund debtors failed to pay.

Government

With of the strongest democratic traditions in the Central American region, Costa Rica is one of the most politically stable nations in the hemisphere. The nation has had only two violent interludes in its history, during the periods of 1917-19 and 1948-49. Of the more than 50 presidents, only six have been considered to be dictators and only three have come

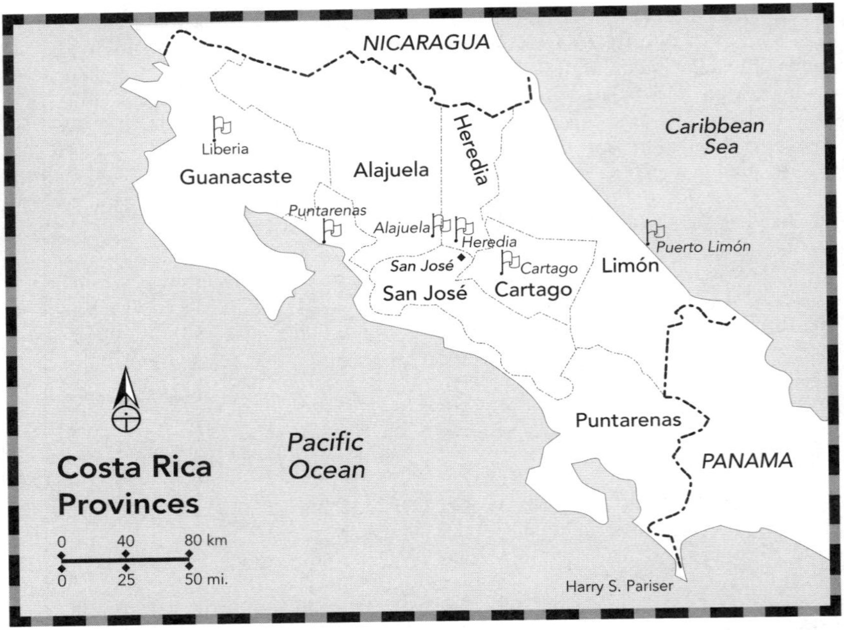

from the military. The nation's relatively homogenous population, its large middle class, traditional respect for the rule of law, geographical isolation, and lack of a large military establishment have all contributed to its political stability.

POLITICAL STRUCTURE: Despite having declared itself a sovereign republic in 1848, Costa Rica has gone through a number of changes in its constitutional format. Established as a democratic and unitary republic by the 1949 constitution, the Costa Rican government is divided into executive, judicial, and legislative branches. The executive branch consists of the president, two vice presidents, and the (Council of Government).

Although there is a carefully designed system of checks and balances and presidential power is (by Latin American standards) limited, the President commands the center position of power. His control is restricted by the legislature's right to override his veto, the Supreme Court's ability to establish the constitutionality of administrative acts and legislation, and the one-term, four-year limit.

There is no official army, and the large police force reverts to the control of the Tribunal Supremo de Eleciones (TSE), which supervises the elections (the so-called *Fiesta Política*) during campaigns. A fourth branch of government are the state's 200 autonomous institutions, including the Pacific Electric Railroad, the Social Security Institute, the Electric Institute, the University of Costa Rica, and all banks, including the Central Bank.

A unicameral body elected for a four-year term, the National Assembly has 57 members, distributed proportionately, with one for every 30,000 Costa Ricans. It may override a presidential veto with a two-thirds majority. No rubber stamp, its exclusive powers include the right to declare war and peace, determine the national budget, impeach the president, and—disturbingly—suspend civil rights for up to 30 days.

LOCAL GOVERNMENT: Ruled by appointed governors, the nation's seven provinces all have capitals of the same name with the exception of Guanacaste, whose capital is Liberia. While Alajuela, Heredia, San José, and Cartago lie entirely inland, Guanacaste, Puntarenas, and Limón border the coasts. Provinces are divided into a grand total of 81 *cantones* (counties); these, in turn, are divided into 344 *distritos* (districts). The *consejo de gobierno* (municipal council) of each canton controls services ranging from trash collection to road maintenance.

POLITICAL PARTIES: Largest and most influential of these is the Partido de Liberación Nacional (PLN, National Liberation Party), founded by the nation's elder statesmen José "Don Pepe" Figueres. Competition for the reins of power comes from the currently-ruling, more conservative Partido Unidad Social Cristiana (PUSC, Social Christian Unity), a loose confederation of four different parties which was known from 1978-1983 as the Coalicion Unidad.

Other, much smaller and less influential parties include the Partido del Progreso (Progressive Party), the religious and conservative Partido Alianza Nacional Cristiana, the Trotskyite Partido Revolucionario de los Trabajadores en Lucha (Revolutionary Party of Workers in Struggle) and the Pueblo Unido, a coalition of two left-wing parties. In recent elections, their combined share of the vote has dropped from eight to around one or two percent.

Some voters, disheartened and disillusioned with the two major parties, turn in blank ballots. In the 1990 polls one witty soul plastered pictures of cattle (including one wearing a suit and tie) and of two pigs (one of them feeding) on his ballot, scrawling the word "no" prominently in three places.

ELECTIONS: Costa Rica has universal suffrage for all citizens over the age of 18, and voting is compulsory for all citizens under 70. Turnout has been about 80% in the past few elections. Voting is by secret ballot with the voter indicating his choice by placing a thumbprint in a box set under the party's name, full color flag, and the candidate's photo; there is also a separate ballot for the congressional and municipal races for which one votes for the party with its full slate of candidates rather than picking-and-choosing.

After voting, each citizen has his or her right index finger dipped in a jar of purple indelible ink. Citizens are automatically registered to vote on their 18th birthdays if they receive a *cedula de identidad*, a numbered identity card complete with name, address, fingerprints, and photo.

The autonomous Tribunal Supremo de Eleciones supervises the electoral process. Composed of three magistrates and three alternates, all selected by the Supreme Court and serving staggered six-year terms, the TSE commands complete control, right down to the ability to ban an already established party. Even though additional advertising is affordable only to the two major parties, all registered parties are granted equal TV and radio airtime.

Although the government also contributes funds for campaign expenses, 5% of the national budget is distributed to parties in proportion to the votes they received in the previous elections. (The catch is that a party must have received a minimum of 5% to qualify). National assemblies (party conventions) choose candidates. Every four years elections are held on the first Sunday in February. The weeks previous to the election are marked by *plazas publicas* (demonstrations featuring sound systems, speakers, and bands), car honking, and flag waving.

If the president and two vice presidents fail to receive 40% of the vote, a special runoff election pits the two top contenders against each other. In the unlikely event that the top two contenders receive the exact same percentage, the oldest will be selected. Of special significance is the fact that the president can not be reelected and is banned from running for the office again. This is perhaps one reason why Costa Rica's history differs from nations such as the Dominican Republic where demagogues such as Balaguer may steal elections over and over again.

Economy

To understand Costa Rica's economy one must take into account a number of factors. The nation's small size and relatively small population have hampered industrial development, and the incessant regional instability, along with socio-cultural and political differences, has served as an obstacle to creating a truly unified regional economic block.

Costa Rica has always been a plantation economy with agricultural exports commanding chief importance. The same lack of industrial development that has hampered the economy in other ways has also made it necessary to import a large number of items from the "developed" world (the US in particular), running up a substantial deficit in the process. A final factor is the government's role as employer: about 20% of the population works directly or indirectly for the public sector.

SOLIDARISMO: Any discussion of the economic situation would be incomplete without mention of *Solidarismo*. Created in 1948 by Alberto Marten as an alternative to the communist-run labor unions, the over 1,300 *Solidarismo* associations operating nationwide are savings associations which work hand in hand with management. The workers invest a fixed percentage of their wage (generally 5%) into a savings fund, an amount which the company then matches with money from a severance pay fund. (Companies are legally obliged to deposit 8.33% of their payroll in a fund which covers payoffs for dismissals).

While some find the system works well for them, there have been compaints of abuses from members as well as from unions, who claim the *Solidarismo* philosophy is designed to destroy their collective bargaining groups. It is also alleged that many *Solidarismo* groups are run by patsies for management who do not have the best interests of workers in mind. In 1993, the AFL-CIO spoke out against what it felt were clear violations of workers' rights and is striving to have Costa Rica excluded from the Caribbean Basin Initiative (CBI), membership in which gives Costa Rican goods preferential tariff treatment.

LIGHT INDUSTRY: The nation's manufacturing industry dates from the early 20th C, when factories to produce such consumables as textiles, cigarettes, and beer were established. The government later adopted the policy of *desarrolo hacia adentro* (internally oriented development). However, its impact has proved disappointing, and the nation is still heavily dependent upon exports.

Since WWII, the government has nationalized many industries. At first this was confined to banking, power companies, and telecommunication. In the 1970s, agriculture and industry began to be nationalized as well. The government set up corporations to manage projects which were either too expensive for or not of interest to private firms. Along with the enactment of the 1959 Industrial Development Law, establishment of the CACM (Central American Common Market) in 1960 accelerated expansion of manufacturing. The CACM established intra-regional free trade along with protective barriers against outside competition.

The nation's open attitude towards foreign investment, combined with its relatively high educational level, has spurred on the economy. The wide variety of goods produced today include bricks, cement, fertilizers, paints, plastics, solar energy collectors, petroleum products, textiles, cosmetics, adhesives, tires, yachts, and motor vehicle spare parts. The textile industry, in particular, has really bloomed during the past decade or so following the establishment of the USAID's CINDE (Coalition for Development Initiatives), a private agency designed to attract foreign investment. New US laws permitting corporations such as Levi Strauss to shut down US operations and import Costa Rican-sewn garments duty-free to the US encouraged this development. There are several hundred or more of these *maquilas* which employ over 50,000 workers, the majority of which are young women. Violations in working conditions are said to be common, and numerous instances of abuse have been uncovered. The companies operate *solodarista* associations in lieu of unions.

The government is in a Catch-22 situation because if it forces companies to comply with regulations, they may move to El Salvador or Guatemala. Costa Rica is second only to the Dominican Republic in total exports. Company profits are sheltered under a 1992 Costa Rican law, and you won't find these goods (as they rationally should be) for sale here. Most of the manufacturing is concentrated in the Meseta Central. Unfortunately, the nation's relatively small population, the vast majority of whom live at or near subsistence level, limits the market for locally produced goods, and the wages are horribly low (around US$.90 per hour in the textile industry).

In 1999, multinational microchip manufacturer Intel ousted tourism as the top foreign exchange earner; Intel brought in an estimated US$957 million as opposed to tourism's US$829 million, textile's US$758 million, banana's US$ 630 million, and coffee's US$409 million.

Economic dependence on Intel is certain to grow as its facilities are under construction. Motorola, meanwhile, closed its plant in 1998.

FREE TRADE AGREEMENTS: In April 1994 President Calderón and Mexican President Carlos Salinas signed a free trade agreement which took effect on

Jan. 1, 1995. The treaty provides for a graded transition in which exports from the two countries will be available duty-free in each others markets. A duty-free trade agreement is hoped for with the US (which purchases some 42% of Costa Rica's exports) within a few years. However, the fallout over NAFTA and the Mexican "bailout" in late 1994 leaves some doubt as to whether such an agreement will ever be enacted.

TOURISM: This "industry" has grown dramatically: some 850,000 foreign tourists arrived during 1998 and an estimated million tourists arrived in 1999.. Future growth is expected: an estimated 1.2 million visitors are projected to arrive during the early years of the 21st Century. The industry now employs half a million Costa Ricans or 17% of the population. Growth in tourism has become a major economic priority, and a large number of new hotels are under construction.

Unfortunately, many of the hotels (especially on the Nicoya Peninsula) are being constructed with only short-term profit in mind, and without consideration of the effect such development will have on the local ecosystem and all of its inhabitants. Some believe that it is unwise for any local economy to place too much emphasis on tourism. Instability in the region, a major earthquake, civil disturbances, hyperinflation, even the whims of tourists could depress tourism — sending the economy into a tailspin.

Investment Scams

Operating under the remarkable delusion that Costa Rica is some kind of paradise, arriving foreigners often exhibit gullible behavior. Con men are everywhere in the world, and Costa Rica is no exception. Recent examples have included a teak "reforestation" (which involves cutting down trees and replanting with teak) project which promised great returns but could not deliver and an unregistered "Rain Forest for Kids Foundation" which launched an aborted attempt to market "Rain Forest Seeds" packets using artwork stolen from a Costa Rican artist. A third scheme — developed in cooperation with the Dutch branch of the World Wildlife Fund — promises exhorbitant profits for investors who put money into its teak farm. One American who operated an investment firm in San José was exposed as a charlatan in late 1994. Such carpetbaggers span all nationalities — from Swiss to Canadian — so let the investor beware!

ECOTOURISM OR EGOTOURISM?: Sadly, many so-called "ecotourism" projects are mostly hyperbole. The government lacks any plan or direction, and there is no control over development. Former Costa Rican Tourism Minister Luis Manuel Chacon was presented an "Environmental Devil" award by Robin Wood and Pro Reginwald, two German environmental groups, at the '93 International Tourism Fair in Berlin on March 6, 1993. Chacon retaliated in the pages of *Conde Nast Traveler* that "those new greens, if you scratch them a little bit, the red will come out." There is considerable debate on what constitutes "ecotourism" in Costa Rica. One travel agency owner actually copyrighted the word "ecotourism" in 1983 and claims all those using it are in violation of his copyright!

The latest attempt to label what is "ecotourism" and what is not has arrived with the Sustainable Tourism Certificate, launched by the tourist board in Aug. 1998. The "five leaf" system is remarkably similar to the one formerly used in the *New Key to Costa Rica*. However, it is likely that the assessments will be biased towards large hotels, and hotels which degraded the environment during their construction will also be eligible for a certificate! Program director Rodolf Lizano maintains that "We cannot condemn for life someone who may have broken the law in the past."

OTHER SECTORS: Much of the mining is of nonmetals — sand, limestone, and clay. Small amounts of gold, silver, and dolomite are also mined. Various projects have been instituted by Citizens Energy Corporation, a nonprofit organization founded by Rep. Joseph Kennedy III. Much of the potential for hydroelectric power remains untapped.

In 1986 the DEA estimated that 20% of the cocaine arriving in the US was funneled through Costa Rica. The largest seizure in history occurred in Nov. 1989 when 568 kg were confiscated at Limón airport along with US$13,500 in cash and the plane belonging to the two Colombian pilots. The fact that no arrests were made of Costa Ricans hinted to many of high level governmental links with drug trafficking.

In Aug. 1995, Spanish police apprehended four Italians, allegedly members of the Calabrian mafia, who are believed to have laundered money through investing in hotels in Costa Rica. They are believed to have been resposible for the smuggling of some 250 tons of cocaine into the US. When they were picked up, they had been trying to cash a US$21-million check in Luxembourg. The money was reportedly destined for Costa Rica.

Agriculture

The economy has always centered around agriculture and animal husbandry — exporting coffee, bananas and, more recently, livestock. Despite a surge in growth, the manufacturing industry's structural emphasis on imports has limited its overall contribution. As there are no mineral deposits of note, the most valuable natural resources are the nation's superior pastures and nutrient-rich fields.

As elsewhere in Central America, the land distribution here is inegalitarian, with a small minority (11,500) of the larger farms monopolizing the largest portion (over two million hectares) of the farmland. Less than one percent of the nation's farms are larger than 1,200 acres (500 ha) but these extend over 27% of the country, and estates with more than 500 acres (200 ha) account for only three percent but occupy more than half of the land area. According to the 1983 census, 71% of the "agricultural" population are landless agricultural laborers. Owing to the topography and the small size of the average farm, mechanization has had little effect on agriculture. It has been estimated that, if the land were used in an ecologically optimal fashion, agriculture could supply employment for nearly half of the nation's labor force, which would relieve the pressure on urban areas.

In the history of agricultural development, government support and regulation has been crucial: The Consejo de Nacional Producción (CNP) buys basic grains from farmers above purchase price and distributes them through its *expendios*. A problem for small farmers has been that loans have been available mainly for export-oriented production. Traditional export crops include bananas, sugarcane, coffee, and cacao.

ENVIRONMENTAL PROBLEMS: Sadly, the Hispanic-American farmers learned little about agricultural methods and techniques from the Native Americans. Whereas the indigenous peoples lived in harmony with the environment—using the forests as a resource, rotating small crops in order to stave off soil depletion—the new arrivals have radically transformed the natural environment, to the point where deforestation, soil erosion, and changes in river ecology have reached crisis proportions.

These ecological colonialists, using monoculture and transforming rainforests into pasture, have wreaked havoc on the environment. Forests on steep slopes and in areas of heavy precipitation, which protected the soil from erosion and regulated water supply to the drainage system, were indiscriminately cut down, setting off a chain reaction. Today, ecologists estimate that 30% of the nation faces serious water and wind erosion.

?!? According to a 1997 report by the Heath Ministry, Costa Rica uses a per-capita average of 6.5 kg of pesticides per year.

PESTICIDES: Pesticide use and its effects are another major problem. Such export-oriented crops as cotton, fruit, vegetables, and cut flowers — temperate products being produced in the tropics—must be deluged with pesticides. Pesticicide bombardment of the mining fly, which plagues the potato fields, has become so heavy that the fly has developed a resistance. Costa Rica spends an estimated US$40 million per year on imported pesticides.

Pesticide use can lead to tragic results. One recent example was DBCP, a pesticide (marketed as Nemagón) used in Standard Fruit's Río Frio banana plantations to control nematodes. After the chemical was found to cause sterility in humans, its use was suspended in 1977 in the US. In Costa Rica, however, it was not banned until 1988. Some 1,000 banana workers were sterilized by the pesticide In 1992, they accepted an out-of-court settlement from Standard Fruit and chemical companies (Shell Oil, Dow Chemical, and Occidental Chemical). However, children in the area have died of leukemia, and local women have developed cancer, suffer from mysterious pains, given birth to deformed children, and experienced miscarriages. All of this may be linked to the chemical. (Ironically, in 1998, Standard Fruit became the first food-growing company in the world to receive the "green seal" that comes with the International Standards Organization's ISO 14001 Certificate).

Paraquat was reported to be the number-one cause of pesticide poisonings between 1986 and 1992. The herbicide is banned in Sweden and restricted in the US. An estimated 500 Costa Ricans are hospitalized each year because of pesticide poisoning, and 445 died during the years 1980-89. In addition to abuse of pesticides, unregistered pesticides have been found in use.

NONTRADITIONAL AGRICULTURE: Termed the *cambio*, nontraditional agriculture is growing in importance. Since the early 1980s the government has stressed the export-oriented production of crops such as coconuts, ornamental plants, flowers, pineapples, macadamia nuts, and melons. Income from these nontraditionals soared from US$336 million in 1984 to US$729 million by 1989. In the near future, the greatly increased acreage planted in macadamias will make Costa Rica the third largest producer of macadamia nuts.

> ?!¿ Costa Rican law formerly prohibited citizens from drinking coffee made with anything other than third-class quality beans. The higher quality were reserved for export.
>
> You may tell the seasons in Costa Rica by the coffee trees. Branches will be laden with fragant white flowers during April and May, small green berries from May through Sept., and ripe red berries from Oct. to Feb.

However, because of the capital requirements and the high interest rates, it is difficult for the small farmer to switch to crops like strawberries, miniature vegetables, mangoes, and flowers. Support for nontraditional farmers has been misdirected because it has been supplied in the form of CATS or tax certificate bonds valued at up to 15% of the value of the nontraditional crops. These can be claimed as discounts on taxes or can be sold to investors for immediate cash. Unfortunately, the small farmer often sells to an exporter who then cashes in, in effect, on the small farmer's benefits.

COFFEE: Coffee (*café*) production began in 1779 in the Meseta Central, an area which has near-perfect soil and climate conditions. A native of Ethiopia, the introduced Arabica blend had been first cultivated in Saudi Arabia. Coffee growing soon surpassed cacao, tobacco, and sugar in importance. By 1829 it had become the major source of foreign revenue. As a nonperishable commodity in an age of slow and costly transport, coffee proved an ideal product and shortly thereafter became the nation's major export, a position it has maintained until recent years. Exports to neighboring Panama began in the late 1820s. After a load was sent directly to Britain in 1843, the British began investing heavily in the industry, becoming the principal purchaser of Costa Rican coffee until after WWII.

The largest growing areas are the San José, Alajuela, Heredia, Puntarenas, and Cartago provinces. Costa Rican coffee is high in both quality and caffeine content; it is often blended with inferior varieties. Local coffee, set at a much lower government-controlled local price, is tinted in order to prevent diversion to the export market. Labor-intensive, coffee production depends upon cheap, seasonal labor: Workers receive a mere pittance per basket picked, and some 75% workers are Nicaraguans.

A major blight struck in 1983. As with any plantation crop, one of the major drawbacks is that income is subject to major price fluctuations, After world coffee prices plunged 40% subsequent to the collapse of the world quota cartel system, Costa Rica joined Honduras, Guatemala, Nicaragua, and El Salvador in June of 1989 in a coffee retention plan which would entail selling their coffee in installments in order to ensure price stability. The export tax on coffee, first initiated in 1955, was abolished in 1994.

A new trend is organic coffee. **Coocafé**, a cooperative of small farmers, sells to CaféDirect in Britain, Equal Exchange in the US, and Max Havelaar in Europe.

> Written by Gregory Nicum and Nina Luttinger, *The Coffee Book* traces its history. Another good title is *Uncommon Grounds: The History of Coffee and How It Transformed Our World* by Mark Pendergrast.

BANANAS: Thought to be a native of tropical Asia, the banana (*plátano, banano*) was introduced into the

Foro Emaus

An umbrella organization working to promoting the rights of workers on banana plantation and towards countering unregulated planatation expansion, Foro Emaus was founded in 1990 in Limón. Members include Catholic clergy, labor union members, and representatives of various environmental groups. The organization's demands include terminating the practice of short-term banana workers and illegal aliens in order to prevent union organizing, terminating the use of dangerous pesticides, and stopping deforestation. The organization is also working to change government policy which currently favors the unions. It has received support only from the Limón diocese. In Costa Rica, as elsewhere in the world, the Catholic Church heirarchy remains devoted maintaining to the status quo. Opposition also comes from the government and the banana multinationals.

members.tripod.com/foro_emaus/

Bamana workers near Siguirres

Caribbean and, subsequently, to Central America sometime after the Spanish invasion. The fruit (which is actually a grain) became well known in the US only after the mid-1860s, and the production of the popular Gros Michael variety was begun by American Minor Cooper Keith. He shipped his first fruit, 360 stems, to New Orleans in 1870. Taking over the nation's debt to cutthroat British bankers in 1883, Keith was offered in exchange control of the completed railway and 800,000 acres or 7% of the national territory. Although much of this land was returned, the remainder became the basis for the company's Costa Rican empire, and Keith's influence seeped into every sector of the economy. A century later, exports surpassed 50 million 40-pound boxes. Financial difficulties in the 1890s drove Keith to merge with the United Fruit Company, a firm which monopolized the nation's banana exports until the late 1950s.

The Standard Fruit Company began production in 1956 with exports beginning in 1959. A third major transnational company, the Del Monte subsidiary BANDECO, the Banana Development Corporation, began operating plantations. United Brands subsidiary Compañía Bananera closed down operations in 1985 following rising costs and a 72-day strike in 1984 which cost the company US$12 million in lost production. In addition to domination of exports by transnationals, another detrimental complication connected with banana cultivation has been the crop's susceptibility to disease, namely Panama disease and Sigatoka (leaf spot) disease. Epidemic diseases in the first quarter of the century led to the temporary abandonment of the Caribbean coastal area and to the establishment of plantations on the Pacific side. With the formation of the Asociación de Bananeros S. A. (ASBANA), a government-subsidized private association, the Atlantic Coast banana plantations took off once more, producing an estimated 75 million boxes of bananas and generating US$440.9 million for the local economy in 1991. In 1994, 450 million boxes were produced. Costa Rica is now the largest banana producer in the world after Ecuador. However, outbreaks of black sigatoka and moka reduced production by as much as 30% on some farms, and a mini-drought hit Limón.

The European Union quotas forced Costa Rica to divert eight million boxes from the EU nations to other markets, resulting in a drop in prices. In 1994 Chiquita cancelled its contract with Difrusa S. A., allegedly because Costa Rica had accepted the controversial quotas mandated by the European Union. The US multinationals fight against the quotas appears hypocritical given the US quotas placed on textiles, sugar, and beef.

Growth has come with a stiff price. Much of the new acreage came through destruction of thousands of acres of virgin jungle near Guapiles. In 1990, Limón's bishop Alfonso Coto denounced the conditions under which workers labor, contending that they are treated unfairly, the wealth is concentrated in too few hands, the industry aggravates deforestation and contamination of rivers, and that the labor organizations (*Solidarismo*, which has replaced the unions) provide neither job security nor adequate working conditions. In Feb. 1992, the Holland-based Second International Tribunal on Water condemned Standard Fruit Company for "severely polluting the eastern region of the country."

In Dec. 1992, the Labor Ministry accused ten banana companies of violating national labor laws by paying substandard wages and refusing to pay overtime. The previous month the banana unions had accused multinationals of hiring some 12,000 illegal workers who are paid less than the minimum wage and denied benefits. Also in 1992, some 1,000 banana workers—sterilized by the pesticide DBCP (marketed as Nemagón) in the late 1970s—accepted an out-of-court settlement from Standard Fruit and chemical companies (Shell Oil, Dow Chemical, and Occidental Chemical).

In May 1994 riot police fired M-16 rifles at a crowd of some 200 striking banana workers at the Geest plantation complex in the Sarapiquí area. The workers had been blocking road access in protest of a wage cut and the dismissal of workers who had joined the union. Private guards also fired on workers who attacked administrative offices. Shortly thereafter the nine-day strike was halted after Geest agreed to recognize the right of SIGTAGA (Agricultural and Ranch Worker Union of Heredia) to organize. On the surface, such an agreement would seem inconsequential as it is merely an affirmation of willingness to respect the nation's labor laws. However, as the banana companies had trampled on workers' rights for the previous decade, it was seen as a major step forward by the workers.

Today, most bananas are shipped to the US and Europe. The developed countries have come to expect that their bananas will have no spots. Originally, banana stems were covered with paper in order to ensure that they were protected. Today, pesticide-imbued light blue plastic bags have been substituted along with polypropylene cord which is used

Cacao

to tie up the top-heavy plants. An estimated 6,300 tons of bags are used annually. Unfortunately, most of these end up in rivers or buried in shallow landfills.

To their credit, Bandeco (Del Monte) and Standard Fruit Company (Dole), which export some two-thirds of all bananas, have constructed the nation's largest plastic recycling facility near Siquirres. In the first stage, the plant is processing some 2,150 tons of plastic into pallets for banana shipping, building materials, and fence posts. If this initial plant (which opened in 1994) proves profitable, the plan is to expand it until it can handle the industry's entire plastic bag supply. In return, Chiquita will receive the "Eco-OK" seal from the Rainforest Alliance. No cure has been proposed with the pesticide problem; the banana industry uses a third of the nation's pesticide imports annually, and the National Insurance Institute maintains that 75% of the labor accidents involving pesticides occur in banana-producing areas.

However, banana production continues to grow unabated, expanding like cancer. Banana companies applied to purchase 8,000 acres (3,227 ha) of land between June and Nov. of 1992. Ironically, US Army Engineers — acting under the "Bridges for Peace" program — had constructed bridges in the Puerto Viejo de Sarapiquí area earlier that year which were suited to the use of the banana plantations. Plans are to expand to cultivation to 123,500 acres (50,000 ha). Current production is around 90 million boxes per year. One possible compromise solution is promised by the Banano Amiga project which proposes to issue management guidelines. Companies followig the recommendations will be issued a seal of approval. No endorsement

Oil palms to the south of Quepos

A girl processes yucca near the Nicaraguan border

will be given to any firm that is cutting down forests to expand production.

The government records 116 million boxes of bananas exported in 1998 generating US$630 million on land covering 51,000 ha.

If you wish to protest the activities of the banana plantations in Costa Rica, you can write to Chiquita Brands International, Apdo. 10036, 1000 San José.

SUGARCANE: *Caña* (*Saccharum officianarum*) probably originated in New Guinea; it has become a major crop only since the late 1950s. While it is grown all over the country, the largest areas for sugarcane growing and processing are concentrated in the Meseta Central, in Guanacaste province, northern Puntarenas province, and in northern Alajuela province. An estimated 113,700 acres (46,014 ha) are under cultivation. Except in labor-scarce Guanacaste, almost all the cane is cut by hand, and the land is burned before harvesting (Jan. to May) in order to expedite cutting. The vast majority of the workers are Nicaraguans. Large sugar mills (*ingenios*) are prevalent although the oxen powered mills (*trapiches*) can still be found.

During the pre-Castro 1950s, little cane was grown, and sugar was imported until the middle of the decade. Stimulated by the Cuban embargo, exports to the US climbed to 60,000 tons by the mid-1960s. In 1989, 45,300 tons were produced.

CACAO: Thought to have originated in the Amazon basin on the E equatorial slopes of the Andes, *Theobroma cacao*, the "food of the gods' has been cultivated for upwards of 2,000 years. After the Spanish conquest, *cacao* (known as chocolate or cocoa in its refined form) became the most important crop, and it was used as currency until the 19th C. when it was replaced by coffee. It only re-emerged as an export crop in 1944. Today, *cacao* is the only export crop grown under adverse conditions.

The vast majority of the crop is produced in the Caribbean coastal lowlands, an area which is really too wet to grow cacao properly. While the NE lowlands are superior, cultivation in the region is hindered by the lack of coastal transport; most of the current crop grown there goes to Nicaragua. Quality of the processed *cacao* is low owing to the lack of controlled fermentation. Devastated by the fungus *monilia* since 1979 and plagued by plummeting prices on the world markets, *cacao* seems to be on its way out. The Ministry of Agriculture has even recommended that farmers substitute other crops.

PALM OIL: Native to W Africa, the African oil palm (*palma de aceite*) was transported to this hemisphere along with the slave trade. The primary oil in use during the Industrial Revolution, it helped to cement the colonial linkage between Europe and Africa. In Costa Rica it was introduced in the 1940s in order to fill the domestic need for cooking oil. After the pullout by United Brands in the 1980s, it replaced bananas on the W coast.

It is cultivated by the Chiquita-owned, government-controlled trans-national monopoly Cia. Palma Tica (formerly Compañía Bananera) whose subsidiary (Grupo Numar) in San José processes the unrefined oil into cooking fat; it also blends it with imported soybean oil to make cooking oil and margarine. Because of its high volume of saturated fats, palm oil along with that from palm kernels and coconuts (the other "tropical" oils) has become a source of worldwide controversy. The oil and its various food products are of major economic importance: Costa Rica exports some 12,000 metric tons of the oil annually, with a market value of over US$4.6 million.

OTHER CROPS: Maize, beans, potatoes, plantains, rice, onions, and sorghum are the main crops cultivated for domestic consumption. The most important cereal grain in Costa Rica, corn is used as a staple food (in forms ranging from *tamales* to *tortillas*), a raw material for industrial products, and as animal feed. Most of the corn is grown on small to medium-sized farms and is usually planted using a digging stick, with two or three seeds inserted in each hole.

Approximately 90% of the rice crop (*Oryza sativa*) is grown without irrigation. Unlike maize, it is grown by large-scale farmers using modern methods. Although Guanacaste has been the traditional stronghold for rice cultivation, irregular rainfall has spurred the development of new areas near Puntarenas. Less important crops include cassava, tobacco, and cotton. Quantities of maize, beans, and sorghum must still be imported.

ANIMAL HUSBANDRY: First brought here in the 1500s, cattle are the most important component of the livestock industry. Until after the end of WWII, beef, the favorite meat of Costa Ricans, still had to be imported. Export of live cattle (*ganado*) to the US began in 1954, but exports switched to beef so that hides and offal could be used locally, and it continues to be the major export after bananas and coffee. Local consumption, however, has actually declined as escalating prices have made beef more and more of an unaffordable luxury. Graded low because the cattle is grass-fed and therefore lean, most of the exported beef is made into pet food, TV dinners, and fast food hamburgers.

Although cattle ranching has been hailed because of its magnetic ability to attract greenbacks, it has had devastating ecological consequences, as the clearcutting of forests has produced severe erosion. The massive deforestation occurring between the 1960s and early '80s was largely the result of a boom in cattle ranching.

While beef exports tripled between 1960 and 1978, the ratio of pasture to agricultural land grew to more than 50%, and an estimated 80% of trees felled were either burned or left to rot on the ground. In a pattern that has become alarmingly typical, small farmers cut down the primary forest, farm the land for a few years until it is depleted, resell the land to a rancher, and then move on to the next virgin tract. Although cattle ranches consume vast areas of land, they provide little employment. At their height, beef exports never surpassed 8.6% of total exports.

During the 1980s, the price of beef began to drop, and a 1988 boycott led by the San Francisco-based Rainforest Action Network led Burger King to stop purchasing Costa Rican beef. Along with the Alajuela province's Llandura de San Carlos region, the largest cattle raising areas are Guanacaste and northern Puntarenas provinces.

Only a few farms raise pigs commercially. Horses far outnumber mules, sheep, and goats. Although all three birds were introduced by the Spaniards, chickens win out numerically over ducks and geese. There are also turkeys and even quail, which produce eggs for export.

FORESTRY: Much of the forest has been sold without directly benefiting the economy. Although the Arias administration claimed to have to have cut the deforestation rate to 30,000 hectares annually while increasing reforestation tenfold, some experts believe the deforestation rate to be much higher now. Although it is now a felony to illegally cut or transport wood, violators are consistently fined rather than jailed. Much contraband wood is transported at times when forestry officials are off work. Although the lumber industry accounted for less than 4% of the nation's agricultural earnings as of 1985, thousands are employed in the process of milling and transporting logs. As wood grows scarcer, the price of timber has risen and the number of mills has dropped from 220 in 1984 to around 150 in 1990. Many of the bankrupt mills were the least efficient wood processors.

At the current rate, the nation's productive forests may be depleted early into the 21st century, and that could cost the government up to US$150 million a year in wood imports. Even though annual reforestation is planned to equal the area cut, there is still a 15-20 year gap between the time of forest exhaustion and the time when the reforested trees are ready for harvest. Although exports of logs and unprocessed timber is prohibited, the nation exports around US$22 million worth of wood products annually.

FISHING: The fishing industry accounts for only a small part of agricultural production. While lobsters are caught in the Caribbean, tuna, herring, sardines, and shrimp are fished in the Pacific waters.

The People (Los Costarricenses)

As is true all over Latin America Spanish influence has been paramount. Although only a few thousand or so Spaniards immigrated between 1502 and 1821, their impact upon the society was tremendous.

Despite the Euro-American "white" Costa Rican image, there has been a great deal of racial mixing over the centuries. Still, Costa Rica is unquestionably the most homogeneous—both lingusitically and ethnically—of all Central American nations. Although there is a definite infusion of African and Native American blood, Ticos share the same language and consider themselves to be Caucasians.

Because Ticos have traditionally viewed themselves as egalitarian yeoman farmers, they sometimes refer to their society as classless despite glaring differences in income and power distribution. In fact, the independent farmer is a dying breed, but other social classes remain strong. In addition to the Spanish stock, French, British, Germans, and Italians have arrived over the centuries and been absorbed into the mainstream.

POPULATION: At the time of Independence, there were approximately 65,000 Costa Ricans. Their numbers grew to around 100,000 by 1850, 250,000 by the early 1900s, to nearly 500,000 by 1927, 2,655,000 in 1985, and an estimated four million today. An average of 13.8 deaths occur for every 1,000 births. With a current annual growth rate of 2.6%, the population is projected to grow to 3.4-3.7 million by the end of the century and to 4.9 million by 2025. Some 20% of households are headed by single mothers. Of the 80,000 births recorded annually, teenage pregnancies account for over 14,000, and more than half of all births are out of wedlock. The average life expectancy is 76.5 yrs., and the infant mortality rate is 16.65 per 1,000 live births, which compares favorably with Guatemala (48.5), Honduras (50.7), and Nicaragua (49.8). Costa Rica ranks 39th out of the 173 nations listed on the Index of Human Development.

Population distribution is inequitable. Average density is 162.2 inhabitants/sq. mi. (62.6/sq. km) as compared with 83.6 in Nicaragua, 83.9 in Panama, 22 in Belize, and 677 in El Salvador. Over half of all Costa Ricans live in the Valle Central which comprises portions of four provinces: San José, Alajuela, Heredia, and Cartago, with the largest portion living in the San José metropolitan area. Although this area encompasses only 5% of the land surface, the population has actually been even more concentrated in the past with many outlying areas becoming significantly populated only in the 20th century. Most emigrants go to the US, and that nation receives a higher percentage of immigrants, relative to Costa Rica's total population, than from any other Latin American nation.

?!¿ Costa Ricans call themselves "*Ticos*" after the special diminutives they add to their words. Throughout Latin America, diminutives are commonly added in speech. For example momento becomes *momentito*, "in a little while." But Costa Ricans change this into *momentico*, using their own unique diminutive form.

?!¿ Many Costa Ricans believe that lacatating mothers can not conceive, and "*lactancia*" is seen as a form of birth control, a quite unreliable one as many come to realize.

CLASS STRUCTURE: In the earliest times, there was a sharp division between the minority *hidalgos* (gentry) and the *plebeyos* (commoners). The former had servants and owned all of the slaves. Although these differences had largely dissolved by the beginning of the 1800s, a small elite still dominated the nation. In fact, 21 out of the 28 who signed the act declaring the nation's independence, were closely related. These *cafetaleros* (coffee barons) came to control the best coffee growing lands along with the beneficios (coffee processing plants). Their political power reached its apex between 1821 and1915. Now known as *la sociedad* (the society), the descendents of the coffee barons—no longer as economically and politically dominant as in the past—still reside in San José. This elite has been joined by other immigrants who made their fortunes in the

If you're planning an extended stay, you may with to read *The Ticos: Culture and Social Change in Costa Rica*. Boulder, CO: Lynn and Bienner, 1999.
www.biesanz.com/book.htm
biesanz@biesanz.com

20th C., and these days wealth is more likely to impress than family status.

Having expanding substantially during the 20th C, the upper and lower middle classes also reside in the capital. The middle class tends to believe manual labor is degrading and has a strong belief in the power of education; conspicuous consumption is their badge of success, even though it may be financed by steep debts. Below the middle class is the working class, traditionally referred to as the *clase obrero* or *el pueblo*. Then come the "marginals"— many of whom are employed in illegal occupations.

One social class which has become virtually extinct is the *gamonal*, well off peasants with a traditional, non-cosmopolitan Tico lifestyle. Usually the wealthiest member of his community, the *gamonal* was highly respected by the villagers and, because they would follow his advice, he was often courted by sharp politicians. If you ask an affluent Tico about poverty in his country, you'll hear about the illiterate, barefoot peasant "who may look as if he has nothing but is very rich." He's referring, of course, to the *gamonal*.

MALE AND FEMALE RELATIONSHIPS: Despite the idealized official version of family life that originates with the Catholic Church, "free unions" are extremely common and 40-50% of all births are illegitimate. In some 20% of these the father is listed as "unknown." Today, to be a *hijo naturale* (illegitimate) is not necessarily shameful. In the upper classes, because patrimony and purity of blood lineage are viewed as being of paramount importance, chastity has been vital for women although men ha ve been free to screw around. The twin pillars of male-female relations have traditionally been *machismo* and *marianismo*. The myth of *machismo* rests on belief in the innate superiority of men in all fields of endeavor, whether in work, in politics, or in the arts and sciences. *Marianismo*, which holds women to be morally and spiritually superior, allows women to feel virtuous through their suffering at the hands of men. The supreme compliment paid to a wife and mother is to call her *abnegada*, self sacrificing.

Traditionally, marriage for women has been a cross to bear which gained her brownie points both with society and with God. It may also be quite a painful cross to bear: a March 1993 report by the Ministry of Health disclosed that some 40% of all women in relationships are physically abused by their spouses each year. Although beatings are the leading cause of injury to women after illegal abortions, only some 5% of the perpetrators are ever convicted. A conviction results in only a small fine.

In a society where men hold the privileges and dominate, females are defined in terms of their relationship with men.

FIRE (Feminist International Radio Endeavor) is available over the Internet It offers programming produced by Latin American women throughout the hemisphere. Topics include the beauty industry, human rights, the environment, and other issues. It is also broadcasts locally on Wed. at 10 AM at 780 AM.
www.fire.or.cr

Unmarried women are called *señoritas* or *muchachas buenas* (a "good girl," therefore a virgin); single, unmarried females are *mujeres* (women); loose women are *zorras*; prostitutes are *putas*; and, *señoras*, married or not, are housewives. Women in consensual unions are legally referred to as , and they have all the legal rights of wives except that they may be forced to testify against their husbands in criminal cases. Common among the poor are so-called "Queen Bee" families in which a grandmother runs the house and looks after the children while the daughters go out and work and bring home the bacon.

While many middle and upper class young women tend to have an idealized view of marriage, with some even believing their match to be predestined, their poorer cousins tend to be more pragmatic, viewing a relationship with a man as a way to weasel out of their parents' clutches. While lower class housewives still find themselves housebound, these days things are changing for upper class women. But many of these women still view themselves as extensions of their husbands' occupations; as is the case with their lower class comrades, many also have little interest in political or cultural affairs and are preoccupied almost totally with their children.

> *In the Land of God and Man: Confronting Our Sexual Culture* by Columbian-born journalist Silvana Paternostro is a great introduction to a feminist's view of Latin American male female experiences. Controversial, informative, anecdotal, entertaining, terrifying, encyclopediac, sobering, intensely personal, informative. Highly recommended.

NAMES: Descent is traced through both male and female lines Children receive both a paternal or first surname and a maternal or second surname, which is frequently abbreviated. If your father is "unknown," you have only your mother's surname.

Minority Groups

As black slaves were few in number and the Indians were mostly assimilated or dispersed, Costa Rica retains few minority groups. Blacks, Indians, and Chinese constitute only 3-5% of the population. But few though they are, these groups are of great importance, for they continue to influence the nation's future just as they have affected its past. All still suffer the sting of prejudice: many Ticos still believe white to be superior, resulting in condescending attitudes not only towards national minorities but also towards citizens of neighboring countries.

MESTIZOS Costa Ricans have often referred to a *mestizo* class. Said to compose 15% of the population by the 1950s, theis numbers had shrunk to 7% by the 1970s. It does seems unlikely they were captured by visiting alien anthropologists for transport to a research lab on a distant planet. Therefore, there is only one possible explanation for the shrinkage: "*Mestizos*" had been classified as such not on racial but on cultural grounds. As they were acculturated, they were accepted, and no longer considered to be separate.

Most *mestizos*, descendants of unions between Spanish and Chorotega Native Americans, today reside in Guanacaste Province and are also known as Guanacasteans. They retain some Indian customs, and they have a distinct dialect.

JAMAICANS: Although the first African-Americans came to Costa Rica as early as 1825 to farm and hunt turtles, most are the descendants of Jamaicans who were brought in to help build the railroad. After its construction, they stayed on to work as railway men, longshoremen, and as banana plantation workers. The newcomers had no desire to assimilate, nor did they have much in common with the Hispanic-Americans. Although they have retained their Jamaican patois and their Anglican religious affiliation, the younger generation can speak fluent Spanish.

During the '30s, the depression, banana disease and falling demand put the Caribbean coast plantations out of business. United Fruit's 1934 contract with the government for the Pacific coast growing plantations prohibited "colored people" from being employed. Many emigrated to the Canal Zone or the US, and the majority of the remainder became full-time farmers. A 1948 decree, sponsored by consummate patriarchal politician Figueres, awarded them citizenship. Discrimination and prejudice against them, however, remain strong and have prevented their full assimilation. Today, there are about 30,000 Costa Ricans of Jamaican descent who are noted not only for their domination of basketball and soccer teams but also, increasingly, for their social and political contributions to the society. Many of them have left farming to enter the professions.

INDIGENOUS PEOPLES: Of the estimated 300,000 Indians in Costa Rica, 65-75% live in Talamanca, the mountainous area to the nation's S where they were either brought or ran for shelter. Although actually quite similar, the Bribri and the Cabecare, who inhabit this area, view themselves as culturally distinct. Widely scattered on both the Caribbean and Pacific sides of the range, the Native Americans settled on the Pacific slope tend to be more acculturated. The Chorotegas of Guanacaste have been almost totally assimilated, as have the Huetares who reside on the Pacific slope of the Meseta Central and the Malekus who live near the San Carlos region close to the Nicaraguan border.

Living in three villages in the SW, the 1,500-2,000 Boruca are the only other remaining Native American tribe of note. Although they are almost totally assimilated, they retain community ownership of the land and some still practice traditional weaving. A 1939 governmental declaration granted the Indians certain lands, and the Council for the Protection of the Native Races was established in 1945. But Indians have lost much of their land through deception or violence. During the 1960s, a congressional investigation revealed that most of them live in extreme proverty and many have succumbed to demon alcohol.

In 1976 President Oduber declared a state of emergency within the Indian areas and established five zones in which non-Indians were prohibited from renting or buying land. Today, although these laws remain on the books, they are unenforced, and the state of the nation's indigenous peoples remains unchanged. Most have made the transition from tribal to peasant culture, and only an estimated 5-6,000 still preserve their culture, including their language. Hunting has been replaced by husbandry, and the Cabaceres, for example, raise pigs for sale. The indigenous cultures appear destined for gradual but inevitable extinction through acculturation and assimilation.

In 1990 Guayami tribespeople came to San José to protest their inablility to secure *cedulas* (identification cards). Many of them emigrated from Panama 50 years ago. The process is now underway to pass a law granting them cards; these cards are of vital importance, as without a you cannot vote, borrow money, or use the benefits of the government health system.

One encouraging development has been the institution of a Council for Indigenous Rights which has been set up under the office of Ombudsman Rodrigo Carazo. The council will attend to complaints concerning the violation of laws by the nation's officials and bureaucrats.

THE CHINESE: Once a separate, socially segregated community, the nation's Chinese (*polequeandos*) are beoming more and more acculturated. While the oldsters still speak Chinese and believe in the old ways, the Spanish-speaking young are intermarrying and converting to Roman Catholicism. Traditionally, Chinese have either stayed out of politics or supported the most conservative candidate. As is true elsewhere in the world, the small, closely-knit Chinese communities exercise considerable economic control relative to their numbers, and this gives rise to resentment on occasion. The Chinese emigrated to Costa Rica from 1873 to work on the railway or as farm laborers. They were harshly exploited. Never confined to the Caribbean lowlands, they soon spread and established shops, inns, and restaurants.

OTHER GROUPS: Sephardic Jews have been in Costa Rica since the beginning of colonization and have been fully assimilated. Before and after WWII, a small number of Polish Jews arrived. Because they earned their living by selling door to door, they were dubbed *polequeandos*. There are also many Panamanian, Nicaraguan, Honduran, and Chilean refugees. Although they are the butt of a considerable amount of resentment and prejudice, the estimated 200,000 Nicaraguan refugees provide badly needed cheap labor, especially in the coffee fields. Because the vast majority lack legal status, they are readily exploited — performing low-paying, low-prestige, and backbreaking work shunned by Ticos. Resident Americans include multinational corporate employees and pensioners. There're also a small but valiant band of Quakers who have set up a cheese factory near Monteverde in Puntarenas Province and a colony of Italians in the town of San Vito in the S.

Festivals and Events

Official Holidays

Jan. 1	New Year's Day
March	Festival in Puntarenas
March 19	St. Joseph
April	Easter (three days or more)
April 11	Anniversary of the Battle of Rivas
May 1	Labor Day
June 29	Day of St. Peter and St. Paul
July 25	Anniversary of the Annexation of Guanacaste Province
Aug. 2	Virgin of Los Angeles
Aug. 15	Mother's Day
Sept. 15	Independence Day
Oct. 12	*Día de las Culturas*
Dec. 8	Conception of the Virgin
Dec. 25	Christmas Day

On each of the 17 official holidays (feriados), most government and professional offices, some banks, and many stores are closed. During Easter and Christmas weeks, the entire country shuts down almost completely.

January

Fiesta Patronales de Alajuelita: Held in honor of the Black Christ of Esquipulas, this festival features a colorful oxcart parade, a pilgrimage to the large iron cross overlooking the town, and plentiful consumption of *chinchivi*, a homemade corn beer.

Fiestas de Santa Cruz: Also held in honor of the Black Christ of Esquipulas, this celebration, held in Guanacaste's cultural capital, includes folk dancing, bullfights, and marimba music.

Copa del Café: This week-long tennis tournament draws an international collection of talented players, all less than 18 years of age.

February

San Isidro de General: This town's *fiestas civicas* are held from the end of Jan. to the beginning of Feb. Activities include a cattle show, agricultural and industrial fair, bullfights, and an orchid exhibition.

Fiesta de los Diablos: The sole remaining native American festival, this takes place in the village of Rey Curre in SW Talamancas. In an allegorical recreation of the struggle between the Diablitos (the local Borucas) and a bull (representing the Spaniards), masked Diablitos pursue the bull, which is made of burlap topped with a carved wooden head. Local crafts, corn liquor (*chicha*), and *tamales* are for sale.

March

Carrera de la Paz: In this footrace, about a thousand people run from San José's National Gymnasium to the campus of the University for Peace in Villa Colón.

National Orchid Show: Featuring 500-plus species, this weekend-long festival takes place in the Colegio de Medicos y Cirujanos headquarters in Sabana Sur.

National Oxcart Day: Taking place on the second Sunday in March, this celebrates the *boyero* (oxcart driver) and the *carreta* (the wooden-wheeled painted cart); the locus for the celebration is in San Antonio de Escazú near San José.

Farmer's Day: Held March 15, this nationwide celebration is headquartered in Tierra Blanca near Poás (whose farmers celebrate deliverance from a plague of locusts in 1877). It is the day devoted to the farmer's patron saint, San Isidro, a humble 12th C. Spanish farmer.

Ujarras Pilgrimage: Held mid-month, this Orosi Valley procession from Paraiso to the ruined church in Ujarras commemorates the rescue from floods of Ujarras by the Virgin. Her graven image returns with the crowd for the occasion.

Bonanza Cattle Show: The nation's cattlemen assemble at the Bonanza Fairgrounds, on the airport highway in San José, for this event. Featured are prize bulls, bullfights, rodeos, horseraces, and mechanical bulls.

San José Day: On this day (Mar. 19), local families traditionally visit Volcan Poás for a hike and picnic.

Crafts Fair: Taking place on the Plaza de la Cultura in San José, 150-200 local artisans exhibit their wares.

Feria Nacional del Agua: This "National Water Festival," a one-week event, takes place at the Parque de la Paz in San José and chiefly features concerts by groups such as Adrián Goizueta and Pura Vida, puppet shows, and mariachi.

International Festival of Arts: One of the best festivals of its kind in the Americas, this festival draws together groups from Costa Rica, Nicaragua, Panama, Cuba, Russia, the US, Ecuador, Chile, and other nations for about 11 days. Inexpensive tickets are sold to events at the Teatro Nacional and other venues, and free performances are held nightly at the Plaza de la Cultura as well as in Moravia and elsewhere around the nation.

April

Día de Juan Santamaría: Held in Alajeula, this day's events—a parade with marching bands and majorettes—commemorate Juan Santamaría, Costa Rica's only national hero and the town's pride and joy.

Earth Day: In San Jose's Plaza de la Democracía, an annual three-day Festival of Native American handicrafts is followed by the celebration of Earth Day.

Semana Santa: Much of the country shuts down during Easter Holy Week from Wed. noon through Sun. The observances begin on Palm Sunday when a small procession bearing the "Lord of the Triumph" wends its way through town via streets festooned with flowers and palm fronds in symbolism of Jesus' march into Jerusalem. Thurs. night devotees pray and chant in church until dawn.

PROCESSIONS: The week's highlight is a series of processions, the most famous of which are held in Cartago, Santo Domingo de Heredia, San Antonio de Escazú, San José, San Isidro de Heredia, and in San Joaquín de Flores—where all the procession's characters are people instead of sculpted images. The **Procession of Silence** takes place at around 8 PM Thurs. night. The **Encuentro procession** takes place at mid-morning on Good Friday, and the Procession of the Holy Burial (in which Christ is slowly marched to the cross accompanied by a grieving Mary, the Apostles, and a band of mourners clad in black) occurs later on between 4 and 5.

Holy Saturday ("Judas Day") is marked by firecrackers and, in some villages, an effigy of Judas is hung to the accompaniment of speeches and petitions. Featuring shepherds and pint-sized angels, the joyous procession of the Resurrection takes place mid-morning on Sunday. If you have a car, you can catch the beginning of a procession in one town and then move on to another town and catch its finale. Procession schedules are available at each Casa Cural.

May

May Day: On the first, workers march and the president gives the annual "State of the Nation Address." The Limón area celebrates with cricket matches, picnics, quadrille dances, and domino matches.

University Week: Taking place around the beginning of the month, University of Costa Rica students crown a queen, and participate in sports events and a parade. Many local bands also perform on campus.

Día del Boyero: May 15 is traditionally the start of the rainy season, and San Isidro Labrador is honored on this day, the "Day of the Oxcart Driver." The celebration takes place in all of the San Isidros and in San Antonio de Escazú near San José. Activities include parades featuring brighly colored oxcarts, the blessing of animals (extending right down to Puss and Fido) and crops by the local priest. The oxen, in turn, show their religious piety by carrying paper money to the church on their horns.

Carrera de San Juan: Taking place on San Juan Day, May 17, around 1,500 run the 22.5 km from El Alto de Ochomongo (near Cartago) to San Juan de Tibás, N of San José.

June

St. Peter/St. Paul: The *fiesta patronales* of these two saints is commemorated in towns of the same name nationwide on the 29th.

July/August

Mango Festival: The highlight of Alajuela's year, this celebration offers nine days of parades, music, outdoor food markets, and arts and crafts fairs.

Puntarenas Carnival: Beginning on the Sat. nearest July 16 in this port town, the Fiesta of the Virgin of the Sea is celebrated with a regatta featuring beautifully decorated fishing boats and yachts. The carnival which follows has parades, concerts, dances, sports events, fireworks, and the crowning of the queen. Similar events take place in Nicoya's Playas del Coco.

Annexation of Guanacaste: Held every July 25, the Anniversary of the Annexation of Guanacaste Province commemorates the province's secession from Nicaragua. Fiestas in Liberia and in Santa Cruz feature folk dancing, marimba bands, horse parades, bullfights, rodeos, cattle shows, and local culinary specialties.

The Virgin of Los Angeles: This festival is Cartago's largest. Every August 1, thousands assemble around Av. Central near Plaza de la Cultura and march towards Cartago. In contrast with the awe that one might expect during such a momentous religious event, the atmosphere is lively, and the devotees display an intimate, convivial relationship with the *I* continue the celebrations on into the month.

Día de San Ramón: In this colorful tradition, nearly 30 saints from a neighboring town are taken on Aug. 31 for a visit to San Ramón, who resides in the town named after him. His image is taken for a spin around town with the others. The celebration continues as the saint's guests reside in the church for over a week.

Semana Afro-Costarricense: Celebrating International Black People's Day and taking place in San José, this cultural week's highlights are lectures, panel discussions, and displays.

International Music Festival: Held in late July or Aug., this two-week music festival is held at luxury hotels throughout the country. Venues include such locations as Villa Caletas, Hotel Capitan Suizo, and Hotel Chalet Tirol. Sadly, this "international" festival is global only in terms of its performers: the music is strictly classical!

September

Festival Marino: This Guanacaste affair, held in Playa Hermosa, features sandcastle making, water ski and jet ski contests.

Día Independencia: Held on Sept. 15, the nation's Independence Day (a date shared by all of Central America) is celebrated with country-wide parades featuring uniformed schoolkids, majorettes, bands, and the like. At 6 PM the Freedom Torch, relayed by a chain of student runners stretching all the way from Guatemala, arrives in San José, and Ticos join in singing the national anthem. That evening schoolchildren march in (lantern) parades, carrying hand-made lanterns along the route.

October

Limón Carnival: Commemorating the natiion's cultural diversity, the former Columbus Day (Oct. 12) is now known as the *Carnaval*, and this port city's annual festival is the nation's most famous. Incorporating the Caribbean Coast's African-American traditions, it's a miniature version of similar festivals found in Río or Trinidad. There are floats and dance groups.

Fiesta de Maíz: Honoring corn, this festival is held in Upala in the uppermost portion of Alajuela Province. Corn Queen contestants don costumes made entirely of corn husks, grains, and silk.

Costa Rica Yacht Club Regatta: Held annually in October and November, this is international regatta is open to sailboats 20 ft. (6 m) and over.

National Artisans' Fair: Held at the FERCORI Exposition Center (C. 23, Av. 1) it is run by the National Artisan's Commission. You may view a wonderful variety of handmade crafts.

November

All Souls Day: Observed nationwide on Nov. 2, special church ceremonies are held and families visit cemeteries to pay homage to the deceased.

Día de Muertos (Day of the Dead): Sponsored by the Mexican Cultural Center (☎ 283-2333), this celebration has a special Mexican flavor. Events are held at the center which is 250 m S of the Subaru in Los Yoses.

International Dog Show: Sponsored by the Asociación Canófila Costarricense, this show features a splendid assortment of dogs.

Coffee Picking Tournament: Held during coffee picking season in the Meseta Central (Nov.-Dec.), *campesinos* compete to pick berries with maximum speed. This televised event includes typical songs, legends, and poems.

International Theater Festival: Held in San José, a variety of theater groups perform plays, puppet shows, and street theater.

December

Fiesta de los Negritos: With wildly costumed dancers in blackface, this festival is on Dec. 8 in the village of Boruca. It is held in honor of its patron saint, the Virgin of the Immaculate Conception, and participants dance to flute and drum accompaniment in time to the , a frame with a horse's head.

Día de la Pólvora: Honoring the Virgin of the Immaculate Conception on Dec. 8, this nationwide festival includes fireworks, the best of which take place in Jesús Maria de San Mateo (Alajuela Province) and in La Rivera de Belén (Heredia).

Fiesta de la Yeguita: Held in Nicoya in Guanacaste on Dec. 12, solemn-faced villagers carry the image of the Virgin of Guadalupe through the streets. To the accompaniment of flute and drums, two dancers, one of whom carries a doll, pass through La Yeguita, "the little mare," a hoop with a horse's face. Other festivities include bullfights, fireworks, band concerts, and traditional foods made from corn.

Vuelta Ciclista: An international cycling tournament which starts in mid-Dec. and lasts until the New Year. Contestants cycle across the country.

Christmas celebrations: Beginning Dec. 15, in a traditional practice known as *los posadas*, children go from house to house asking for a place to stay—just as Mary and Joseph supposedly did in Bethlehem thousands of years ago. Accompanied by musiciansand carolers, they are given refreshments at each house and are treated to songs in exchange. Confetti battles take place along Av. Central on Christmas eve. Creches of the nativity scene are very popular and a competition is held in San José. Before they are taken down on Candelaria in Feb., families gather to pray, sing, drink corn liquor and eat traditional sweets.
Year's End Fiestas: Most events take place in and around San José. These begin during the last week of Dec. and extend through the beginning of January. Bullfights are held at the Zapote ring daily; the, a procession of horses, departs from Paseo Colón, proceeds along Av. Central and ends at Plaza Viquez. Finally, a dance in Parque Central welcomes the New Year. While the Christmas season is a time of partying and all the bars stay open, people turn solemn at New Year's Eve. Some Ticos believe that if God sees them in church on the first day of the year, he'll make allowances if they are absent during the remainder.

Easter shrine near Turriaba shows the intimate connection between Costa Ricans and the Catholic religion..

Religion

As in every other Latin American nation, the Roman Catholic Church reigns supreme here. Although 95% of Costarricenses claim to be practicing Roman Catholics, and most of these attend church, the strength of religious belief and practice varies widely. With the ratio of one priest for every 4,000 Costa Ricans, there are more clergy per capita than in any other Central American nation and Costa Rica is touted as the most staunchly Catholic country in the isthmus.

Surprisingly, the government has frequently shown itself to be anticlerical. This attitude, combined with 19th C. liberal values, culminated in the Liberal Laws, which permitted divorce, ended religious instruction in public schools, secularized cemeteries, and drove a firm wedge between Church and State. These laws were repealed in the 1940s by President Rafael Angel Calderón Garcia, a staunch Catholic, who re-introduced religion to the public schools.

Today, Catholicism remains the state religion, and the only church marriages that have civil validity are those performed by Roman Catholic Priests. Although the official Church teaching is that God is all powerful and the saints are only intercessors on behalf of the petitioner, in practice Ticos act as if the saints are all powerful and have the ability directly to grant their requests.

Undoubtedly a reaction to the popularity of evangelical Protestantism, a new movement has emerged in recent years. Known as Catholic Pentacostalism or Spiritual Renovation, this intensified Catholicism involves speaking in tongues, uttering prophesies, and other such activities. Although the Church leadership initially looked askance at such practices, they are now accepted. Another innovation is the *Cursillos de Cristianidad*, three-day intensive study courses which have attracted tens of thousands of participants over the past 25 years.

PROTESTANTISM: When the Central American Mission arrived in 1891, they encountered vehement hostility. They were stoned and beaten and the Catholic Church attacked them. The missionaries responded to these attacks by calling the Church "utterly debased and idolatrous." Although the government refused to expel them, in 1901 it forbade them to preach in public, advertise their meetings, or establish schools. Despite this, the Protestants perservered, and other sects arrived.

When Billy Graham arrived in 1958, the Catholic Church not only suppressed any announcement but blacked out all media coverage — including a service attended by 8,000. Similarly, the Church was able to block a 1961 parade of various sects commemorating the 70th anniversary of Catholicism. Today, it is common to see the declaration *"Somos Catolicos"* posted by the door — not as an affirmation of faith but to deter annoying door-to-door religious peddlers.Over the decades, however, the prejudice has abated.

Ironically, as Catholic-Protestant relations have improved, the sects have grown apart from each other. Today, there are an estimated 40,000 Protestants. With Costa Rica the headquarters for the Latin American missionary movement, there are a many bible colleges and publishing houses. Evangelical Protestant sects include Methodists, Baptists, and Pentecostals. They make up a growing percentage of the population. Most Anglicans are Jamaican emigrants and their descendants. Small sects include Jews and Indian religions.

Food

No one would ever accuse Costa Rica of having great cuisine overall. With the exception of a few gourmet restaurants, this is not a place to visit for its food. All too frequently overcooked and greasy fried foods dominate in small local restaurants. It is a simple and unvarying fare, the product of a nation of farmers struggling to eke out a living on small plots. Despite the spicy reputation of Latin food, Tico chefs appear unfamiliar with the use of spices. During your stay, however, you will find that Tico cuisine has its own charms and, back at home, you may find yourself pining for a breakfast of *gallo pinto*.

TYPICAL FARE: *Campesino* food has historical roots. The maize and beans grown by the Native Americans, have become staples which along, with rice, have become the principal source of protein in the average Tico's diet. The standard diet consists of ***tortillas*** (thin corn pancakes), rice, beans, salad, and bread. ***Agua dulce*** (water sweetened with raw sugarcane) is the national beverage.

In a typical restaurant, there's one surefire bet: the ***casado***. A plate of rice served with salad, beans, and meat, chicken, or fish, this dish—as ubiquitous as the hamburger in the US—will probably be your staple meal. ***Arroz con pollo***, one of the most popular local dishes, is chicken with rice and vegetables.

OTHER DISHES: Traditional dishes include ***olla de carne*** (a beef stew including local vegetables like *yuca, ñanpi,* ***chayote***, potato and plantain), ***mondongo en salsa*** (ox in tomato sauce), ***chilasquiles*** (meat stuffed *tortillas*), A ***sopa negra*** is made with black beans and sometimes includes a poached egg. Other soups include ***pozol*** (corn soup) and ***guiso de máiz***, fresh corn stew.

***DESAYUNOS*:** "Breakfast" appears on

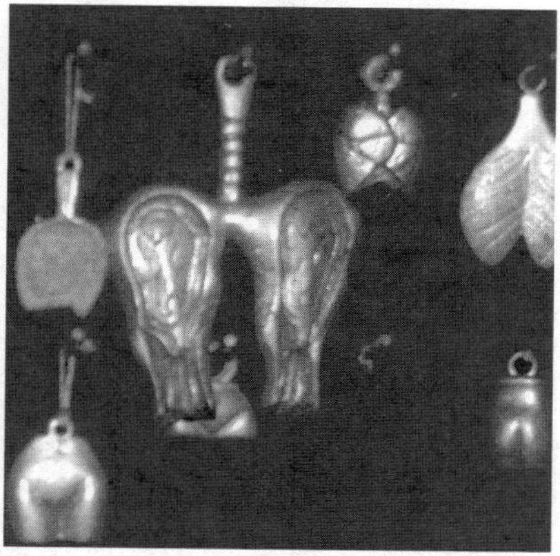

Costa Rica's most famous religious shrine is the Cartago Cathedral where supplicants arrive to pray to the Virgin (left) for cures and leave silver offerings (right) after their prayers are met.

Costa Rican Food: A to Z

Agua dulce — water sweetened with raw sugarcane.
Almuerzo ejecutivo — a specially priced "executive" lunch.
Arreglados — sandwiches which contain meat and vegetables.
Arroz con camarones — fried rice with shrimp.
Arroz con pollo — chicken with rice and vegetables.
Café con leche — coffee with milk.
Café negro — black coffee.
Cajeta — a traditional fudge-like treat.
Camarones — very small shrimp.
Carne — beef.
Casado — a plate of rice served with salad, beans, and meat, chicken, or fish.
Ceviche — a chilled fish cocktail made using corvina (sea bass) pickled in lemon juice and mixed with cilantro and onion.
Chilasquiles—meat stuffed tortillas.
Chorreados—corn pancakes which are often sold by street vendors in San José.
Corvina—Sea bass.
Desayunos—breakfast.
Elote asado—roasted corn on the cob.
Elote cocinado—boiled corn.
Empanadas—corn turnovers filled with cheese, beans, or meat and potatoes.
En escabeche—foods that have been pickled Spanish-style.
Enyucados—empanadas made with yucca.
Flan—a sweet custard.
Gallo pinto—rice and beans fried together, the staple breakfast food.
Gallos—tortillas filled with cheese, beans, meat, etc.
Guaro—a firewater popular among *campesinos*.
Guiso de máiz—fresh corn stew.
Langostinos—prawns.
Langosta—lobster.
Masamorra—corn pudding.
Melcochas—candies made from raw sugar.
Mondongo en salsa—ox in tomato sauce.
Natilla—Costa Rican sour cream.
Olla de carne—a beef stew.
Pan de maíz—a thick and sweet cornbread.
Pañuelos—a type of pastry.
Papas francesas—french fries.
Patacones—mashed and fried plantains which are served like french<R>—fries.
Patí—snacks made of empanadas filled with fruit or spicy meat.
Pescado ahumado—smoked fish made from marlin.
Plátanos—plantains, large banana-like grains which must be fried or baked. They are often sliced and fried like potato chips.
Pozol—corn soup.
Pupusas—two tortillas fried with cheese inside.
Queque seco—pound cake.
Refrescos — tropical fruit shakes made with milk or water.

Sodas — small alcohol-free restaurants.	
Sopa negra — black bean soup which sometimes includes a poached egg.	
Tamal asado — a sweet cornbread cake.	
Tamales — ground corn and pork wrapped in plantain leaves; traditionally served at Christmas.	
Torta chilena—a multi-layered cake filled with *dulce de leche.*	
Tortas — a type of bread filled with meat and vegetables.	
Tortilla — refers either to an omelette or a small thin *tortilla* (thin corn pancake).	
Tortilla de queso — a with *tortilla* cheese mixed in the dough.	
Vigorones — a combo of cabbage, cassava, tomato, and — onion topped withpork rinds.	

the menu throughout the day. ***Gallo pinto*** ("spotted rooster"), rice and beans fried together, is the staple breakfast food which varies little from place to place except in price. It comes *con* (with) (eggs) , *jamon* (ham), etc.

SEAFOOD: ***Ceviche*** is a chilled fish cocktail made using *corvina* (sea bass) pickled in lemon juice and mixed with cilantro and onion. It's a meal in itself. ***Pescado ahumado*** is smoked fish made from marlin, which resembles salmon. ***Camarones***, usually very small shrimp, are served with fried rice. ***Langostinos*** (prawns) and ***langosta*** (lobster) are available but expensive. Fish dishes served ***en escabeche*** have been pickled Spanish-style. Canned locally, Costa Rican tuna may or may not be tainted with dolphin blood.

Other Food

JAMAICAN CUISINE: It is largely confined to the Caribbean coast, and little has survived the voyage across. The most common dish you'll find is rice and beans cooked with coconut milk and spices, a version infinitely more appetizing than the Tico rice and beans.

Patacones are mashed and fried plantains which are served like french fries, and patí are snacks made of empanadas filled with fruit or spicy meat. Two other specialties to watch out for are ***johnny cakes*** (originally "journey") and ***pan bon*** (from the English word "bun"), a sweet and dark bread with designs etched in the batter on top. In some *sodas*, you'll also find ***agua de sapo***; this "toad water" is iced lemon and raw brown sugar. If you're fortunate you may be able to find delicacies such as fritters, fry-bread, roasted breadfruit, ackee, and herbal teas.

CHINESE FOOD: You know you're really in a small town when there is no Chinese restaurant! The quality varies from gourmet to grease galore. You may want to ask them to leave out the *ajinomoto* (monosodium glutamate, MSG), a Japanese flavoring derived from soy sauce that, along with cornstarch, ruins the quality and flavor of traditional Chinese cuisine. Curiously, Chinese food is generally accompanied by twin slices of styrofoam-like bread. Some of the most common Chinese dishes have become an integral part of the Costa Rican diet. One example is **arroz con camarones** (fried rice with shrimp) which may be accompanied by greasy (french fries).

ON THE QUICK: Fast food franchises, whose prices and "cuisine" replicate the US originals along with the US prices (although their workers are paid a pittance by comparison) include McDonald's, Pizza Hut, Burger King, and Colonel

Sanders. And, regrettably, a Denny's may be opening in the Hotel Irazú.

One dish you can order quickly and conveniently is **pizza** which is best ordered in an Italian restaurant, not at vile Pizza Hut. Terms you should be familiar with when ordering pizza include *hongo* (mushroom), *aceituna* (olives), and *cebolla* (onion).

SNACKS: ***Tamales*** are ground corn and pork wrapped in plantain leaves; they are traditionally served at Christmas.

A ***tortilla de queso*** has cheese mixed in the dough. The term tortilla can refer either to an omelette or to the thin corn pancake which is a common Latin American dietary staple.

Pupusas are two *tortillas* fried with cheese inside. Gallos are tortillas filled with cheese, beans, meat, etc.

Arreglados are sandwiches which contain meat and vegetables, and ***tortas*** are a type of bread filled with meat and vegetables.

Invented in Nicaragua, ***vigorones*** are a combination of cabbage, cassava, tomato, and onion topped with pork rinds.

Empanadas are corn turnovers filled with cheese, beans, or meat and potatoes, and ***enyucados*** are *empanadas* made with yucca.

Masamorra is corn pudding, ***pan de maíz***, is a thick and sweet cornbread, and ***chorreados*** are corn pancakes which are often sold by street vendors in San José.

While ***elote asado*** is roasted corn on the cob, ***elote cocinado*** is the boiled variety.

Plátanos (plantains) are large banana-like grains which must be fried or baked. They are often sliced and fried like potato chips.

Huevos de tortuga are sea turtle eggs, which are thought to have aphrodisiacal properties and can be found in bars. As with the sea turtle meat served in restaurants, eating this food supports further killing of an endangered species.

DESSERTS AND TOPPINGS: The best ice cream is served at the Pops chain. Competitors are Mönpik and Baloons.

Capuchino is a cone dipped in chocolate. ***Cajeta*** is a traditional fudge-like treat.

Made with coconut, tapa dulce, and orange peel, ***cajeta de coco***, is a delicious variety.

Tres leches is a cake with filling and frosting.

Flan is a sweet custard.

Pañuelos (lit. handkerchiefs) are a type of pastry.

Melcochas are candies made from raw sugar.

A ***torta chilena*** is a multi-layered cake filled with dulce de leche, and a pound cake is called **queque seco.**

Tamal asado is a sweet cornbread cake.

Tapitas and ***milanes*** are foil-wrapped chocolates.

Popcorn is known as ***palomitas de maíz*** or "little corn doves."

Tapa dulce is strong-tasting unrefined sugar which is sold in brown hunks.

Dulce de leche is a thick syrup made with milk and sugar.

Natilla, cream left out overnight, is a popular topping on many dishes.

A common dessert, fruit salad (***ensalada de fruitas***) often comes with jello and whipped cream.

FRUITS: ***Papaya*** is available much of the year. The two varieties are the rounder, yellow-orange ***amarilla*** and the elongated red-orange ***cacho***.

Watermelon (***sandia***) are also plentiful in season. Don't mistake them for the chiverre, a gourd which is candied during Easter.

Fruit stands are a definite delight. This one is along a road in the nation's far north.

You'll find the pineapple (***piña***) to be sweeter than those you know from home. Avoid eating the core which is packed with papain, an enzyme used in making meat tenderizers. (For similar reasons, avoid eating green papayas).

Originally introduced from Asia, citrus fruits include grapefruit (***toronja***), four types of lemons (***lemones***), mandarins (***mandarinas***), and oranges (***naranjas***).

Mangoes come in several different varieties and are excellent.

Guayabas (guavas) have a pink, very seedy pulp commonly used in jam or paste.

Cas is a similar but smaller and rounder sour-tasting, green or yellow fruit, which is used in drinks and ices.

Resembling an extraterrestrial beverage, ***chan***, a relative of mint, contains furry purple seeds which taste like gelatin as they go down.

Another fruit that is commonly served only in beverage form, ***maracúya*** is an acid sweet fruit which makes an exotic drink. Introduced from Brazil, its taste but not its appearance resembles passion fruit.

Resembling a cross between a prune and a fig when dried, ***marañón*** is the fruit of the cashew nut.

Brown and similar to avocadoes but with bright orange sweet pulp, ***zapotes*** are another exotic fruit.

An unusual delicacy is ***palmito***, the tender and delicous heart of the pejibaye palm, which may be boiled or eaten raw. The fruit of the ***pejibaye*** (pay-hee-BAY-

> If you wish to cut down or quit, Costa Rica is an excellent place: single cigarettes are priced at about five cents each and are commonly sold on the street or in small shops..

yay) palm is treated as a delicacy; it was once a major source of protein for the Indians. Fibrous in texture, these bright orange fruits are usually boiled in salted water, peeled, halved, and eaten. The fruit is celebrated in an annual festival held in the village of Tucurrique near Cartago.

Other fruits include ***granadillas*** (passion fruit), ***mamones*** (lychees), ***mamón china*** (rambutan), ***carambola*** (starfruit), ***aguacate*** (avocado), ***melocoton*** (peach), and níspero.

TOBACCO: Nicotine junkies can choose their poison from well over half a dozen local brands. Males smoke like chimneys as do many *joven, señoras, y señoritas*, or at least those who can afford it.

Drinks and Beverages

FRUIT DRINKS: ***Refrescos*** are tropical fruit shakes made with milk or water. These drinks are made from *tamarindo* (the seed pod of the tamarind tree), *mora* (blackberries), *cas*, and other fruits.

Some of the most popular items are ***pipas***, green or gold drinking coconuts. The vendor opens these with a machete. He hacks off a piece from the edge which, after you're finished eating, serves to scoop out the soft white creamy jelly inside. If you want more water than jelly or lots of jelly, just tell the vendor, and he'll hand pick for you.

ALCOHOL: Drinking is a very popular activity, and establishments selling liquor outnumber schools almost three to one. Excellent, locally brewed **beers** are available in 350 ml bottles in supermarkets, restaurants, *cantinas*, and bars. The brands are the ultra-popular Imperial, the locally brewed Heineken, Bavaria and Bavaria Light, the recently-introduced Bremen (try the extra-strong 5.0 version) and Pilsen; another brew, Tropical, is a type of ale. All are produced by the same brewery.

Cerveza cruda (draft beer) is also available in some local bars. Local bars sell beers for around US$.50-70 and you are expected to drink it there unless you ask for a cup. Stores sell beers in two varieties of bottles, nonreturnable and returnable—so identified in raised letters on the glass. While in the supermarkets, you have to get a receipt written out if you want to return them, shopowners generally just rely upon appearance (i.e., if it has a price tag it's not ours!)

Costa Rica also produces a few inexpensive varieties of **rum** as well as sugarcane-distilled ***guaro***, a firewater which is the hands-down popular favorite among . Often drinks are accompanied by ***bocas***, small dishes of fried fish, *ceviche*, or other snacks. Sometimes you have to pay extra for these; other times they are included in the price.

CAFÉ: Aside from alcohol, the most popular drink in Costa Rica must be coffee — the nation's only other legal drug. It is served either as ***café negro*** or ***café con leche*** (coffee with milk) and is customarily combined with generous quantities of sugar.

The traditional fashion of serving coffee is to deliver one small pitcher of coffee along with another of heated milk, which one mixes together according to taste. Sadly, this custom has largely fallen by the wayside. However, it is still served this way in the better restaurants and cafes.

Coffee can be had ***en taza*** or, somehow more delicious, ***en vaso*** (in a glass). It comes in two sizes: *pequeno* (small) and *grande* (large). Despite claims to the contrary, the coffee generally served in Costa Rica is not all that good, unless one compares it with watered down truckstop brew found in the States. Most of the ordinary *sodas* sell coffee made from preground powder which has been either made in a large metal percolator and left to sit, or filtered through a ***chorreador***, a cloth filter mounted on a wooden stand. A cup sells for around US$.45.

SOFT DRINKS: Colored sugared water is very much in vogue here, and imbibers will find a choice selection practically everywhere. Brands include Coke, Canada Dry Ginger Ale, Squirt, and most of the others. While there is no mineral water, you can ask for soda blanca. Although soft drinks come in 500 ml plastic disposables, you might wish to set an example for the locals and send a message to the multinationals by sticking to glass. Milk costs about US$.50 per liter, and long life milk is also available at a higher price. Both are 2% fat.

Dining Practicalities

TAXES AND TIPS: One thing very confusing for foreign visitors is the system of taxes and tipping. At the better quality restaurants, a 10% service charge is levied on all meals , and a 13% sales tax is added on top of this. At the cheaper restaurants, the 13% tax is incorporated in the cost of the meal. The least expensive places, such as *sodas*, incorporate taxes and service in their prices. Costa Ricans almost never leave an additional tip; you can do so if you feel the service made it worthwhile.

DINING OUT: Most of the nation's finest restaurants—representing cuisines ranging from Swiss to Chinese to Italian—are found in the San José area. While shrimp and lobster are available, they are not cheap. Usual hours for gourmet dining are 11:30-2:30 for lunch, and from 6 or 6:30 to 10 or 10:30 for dinner.

While some restaurants are open only for dinner, the ones open for lunch usually feature an *almuerzo ejecutivo*, a specially priced "executive" lunch. To find gourmet restaurants check the pages of this guide, the yellow pages, or the restaurant reviews in the *Tico Times*. Out in the country, high quality restaurants are fewer and are generally connected to a hotel.

BUDGET DINING: You'll find no lack of of places to eat. There are a small number of local restaurants in every town. Alcohol free *sodas*, which serve everything from *casados* to hamburgers to sandwiches, are your best bet. In a typical *soda*, the menu (which usually includes a *plato del día*, special of the day) is written on a blackboard or painted on a wall. A glass cabinet on the counter contains baked goods and other snacks. Expect to spend about US$2-7 per meal. Restaurants offering counter service are generally less expensive.

It's always best to ask the price of food before consuming. Although Ticos are not price gougers like the Mexicans, there *are* some unscrupulous people who don't hesitate to jack up the price when the opportunity beckons.

TIPS FOR VEGETARIANS: This is most definitely a carnivorous society so the more you are able to bend or compromise your principles, the easier time you'll have. If you're a vegan (non dairy product user), unless you're cooking all of your own food, you will find it even more difficult, but the quantity and variety of fruits readily available may be your salvation. Locally grown fruits such as papayas and mangoes tend to be much more reasonable when purchased from vendors, and prices go down at the end of the day.

Fruit salads are often drowning in gelatin (an animal product) and ice cream. Ask to have it *sin helados* and *sin gelatina*. If you do eat fish, you should be aware that locals eat it fried and that it may have been fried in lard or in the same oil as chicken or pork. At the very least, it will have been fried in *manteca*, a type of shortening made from hydrogenated palm oil.

Be aware that the word *carne* refers only to beef; a dish may still have pork, chicken, or fish in it. If you are in a rush a cheese sandwich (*sandwich de queso*) will serve you well. If you eat a lot of nuts, plan on bringing your own because those available locally are expensive. The same goes for dried fruits such as raisins. Finally, semi-vegetarians should bear in mind that — outside of tourist restaurants — fish may be in short supply at times. Places serving vegetarian food are highlighted throughout the text.

Sports and Recreation

Water Sports

BEACHES AND SWIMMING: Aside from the innumerable beaches and rivers, most major hotels and "aparthotels" have their own pools; olympic size ones are found at the Cariari Country Club and in Parque de Sabana where swim meets are held on occasion.

Located S of the international airport, the pools fed by Ojo de Agua springs are cold and fresh.

Ironically sponsored by unhealthy McDonald's, the International Swimming Tournament is held at the outdoor club in the E part of San José every July or August.

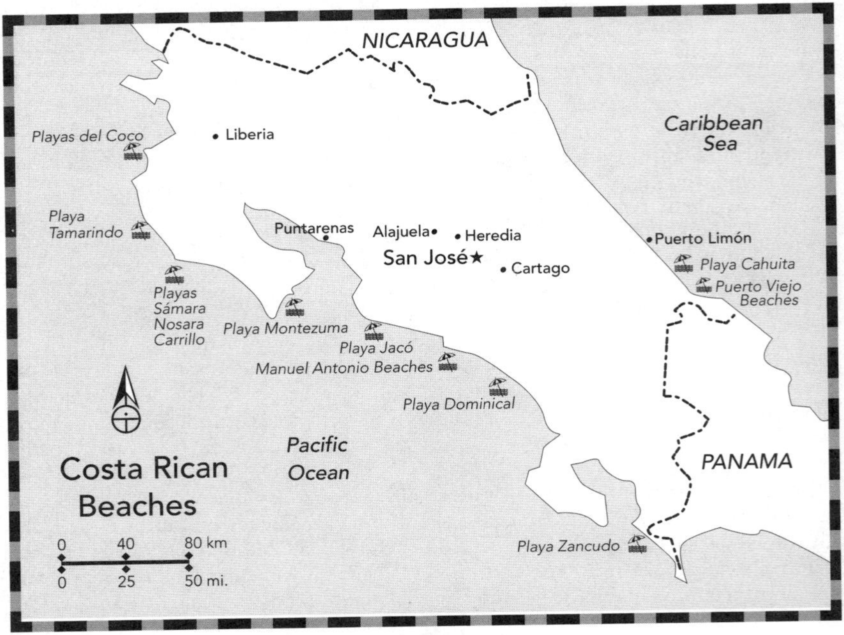

BEACHES TO AVOID: According to the National Water and Sewage Service, currently contaminated beaches are Playa Taracoles, Playa Azul, Playa Guacalillo, Playa Quepos, Playa Limon, and Playa Limoncito. Beaches that have a "blue flag" are safe for swimming. Some 30 beaches have been so certified since the government began the program in 1997.

SCUBA AND SNORKELING: Although the former is still an emerging sport here, Costa Rica is an exceedingly fine place to do either. The Caribbean coast's only coral reef is at Cahuita, S of Limón.

One excellent area located in Guanacaste's Nicoya Penninsula is Playas Hermosa, and the nearby Islas Murciélagos is also one of the best locations. El Jardín — an area just off of Bahía Herradura — is famous for its sea fan and soft coral formations. A visit here would have to be arranged by special charter from Quepos or Puntarenas.

Just offshore from Limón, the waters surrounding Isla Uvita have a wide variety of fish, sea fans, and coral as well as the wreck of the *Fenix*, a cargo ship. This is recommended for experienced divers only. Other sites include the Isla de Caño off Osa peninsula in the NW (best accessed from Drake Bay lodges) and the distant Isla de Cocos.

Diving Web Sites
www.costaricadiving.com
(Jinetes de Osa in Drakes Bay)
www.diving-safaris.com
(Bill Beard)
divecostarica.com
(Playa Coco)
www.centralamerica.com/cr/scuba/escenar.htm
(Agencia de Viajes Escenarios Tropicales)

SURFING: Although there is also surf to be found along the Caribbean, the Pacific coast is famous for its waves.To buy or sell your surfboard, try the Mango Surf Shop, 75 feet W of the Banco Popular in San Pedro, or the Tsunami in Los Yoses. Other rental shops are in Limón, Cahuita, Puntarenas, Jacó, and Manuel Antonio.

GUANACASTE LOCATIONS: The season in Guanacaste runs from late Nov. to early April. Surfing spots are numerous but hard to reach.

To get to **Potrero Grande** in Parque Nacional Santa Rosa, which features a fast and hollow right point break, rent a boat at Playas de Coco.

On the N side of the same park, **Playa Naranjo** has one of the country's best breaks.

Points at **Playa Tamarindo** are found at Pico Pequeño, El Estero, and at Henry's Point in front of the Third World Bar. Featuring a R and L point break that curls in front of a small rivermouth, Langosta is located a km to the S. Avellanas (which has the beach break "Guanacasteco") lies 10 km S, and Playa Grande is a 20 min. walk (or a shorter drive) to the N.

Farther S along the coast are **Playa Negra** and **Nosara**. **Coyote Manzanillo**, and **Mal País** can be reached by four-wheel drive during the dry season, but there are no hotels.

PUNTARENAS AND S: To the S from **Puntarenas** are Boca Barranca, Puerto Caldera, Playa Tivites (and Valor, a rocky point), and Playa Escondito—for which you should rent a boat at Jacó.

Near famous **Playa Jacó** are Roca Loca set 1.5 km S, Playa Hermosa (best in front of the almond tree), and other points to the S like Esterillos Este, Esterillo Oeste, Bejuco, and Boca Damas.

i Fishing doesn't have to be super expensive. While you can't go after sailfish or marlin, you can find a local who will take you out for tarpon or snook. During the snook season (Sept. and Oct.), fish may be caught around the shore area or river mouths. If you obtain a license, you can fish inland. Spanish speakers can get information on fishing at Deportes Keko (Av. 20, C. 4/6) in San José.

Tico Times columnist Richard Krug (☎ 223-4331, fax 221-0096) has a desk in the Hotel Del Rey (near the Parque Morazon) in San José. He'll hook you up with a fishing expedition suited to your needs.

fishing@sol.racsa.co.cr

There's good surfing (but polluted water) in the town of **Quepos** and, to a lesser extent, up at Manuel Antonio.

Set 11 km to the R of Ronacador off the road to Dominical, **Playa El Rey** features R and L waves. Father S are Playa Dominical and (accessible only by boat), **Drake Bay** and **Boca del Río Sierpe** in Peninsula de Osa.

Reachable either by road or by rented boat from Golfito, the L point at **Pavones** is considered to be one of the world's finest.

The southernmost Pacific surfing spot is **Punta Burica** which can only be reached by boat; there's no accommodation.

THE CARIBBEAN COAST: On the Caribbean side, located to the N of Limón, are **Playas Bonita** and **Portete**; conditions at the former are dangerous. To the S, a long beach break termed **Westfalia** extends S from Limón to Punta Cahuita. Other places are Cahuita's **Black Beach**, "Salsa" at **Puerto Viejo** and **Manzanillo** to its S, and beaches near Herradura.

AGENCIES: Contact **Tico Travel** (tel. 800-493-8426) regarding surf tours.

WINDSURFING: Conditions for windsurfing are said to be among the best in the world. Chilly **Lake Arenal** features 35-knot gusts every afternoon. (For more details see Parque Nacional Arenal and Environs in the text). **Other spots** include Puerto Soley (a half hour from Cuajinquil), Playas del Coco, Playa Tamarindo, Playa Puntarenas and the nearby Boca Barranca.

WINDSURFING PACKAGES: Practically any travel agent can put one of these together these days. Contact **Surf Costa Rica** (tel. 800-771-7873), **Destination Costa Rica** (tel. 223-0656, fax 222-9747; Apdo. 590, San José), or the Ecoadventure Lodge's **Tikal Tours** (tel. 223-2811; fax 223-1916; Apdo. 6398, San José).

River Fish

Although Costa Rica is famous for its deep-sea fishing, it also has a number of freshwater fish that might delight many an angler.

"Most handsome" in Spanish, the **guapote** (rainbow bass) is a relative of South America's peacock bass. Although it is found in warmer rivers, coastal lagoons, and lakes, it is most abundant in Lake Arenal where a tourney is held each May. It fights like the devil once hooked.

Related to the piranha, the high-jumping **machaca** is said to eat anything that hits the water. Unfortunately, they're hard to hook and make bony eating.

The **mojarra** is said to resemble a blue gill and are often found near the shore, concealed beneath shrubbery and logs. They are known to swim right up to the lure, but their small mouths may make them difficult to hook.

Other river fish include **bobo** — a semi-vegetarian mullet which may be caught with lettuce, tomato, or bits of banana—and as well as snook, vieja, guavine, giant bull sharks, sawfish, and the alligator gar.

WHITE WATER RAFTING: Some of the world's best is found here and it's at its best during the rainy season when the rivers fill up. Beginners will want to try the Reventazón. (See description in "Meseta Central" section). It also has Class V on its upper end.

Endangered by a proposed hydroelectric project, the **Pacuare** flows from the Talamancas to the Caribbean; it is ideal for two- or three-day trips through the tropical jungles. Some 10,000 people raft the river each year according to the *Tico Times*.

Larger, wider, and more powerful than the Pacuare, the **Chirripó** is less difficult to navigate.

A comparative newcomer on the scene, the **Río Savegre** is a class II-III run which offers attractive scenery.

For a relaxing trip, Guanacaste's gentle **Corobicí** is ideal, but don't allow the gentle current to lull you into letting your guard down: drownings have occurred here.

COMPANIES: Most offer a series of one-day tours—ranging from Class I to V in difficulty—on the Reventazón, Pacuare,

Selected Fishing Lodges

Atlantic/Caribbean Coast

Casa Mar Fishing Lodge: In Barra del Colorado. Write PO Drawer 787, Islamorada, FL 33036, ☎ (800) 327-2880 or (305) 664-4615. In Costa Rica call 433-8834 or fax 433-9237.

Isla de Pesca: With housing in A-frames, this is another major fishing lodge. Write Apdo. 8-4390, 1000 San José. ☎ 23-4560 or 21-6673 in San José; fax 255-2533. In the US ☎ 800-245-8420 or 305-539-1630/1631; fax 305-539-1123. Or write Costa Sol International, 1717 N Bayshore Dr., Ste. 3333, Miami FL 33132.

Parismina Fishing Lodge: This lodge features rooms in wooden cottages. Write Apdo. 7127, 1000 San José, ☎ 222-6055, or fax 222-1760.

Río Colorado Lodge: Located in Barra del Colorado, it offers simple cabins. Write Hotel Corobicí, PO Box 5094, 1000 San José. Call 232-8610 in San José. In the US, write 12301 North Oregon Ave., Tampa FL 33612 or ☎ 800-243-9777. From outside the US ☎ 813-931-4849.

Silver King Lodge: Opened in 1993 and offering facilities which are a bit upscale compared to the others in the area. In Costa Rica call 288-0849 or phone or fax 288-1403. In the US call 800-VIP-FISH or write Aerocasillas, Dept. 1597, Box 025216, Miami FL 33102.

Tortuga Lodge: A comfortable lodge in Tortuguero run by Costa Rica Expeditions. In San José ☎ 222-0333 or 257-0766; fax 257-1665. Write Apdo. 6941, 1000 San José or, from the US, ☎ 800-225-2272. **www.expeditions.co.cr costa-rica@expeditions.co.cr**

Pacfic Coast

Río Sierpe Lodge: Deep sea and tidal basin fishing lodge located in the NE section of the Osa peninsula. Scuba and snorkeling day trips to Isla de Caño can be arranged, as can two-day RT cruises to Isla de Coco. Write Apdo. 818, 1200 Pavas; ☎ 220-1712/2121 or fax 232-3321.

Aguilar de Osa: Aguila de Osa (☎ 296-2190, fax 232-7722' Apdo. 10486-1000, San José) has 14 thatched-roof cabins with verandas. Perched on a hillside, its garden setting includes a gourmet restaurant and a pool. It offers sportsfishing (four boats), scuba, birding, and kayaking. In the US, Write Cuenta # 250, 7500 NW 25 St., Miami FL 33122.

Serapiquí, and Corobicí. Two-day tours on the Reventazón-Pascua (Class IV), two- and three-day trips on the Pacuare (Class III-IV), and three-, four-, and five-day trips on the Chirripó (Class III-IV) are also available. Special rates for residents and Ticos are offered by some companies.

The best established company is **Costa Rica Expeditions** (tel. 257-0776, 222-0333, fax 257-1665; Dept. 235, 1601 NW 97th Av. Unit C-101, Miami, FL 33172).
www.expeditions.co.cr
costa-rica@expeditions.co.cr

Another well known firm is **Ríos Tropicales** (tel. 233-6455, fax 255-4354; Apdo. 472, 1200 San José). They run three-day trips up the Pacuare where they run a lodge.
www.riostropicales.com
www.riversearch.com
info@riostropicales.com

Pioneer Tours is a comparative newcomer on the scene. In Costa Rica, ☎ 253-9132, 225-8117. 225-4735, or fax 253-4687. In the US, ☎ (800) 288-2107 or (408) 626-1815, fax (408) 626-9013. Or write Box 22063, Carmel CA 93922.

Based in Costa Rica, **Aguas Bravas** offers whitewater rafting as well as other adventures.
xijansa@sol.racsa.co.cr

KAYAKING: Interest in kayaking has grown dramatically in recent years. Featuring Class IV and V rapids, the Reventazón has become world renowned as a winter kayaking training ground. Flowing N from Volcán Poás through the province of Heredia, the Sarapiquí has moderate rapids. Other destinations include the Pacuare, General, and the Corobicí. An alternative to going out on the rivers is sea kayaking. Companies in the Golfito and Osa Peninsula areas offer trips, and the Almonds and Corals Tent Camp on the Caribbean Coast also offers rentals. Check with your lodge or the specific location in the travel section for details.

Ríos Tropicales (☎ 233-6455, fax 255-4354; Apdo. 472, Pavas) offers sea kayaking at Curú off of the Nicoya Peninsula and from Manuel Antonio.
www.riostropicales.com
www.riversearch.com
info@riostropicales.com

CANOEING: A variety of lodges rent canoes or allow their guests to use them. Some of the best places to canoe are in Tortuguero National Park and Barra Del Colorado reserve. **Battenkill Canoe** (☎ 02-362-2800; Box 65, Arlington, VT 05250) offers canoeing tour packages.

ANGLING AND DEEP-SEA FISHING: Some of the planet's best sport fishing is to be had here. You can expect sailfish, red and culbera snapper, roosterfish, wahoo, crevalle, snook, tarpon, blue and black marlin, corvina (sea bass) and yellowtail. For the competitively-minded, sportsfishing lodges and fishing lodges hold tournaments.

A **fishing license** (US$30) may be obtained from any agency of the **Banco Credito Agricola** (☎ 223-8855; Av. 4, C. Central/1, San José, 233-0829. You will need your passport, tourist card, and two passport-sized photos, but call first to doublecheck on current requirements. It's probably best to bring your own gear for freshwater fishing; note that guapote require a medium rod and a ten-lb. line.

AREAS AND SEASONS: Lake Arenal's guapote season stretches from Jan. 1 through Sept. 30. Although they peak in size from August through mid-Oct., snook may be caught—near river mouths and along beaches—all year round. Although they may be caught in other months, tarpons are caught off the Caribbean coast from Jan. through mid-May. Sailfish and dorado (dolphinfish) are best caught in July through Sept., roosterfish in May and June, yellowfin tuna in July and Aug., and wahoo from June through Sept.

CHARTERING: Along the Pacific coast, charters are centered at hotel resorts. In the Gulf of Papagayo (Nicoya Peninsula), modern craft can be found at Ocotal, Pez Vela, Flamingo Marina, and at Tamarindo. From Puntarenas, charters operate from The Yacht Club and the Pacific Marina. Other locations include Playa Naranjo's Oasis del Pacifico, and fishing camps near Golfito and on the Osa Peninsula.

J. P.'s Sportfishing Tours (☎ 257-8503, 257-7829, fax 222-8134; Quepos; ☎/fax 777-0757, 777-1613; 800-308-3394) works primarily out of Quepos from Dec. to May.

Adventuras Poseidon (☎/fax 77-0935; Apdo. 185, 6350 Quepos) is another Manuel Antonio-based operation.

GOING AFTER TROUT: The most accessible rivers for fishing are the Tapantí, Copey, and Providencia. Most average around 1 lb. (454 g) although larger ones have been caught. Chacón farm at San Geraldo is one of the locations stocked for trout.

SEA EXCURSIONS: Many boat trips are available. The best known is the cruise to Tortuga Island (See the "offshore islands" section under "Puntarenas to Panama.") Another is the trip to Isla del Coco which many live-aboard dive ships make.

HOT-AIR BALLOONING: Serendipity Adventures (☎ 556-2592, fax 426-5026; Apdo. 76, CATIE, Turrialba) offers air tours at sunrise from Naranjo, Turrialba, and Arenal; there is a maximum of five passengers per balloon; tours are combined with optional activities such as white water rafting.

While the Naranjo and Arenal options involve pickup at your hotel in San José, the Turrialba flight involves an overnight at Casa Turire before the flight. In the US call 800-635-2325, fax 313-426-5026, or write Box 2325, Ann Arbor, MI 48106. (They can also arrange a number of other excursions ranging from tree climbing to canyoning).
www.serendipityadventures.com
serendip@ix.netcom.com

Competitive Sports

BASKETBALL: One of the national avocations. Hoops may be had at many a village court, and national games are played at San José's La Sabana.

BOWLING: There are a number of alleys in San José. Considered to be the most prestigious bowling contest in Latin America, the **Tournament of Nations** is held on Columbus Day, Oct. 12.

CYCLING: Despite the dangers of diesel exhaust, cycling is a rewarding experience. The major annual event is the ***Vuelta a Costa Rica,*** a 12-day marathon held in Dec. For mountain biking excursions contact the companies listed in the chart .

GOLF: Golf courses have grown in number as the type of visitor coming to Costa Rica has changed.

Set some km W of San José enroute to Alajuela, **Cariari Country Club** has one of the nation's oldest 18-hole golf courses. There is an annual international tournament here.

Other 9-hole courses are at Los Reyes Country Club near Alajuela, **El Castillo**

Mountain Bike Rentals/Tours

Company/ Tel./Location	Rentals	Tours
Bike N'Hike 289-8191 Centro Commerical, Escazú	X	X
C. R. Mountain Biking 222-4380 Apdo. 3979, San José 1000	X	
Costaricabike 225-3939 Apdo. 812, 2050 San Pedro	X	
Geoventuras 221-2053		X
Horizontes 222-2022 Apdo. 1780, San José 1002		X
Mountain Biking Costa Rica 255-0914	X	X
Rios Tropicales 233-6455 Apdo. 472, Pavas	X	X
Safaris Corobici 669-0544	X	
Tikal Tour Operators 223-2811 Apdo. 6398, San José 1000X		X

Travel Agencies Abroad: Mountain Bike Tours and Excursions

Backroads	800-245-3874
Canadian BackRoutes	*416-588-6139*
Journeys	800-255-8735
Mariah Wilderness Expeditions	*800-462-7424*

Country Club above Heredia, Escazú's **Costa Rica Country Club**, and **Tango Mar** near Playa Tambor on the S coast of Nicoya Peninsula. the **Parque Valle del Sol** (☎ 282-9222, ext. 3) in Santa Ana has nine holes but another nine are planned. The **La Roca Country Club** in Caldera has 18 holes. A six-hole course is at the **Casa Turire** near Turrialba.

The **Rancho Las Colinas** (☎/fax 654-4089) has an 18-hole course as does the **Melia Playa Conchal Resort** (☎ 654-4123).

The **Los Sueños Marriot Golf Club** at Playa Herradura is scheduled for completion by 2000.

Resort Rancho Mary at La Cruz has 18 holes.

The **Tamarindo Golf**, the **Monte del Barco** at Playa Panamá, and the Vistas del Flamingo are all planned for the future in Guanacaste.

> ***URL*** **www.centralamerica.com/gr.golf**
> *Site of golf course promoter Landy Blank (☎ 446-6489)*

RUNNING: The best place to jog in San José is in the park (La Sabana). Attracting competitors worldwide, there's also a Hash House Harriers Club (☎ 228-0769) which runs on Mondays and drinks beers afterwards.

SQUASH: Courts include Monte Real in Sabana Sur and Top Squash (right behind McDonalds in the Sabana area).

TENNIS: In addition to those found at hotels, public hard and grass courts are maintained at Sabana Park and the nearby Costa Rica Tennis Club, the Costa Rica Country Club, and the Los Reyes Country Club. The Cariari Country Club also hosts the annual World Friendship Tournament in March and April and a tournament for the younger set, the Copa del Café, every Jan.

> "Costa Rica needs golf like a fish needs a bicycle.. The best thing to do would be to let the land go back to tropical dry forest." — Costa Rica Expeditions owner Michael Kaye as quoted in *Conde Nast Traveler*, Nov. 1998.

Other Sports

HORSEBACK RIDING: Noted for its Paso Fino and Andalusian breeds, horses are a national pastime. Instruction is available at the **Porton del Tajo** (☎ 239-2248) at Cariari Country Club and the **Hipico La Caraña** (☎ 228-6106, 28-6754), located about 20 km W of San José in Río Oro de Santa Ana, where international competitions are held annually.

Santa Ana's **Club Paso Fino** (☎ 249-1466) specializes in these purebreeds; it gives lessons and offers accommodation and meals. Horse lovers won't want to miss the Horse Parade, held in San José during Christmas week.

A large number of lodges have horses and riding is available in places as diverse as Manuel Antonio, Rincón de la Vieja, Cahuita, and Puerto Viejo de Talamanca. Specifics are given in the travel section, with a special section included under "Vicinity of San José."

BULLFIGHTS AND RODEOS: Cattle capital of Costa Rica, Guanacaste Province holds rodeos and bullfights from Nov. to April in the towns of Santa Cruz, Nicoya, and Liberia. The Cariari Country Club also has rodeos, and rodeos and bullfights are held in San José during the Christmas holiday season.

YOGA: The luxury **Nosara Retreat** (☎ 682-0071, fax 682-0072; 888-803-0580) offers a "Wellness Adventure Program."
yogaretreat@nosara.com
www.nosara.com/yogaretreat

Practicalities

WHEN TO COME: When you should come depends upon your motives for coming. The best time is generally off-season, when rates for hotels plummet and there are few visitors to be found in the more popular spots. While it does rain quite a bit during this period, white water rafting improves, the Guanacaste region greens over, and showers (largely confined to the afternoon) cool things down.

The rain is heaviest in the region surrounding San José. In other regions, such as the Caribbean Coast and around Golfito, there is no clearly defined rainy season: it rains much of the time year round. If you check an issue of the *Tico Times* after arrival, you can window shop rainfall levels and decide which locations to visit. *La Nación* has a daily report.

If you arrive during the rainy season (the Costa Rican "winter"), you can beat the heat you'd find at home; things can actually be cooler in Costa Rica! If camping and hiking are important items on your itinerary, it would definitely be preferable to come in the dry season. If you go to the more inaccessible or untouristed towns, parks, and reserves, crowds shouldn't be a problem, whatever the season.

DEALING WITH HOLY WEEK: During Holy Week, most *josefinos* flee the capital and the streets are deserted. Since this is the only time when you can cross the streets safely, it is the perfect time to visit San José. The drawback is that almost everything is closed. This is not the time to visit the beaches because that is where everyone goes. If you need to hide away, the best bets are the smaller inland towns.

You can generally find places to eat, but there won't be much to do other than to watch the festivities. No alcohol is sold on Thursday or Friday, so all bars, cantinas, and restaurants that usually sell alcohol are shut tight with *guardia* seals plastered across the door to ensure that no violations occur. Even cases of liquor in the supermarket are sealed up, so if you're an imbiber be certain to stock up beforehand. Also note that most buses stop running from noon on Thursday through Friday.

WHO SHOULD COME: Costa Rica is definitely not the destination for everyone. If the least little sandfly bite, mosquito sting, or insect sighting takes you aback, then this isn't the place for you, and you won't like it much unless you confine yourself to the most luxurious resorts along Guanacaste's coast. Much of Costa Rica is truly for adventurous people who don't mind being a bit uncomfortable if that's what it takes to really experience things.

Unlike traveling to Hawaii or even the Americanized Cancún, a visit here *definitely* requires some degree of adjustment on your part. Althought available, posh resorts are definitely *not* what Costa Rica is about, nor is great nightlife. You absolutely must have to have an appreciation of and an interest in nature; a desire to try to speak even *a bit* of broken Spanish will get you quite a long way. If you drop a lot of your expectations and attidudes, you'll find that the rewards are worth every bit of the discomfort you endure.

SUGGESTED ITINERARY: There is no set of "must see" attractions. Everything depends upon your priorities, finances, time, and your interests. In a two-week trip, you might sample some of the museums of San José, visit one or more parks or reserves, and swim at a beach on either coast. Another possibility is to stay longer and become a volunteer or study Spanish. Whatever you do, don't try to see the whole country in a week or so. Spend some time in a single area and really get to know it! You can always come back for another visit. In general, it's better to avoid such over-touristed areas as Manuel Antonio, Monteverde, and Jaco and some of the horrendous resorts and overpriced mega-hotels.

PLANNING EXPENSES: There are facilities available to match every pocketbook. Generally speaking, the more you want to do in a shorter space of time and in an organized fashion, the more you can expect to pay. Doing your own chartering and/or using local transportation takes more time, requiring schedule flexibility and initiative. If you're seeking comfortable accommodation or taking a tour, you may not find that large a price differential with the US, Canada, or Britain. You may want to compromise—staying in an inexpensive hotel and then splurging on a Tortuguero river trip for example.

ON A BUDGET: Expect to spend from US$20 per person per day at a minimum for food and accommodation. (Information on budget acccommodation is listed under "Accommodation" below). Generally, you'll find yourself spending at least US$25 total and, depending upon your needs, probably more. The best way to cut down on expenses is to stay in one (relatively inexpensive) location for a time and to prepare some of your own food. Renting a car is an expensive proposition, but the buses are reasonably priced and service is extensive.

A decade ago, Costa Rica could truly be considered a low-budget destination, but its rise in popularity has pushed prices up dramatically. Consequently, despite a sharp decline in the value of the *colón*, Costa Rica, while cheaper overall than Belize and the US, no longer compares with places like Honduras. Many of the parks—such as Tortuguero and Manuel Antonio—are becoming too expensive (the entrance fee issue aside) for all but the well-heeled and the average Tico has been priced out as well. Consequently, you may prefer to focus on some of the less well known places. You'll not only cut costs but also get more out of your trip.

note: Be aware that anything calling itself a "youth hostel" has no official status as such and may be more expensive than other, comparable accommodation.

Arrival

BY AIR: The best way to get a deal on airfares here is by shopping around. A good travel agent should scan for you to find the lowest fare; if he or she doesn't, find another agent, or try doing it yourself. If there are no representative offices in your area, check the phone book — most airlines have toll-free numbers (see chart). In these days of airline deregulation, fares change quickly so it's best to check the prices well before departure — and then again before you buy the ticket. The more flexible you can be about when you wish to depart and return, the easier it will be to find a bargain.

Whether dealing with a travel agent or directly with the airlines, make sure that you let them know clearly what it is you want. Don't forget to check both the direct fare and the separate fare to the gateway city and then on to San José; there can be a price differential.

Although you should reserve several months in advance, you should also recheck fares before paying for your ticket. Allow a minimum of two hours connecting time when scheduling.

Continental flies nonstop from Houston and New York to San José. Connections are available through Houston to most US cities; there are also nonstop flights from Houston to Paris and London.

Mexicana flies to San José from Los Angeles via Mexico City.

United also flies to San José from Guatemala City and Washington, DC.

LACSA, the national airline of Costa Rica, flies nonstop from Miami, from NY (via Guatemala and San Pedro Sula), from New Orleans (via Cancún and San Pedro Sula, Honduras), LA, and from San Juan, Puerto Rico. It also flies from San Francisco. It now code shares with American.

TACA flies from Los Angeles, Houston, Miami, New Orleans, New York, San Francisco, and Washington.

Delta began service to Costa Rica from Atlanta in 1997.

American Airlines flies from Dallas and out of its Miami hub.

United Airlines flies daily from Los Angeles and Miami to San José.

Airlines Serving Costa Rica	
American	☎ 800-433-7300
Continental	☎ 800-537-3444
Delta	☎ 800-221-1212
LACSA	☎ 800-225-2272
Mexicana	☎ 800-531-7921
TACA	☎ 800-535-8780
United	☎ 800-241-6522

TO LIBERIA: Although theoretically an international airport, traffic is scarce to Liberia's airport. The advantage with coming here is that you would be much closer to the beach resorts in Guanacaste. A few airlines offer charter flights, and LACSA now flies via San José. Local airline Travel Air also flies into this airport from San José.

CHARTER: Travel Charter International (☎ 248 641-0875) in Troy, Michigan offers charter flights as do Allegro (from Boston, Atlanta, Dallas), North American (from Phildelphia), Skyservice (from Toronto), and American TransAir (from Detroit).

When making reservations for your flight to Costa Rica, make sure you receive a ticket issued on a carrier which has an office in San José in the event that the ticket needs to be reissued.

FROM CANADA: While there are few charter flights from the US, many charter flights operate from here during the winter months for around C$600. Contact Go Travel (☎ 514-735-4526) in Montreal, Fiesta Wayfarer (☎ 416-498-5566) in Toronto, and Fiesta West (☎ 604-688-1102) in Vancouver. Charter flights may also run into Liberia's airport.

FROM EUROPE: Iberia, Condor, Avianca/SAM all fly. Continental flies from Paris and London via Houston. British Airways flies to Miami and has a direct flight to San José. If you are coming from this direction, you should be aware that many of the flights stop in the Caribbean enroute so they may be heavily booked. Ask about possible stopovers. Costa Rica may also be reached by air from everywhere in the Central and South American region. Finally, if you wish to arrange a trip out of Costa Rica by air, you'll do well to purchase your ticket in advance: All tickets purchased in the country are subject to a 10% sales tax.

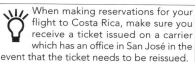

BY BUS: Unless you have a damned hard ass and a hell of a lot of patience or plan on taking a month or so to complete the trip, this isn't really a viable alternative. It will cost you less than US$100 for the total fare from Texas or San Diego.

FROM NICARAGUA: When you enter Costa Rica through the border post at Peñas Blancas, you may be asked if you've been taking malaria pills and, if so, you may be asked to produce them. At the border, you'll find a branch of the tourist bureau, moneychangers (poor rate for ***cordobas***, the Nicaraguan currency; change these before leaving) and a restaurant. If you travel by bus, make sure that you get the correct passport back from the driver after he receives them from the immigration officer.

BY SEA: Unless you are willing to take one of the cruise ships—which occasionally dock at Puntarenas and near Limón for brief stopovers—there is no regularly scheduled alternative from N America or other Central American nations.

However, a **vehicular ferry service** does run three times a week between Cristóbal in Panamá and Cartagena, Columbia. This eliminates the need to ship your vehicle to S America. For more information, call Rodrigo Gómez or Harry Evetts in Panamá at 507-64-5564 or 64-5699.

Tours

One option for visitors without a great deal of time, or with an urge to savor different experiences, is a tour or excursion. Most of these include hotel pickup, meals, and dropoff in their pricing. The advantage is that you avoid crowded buses, you can cover a lot of territory, and your driver will not only speak English (or whatever your native tongue) but is likely to be very informative. Disadvantages are the added expense, isolation from the locals, and loss of flexibility. They do provide an easy way to visit many of the national parks, reserves, and wildlife refuges. Although most tours operate out of San José, an increasing number are starting up in other areas. In addition to those listed here, large hotels may offer their own tours for guests.

PACKAGE TOURS: As they say, all that glitters is not gold. And this cliché may be old but certainly pertinent when it comes to package tours! If you want to have everything taken care of, then package tours are the way to go. However, they do have at least two distinct disadvantages: Most decisions have already been made for you, which takes

Humanitarian Tour

Are you tired of the same old touristic sights? The Educational Resource Center in Santa Ana has put together a group of tours that takes you into the heart of Costa Rican realities. The center helps collect donations for a number of local social change enterprises, and the tours are a way of helping fund the projects. Trips run from one to eight days and begin either with a walking tour of Santa Ana or a visit to Guayabo National Monument. In the afternoon, you visit one of eight centers: a State-run orphanage, a Catholic nun-run home for abused or neglected girls, a day care center, an indigenous reserve, a project which employs street children, or others. Rates run at US$60 pp, pd. Call the Educational Resource Center (☎ 282-7368) or Via Nova America Tours (☎ 255-1825, fax 255-0061) for more information and bookings.

much of the thrill out of traveling, and you are more likely to be put up in a large characterless hotel (where the tour operators can get quantity discounts), rather than in a small inn (where you can get quality treatment). So think twice before you sign up. Also, if you do sign up, read the fine print and see what's really included and what's not. Don't be taken in by useless freebies that gloss over the lack of more important features such as paid meals.

ENVIRONMENTAL AND ADVENTURE TOURS: If you're pressed for time and convenience is more important than money, you may want to sign up for one of these. It's possible to get any package you want from the US and a good travel operator can put a custom package together for you. A list follows under "tour operators and agencies."

TOUR OPERATORS AND AGENCIES: There are hundreds of these, many of which are listed below alphabetically. Note that wholesalers also work with individuals, and that many of those listed have 800 numbers: call 800-555-1212 for information. E-mail and web sites are current as of publication of this book. Launch a search should these prove invalid.

Adventure Dive Travel & Tours (☎ 650-364-7259, fax 650-364-9289) specializes in nature travel and tours in Costa Rica.
costarica@adventuredive.com

Adventures (☎ 406-586-9914) specializes in fishing and adventure travel to Costa Rica.
advent2@avicom.net

American Escapes (☎ 510-935-5241, fax 510-945-0154) is based in Walnut Creek, CA and specializes in designing packages for groups or individuals with special interests.
laescapes@aol.com

Avanti Destination (☎ 503-295-1100, fax 503-295-2723) is based in Portland and offers special packages.
www.avantidestinations.com
avanti@avantidestinations.com

Bahia Tours (☎ 954-929-0090, fax 954-922-7478) is a Florida-based wholesaler which offers a wide variety of trips to Costa Rica.
bahia@gate.net

Baja Expeditions (☎ 800-843-6967) is the US representative for Ríos Tropicales.
Biological Journeys (☎ 800-548-7555 and, in CA, 707-839-0178; 1696 Ocean Drive, McKinleyville, CA 95521) is another agency.
Caprice Tours (☎ 305-436-0842, fax 305-436-0843) is a Miami-based wholesaler who specializes in Latin America.
caprice@worldpass.net

Cardonna Caribbean Tours (☎ 407-774-9000, 407-682-6000) specializes in dive packages with other adventure excursions tacked on.
caradonna@aol.com

Caribbean Selections (☎ 281-363-4051, fax 281-292-0315) is Texas-based.
caribsel@flex.net

Carolina Meeting & Incentive (☎ 919-782-1900, fax 919-787-1952) is based in North Carolina and helps plan business trips.
alasky@netstart.net.

Costa Rica Experts (☎ 773-935-1009, fax 773-935-9252) is based in Chicago and provides customized packages.
crexpert@ais.net

Costa Rican Experience (☎/fax506-268-4350, cellular ☎ 506-390-6970, 800-584-8529; SJO 782, 1601 NW 97. Ave. Unit C-101, BOX 025215, Miami, FL 33102-5216 run by Fred Solomon who is based in Costa Rica. He sets up hand-tailored tours for families, including waterfall tours.
cretour@sol.racsa.co.cr

Costa Rica Travel Exchange (☎ 504-482-2800, fax 504-488-6144) is a New Orleans-based wholesaler and tour operator specializing in Costa Rica.
costatrvl@aol.com

Creative Tours (☎ 504-861-2639, fax 504-866-0791) is a wholesaler and tour operator specializing in naure tourism.
creattour@aol.com

Da Costa Tours (☎ 916-927-6087, fax 916-927-6089) offers nature tours and packages.
dacostatours@juno.com

DFW Tours (☎ 972-980-4540, fax 972-386-3802) is Texas-based and caters to "upscale" tourism.
dparrish@dfwtours.com

Exito Latin America Travel Specialists (☎ 510-655-2154, fax 510-655-4566) is based in Oakland, CA and focuses on small group tour and Spanish language immersion program travel.
exito@wonderlink.com

Extraordinary Expeditions (☎ 800-234-1569, 208-788-2012) is based in Indiana.
Experience The Adventure Tours (☎ 305-267-6644, fax 305-261-6648) is a Miami-based; it offers dive and adventure packages.
etatours@aol.com

Festival Tours (☎ 407-859-5712, fax 407-240-8616) offers a wide variety of Costa Rican trips.
festival@internetmci.com

Freegate Tourism (☎ 516-22-0855, fax 516-222-0848) specializes in Central and South America.
freegatetours.com
mail@freegatetours.com

Geo Expeditions (☎ 800-351-5041, 209-532-0152; Box 3656, Sonora, CA 95370) and **Geostar** (☎ 800-633-6633, 707-584-9552; 6050 Commerce Blvd., Ste. 110, Rohnert Park, CA 94928) are other options. **GL Tours** (☎ 414-275-6873, fax 414-275-3996) is located in Wisconsin and sells small-group tours as well as individual packages.
gltours@leknet.net

Holbrook Travel (☎ 352-377-7111, fax 352-371-3710) is the owner of Selva Verde Lodge.
debbie@holbrook.usa.com

Formerly Costa Rica Connection, **InterConnections** (☎ 800-345-7422; 805-543-8823. fax 805-543-3626; 975 Osos St., San Luis Obispo, CA 93401) is the part-owner of the Arenal Observatory Lodge, Tiskita, and Costa Rica Sun Tours. It is run by affable Costa Rican John Aspinall, whose brother runs Tiskita Lodge; it offers a wide range of tours and is recommended.
www.crconnect.com
tours@crconnect.com

Interesting Travel Company (☎ 888-647-7033, fax 305-296-9457) is a travel agency which actively tries to introduce its clients to locals.
www.interestingtravel.com
info@interestingtravel.com

International Expeditions offers 10-day, all inclusive tours departing from

Miami. These explore the Monteverde, Puntarenas, and Tortuguero areas. A special three-day additional visit to Manuel Antonio is also available. Call 1-800-633-4734 or write 1776 Independence Court, Birmingham, AL 35216.
www.ietravel.com

Intervac (☎ 305-670-8990, fax 305-670-6168) is based in Miami and specializes in Latin America.
alain@intervactours.com

Intratours (☎ 713-952-0662, fax 713-952-2631) is in Houston and offers "spiritual and cultural" as well as other trips.
intratour@america.net

Island Flight Vacations (☎ 212-567-2050, fax 212-942-0501) specializes in vacation packages.
mailisland@aol.com

Journeys (☎ 800-345-4453, 206-365-0686; 3526 NE 155, Seattle, WA 98155),
Kam Tours International is a NYC-based consolidator and wholesaler.
kamtours@aol.com

Magic International Tours (☎ 813-933-0633, fax 813-932-7287) offers group tours.
magictour@aol.com

Magnatours (☎ 516-424-2000, fax 516-424-6700) is a tour operator and wholesaler offering Costa Rica packages.
magnat@ix.netcom.com

Mariah Wilderness Expeditions (☎ 800-462-7424, fax 510-233-0956) specialize in custom itineraries for the individual traveler. They also have special programs for rafters as well as groups for women.
www.mariahwe.com
rafting@mariahwe.com

Picking a Tour

- ☞ Find out who your tour leader is. The best tours combine local guides with well-known scientists, and these are generally the most expensive.
- ☞ In order to fully experience the rainforest environment, choose a tour that doesn't move around too much. Otherwise, you'll end up paying for transport and spending time on buses while you could be out in the wild.
- ☞ Be sure that non-park and reserve excursions are optional.
- ☞ If luxury lodging isn't important to you, you can save by choosing a tour that stays at less expensive abodes.
- ☞ Although small group tours are more expensive than larger ones, they may not be superior. Ten people marching through the rainforest will not necessarily see more than will 30 or 40. And, if you don't get along with the others on your small tour, it can be unpleasant. The best tour is one that also allows you time to explore on your own.
- ☞ Keep in mind that you can't follow your normal three-meal schedule and expect to see much wildlife. You should be in the forest before sun-up. You can sleep during the hot afternoon — when the animals do. If you're an avid birder, birding trips aren't necessarily the way to go.
- ☞ It's also important to experience the jungle in the night as well as the day, and tours which feature a night hike are desirable.
- ☞ Ornithology tour leaders can sometimes be preoccupied with trying to spot as many species as possible. If you're not a birder, a general natural history tour may be better.
- ☞ The *real value* of this type of tour is in the learning experience. For that you need people who know what they are doing.

Maya Tours (☎ 561-477-4848, fax 561-477-4879) is based in Florida and offers tours throughout the "Mundo Maya."
www.mayatour.com
info@mayatour.com

Miller and Associates (☎ 509-996-3148; Box 819, Winthrop, WA 98862)
Nature Tours (☎ 504-895-0970, fax 504-895-0092) is a wholesaler for Central America.
naturetours@worldnet.att.net

Ocean Connection (☎ 281-966-7800, fax 281-996-1513) is an ecodadventure and dive wholesaler specializing in the Caribbean and Latin America.
www.oceanconnection.com
adventure@oceanconnection.com

Paradise Marketing (☎ 702-896-8336, fax 702-896-8325) is based in Las Vegas and specialize in Latin America.
2bbeck@concentric.net

Run by friendly Karen Johnson, **Preferred Adventures** (☎ 651-222-8131, 800-840-8687, fax 651-222-8687) is based in St. Paul, MN and invites visitors to "touch the wild."Karen has set up a Costa Rica-Minnesota Foundation, and sells unique playing and greeting cards.
www.preferredadventures.com
paltours@aol.com

Located in Alabama, **Pura Vida Excursions** (☎ 334-981-4811, fax 334-981-4812) is a Costa Rica-only whoelasler who generally works in tandem directly with service providers.
puravida@gulftel.com

Reserve Costa Rica (☎ 305-229-9639, fax 305-229-3058) is based in Miami.
reservecr@aol.com

Safaricentre International (☎ 310-546-4411, fax 310-546-3188) is an adventure-tour company specializing in "safaris."
www.safaricentre.com
info@safaricentre.com

Star Tours (☎ 800-466-6069, fax 407-299-3874) is family-run and based in Florida
startours@netpass.com

Tara Tours (☎ 305-871-1246, fax 305-871-0417) is Miami-based and is a wholesaler.
taratours@aol.com

Tico Travel (☎ 213-644-0505, fax 213-644-0808) is an LA-based company run by a genuine Tico.
ticosla@pacbell.net

A second **Tico Travel** (☎ 954-493-8426, fax 954-493-8466) is a wholesaler dedicated to Costa Rica.
tico@gate.net

Toro Tours (☎ 305-265-2233, fax 305-265-0402) is Miami-based and wholesales Costa Rica.
torotour@icanect.net

Tour Costa Rica, Inc. (☎ 954-568-2838, fax 954-493-7925) is based in Ft. Lauderdale, and the Tico owner has a number of unsusual offerings.
tsacora@gate.net.

Tour Du Jour (☎ 504-780-8637, fax 504-456-0237) is a Louisiana-based wholesaler specializing in Mexico and Central America.
tourdujour@aol.com

Tourtech International (☎ 949-476-1912, fax 949-476-2210) is based in Irvine, CA and specializes in Latin America.
tourtech@worldnet.att.net

Tread Lightly (☎ 860-868-1710, fax 860-868-1718) is a Connecticut-based wholesaler and

tour operator that promotes environmental-friendly properties.
patread@aol.com

Vargas Travel (☎ 925-943-6588, 800-548-2742, fax 925-943-6560) is a Costa Rican-run wholesaler.
vargastravel@msn.com
www.vargastravel.com

Wildland Adventures (☎ 800-345-4453, 206-365-0686; fax 206-363-6615; 3516 NE 155th St., Seattle, WA 98255) act as an agent for many Costa Rican firms and offer a tremendous variety of trips; call friendly Anna or Kurt and ask for their brochure.
info@wildland.com
www.wildland.com

World of Adventure Vacations (☎ 303-708-9183, fax 303-792-2954; 888-792-4384) is based in Colorado and has a special interest in ecotourism.
www.latinadventures.com
mail@latinvacations.com

Worldwide Adventures (☎ 407-773-4878) is a Florida-based agency specializing in surfing and family vacations.
www.surfingadventures.com
surfer@surfingadventures.com

IN SWITZERLAND: **RDR Travel** (☎ 1-389-9289, fax 1-383-9280) is the leading Swiss wholesaler dealing with Costa Rica.
rdrtravel@swissonline.ch

IN GREAT BRITAIN: **Journey Latin America** (☎ 818-74-78315, fax 818-74-21312) specializes in Latin American tourism.
tours@journeylatinamerica.co

Based in Bristol, **Trips Worldwide** (☎ 117-987-2626, 117-987-2627) arranges individual itineraries and specializes in hotels and lodges which are off the beaten track.
post@trips.demon.co.cr

IN CANADA: **Global Connections** (☎ 604-681-1221, fax 604-681-2754) specializes in all of Latin America
glblconx@istar.ca

Another Canadian alternative is **Grulex** (☎ 604-988-5533, fax 604-988-5559), a Vancouver-based center which focuses on Costa Rica and Central America.
Tours Mont-Royal (☎ 514-871-5100, fax 514-871-5140) operates a number of charter flights to Costa Rica.
tmr@videotron.net

TEMPTRESS **CRUISE TOUR PACKAGES:** Truthfully advertised as a "Back Door to Costa Rica," Temptress Cruises runs a variety of superbly organized cruises down the Pacific coast. Whereas they once catered to singles and couples, the stress is now on "family adventures." Three routes run year 'round from the port in Puntarenas. Easter Cloud, Profusion Voyage, and Java Adventure. At each day's anchorage, you can choose between a natural history tour conducted by a professional biologist, or a recreational/cultural tour, which might include horseback riding or sunbathing.
A 1785-ft. a/c diesel-powered vessel, the *Temptress Explorer* is equipped with sun deck, swimming platform, small store, and wet bar. Its rooms hold up to 99 guests. Snorkeling gear, kayaks, and hydro slides are also part of the package. Water skiing, scuba (if you are certified), and fishing charters (in the two 17-ft. Boston Whalers) are available as well.
These tours are for those who want to experience the range of what Costa Rica has to offer without sacrificing comfort or spending the time required to reach the various ports of call by road. Taking

the sea route, you are generally within minutes of your destination each morning. The more energy you have, the more you'll get out of the cruise. With swimming, snorkeling, diving, kayaking, nature tours, and other activities, there is more than enough to keep anyone busy. Contact Temptress Cruises at 1600 NW Lejeune Rd., Ste 301, Miami FL 33126. In the US, ☎ 800-336-8423, 305-871-1663, or fax 305-871-1657. In Costa Rica, ☎ 220-1679. Buses to Puntarenas (and the boat) depart from Sabana Norte, Frente Al Colegio Los Angeles (Por ICE de la Sabana), Centro Comercial La Torees, Local #11.
www.temptresscruises.com
info@temptresscruises.com

***CLIPPER* CRUISES:** Larger and more like a conventional cruise ship, they take passengers to San José, Carara, Manuel Antonio, and Marenco, before going on to Panama aboard their 138-passenger ship. Prices range from US$2,390 on up for the 10-day cruise plus three nights on land (☎ 800-325-0010. In MO, ☎ 314-727-2929 collect).

SENIOR CITIZEN TOURS: Elderhostel, a sponsor of inexpensive tours, has a Costa Rica trip. Call 617-426-8058 or write 80 Boylston St., Ste 400, Boston MA 02116. Grand Circle (☎ 800-321-2835, 617-350-7500, fax 617-728-8840) gears itself towards tourists 50 and over. For those who want to explore the possibility of retiring in Costa Rica, write **Lifestyle Explorations** (☎ 209-577-4081), PO Box 6487, Modesto CA 95355.

LOCAL NATURE AND ADVENTURE TOURS: It's in to be green these days among tour operators. So many people have jumped into the business of "ecotourism" so fast that many can not deliver on their promises. You must choose carefully. The tours offered by the organizations described above generally use one or more of the following Costa-Rica-based operators to handle their logistics.

Costa Rica Expeditions (☎ 257-0776, 222-0333, fax 257-1665; Apdo. 6941, San José) offers tours to all the major wildlife sanctuaries in the country and operates Monteverde Lodge, Tortuga Lodge, and Corcovado. With a large staff, there's someone in the office from 5:30 AM to 9 PM in case you have a problem or want to make a booking.
costa-rica@expeditions.co.cr
www.expeditions.co.cr

Dealing with groups as well as individuals, **Horizontes** (☎ 222-2022, fax 255-4513; Apdo. 1780, 1002 P.E. San José) retails a large number of tours including mountain biking. Seminars and conventions can also be arranged. They're located off of Paseo de Colón on C. 28, Av. 2/3.
www.horizontes.com
horizont@sol.racsa.co.cr

Run by a Costa Rican architect, **Caña Dulce** (☎ 258-3535, fax 222-0201) offers "cultural tourism." They have small-scale tours to coffee plantations, churches, local festivals, and other historical sites.
canadulc@sol.racsa.co.cr

Cultourica (☎ 249-1761, 249-1271) offers inexpensive nature tours which focus on community-oriented cooperatives and other projects.
cultourica@sol.racsa.co.cr

Conexiones (☎ 231-3637, 290-6149, fax 231-5221; Box 025216 SJO 210, Miami, FL 33102-5216) is a new San José-based travel agency who offer a number of innovative trips and packages all over the nation.
connexion@sol.racsa.co.cr

Expediciones Tropicales (☎ 257-4171, fax 257-4124), Ave. 11/13, 3 bis, is a tour operator which offers a wide range of tours; it has a good reputation.
www.costaricainfo.com/expetrop.html
expetrop@sol.racsa.co.cr

Ecoscape Nature Tours (☎ 297-0064, fax 297-0549) offers a "Highlights Tour" which visits Poás, Braulio Carrillo, and other attractions in one ten-hour day tour.
ecoscape@sol.racsa.co.cr

Kapi Tours (☎/fax 231-7071; Apdo. 566, 1200 San José) offers a variety of package tours which last as long as 13 days.
www.zurqui.com/crinfocus/kapi/kapi.htm
kapijm@hotmail.com

Costa Rica Sun Tours (☎ 233-6890, fax 255-1665; Apdo. 1195, 1250 Escazú.) specializes in Arenal and the Tiskita Lodge, S of Golfito. Bicycle tours of Orosi Valley are also offered.
www.crsuntours.com

Ecole Travel (☎ 223-2240, fax 223-4128) offers inexpensive tours.
ecolecr@sol.racsa.co.cr

Ecoscape Nature Tours (☎ 297-0064, fax 297-0549) operates the Costa Rican Highlights Tour which offers a ten-hr, trip to Poás, Braulio Carrillo, and other wonders.
ecoscape@sol.racsa.co.cr

Tours by **Río Tropicales** (☎ 233-6455) include white water rafting and stays at their lodge on the Pacuare.
www.riostropicales.com
www.riversearch.com
info@riostropicales.com

Specializing in rafting and kayaking, **Adventuras Naturales** (☎ 233-6455) has packages which include trekking.
www.toenjoynature.com

Caminos de la Selva or **Jungle Trails** (☎ 255-3486; Apdo. 5941, San José) has an unusual variety of hiking and camping trips.

Adventure Tours (☎ 232-8610, 231-5371), headquartered at the Corobicí Hotel, offers a variety of tours and a special trip up the Río Sarapiquí. Private tours are also available.

Caribbean Treks and Expeditions (☎ 223-2125, 233-3993, fax 223-5785; Apdo. 363, San José) runs a gamut of tours from surfing to rafting and biking.

Interviajes (☎/fax 238-1212; Apdo. 296, 3000 Heredia) in Heredia offers a number of inexpensive tours.

Based at Playa Tamarindo, **Papagayo Excursions** (☎ 680-0859, 680-0652, 232-6854) operates cruises through mangrove swamps and past turtle nesting sites.

Liberia's own **Guanacaste Tours** (☎ 666-0306, fax 666-0307), one of the nation's best tour companies, runs tours to Santa Rosa, Palo Verde, Arenal, and other destinations. Write Apdo. 55, 5000 Liberia.

Costa Rica Coast to Coast Adventures (☎ 225-6055, 280-8054, fax 225-7806, Apdo. 2135, 2000 San José) offers spectacular trips which include hiking, biking, rafting, rock climbing, and other adventures.
www.ctocadventures.com
info@ctocadventures.com
ctocsjo@sol.racsa.co.cr

Serendipity Adventures (☎ 556-2592, fax 426-5026; Apdo. 76, CATIE, Turrialba) offers balloon tours at sunrise, white water rafting, tree climbing, canyoning, and other activities.
www.serendipityadventures.com

Internal Transport

Owing to its compact size and relatively developed and professional infrastructure, Costa Rica is one of the easiest Latin American nations to get around in. If there's no bus going directly to a place, it's generally possible to take a bus to the nearest dropoff point and hire a taxi from there. Another option, especially for those who have more money than time, is flying.

BY AIR: Government owned and subsidized, **SANSA** flies daily or several times weekly between San José and Tamarindo, Nosara, Samara, Quepos, Golfito, and Coto 47 near the border with Panama. It offers lower fares for Costa Rican nationals and residents and departs from the international airport in San José.

During the tourist season, flights (which seat only 25-30 passengers) should be booked well in advance. If you don't have a booking, keep in mind that you can always try to fly standby. SANSA has a bad track record for reliability, and it is not uncommon to find your flight cancelled without prior notice. Their office (☎ 221-9414, fax 255-2176) is in the Grupo TACA building which is off the far end of Paseo de Colón. Remember that SANSA considers confirmed reservations only those for which a cash payment has been received, and you must pay for your ticket the day before you leave! SANSA operates shuttle buses to and from the airport.

www.grupotaca.com

Another, newer airline is the more expensive **Travelair** (reservations ☎: 220-3054, sales: 296-1102, fax 296-2316; SJO 788, PO Box 025216, Miami, FL 33102-5216) which flies from San José to Tortuguero (US$51 OW), Quepos (US$50 OW), Golfito (US$84 OW), Palmar Sur (US$113 OW), Tamarindo (US$92OW), Liberia (US$92 OW), Punta Islita, Puerto Jiménez (US$90 OW), Tambor (US$69 OW), and Carrillo (US$82 OW). (RT fares are lower). It leaves from the smalll Pavas airport on the W side of San José but has a shuttle to the international airport. They fly passengers in 15-passenger turbo prop LET planes.

Travelair's reservation offices are open.daily from 6 AM-11 PM. Reservations may also be made on the web. Children under 11 are offered a discounted rate. If you have a ticket, you are guaranteed a flight. Carry-on and baggage are limited to 25 lbs. (as compared to 12 lbs. with SANSA). Excess baggage is billed at US$.45/lb, and bikes are US$25 each way (which is higher than SANSA). Charters are available to all of these destinationa as well as Barra del Colorado. Fax 220-0413 (attn. Sylvia or Vanessa) for prices.

www.travelair-costarica.com
information@travelair-costarica.com

SEAPLANE: (☎ 296-4244) has a seaplane available for charter for around $300 ph. Other charter planes depart from the smaller Aeropuerto Tobías Bolaños near Pavas, to the W of San José.

AIRTOURS: A new company, Pitts Aviation (☎ 383-3673, ☎/fax 228-9912; Apdo. 1442, 1250 Escazú) offers air tours of the nation from US$99 pp.

skytours@sol.racsa.co.cr

Land Transport

BY TRAIN: Alas, there are no more trains!

BY BUS: Buses run practically everywhere, although runs are less frequent to more remote destinations. There are

URL Check bus schedules online at **www.yelloweb.co.cr/crbuses.html** A printed form is available in Costa Rica under the title *Get on the Bus!*

comfortable and inexpensive runs on main highways to Puerto Limón, Puerto Viejo de la Talamanca, Golfito, Puntarenas, Liberia, and other major towns. Travel times anywhere within the country are reasonable. It takes about eight hours from San José to Golfito for example. It's essential to know a bit of Spanish, but only a bit will go a long way. Remember not to flash money around and to keep a close watch on your things while in transit. Baggage can be a problem. Although some buses may have storage below, many do not — including the local buses. Overhead racks inside won't hold large backpacks or suitcases; it's preferable to carry as little as possible. Try to store excess bagage in San José. If there's no buzzer on your bus, yell out *"La parada por favor."*

RESERVATIONS: If you're planning to travel on weekends or during three-day holidays, it's advisable to obtain tickets in advance, particularly to and from places such as Puntarenas, Manuel Antonio, the Caribbean coast, and beaches on the Nicoya Peninsula. In any event, if you know exactly how long you're staying, it's always good practice to buy a return ticket upon arrival.

BUS ROUTES: There are over 700 bus routes covering virtually every hamlet, village, and town. Local buses link towns to each other, and long distance bus services link them to San José. They generally leave on the button, and the fare is collected onf board. (It is advisable to buy your ticket a few days in advance on major routes if you will be traveling on weekends or holidays or are on a tight schedule).

The quality of the bus employed ranges from the huge white buses used on the San José-Puntarenas route to the geriatric Bluebirds found frequently in the countryside. On board, decorations near the driver may include painted murals of seascapes and pictures of Jesus. On the better roads—particularly along the smooth Interamerican Highway, travel is inexpensive and fast. But, on the rougher rural roads, fares and travel times escalate. You'll need to have patience! One problem with bus travel is that buses to more remote areas may leave only once or a few times per day. Your hotel, the ICT, and a bar or restaurant near the bus stop are all good sources for information on departures.

NOTE: *Because schedules seldom change, the times in this book should be accurate. But, if you're on a tight schedule or have an early departure, you would do well to double-check.*

HITCHING: Hitchhiking is slow but very possible and a good way to pass the time while waiting for buses in the boonies. In some places, where there are no buses, it may save you a taxi fare. In the rural areas, Costa Ricans with cars are generally conscious of the transport situation and, although there may not be many cars, a high percentage of those that do pass will stop for you.

BY TAXI: Generally reasonably priced, cabs are meterless, and the fare depends largely upon your ability to bargain in Spanish. Be sure to agree on one before getting into a cab.

The exception to the rule is San José where the meters (*marías*) are used upon insistence. Taxis may be easily identified by their red color and the inverted gold triangle on their front door. Especially if you have a group of people, taxis can also be a reasonable alternative to renting a car, but you should negotiate as well as ask around.

> ?!¿ Only around 16% of Costa Rican roads are paved.

DETERMINING A FARE: Unmetered taxi fares may change like the weather. Factors include your apparent affluence, the driver's current psychological state, your own psychological state, your dress, and your pickup point or destination. If you are going to an expensive hotel, it's better just to give the nearest intersection. If you're unsure or the fare appears too high, an effective technique is to ask several drivers.

If a San José driver refuses to use his meter, take his permit number and car license (*numero de placa*); the ICT office has the Ministry of Public Transport complaint forms. As the meter only goes up to 15 km, it's necessary to bargain for a longer trip.

Buses run until 10 or 11 in San José, but stop earlier in the smaller towns, after which you'll be dependent upon taxis. In the outback, many cabs are four-wheel drive. Finally, remember that the drivers are not tipped.

CHARTERING: If you are in a group, you might consider chartering a taxi as a less expensive alternative to tours or as a method of getting to and from national parks. Be sure to bargain and set the fare beforehand.

Car Rental

Although renting a car may be an option you'll want to consider, you should know exactly what you're getting into. With one of the world's highest per capita accident rates, Costa Rica is not one of the easiest places to drive. Macho is often the rule here, and passing on narrow two-lane highways can be dangerous. Even on steep and winding grades, buses and trucks pass in both directions. In San José itself, the streets are narrow and one way; few parking lots or spaces are available.

In defense of driving, however, it can truthfully be said that once you leave the San José area, the accident rate drops as, due to lower population and income levels, there are fewer cars. And, with over 18,020 miles (29,000 km) of roads, there's plenty of territory to explore.

You can use a valid US or International driver's license here for up to three months. A permit is necessary to drive a motorbike of up to 90 cc. Cars may also be rented at the airport. You can expect to pay around $350/wk for an insured subcompact plus gas. Unless you have a credit card, you'll have to fork over a whopping deposit. The most useful vehicle, a four-wheel drive jeep, is the most expensive at around US$70 pd.

Taxi Rates

Taxis charge 165 *colones* for the first km and 90 *colones* for each additional km. Outside of San José, the charge is 95 *colones* per additional km. These fares apply to trips of up to 12 km; fares must be negotiated for longer distances. From 10 PM until 5 AM, a surcharge of 20% is applied. Be sure to watch out for drivers who add an extra zero on to the meter and who use a nighttime rate during the day. Avoid pirate cabs at your own peril

Don't rent a four-wheel-drive vehicle unless you really need it to get where you're going. Gas costs a bit more than in the US. A state-run monopoly, mandatory car insurance (a steep $8.50-$12/pd with $250 deductible) will be supplied by the rental company. As you should do everywhere, read the contract thoroughly — especially the fine print. Ask about unlimited mileage, free gas, late return penalties, and drop-off fees. Check the car over for dents and scratches and make sure that the agent notes any damage so you won't be charged later.

A problem surfacing in recent years has been attempts by rental companies to charge for nonexistent damages. It's preferable to bring your car back in plenty of time for your flight. If you have a video camera, you may want to film your vehicle (inserting a view of a digital watch which shows the date and time).

DRIVING: Road hazards at night include pedestrians, holes, and livestock.Signs you should know the meaning of include *siga con precaucíon* (proceed with caution), *ceda el paso* (yield), *peligro* (danger), and *despacio* (slowly). Be sure to fill up at the main towns before heading out to the sticks where there may be no service stations. Also, while you'll find stations that are open 24 hours in San José, many in the countryside run only from dawn to dusk. Bring a rag to wipe the inside windows in the rain. Unless otherwise posted, speed limits are usually 80 kph (50 mph) on toll roads and highways. Speeders are subject to stiff fines, and you must also remember to use your seatbelt in the front or face a ticket.

It's preferable to avoid driving in congested San José, and you may even wish to consider beginning your car rental elsewhere. (Hotels in Jacó Beach, Manuel Antonio, and in Guanacaste as well as elsewhere have car rental agencies: National rents out of Liberia).

Be sure to allow twice the amount of time to find someplace that you might if you were to drive the same distance in the US or Canada.

> ☛ It may be better to reserve your vehicle rental in the US because you may get a better rate. Call the 800 nos. for the major agencies and shop around. (Avis: 800-331-1212; Budget 800-527-0700; Hertz 800-654-3131; National 800-328-4567 Thrifty 800 367 2277). Also, certain rental companies have bad reputations. For example, a posting on Compuserve's Travel Forum accused one rental company of claiming scratches that were not there and of using their credit card number to buy things.

FINDING PLACES: One way to find things is by using your odometer; another is to look out for the rather blaring ads for Delta cigarettes which have the names and pointers for major destinations on them. There are also signs denoting the entrance to various *playas* (beaches) along both coasts; your car gives you the advantage of driving in and actually exploring.

CORRUPT COPS: If a policeman stops you for speeding, don't pay the fine on the spot because this will go straight into his pocket (and is illegal). Insist on a citation ("*deme un parte*") "give me a citation") which you will then have to go to court to pay. If he appears to have stopped you just to hassel you, pretend to speak no Spanish even if you are fluent. Maintain your politeness. If you are maltreated, get his ID number and report it to the Dirección de Tránsito.

OTHER TIPS: You may use your own license for up to three months. Be sure you have your passport (or a photocopy of it) on you at all times. Expect to rent a four-wheel-drive if you intend to travel on the back roads which can be extremely muddy. Drive defensively.

> If possible, park in a *parqueo* which will also be safer than on the street. In San José, you will need tokens for the meters; these are sold in *sodas* and in shopping centers.

PARKING: Never park illegally. Yellow curbs mean no stopping, even if you are in the car. Getting towed is no picnic.

CAR TROUBLE: Costa Rican law mandates that you must have flourescent triangles to place on the road in front and to the rear of your car in case of a breakdown. Call **Coopetaxi** (☎ 235-9966) if you do break down.

IN THE EVENT OF ACCIDENT: If you have an accident call 227-7150 or 227-8030 for a traffic cop. Wait for their approval before moving your car, and be sure to get the names and ID numbers of any witnesses. Sketch the area with the positions of the vehicles before and after the accident indicated. Obtain the names of witnesses. Give no statements. Take the set of reflective triangles (which you must legally have) and put them out in front of your vehicle. It is mandatory that you report the accident to the local municipality or Tribunal de Tránsito within eight days. Take a copy of their report—along with your driver's license, police report, insurance policy, and any other relevant information — to the INS (☎ 223-5800, 223-3446) at Av. 7 between C. 9/11.

RENTAL AGENCIES: For a full list check the yellow pages under "Alquiler de Automóviles." Some of the more prominent are **ADA Rent-a-Car** (☎ 233-6957), Budget (☎ 223-3284), **Dollar** (☎ 233-3339), Poás (☎ 221-2331), **Viva** (☎ 231-3341, 232-4333), **Toyota** (☎ 222-2250, 223-8979), Hertz (☎ 221-1818, 223-5959), **Tropical** (☎ 232-2111), **Elegante** (☎ 221-0136, 221-0284, 233-8605), **Avis** (☎ 322-9922, 442-1321). Many of these also have branches at the airport.

OTHERS: **Elegante** has branches in Quepos (☎ 777-0115), Puntarenas (☎ 661-1958), and Tamarindo (☎ 653-0115). **Ada** operates from Liberia (☎ 666-2998) and Jacó (☎ 643-3207). **Economy** has branches in Jacó (☎ 643-3280) and Flamingo (☎ 654-4152). **Toyota** (☎ 666-0016) has a branch in Liberia as do Sol (☎ 666-2222) and National (☎ 666-1211).

In Liberia to the N, **Adventura Rent A Car** (☎ 666-2349), El Bramadero, Liberia. Most beach resort hotels can also arrange rentals.

MOTORBIKE RENTAL: Rent-a-Moto (☎ 257-3831, fax 256-1670) rents bikes for around US$210/wk. A US$500 credit card deposit is required.
www.online.co.cr/peisa
peisainc@sol.racsa.co.cr

Motorcycles Costa Rica (☎ 446-5015, fax 446-6635) offers rentals as well as guided trips. They are based in Atenas.

AMIGAM

AMIGAM (☎ 257-6198, 296-3751, fax 222-7924) is a reservations and promotion service run by an association of small businesses. It offers the opportunity visitors to make reservations with small hotels and lodges (over 200, priced from US$20-65) as well as find tours .
www.amigam.com
sabanabb@sol.racsa.co.cr

Accommodations

Costa Rica has thousands of hotels — everything from luxury resorts to simple hostelries. It all depends on what you want, and what you want you can find. ***A 13.4% tax is added***. Keep in mind that listing of a hotel in this guide does not necessarily constitute a recommendation.

MAKING RESERVATIONS: Reservations should be made a month in advance during the dry season and three months in advance for Christmas and Easter. Be sure to reconfirm three days in advance. During the rest of the year, reservations are a good idea, but you generally can have your pick of rooms. Couples should state if they prefer twin or double beds. Rooms with a shared bath down the hall are the least expensive. Remember that most tourist-oriented hotels give a 20-30% discount during the low season. The major resorts and hotels have three or four sets of rates: winter, summer, shoulder, and (sometimes) Christmas.

TERMINOLOGY: You will frequently encounter the "***apartotel.***" This is an apartment hotel which has rooms with kitchen facilities. These are often suites and, in addition to daily, usually have weekly and monthly rates.***Cabinas*** — literally cabins — are sometimes similar to motels and sometimes identical with apartment hotels.

"***Villas***" and "***chalets***" are fancier cabinas. Found on the outskirts of San José, motels cater to the tryst trade. Finally, "***pensións***" and "***hospedajes***" are other names for inexpensive hotels.

PRICING: For the reader's convenience, prices (generally inclusive of 13.4% tax) are listed in US dollars. They are subject to fluctuation and should be used only as a guideline; the 1990 oil price rises have hit the economy hard, and while the currency continues to devalue, it is impossible to say whether prices will increase at a slower or faster pace. Wherever you go, there are likely to be one or more newer places not listed in this guide. are generally more expensive for just one person, cheaper per person for two, and lower thereafter. Local hotels either charge double the single price for a couple or reduce the price slightly.

Establishments for which no prices are listed are classified as follows: **low budget** (les than $20 d), **inexpensive** ($20-30 d), **moderate** ($31-50 d), **expensive** ($51-90 d), **luxury** ($90-120), and **ultra-luxury** (over $120 d). It's a good idea to get the current rates from the tourist board; they can print them out if you request it at the Plaza de la Cultura office. If they don't list the rates, it's just that they haven't supplied them to the board, so use the address or phone number listed to contact them. There are also rental agents on the island.

FACILITIES: In Costa Rica, you don't necessarily get what you pay for. Some owners have gotten greedy and boosted prices higher than inflation (and their services) should allow. Also, things may not quite be what they seem in the brochure. A scarlet macaw may be a pet (as opposed to flying overhead with its mate) and an exploding volcano may be an hour or more away. In some of the less expensive establishments (and in many of the expensive lodges as well), "hot" water may mean an electrical device attached to the showerhead which warms the water. It's clever, and it does the trick, but it's not as hot as a gas heated shower.

Selecting a Rainforest Lodge

With tourism's growth in Costa Rica, the number of private reserves has grown apace. As any reader of this book will notice, it has become increasingly difficult to catalog the accommodations available, let alone evaluate them all. Practically everyone who has a patch of forest (or even a denuded cattle farm) wants to jump on the "eco-tourism" bandwagon, some without really understanding what's involved.

As parks (such as Manuel Antonio and Tortuguero) are becoming more clogged with tourists and raise entrance fees for foreigners to extortionate levels, private reserves are playing a more important role. But they are generally not for people on a budget. Costs usually run around $50 per person per day for room and board, not including transportation, a guide, horses, or other extras. If you can't afford this, you're better off hiking and camping in a less frequented park or reserve.

On the other hand, these lodges are not for those who are especially demanding about their accommodations. While most are well constructed and fairly new, the occasional bug is going to get into your room and, if there a generator, it will probably not run all night. You almost certainly won't be near a shopping mall or a boutique—at best, there may be a small store in the lodge or a nearby.

The best way to select a lodge is by asking the right questions. *Is there electricity?* Hot water? *What kind of food is served?* How close is the lodge to the main road? *What is the fastest way to get there?* How much does the transportation cost? *What's the least expensive way to get there?* Do they have horseback trips? *Do they have night hikes?* Do the prices include taxes and service charges? *Do they have a biologist/naturalist on the premises?* What is his or her nationality and qualifications? *Are guided hikes included in the price or are they additional?* What other tours and excursions are available?

These are some of the questions you may want to ask. Depending on your situation, you may come up with others. Some answers are found in this book; others are not. Keep in mind that some details will have changed from the time this book was written. Allow plenty of time for correspondence with the lodges. Many do not have direct telephones. Whenever possible, deal directly with the lodges and avoid travel agencies. They will save 15-20%, and you'll get the details from the horse's mouth.

Another alternative is to talk to any friends who have recently returned from Costa Rica or to travellers you meet there. But make sure that, in weighing their recommendations, you take stock of any differences in their experience and outlook. A lodge that may seem wild to a Sunday stroller could be too civilized for an avid backpacker. In any event, do write and let us know your recommendations.

RESERVATIONS: If you arrive without reservations, the ICT has offices to help you in the airport (which may not be open if you arrive late). However, they will not be much help if you're on a budget. Although reservations may not be necessary for the large hotels except during the season, it would be prudent to both reserve and send a deposit to the smaller establishments which do accept reservations so you can be certain of your booking. If you need to make reservations ahead, you should note that many of the coastal hotels have a San José number. It will be difficult to make reservations for the lower priced hotels unless you can speak Spanish. However, the cheapest of these often do not take reservations. Fax numbers (when available) are listed throughout the text, and faxes are appropriate ways to make reservations.

CHOOSING ACCOMMODATIONS: Remember that every dollar, pound or DM you spend while in Costa Rica constitutes a vote. By staying near the parks and reserves in Costa Rican-owned accommodation, you emphasize to local people the importance of conservation and its economic potential. Locals who can see the benefits of preserving the forest are less likely to destroy it. And the money stays in Costa Rica and benefits Costa Ricans rather than being repatriated. You don't necessarily need to sacrifice comfort to stay outside of San José: rainforest lodges are getting more and more deluxe all of the time. They are all listed in the travel section.

TWO-TIER PRICING: In the old days, Tico and visitor suffered the same and paid the same. These days, with a growing number of hotels affordable only to the wealthiest of the nation's elite, a two-tier pricing system has been instituted (with tacit ICT approval) across the country. This practice is generally found in the tourist spots along with the more expensive hotels.

Ticos and foreign residents—including American Embassy employees and banana plantation execs—get a secret discount of as much as 40% at many hotels and lodges. Ticos argue that the lower prices help support hotels which suffer in the off-season and that they cannot afford to pay more. These are, however, often the same Costa Ricans who can afford to pay premium prices in Hawaii and Europe.

Costa Rica is not the only "tropical paradise" to practice this system. It is common in Mexico and in Jamaica, but is unknown in Europe, North America, Japan, or anywhere workers are paid a wage in line with costs. A better approach would be to charge everyone the same price but with off-season discounts.

It's always a good idea to consider your eating habits while booking accommodation. For example, if you eat breakfast, you should think about what you may need or want to eat and when. Check to see when breakfast (or even coffee) will be available. Many hotels serve a complimentary breakfast which is often continental. Consider whether this will satisfy you or not. Find out what other meals are available and how far it is to other restaurants. Vegetarians or those who simply shun meat and dead fowl will want to know if the restaurant will have anything for them to eat. Remember, it always pays to inquire before rather than after!

For a list of **bed-and-breakfasts** throughout Costa Rica which are booked by long-time resident Pat Bliss see www.savethemanatee.com/b&b or www.jps.net/vudu/bliss2.html

BED AND BREAKFASTS: A recent feature on the Costa Rican accommodations landscape, the B&Bs fill a niche. Generally staffed by expats (although a few have Tico owners), they provide hospitality and information in addition to a room. You can't expect the services you find at a high-priced hotel, but the homey atmosphere more than makes up for it.

PRIVATE NATURE RESERVES: These present one of the best opportunities you'll have to gain a deeper understanding of the ecology while simultaneously meeting residents. You can usually expect spartan but functional accommodations, although

Selected Ecotourism Projects in Costa Rica

"Ecotourism" is a loosely defined term to say the least. The best bring visitors to a community under terms which the community benefits financially, learning takes place, and the environment is preserved for the future. Here are a few places that attempt to do just that.

Albergues Ecoturisticos & Coopeunioro *This set of village cooperatives (☎ 259-3401/8442, fax 259-9430) offers activities for visitors. Members include the Ecopavones Ecotouristic Lodge (near Pavones), the Silencio Community Ecolodge (in Silencio near Savegre 25 km NE of Dominical and 30 km from Quepos), the Coopesanjuan Community Ecolodge (in La Gloria de Aguas Zarcas de San Carlos) and Coopeunioro (a 13-family cooperative is operated by former goldminers near Corcovado National Park). All are similarly priced and offer a wealth of activities.*

MINAE

SINAC

www.novanet.co.cr/cooprena
cooprena@sol.racsa.co.cr

Esquinas Rainforest Lodge *Set on the border of a national park to the N of Golfito in southwestern Costa Rica, this lodge (☎ 382-5798, fax 775-0631; Apdo 183, Golfito) was financed largely by donations from Austrians and is intended to benefit the community.*
esquinas@sol.racsa.co.cr

ATEC *This cooperative has an office is in the village center of Puerto Viejo on the Caribbean coast. They offer offer a number of trips, and your fees go to your guide directly. Call 750-0188, 750-0191.*
atecmail@sol.racsa.co.cr

Las Delicias Ecotourism Project *Located near Barra Honda National Park on the Nicoya Peninsula. Three inexpensive cabinas, a campsite, gift shop, and restaurant. Guides to the caves in the national park are also available through them. To reserve, leave a message in Spanish at 685-5580.*

some are fairly luxurious. Although most are out of the way, many provide transport either included in the rate or for an additional fee. Most are relatively expensive so they are not for low budget travelers, although some (such as Rara Avis) do give a discount for IYHF card holders. And there are a few conmunity tourism projects that provide a natural experience at a more reasonable cost.

ON A LOW-BUDGET: Low-budget travel is the best way to see any country, and it is definitely the best way to experience Costa Rican life as Costa Ricans experience it.

Out in the boonies, hotels can be found for a few dollars or so, and nearly every village has basic hotel rooms. Among the difficulties you might encounter include blaring TVs, clucking chickens, mosquitoes, spiders, and cockroaches. Some of the rooms are dimly lit. In spite of these drawbacks, the smaller hotels offer a genuine Tico experience, one which often brings you closer to the local people and their lives. Your neighbors will be ordinary, hardworking Costa Ricans, and not wealthy tourists on holiday. And your money goes directly to the local people who really need it. If you try it, you'll find that you can survive quite well without a/c—a fan, or sometimes no fan at all, will suffice. And, after you make the adjustment, everything else just falls into place.

Don't even think about camping during the rainy season unless your idea of fun is spending 12-16 hours in your tent waiting for a downpour to end! The exception to this would be if you have a car and can escape to a restaurant or other lodging.

CAMPING: Camping is not only a practical alternative to hotels; it may well be that you have no choice if you really want to get close to nature. When you're visiting one of the national parks, the nearest place to stay may be many kilometers away. Day trippers arrive after things warm up and animal movement has decreased. For camping at high elevations, a good bag and tent are required. Avoid staying in pastures which have ticks and chiggers. Although there are few organized camping areas, more are being added — in places such as Jacó and along the Caribbean coast. If you decide to camp be sure that your things will be safe.

Entertainment

Outside of San José, you may have to invent your own nightlife. At worst you might have to watch the stars overhead. Inside the city, there's generally plenty to do. Good sources are the *Tico Times*, Friday's issue of, and posters in front of the National Theater. Suggestions are also noted in the San José chapter as well as under specific listings for other towns.

MUSIC AND DANCE: The Punta Guanacasteco, the national dance, is performed to the accompaniment of the marimba and guitar. The nationk music

Marimba players perform in San José

is played on the *quijongo*, *ocarina*, and the *chirimia* —wind instruments dating back to the pre-Columbian era. These are from Guanacaste Province and are not commonly seen. Modern dance performances take place at the Teatro Nacional as well as other venues from time to time. Discos abound everywhere as do jukebox-equipped bars. Many discos play song after song of , mushy rock songs translated into Spanish. Watch as the couples cling to each other, tune after tune. With the distinct exception of San José, where they are basement-class prostitute pickup bars, a bar marked "Centro Social" connotes a community center with live music. al folk music is played on the *quijongo*, *ocarina*, and the *chirimia* —wind instruments dating back to the pre-Columbian era. These are from Guanacaste Province and are not commonly seen. Modern dance performances take place at the Teatro Nacional as well as other venues from time to time. Discos abound everywhere as do jukebox-equipped bars. Many discos play song after song of , mushy rock songs translated into Spanish. Watch as the couples cling to each other, tune after tune. With the distinct exception of San José, where they are basement-class prostitute pickup bars, a bar marked "Centro Social" connotes a community center with live music.

CONCERTS: There are a number of venues. Major groups seldom visit, but the National Symphony performs at Teatro Nacional as do some other local bands including the local "new song" band Adrián Goizueta and Grupo Experimental.

MOVIES: Most are dominated by the three themes of Kung fu, sex, and violence. Generally, the worst of American movies are shown with some finer films being shown in San José at such theaters as the **Sala Garbo** and at some of the cultural centers. There are few theaters out in the boonies these days. You can learn a lot about cultural attitudes by going to the movies and noting the audience reaction.

GAMBLING: Black jack and other games are found just about everywhere in and around San José. Specific listings are found in the travel section. Some casinos also offer craps. This is called *Domino Chino* (Chinese Dominos) here, and you'll find workers shuffling tiles instead of rolling dice; two dominos are turned over at each turn. Bingo is popular out in the provinces. The biggest and most widespread scam is the National Lottery.

Visas, Services, and Health

VISAS: American citizens may enter with a passport, driver's license, or voter's registration card and stay for 90 days, but they may not extend their visa for more than that if they do not have a passport. Canadians must have a passport if traveling by a charter flight. All visitors should note that they will be expected to show sufficient funds and a return ticket.

FOR OTHER NATIONALITIES: Citizens of the following nations do not require visas for stays of up to 90 days: Great Britain, West Germany, Spain, Argentina, Austria, Columbia, Denmark, South Korea, Japan, Netherlands, Finland, France, Italy, Israel, Norway, Roumania, and Luxembourg. Citizens of the following nations do not require visas for stays of up to 30 days: Honduras, Guatemala, Liechtenstein, Iceland, Sweden, Republic of Ireland, Switzerland, New Zealand, Brazil, Ecuador, Australia, Venezuela, and Mexico, Monaco, and Belgium. All others must have visas.

EXTENDING YOUR VISA: If you wish to avoid the lines, language difficulties, and the general hassle, you can go to a travel agent and receive an exit permit, which will permit you to stay an extra 30 days. This must be done prior to your tourist card's expiration date, and you must bring along your passport, tourist card, three passport photos, and airline ticket. You should make a copy of the first few pages of your passport for use while the agent is obtaining the permit. You'll be charged a fee, but this will save you two trips to Immigration and a half-day or so of standing in line. At the permit's expiration, you will be required to leave the country for at least 72 hours. In order to extend it more than a month, you must do so at Immigration, although you may go through a travel agent to receive your exit permit before you leave.

If you stay more than 92 days, a statement is required from the Ministerio de Haciendo showing that you owe no taxes. The travel agent may be able to get one of these as well. In any case, you'll be expected to show at least US$200 for each month you plan to extend. You may stay up to six months without departing so a 90-day extension is the maximum you will be granted. You should arrive at Immigration (located in the outlying suburbs of La Uruca) by 7:15 AM in the earlier part of the week. Go to the window labeled "Prorogas de Turismo" where you'll receive a form. Inquire as to the amount of revenue stamps you'll need and purchase those before going to the third (and hopefully final!) line. You'll receive a receipt for your passport which you'll have to come back for after several days.

Costa Rican Tourist Board Offices
SAN JOSE
Plaza de la Cultura Avenidas Central/2, Calle 5 ☎ 222-1090 ☎ 223-1733, x 277 ☎ 242-1820 (airport office)
MIAMI
1101 Brickell Avenue BIV Tower, Suite 801 Miami, FL 33131 ☎ (305) 358-2150 ☎ (800) 327-7033 Fax 305-358-7951
LOS ANGELES
3540 Wilshire Blvd. LA, CA 90010 ☎ (213) 382-8080

OVERSTAYING: A July 1995 crackdown on overstayers resulted in the issuance of deportation orders for 180 foreigners. While it was once possible for you to overstay practically forever, and pay a fine at the airport, the government has toughened restrictions and now offenders who may not re-enter the country for 10 years.

BRINGING YOUR PET: It's much simpler to leave Fido at home! If you want to persist, you should write far in advance of your visit to Jefe del Departamento de Zoonosis, Ministerio de Salud, 1000 San José, and ask for an importation form.

i In the US call 800-343-6332 for information courtesy of the Costa Rican Tourism Institute. It's available from 8-5 Costa Rican time. Inside Costa Rica itself you can dial 800-012-3456.

SERVICES AND INFORMATION: Tourist information centers are at the airport and in San José at the Plaza de la Cultura (☎ 222-1090). These are said to be the biggest "white elephant" the government has, and service in the offices can range from excellent to execrable depending upon who is in charge and if they feel like abandoning their newspapers or not. Generally, they only give you what you ask for, so be sure to ask for as many things as possible including the bus transport sheets. You may borrow these and photocopy them in the film shop across the street. Although better maps are available, the giveaway maps (also on sale at bookshops) should be sufficent for ordinary use. The best **map** available is put out by ITMB in Vancouver and is sold at select bookstores in Costa Rica nationwide.

LAUNDRY: Although laundromats are scarce and incredibly expensive, your hotel can usually arrange to do laundry or hook you up with a launderer. Cheaper hotels have sinks () where you can do your laundry yourself. Located next to Spoon in Los Yoses to the E of downtown San José, Lava Más is one of the few self-service joints found in the country. Check with your hotel for possible others.

Phone, Mail, Telephone & Internet Access

TELEPHONE SERVICE: Unlike some other nations, Costa Rica has a fairly reliable phone system, including a good supply of pay phones. Unfortunately, as Costa Ricans love to telephone, there's almost always a line! Pay telephones take either the new or antiquated varieties of coins, so it's best to carry a supply of both varieties. Always in short supply, the two *colones* coins are being replaced by the five *colones* coins, leading one to suppose that the government has chosen to rectify the shortage by raising the price. Many pay phones also use 10 and 20 *colones* coins, but they love five *colones* coins the best.

To use a pay phone, wait for a dial tone *before* inserting your coins. Call times are limited and at the end of your time you'll need to pay again. Although one species of machine has you place your coins on a rack to be digested as required, others will give you a signal. But be quick in depositing additional coins or face being cut off! If you dial and hear nothing or get a busy signal, be sure to redial: it may be a problem with the central exchange.

No calls within the country require a prefix. An increasingly smaller number

Using Pay Phones

When using the pay phones keep the following in mind:

- Obtain a good supply of five *colón* coins and keep them handy
- Redial several times if you get a busy signal.
- In Spanish query *"Aló"* and follow this with *¿se encuentra (name) por favor?* You will be asked *"?de parte?"* (who's this?) so give your name.
- If you are using a phone card be sure to get one (197) which is good for domestic and not one which is valid only for international calls (199).

Exploring Costa Rica Guide, an annual put out by *The Tico Times*, the English-language weekly, provides useful updates on new hotels which may not appear in any of the other comprehensive travel guides. It is sold in Costa Rica and comes free with a year's subscription. (A sub. brings the current issue).

largely by extensions. In areas where there are no regular public phones, shops, bars, and restaurants rent out their phones.

It's best to ask the price before dialing to make sure that it is fair and not a *gringo* rate. The cost can add up and there can also be a wait. If you have a large number of calls to make, you may want to wait until you are in a place with a regular pay phone. Some hotels tack on a surcharge to the bill which allows you unlimited dialing within the country. So, if your hotel has a phone in the room, ask about their policy when you check in.

CALLING TO AND FROM ABROAD: When dialing the US or Canada direct from a local phone, call 001, 116, and the number. Other useful numbers are 112, time of day; 117, San José police; 118, fire department; 127, local police.

For an AT&T overseas operater, dial 114. At the Radiográficia (C. 1, Av. 5) in San José, you can phone or wire abroad; either are very expensive. If you wish to make a credit card or collect call, you can reach AT&T operators directly from USADirect phones at the airport, Radiográfica, and at the Holiday Inn, Av. 4, C. 5.

PHONE CARDS: Phone card phones are chiefly found in San José and are slowly spreading to the boonies. Cards are be available in denominations of C 200, 500, and 1,000. Purchasing one makes sense chiefly if you are going to be spending a lot of time in and around San José.

POSTAL SERVICE: Window service at the main post office (Correos y Telegráphicos or Cortel, C. 2, Av. 1/3) run from 7-6 weekdays and 7-2 on Sat. Other offices are located nationwide. The philatelic department is upstairs. Rates are inexpensive; your color postcard is likely to cost you more than the stamp! Although owing to the vagaries of the postal systems involved it may take much longer, mail generally takes about five days to the US, Canada, or Europe.

Sea mail (*marítimo*) generally runs about four to six weeks to North America. To ensure prompt delivery, send mail from your hotel desk or a main post office and avoid enclosing anything other than a letter.

RECEIVING MAIL: You can have mail sent to you at your hotel or to *Lista De Correos* (General Delivery); the latter is at window 17 in the main post office. Have your correspondents send it in your name (have the last name written in capital letters), c/o Lista de Correos, Correo Central, San José.

Currently, letters (up to 20 g) cost C 20 locally, C 35 to Central America, C 45 to S and N America, and C 55 to Europe. Postal codes are placed *before* the city or town. In order to bypass the convoluted bureaucracy and absolutely outrageous customs duties, avoid having anything sent to you save letters and perhaps a few snapshots.

If you do receive a package, you may

Important Costa Rican Phone Nos.

AT&T	0-800-011-4114
MCI	0-800-012-2222
Sprint	0-800-013-0213
Canada Bell	0-800-015-1162
Nat. Parks Office	192
Emergency	911
Fire Department	118
Directory Assist.	113
Travel Air	220-3054
Sansa	221-9414
Caribbean Bus Schedules	256-4248

Costa Rican on the Internet

There are now more Costa Rican sites than you could ever check out. Many are listed in this book. Others can be found through search engines. Here is a list of some of the more interesting and useful ones.

www.nvmundo.com	volunteer opportunities
www.savethemanatee.com/costarica	Manatee Press
www.incostarica.net	The Costa Rica Supersite
www.ticotimes.co.cr	The Tico Times (newspaper)
www.nicoya.com	Nicoya
www.tamarindo.com	Tamarindo
www.nosara.com	Nosara
www.zancudo.com	Zancudo
www.crdirect.com	Hotels
www.costarica.tourism.co.co	Hotels
www.crica.com	Information
www.ots.ac.cr	Organization of Tropical Studies
www.maqbeach.com	Manuel Antonio/Quepos
www.playa-junquillal.com	Playa Junquillal
www.horizontes.com	Horizontes (travel agency)
www.cocori.co.cr	Completely Costa Rica (Web Site Overview)
www.yellowweb.co.cr	Bus schedules and weather
www.centralamerica.com	Expensive hotels
www.ecotourism.co.cr	Southern Zone
www.jacobeach.com	Jacó Beach
www.cahuita.com	Cahuita
www.greencoast.com/index.htm	Useful list of Costa Rica eco-travel links
www.expeditions.co.cr	Costa Rica Expeditions
wwwinbio.com	The Institute of Biodiversity
www.biophotos.com	Videos and photos by Richard Whitten
costaricapages.com	Costa Rican Yellow Pages (directory)
www.infocostarica.com	Costa Rican Information

Web Surfing Tips

Always search for a site twice if it is not found the first time.

If a site is down, try a variation of the domain name: It may have gotten its own domain.

Sign in at www.savethemanatee.com/innersoul to receive free updates.

When visiting Costa Rican sites check for links to other useful sites...

have to make two trips to the office way out in Zapote and pay a customs fee which could be more than the value of the package. Have your friends underline both "Costa Rica" and "Central America" to ensure that your letters won't languish in Puerto Rico!

If you have American Express traveler's checks or a credit card, you can have mail sent c/o Tan Travel Agency (☎ 233-0044), Apdo. 1864, San José). They're at Av. Central, C.1.

NOTE: Although things are said to be better, mail theft has been endemic. In 1993, following a two-year investigation, eight postal workers were fired for allegedly stealing thousands of checks, credit cards, and other valuables sent through the mail. The workers remained on the job during the investigation because Costa Rica's Civil Service laws require such an investigation before workers can be fired.

> If you send a fax to a post office with the address clearly written on it, the post office will deliver the fax to the recipient.

FAX: If your hotel has a fax machine, they will generally send one for you and allow you to receive one for a fee. The cheapest place to send a fax is at a CORTEL office. In San José, the main office is at C. 2, Av. 1/3. Go to the CORTEL Fax window, fill out the form, and head to the telex office upstairs (follow the arrow). Faxes can also be sent via Radiográfica (☎ 223-1609, 323-7932); their offices are at C. 1, Av. 5, open 7 AM-11 PM. If your correspondent includes your hotel's phone number, they will notify you. Call 287-0513 or 287-0511 to see if you have received a fax.

INTERNET ACCESS: While there are several Internet cafes in San José, access is limited, and you should limit receiving e-mails to important messages at the place or places where you will be staying. (Check with the management first). If you are going to be here a long time, you can connect up to the Internet, but it will be comparatively expensive to do so.

Broadcasting and Media

A media censorship board is in operation; its effect is most directly apparent in movies. In the past, all journalists had to be registered with the Colegio de Periodistas which was a clear violation of the nation's obligations under the Human Rights Convention to which it is a signatory. In a May 1995 ruling, the Supreme Court ruled the licensing unconstitutional. In Jan. 1999, *La República* columnist Julio Suñol was summarily fired and barred from entry to the building, presumably because of his atttack on the president's individually-initiated 155% raise in pay.

NEWSPAPERS: There are four daily papers: The daily *La Nación* is a horrifically propagandistic right-wing tabloid said to be manipulated by US interests. Its vice-director is vice-president of the Free Costa Rica Movement (MRCL), a right-wing civic organization with an armed militia. Others are *La Prensa Libre* and *La República* (originally founded by Figueres and his supporters in 1950). They aren't much better.

There are four weekly newspapers including *Esta Semana* (the best Spanish language source for news) and the equally fine *Universidad*, published by the University of Costa Rica.

Muckraking journalist Martha Honey has called English language *Tico Times* "definitely the best newspaper in Central America." It covers local poli-

tics, the environmentally-destructive activities of unethical hotel chains. and has a very useful "Weekend" section. Subscriptions are available, and portions may be accessed online.
www.ticotimes.co.cr

Essential for anyone concerned about Central American politics and economics, ***Mesoamerica*** (☎ 235-3195, ☎/fax 234-7682; Apdo. 1524, 2050, San Pedro, San José) is published in San José's suburb of San Pedro. The library at the Friend's Peace Center sells copies.
www.amrisol.com/costarica/edu/mesoamer.html
mesoamer@sol.racsa.co.cr

Costa Rica Outdoors is a bimonthly full-color magazine geared towards sportsfishing.

RADIO: All radio stations are privately owned, either by commerical interests or by religious broadcasters. Most stations play an amalgam of salsa and American rock and schlock.

Radio Universidad, at 870 AM and 96.7 and 101.9 FM specializes in classical music and educational programing. It also offers New Age and jazz.

Radio Azul, 99 FM, plays chiefly jazz and "new age" music.

Radio 2 at 99.5 FM offers news in English on the half-hour, hits from the 1960s on, and other information. For those missing the concrete jungles of LA, you can tune in for Dick Barkley's "American Gold" from 10 to noon on Sat. and Sun. From 6-9 weekdays, you can hear Dick Barkely's "Good Morning, San José" program.

Radio Uno 102.7 FM offers rock music introduced by bilingual djs.

Colorín Radio at 91.1 FM offers broadcasts for children; the bulk of the programming consists of stories. Radio for Peace International transmits on shortwave and broadcasts in English, Spanish, German, and French Creole.

Radio 107.5 offers all-English broadcasts and promises "100% Rock at the End of Your Dial." It also offers BBC news broadcasts at 8 AM and 5 PM.

Radio Stations

Frequency	Station Name/Programming
500.9 AM	Radio Nacional Popular (mixed)
670 AM	Radio Monumental (romantic)
700.3 AM	Radio Reloj (Latin pop)
760 AM	Radio Columbia (talk radio)
780 AM	Radio America (Latin pop)
850 AM	Radio Viva (US/Latin pop)
870 AM	Radio Universidad Classical music, educational
900 AM	Radio Nacional Popular (mixed)
1080 AM	Radio Alajuela Latin dance music
1440 AM	Radio Puntarenas Latin pop
1420 AM	Radio Pompa Popular
88.7 FM	Radio Lira Popular
91.1 FM	Colorín Radio (Children)
91.9 FM	Radio Puntarenas (Latin pop)
93.5 FM	Radio Monumental (romantic)
94.3 FM	Radio Reloj (Latin pop)
94.7 FM	Radio Joven (rock)
95.1 FM	Radio Fabulosa (US/Latin romantic)
96.7 FM	Radio Universidad (classical music/educationa)l
96.9 FM	Radio 96 Classical
97.5 FM	Radio Musical Romantic
97.9 FM	Radio Titania US/Spanish pop
98.3 FM	Radio Alajuela (Latin music)
98.7 FM	Radio Columbia Talk radio
99 FM	Radio Azul Jazz /"new age"
99.1 FM	Radio Sabrosa (Latin music)
99.5 FM	Radio 2 1960-90s hits
101.5 FM	Radio Ultra-Sonic Popular
101.9 FM	Radio Universidad (classical music/educational)
102.3 FM	Super Radio 1960s/70s US rock
102.7 FM	Radio Uno (US/Latin rock/pop)
104.3 FM	Radio Sensación (Spanish pop)
105.1 FM	Radio Omega New popular
106.3 FM	Radio Stereo 106 Muzac
107.5 FM	"Rock at the End of your Dial"

TELEVISION: First introduced in 1960, there are now six TV stations. TV serves up a combination of the worst of American programming rendered into Spanish and bad local imitations of the worst of American programming. It is rather dismaying to see MTV in Spanish, featuring videos by heavy metal bands from El Salvador! Cable Network News (CNN) and other cable service in English is available. An interview program in English, Costa Rica Update appears every Thurs. at 7 PM on Channel 19; it's rebroadcast at 1 PM.

Health and Hygiene

Costa Rica is perhaps the most sanitary of the Central American nations. Although tap water in San José is safe to drink, you may wish to exercise caution elsewhere.

If hiking and camping, either drink boiled water or have iodine tablets on hand. If the taste bothers you, add a little powdered drink mix or squeeze lemon or lime into your water bottle.

Take basic precautions such as washing both your hands and pocketknife before peeling fruit.

No immunizations are required. You may wish to get a gamma globulin shot to stave off hepatitis A, but the incidence of the disease is low here. **Diarrhea** (easily remedied by over-the-counter medicines) is much more common than dysentery, the symptoms of which include fever and blood in the stools.

Malaria is nonexistent except near Panama on the Caribbean coast and in the Sarapiquí and Limón areas—an effect of poor health practices on the banana plantations. Some 6,000 cases were reported in 1992, the highest incidence in two decades. If you plan on spending a

- painkillers
- antihistimine tablets
- hydrocortisone cream (1%)
- sunscreen
- insect repellent
- band-aids
- antiseptic
- water purification tablets
- prescription medicines

long time in these areas, prevent an occurrence with a dose of chloroquine (marketed in Costa Rica as Aralen) and begin two weeks before your arrival. Keep in mind that these mosquitoes bite mainly at night.

Outbreaks of **dengue fever** have also been reported since 1994, but this mosquito-borne viral disease should not affect short-term visitors. Dengue victims have a sudden high fever and body aches coupled with diarrhea and vomiting, a sour aftertaste, and (frequently) dots of blood on the skin.

Leptospirosis, a disease caused by a microorganism, is transmitted to humans from animals through contaminated water. Again, cases have been reported, but it should not be a problem with visitors.

Another disease which may infect long-term residents but is unlikely to affect casual visitors, **legemaniasis** is a sand flea-borne viral infection which causes a cutanaceous ulcer under your skin. It can only be cured with injections, and it results in a depressed, depigmented scar.

There are plenty of *farmacia* around should you require medicine, but most medications are imported (largely from Europe and the US) and expensive. Costa

Rica's health system is reputed to be among the world's best; hospitals and other information are listed in the San José section of this book.

PRECAUTIONS: While San José water is safe to drink, visitors should exercise caution with water in other locales. If you should believe you might have amoebic dysentery, go to Clinica Biblica (☎ 223-6422) or Clinica Americana (☎ 222-1010) and have a urine test. Medicine can be purchased at any pharmacy. Be sure to wash with soap and water after swimming in a pool or river and, to stave off ear infections, swab yourself.

> If you should need to wash your hands and/or use a toilet pop into the nearest fast food restaurant in San José. While no one who values their health would ever eat in one of these, they do have clean restrooms.

SNAKEBITE: In the *extremely* unlikely event that you should be bitten by a snake, don't panic! Stay still and try to take note of its characteristics (size, color, pattern, and head shape). Non-poisonous snake bites show two rows of teeth marks, but fang marks are lacking. Suck venom from the wound or push it out with your fingers and apply a loose tourniquet. Walk back to your lodge. You still have several hours before the venom takes effect.

The best way to prevent snakebite is to avoid stepping on one. Birders should have friends who occasionally focus their eyes on the ground. Keep to trails, wear rubber boots, and avoid reaching into holes or under fallen logs. Never chase a retreating snake; instead, immediately retreat. Keep in mind that low-lying branches may also have snakes. If you leave snakes alone, they'll do likewise.

PROTECTION AGAINST INSECTS: Although scarce at higher altitudes, mosquitoes are prevelant in the lowlands. Buy insect repellent containing DEET (diethylmetatoluamide) at a 90 concentration or higher prior to your arrival; Seattle-based REI has a comparatively inexpensive brand.

A mosquito net is a handy appurtenance as are the boxes of mosquito coils (***spirales***) which keep the numbers down when you relax or sleep. *Pulperías* will sell you one or two if that's all you need, but make sure you get a stand (suporte). Avoid inhaling the smoke.

Tiny mites barely visible to the naked eye, **chiggers** (*coloradillas*) are some of the worst pests around. They wait on vegetation, then leap aboard and seek out a nice warm place—generally between your clothing and skin—and burrow in. (It loves to squeeze into protected places such as bra and belt lines and the genital area where it injects histamines). Itches can last for weeks. If afflicted, you can try running hot water on top of them, which will kill them. Dust your clothes and lower body with sulfur powder in order to stave them off. Or dissolve locally-available *azufre sublimado* under your tongue; it gives your sweat an odor noxious to chiggers. Avoid grassy areas whenever possible. Try antihistamine cream, Euthrax, or Caladryl to help soothe bites.

You have to watch for **ticks** (*garrapatas*) when you undress because they may not be evident otherwise. If you pull them straight off, you risk leaving their pincers in you. Hold a lighted match or cigarette to the bite and squeeze the area to extract the tick. Gasoline, kerosene, or alcohol will encourage the tick to come out. Repellents are ineffective against sand gnats; use some antibiotic ointment and, as is the case with all bites, avoid scratching or risk infection.

Small gnats which favor the tender skin of the ears and neck, **purrujas** (no-see-ums, biting midges) are almost invisible and are most active on warm days and windless evenings. Only the females bite humans.

Should you be stung by a wasp, scrape the detatched stinger out carefully with your fingernail. If you pull or squeeze it out, you'll pump more venom in! Unless you're an amateur or professional entomologist, give other insects space to be themselves. Touching seemingly adorable fuzzy or spiny caterpillars may cause painful caustic rashes. Colorful stinkbugs may spray cyanide.

In summary, prevention is the best cure: take the precautions listed here and wear protective clothing. Except for those that feed upon us directly, most insects harbor no animosity and would prefer a live-and-let-live peace accord.

Money and Shopping

MONEY: Monetary unit is the *colón* which is divided into 100 *centimos*. Notes are issued in denominations of 500, and 1,000 and coins are minted in amounts of 10, 25, 50, and 100 colones. Coins of 25 and 50 *centimos* and five and ten *colones* notes are still in circulation, anachronistic holdovers from an era when a single *colón* was of tremendous value. The current floating exchange rate is around US$1= C 295; this may be somewhere in the 300s when you visit.

Owing to the continuing devaluation of the currency, prices in this book are listed in US dollars. Depending upon the correlation between the exchange rate and inflation (currently around 20%), things may cost more than listed here or about the same. In compliance with IMF demands, Costa Rica's currency exchange was liberalized in Feb. 1992, and dollars may now be exchanged anywhere.

CHANGING MONEY: Most banks impose a service charge for cashing travelers checks. Currency other than US$ can be exchanged only with difficulty. Canadian dollars and British Sterling can be exchanged at Banco Lyon, C. 2, Av. Central. Canadian dollars can also be exchaged at Banex, C. Central, Av. 1. German marks can be exchanged at the Banco Nacional in San José. Banks are generally open Mon. to Fri., 9-3 or 9-4; a few in San José are open later. It's desirable to carry at least some cash with you. Be sure to carry small bills (less than 1,000 *colones*) and coins when visiting villages where change may not be readily available for larger denominations. Unlimited exchange of *colones* is permitted; losses are limited. Major credit cards are accepted by banks, established shops, and large restaurants.

CREDIT CARDS: Although there are a large number of establishments (mostly high-priced) accepting credit cards, don't make them your chief source of cash. At the American Express office (☎ 257-0155, ext. 351) in the Credomatic/Banco de San José office (C. 3/5, Av. Central), you may write a personal check to purchase traveler's checks in dollars if you have one of their credit cards. Visa and Mastercards are accepted at this bank, and emergency cash advances may be negotiated.

Located in the same building as Paprika restaurant (Av. Central, C. 29/33), Credomatic accepts both Visa and

In recent years counterfeit bills have proliferated. Most are of the 5,000 *colónes* denomination. The bills are generally brighter blue than the regular issue and are likely to fell thinner. Check to see if the watermark (which shows up in regular light) is visible. Also check for the fine-line grid on the blue part of the bill which is missing from the counterfeits.

Black marketeers operate openly on Av. Central between Calles 2 and 4 and at many other locations. Changing on the black market brings only a slightly better rate. Once trustworthy, the black market has become increasingly inflitrated by con men who will steal your money or give you counterfeit US$50 and US$100 bills which are printed in Colombia. The best alternative is the moneychangers who operate in shops around the PO in San José.

Mastercard. To get here take the San Pedro bus and get off at KFC. Located near the cathedral at Av. 4, C. 2, Banco Credito Agrícola de Cartago accepts only Visa.

note: *Be sure you investigate all of the charges before going this route. Also note that paying by credit card at hotels and restaurants may result in a surcharge being added to your bill.*

If you are a guest at some select hotels, Visa and Mastercard can secure you cash advances in *colones* but not dollars. (Visitors should note that Visa traveler's checks have a bad reputation with regard to refunds).

SHOPPING: Opening hours vary but stores are generally open 8-6 from Mon. through Fri. with some stores closing from 12-2:30 in the afternoon. Most close down Sat. afternoons and are closed on Sundays. Aside from local handicrafts, there isn't much to buy that can't be found cheaper (or at the same price) somewhere else. Many of the handicrafts are imported and then sold at inflated prices. Recently, there have been some interesting souvenirs produced such as Ecopapier, the gorgeous handmade 100% recycled paper made at Upala. It is dyed with organic dyes and is pulped with agricultural byproducts. Locals, initally funded by a USAID grant, produce it in a small factory.

As is the case with all luxury items, there's an import tax on photographic equipment and accessories so bring your own. T-shirts make good souvenirs, as do local coffee beans (about US$3-8 lb. depending on quality and where you buy them).

SOUVENIRS: Unique and inexpensive souvenirs include vanilla beans, vanilla extract, Café Rica (the national equivalent of Kahlua), and bags of coffee beans. Buy beans marked "puro," indicating that no fillers or sugar has been added during the roasting process. Kábata makes a line of herbal teas and comsetics; Manza-te also offers a line of tea.

Palmito (heart of palm) preserves and preserved *pejibaye* (a scrumptious palm fruit that tastes like a cross between a chestnut and a pumpkin) are good for your jaded and worldly friends. Although high-priced, local woodwork and other crafts make good souvenirs. One souvenir that is functional during your visit is the shopping bag fashioned from a rice sack; another is the traditional *campesino* sun hat made from cotton canvas. More recent local creations include banana paper items as well as rope sandals.

Souvenirs you won't want to bring out are things made from marguay, jaguar, or alligator skins — endangered species all.

Should you come across it, black coral jewelery is another product to avoid buying.

> ?!¿ Opened in 1998, Galería Namú is on C. 7 directly behind the Holiday Inn and combines campesina paintings with indigenous crafts. You will find items here which are unobtainable elsewhere.
> **befrench@sol.racsa.co.cr**

SHOPPING: Many vendors sell in the streets of San José. Craft shops are listed in the travel section under San José. Also, you can buy a selection of handicrafts in Moravia (take a bus from Av. 3, C. 3/5) and get off before the gas station.

BARGAINING: It's customary to bargain in nearly every country of the developing world, and Costa Rica is no exception. Although most of the stores have fixed prices, you can bargain in market stalls, and you should definitely do so with meterless taxi drivers and on boat charters. Hotel room prices are generally fixed, but you can try. Discounts may be given for longer stays or when hotels are empty. In general, no matter how much you can afford to pay, don't agree on the first price. The next person may be a student on a meager budget.

And there is another reason to get the most for your money. With the onslaught of well-heeled tourists, Costa Rica is becoming more and more expensive for the Ticos themselves, who are finding it difficult to vacation or even get by day to day. Don't act as if you are here with your dollars ready to buy the country.

Bargaining Tips

Here are some bargaining techniques: First ask the price of the item: "*¿Cuánto es?*," *¿Qué precio tiene?*, or "*¿Cuánto vale*?" Then respond with "*Le doy.*" or "*Le ofrezco*" and indicate how much you wish to pay. If you don't wish to make an offer yet, exclaim "*¿Cuanto*?" ("How much?") in a tone of astonishment or declare "*Es un robo!*," ("It's robbery!)

Follow this up by querying "*¿No puede rebajar?*" ("Can't you lower the price?") If this has no effect, repeat it. Then, if the counter-offer does not come or is unacceptably high, follow this with "*No puedo pagar más*," ("I Can't pay more than that.") To close the deal, say "*Me lo llevo*" or "*Lo tomo.*" ("I'll accept that.")

Customs

AMERICAN CUSTOMS: Returning American citizens, under existing customs regulations, can lug back up to US$400 worth of duty-free goods, provided the stay abroad exceeds 48 hours and that no part of the allowance has been used during the past 30 days. Items sent by post may be included in this tally, thus allowing shoppers to ship or have shipped goods like glass and china. Over that amount, purchases are dutied at a flat 10% on the next US$1,000. Above US$1,400, duty applied will vary. Joint declarations are permissible for members of a family traveling together. Thus, a couple traveling with two children will be allowed up to US$3,200 in duty free goods.

Undeclared gifts (one per day of up to US$50 in value) may be sent to as many friends and relatives as you like. One fifth of liquor may be brought back as well as one carton of cigarettes. Plants in soil may not be brought to the U.S. If you're considering importing large number of items or are simply bringing back a quantity of souvenirs, you'll want to consult "GSP and the Traveler," a booklet which outlines the goods admitted duty free to the US from Costa Rica. It's obtainable from the Department of the Treasury, US Customs Service, Washington, DC 20229.

CANADIAN CUSTOMS: Canadian citizens may make an oral declaration four times per year to claim C$100 worth of exemptions, which may include 200 cigarettes, 50 cigars, two pounds of tobacco, 40 fl. oz. of alcohol, and 24 12-oz. cans/bottles of beer. In order to claim this exemption, Canadians must have been out of the country for at least 48 hours. A Canadian who's been away for at least seven days may make a written declaration once a year and claim C$300 worth of exemptions.

After a trip of 48 hours or longer, Canadians receive a special duty rate of 20% on the value of goods up to C$300 in excess of the C$100 or C$300 exemption they claim. This excess cannot be applied to liquor or cigarettes. Goods claimed under the C$300 exemption may follow, but merchandise claimed under all other exemptions must be accompanied.

BRITISH CUSTOMS: Each person over the age of 17 may bring in one liter of alcohol or two of champagne, port, sherry or vermouth plus two liters of table wine; 200 cigarettes or 50 cigars or 250 grams of tobacco; 250 cc of toilet water; 50 gms (two fluid ounces) of perfume; and up to £28 of other goods.

GERMAN CUSTOMS: Residents may bring back 200 cigarettes, 50 cigars, 100 cigarillos, or 250 grams of tobacco; two liters of alcoholic beverages not exceeding 44 proof or one liter of 44-proof-plus alcohol; and two liters of wine; and up to DM300 of other items.

Life, Language, & Study

LIVING IN COSTA RICA: Many American retirees have opted for the opportunity to be in Costa Rica. There are three categories which will allow you permanent residency: ***inversionistas*** (investors), ***rentistas***, and ***pensionados***. To qualify for the first, you need substantial funds to invest. The latter two categories require that you show evidence of an adequate fixed income.

Applying for residency is a three-ring circus of red tape. You'll require a statement from your local police headquarters certifying that you have no criminal record, plus naturalization and/or birth certificates for you and any dependents, along with any and all marriage and divorce certificates. You'll also need two copies of your passport, one copy of the passport for each dependent, and 12 passport-size photos (six profile and six front) for each individual involved. Blood tests (VD and AIDS) and a TB chest X-ray are also required.

In addition, all signatures on foreign documents must be notarized, and the notarized signature must in turn be authenticated by the county commissioner or secretary of state. The signature must also be authenticated by the nearest Costa Rica consul, who will charge a hefty US$40 per document for this service. Additionally, all documents must be translated into Spanish—not by just any translator, but by one that carries the Costa Rica Ministry of Foreign Relations' stamp of approval. Finally, you must swear on paper that you will live in Costa Rica for a minimum of four months each year.

The most popular category is that of *pensionado*. *Pensionados* are required to show evidence of US$600/month income from Social Security or a qualified pen-

Options for Living in Costa Rica

Pensionado You must receive a minimum of US$600 per month from Social Security or a qualified pension or retirement plan. A minimum of US$600 must be changed into *colones* monthly. You must reside in Costa Rica for a minimum of four months each year. Taxes must be paid on any household goods or cars imported. Although you may set up your own business, you may not work for anyone else.

Rentista You must prove that you have investments outside the nation which will guarantee $1,000/mo. for the next five years. An alternative is to purchase a CD from a Costa Rica bank that will guarantee you the same level of income. A minimum of $1,000/mo. must be changed in to *colones*. You must reside in Costa Rica for a minimum of six months each year. Although you may set up your own business, you may not work for anyone else.

Rentista-inversionista (investor) A minimum of US$50,000 must be invested in projects involving export, tourism, or reforestation or US$200,000 in a Costa Rican business. Temporary residency will be granted for two years. Permanent residency will follow if there are no problems. You must reside in Costa Rica for a minimum of six months each year.

Residency You must prove a tie to Costa – through blood or by proving that you can support yourself without employment. Although unconditional residency gives you the legal right to work, you must prove that you will not take jobs away from Costa Ricans.

Work permit This is obtainable through an employer who must prove that there is no Costa Rican qualified to do the job. The permit is valid only so long as you remain employed. Taxes must be paid, but you will receive the same benefits as Costa Rican workers.

Temporary Residency Granted to teachers, Peace Corps volunteers, diplomats, and other international workers.

Student Visa If you can show the ability to support yourself and enrollment in a school or university, temporary residency will be granted.

Tourist You may stay in the country up to 90 days with a passport. If staying for more than 90 days, you need to get an exit permit when you leave, and you must pay for the time you overstay which can be expensive.

sion fund. To be "qualified" means that the company must have been in existence for at least 20 years. It must supply a CPA-certified statement of incorporation and financial solvency, which must in turn be certified by a Costa Rican consul. Reference letters from two banks affiliated with the pension plan are also required. You will need to present a letter, either from Social Security or from your pension fund, stating that your pension is for life and will be paid to you in Costa Rica. Finally, before receiving your residency permit, you must hand over additional photos and allow yourself to be fingerprinted so that Interpol can check to be sure your documents are not falsified and that you are not a criminal.

Pensionados possess rights identical with citizenship, except for the right to work and to vote. They once had advantages over the locals, being allowed to bring in their household goods one time and import a car once every five years

Buying Property and Land

If you decide during your stay that you'd like to buy some land, don't expect to do so during five minutes of your vacation! Land titles are a problem here: you must check with a lawyer to make sure that they are correct. Be sure you understand what's written in Spanish. Some of the land has been sold two or three times over. Expect to spend around US$100,000 or up for an attractive home with around 250 sq. m of land in the Meseta Central.

Keep in mind that the sight of a foreigner frequently sends prices rapidly skyward so it might be advisable to send a Tico to scout for you! Find one who's bilingual and pay him or her. Don't depend upon the land values assessed by the National Registry. One way to assess current rates is to find out the sale price of similar properties in the area during the recent past.

Don't rely upon advertisements; word-of-mouth is more important. The local *pulpería* is a good source for who wants to sell what. The more information you can obtain the better so don't hesitate to talk to everyone you meet! Take your time and bargain hard; don't be in a rush. Always use *colones* when drawing up a contract. Find a lawyer who is a real estate specialist to draw up a contract. Finally, think everything through and make a considered choice.

duty-free. New laws have taken those privileges away and you must now pay duty on all imports.

Rentistas differ from *pensionados* in that they must have investments which will guarantee them a monthly income of $1,000. Both *rentistas* and *pensionados* can start their own businesses. They cannot, however, be employed in the country.

Life is not a bed of roses here; one of the complaints *pensionados* have is of the complex bureaucracy and the frequent switches in government policy towards them. Living in Costa Rica is a tremendous opportunity for retirees—not to isolate oneself in a "tropical paradise" but to open new horizons—learning a new language and becoming immersed in a foreign culture by volunteering one's skills. For information contact the **Departo de Jubilados, Instituto Costarricense de Turismo**, Apto. 777, (Av. 4, C. 5) San José, call 223-1733, ext. 264.

Located next to the Jubilados office on the ground floor of the ICT building is the **Foreign Residents Association** (call 233-8068, fax 222-7862; write Apdo. 700-1011, San José). For around $900, they will speed your application through in two-four months. Going through a lawyer will cost more and take longer; doing it on your own is only for the most perservering souls among us.

NOTE: This association encountered financial dificulties after uncovering bookeeping irregularities in 1994, so check about its current reputation. If you do decide that you want to relocate, it would be better to stage a dry run of six months to a year so you can be sure that you've made the right decision.

GETTING A JOB: Although foreigners are discouraged from working in Costa Rica, there are various positions that cannot be filled by Ticos and that will help you establish *residencia temporal*. For example, teachers are needed at schools for expatriate children (French, English, German, and Japanese) in the San José area. Language schools require native speakers, the *Tico Times* needs reporters, and the symphony can use musicians. None of these options pays a great deal, but they will allow you to stay longer.

VOLUNTEERING: This may be the best way to really experience the country.

> If you're young and have more money than time you should be aware that it is fairly easy to find a job working at a small lodge or hotel or bar. Strictly speaking, you will be "working" illegally (more than likely your pay will consist of room and board), but it can be done.

Opportunities range from sea turtle banding to journalism.

For those with an interest in regional politics, an excellent opportunity is a six-month internship for qualified Spanish-speaking college students and graduates at the Institute for Contemporary Studies (☎ 235-3195, ☎/fax 234-7682; Apdo. 1524, 2050, San Pedro, San José). They publish *Mesoamerica*, an outstanding monthly that covers regional politics. Participants gain valuable experience in professional journalism.

It's possible to support yourself by teaching English (about US$3/hr) but you must be available at least half-time. Send a resume along with recommendations and the months you could be available.

www.amerisol.com/costarica/edu/mesoamer.html
mesoamer@sol.racsa.co.cr

The **Association of Volunteers for Service in Protected Areas**, ASVO (☎ 233-4533, fax 223-4989; apdo. 11384, 1000 San José) is a governmental organization which will hook you up with park guards searching for poachers or you may write newsletters. You must volunteer for a two-month minimum as well as pay for lodging and meals.

asvo89@sol.racsa.co.cr

The **Association of Volunteers in Research and Environmental Devlopment**, VIDA (☎ 233-7203) matches volunteers with organizations.
voluntariado@vida.org

Fundación Pamiamor (☎ 225-5031) places Spanish-speaking volunteers in positions where they can help to prevent child abuse. Non-Spanish speakers can help with administration.

paniamor@sol.racsa.co.cr

Rara Avis (see description in "Meseta Central" chapter) also needs qualified volunteer guides on occasion. Contact Amos Bien (☎ 764-3131; fax 764-4187; Apdo. 8105, 1000 San José)
www.intelog.com/~rainfrst
www.rara-avis.com
raraavis@sol.racsa.co.cr

If you have six months and some skills to offer in a relevant field (agriculture, aquaculture, forestry, ecology, photography, etc.) and want to live in the Talamancan sticks, then **ANAI** might have a volunteer position. A sometimes controversial organization, ANAI is involved with the concept and practice of "Earth Stewardship" in the lowland tropics, resolving the conflict between conservation and development in rural communities. Volunteers are expected to have reasonable conversational experience in Spanish, have their own insurance, and provide their own transportation. ANAI can provide housing and limited assistance with food.

A three- to six-month commitment is required for volunteering on their experimental farm, and volunteers are needed to monitor the beaches in the area during the turtle egglaying season (May-July); a US$10 pd contribution for food and housing is asked.

Call 224-5090/3570, fax 253-7524, or write Apdo. 902, Puerto Limón 7300,

Costa Rica. Or, from May to Dec., write Dr. William O. McLarney, 1176 Bryson City Road, Franklin, NC 28734, call (704) 524-8369.
anaicr@correo.co.cr

If the sea and sea turtles interest you, a fantastic opportunity is to volunteer at the **Caribbean Conservation Corporation's** John H. Phipps Biological Field Station at Tortuguero National Park. One- and two-week packages are available. The fee is high because you are helping fund their sea turtle program, and a substantial portion of the amount may be tax deductible. A limited number of positions are also available for research assistants who receive no salary but are granted room and board. Programs involve both green and leatherback turtles. They also have a bird identification project. For more information contact the Caribbean Conservation Corps (☎ 800-678-7853, 352-373-6441, fax 352-375-2449), PO Box 2866, Gainesville, FL 32602.
wwwcccturtle.org
baulas@sol.racsa.co.
crresporg@cccturtle.org

An ultra-worthy organization sending volunteers into the field is **Earth Island Institute's Sea Turtle Restoration Project** (☎ 415-488-0370, fax 415-488-0372, PO Box 400, Forest Knolls, CA 94933) which features trips to Costa Rica's Ostional and Playa Nancite as well as trips to Nicaragua's Playa La Flor, a beach near the Costa Rican border.
www.igc.apc.org/ei/strp/strpindx.html
seaturtles@earthisland.org

The **Reserva Pacuare**, a leatherback turtle reserve on the Caribbean coast, also needs volunteers (US$100 pw donation). Contact Carlos or Maggie Fernández (☎ 233-0451, 233-0508, 391-9975, 383-1064 fax 221-2820).
leatherback@yahoo.com

The University of California at Berkeley (☎ 510-642-6586) also sends volunteers into the field in the company of researchers to locations that include Lomas Barbudal. Write UREP, University of California, Berkeley, CA 94720.

APREFLORAS (☎ 240-6087; Apdo. 917, 2150 Moravia), the Association for the Preservation of Wild Flora and Fauna, accepts volunteers who will work as guards for the parks (some risk involved) or act as environmental educators in schools.
www.preserveplanet.org
preserve@sol.racsa.co.cr

The **Asociación de Amigos de Aves** (☎/fax 441-2658; Apdo. 32-4001, Rio Segundo de Alajuela) works to re-introduce macaws to the wild through breeding, and volunteers are needed to help care for the birds. They accept volunteers but can not offer room and board

Aspiring organic farmers can volunteer to work for Erich Orlich (lodging amd meals provided) of the **National Association of Organic Farming** (ANAO; ☎ 223-3030).

Researching laws relevant to topics such as forestry, land use and tenure, urban air pollution, and marine and coastal resources, the **Centro de Derecho Ambiental y de los Recursos Naturales** (CEDARENA, ☎ 225-1019, fax 225-5111; Apdo. 134, 2050, San Pedro) is compiling an information bank which they hope will be used to institute the environmentally-optimal developmental decisions.
cedarena@sol.racsa.co.cr

Founded in 1986, the innovative

Monteverde Institute (☎ 645-5053, fax 645-5219; MVI, Apdo. 69, 5655 Monteverde) coordinates a limited number of international volunteer service projects which usually center around farming or building with added courses such as Spanish, "Sustainable Futures," biology, or workshops on regional issues. They can also hook you up with a volunteer teaching position in a local school. A total of 25% of profits are donated to the community.
www.mvi.cea.edu
mviimv@sol.racsa.co.cr
mvipac@sol.racsa.co.cr

Volunteers are also always needed at the reserve itself. Lodging but not food is provided. Contact **Monteverde Cloud Forest Reserve** (☎ 645-5122; Apdo. 8-3870, 1000 San José).
volunt@ct.or.cr.

Earthwatch (☎ 617-926-8200) sends paying volunteers out to assist researchers working in the field. Recent projects include work at the Wilson Botanical Gardens with birds, studying the courtship practices of long-tail manakins in Monteverde, and research on olive Ridley egglaying on Tamarindo beach. Costs are tax deductible except for airfare. Write 680 Mt. Auburn St., Box 430-P, Watertown, MA 02272 or call 1-800-776-0188.
www.earthwatch.com

The Volunteer Coordinator for the **School for Field Studies** (☎ 508-927-7777) offers volunteer opportunities in Costa Rica Write 16 Broadway, Beverly, MA 0195-2096.

If you are a Spanish-speaking person with knowledge of environmental law and research the **Centro de Derecho Ambiental y de los Recursos Naturales** (CEDARENA, Apdo. 134, 2050, San Pedro; 224-8239, fax 225-5111) needs volunteers. a three-month stay is requested.

One of the best-established organizations, the **Costa Rica Association for the Protection of Nature** (ASCONA, call 222-2288/2296; Apdo. 8-3790, 1000 San José) works on sustainable development and needs volunteers with scientific or technical backgrounds.

VIDA (☎ 233-7203, fax 222-3620) places volunteers with organizations as well as arranging educational tours for high school students.
www.vida.org
voluntariado@vida.org

Retired businessmen and technical advisors might join the **International Executive Service Corps**, (☎ 233-9855; Apdo. 70, Centro Colón, San José; Box 1005, Stamford, CT 06904-2005) a non-profit partially sponsored by US AID and based in Stamford, CT.

The **Ministerio de Educacíon** (Departamento de Inglés, San José 1000) now accepts volunteers to teach English.

If you have a minimum of six weeks you can commit, **Finca Brian y Milena** (Apdo. 2, 8000 San Isidro de El General) is looking for volunteers who will be willing to work on their fruit farm near Dominical; you will be expected to contribute $30 pw towards your food.

The oldest and largest organization of its kind in the US, **Global Volunteers** (☎ 612-482-1074, fax 612-482-0915; 375 East Little Canada Rd., St. Paul, MN 55117) now sends teams to Costa Rica.
www.globalvlntrs.org
email@globalvlntrs.org

> It never hurts just to go to the office of a park or reserve and offer to volunteer on the spot.

Sarapiquí Conservation Learning Center (☎ 766-6077) needs vounteers for community work including teaching English. **selvaver@sol.racsa.co.cr**

Barú Adventures (☎ 800-297-2278) offers environmental adventure tours for high school teachers.
www.cool.co.cr/usr/baru/baru.html
sstroud@sol.racsa.co.cr

FOUNDATIONS: If you would like to help conservation in Costa Rica, there are a number of organizations which welcome donations. If sent directly to Costa Rica, these are not tax deductible.

One of the best new organizations on the scene is the **Cecropia Foundation** (☎/fax 735-5532) which is attempting to halt logging in the Osa Peninsula near Corcovado National Park.
cecropia@sol.racsa.co.cr

If you want to support the parks, the **Fundación de Parques Nacionales** (Apdo. 1008, 1002 San José) works on management, development, and protection of parks and reserves.

Working with communities near the parks, the **Fundación Neotrópica** (Neotropical Foundationl; ☎ 253-2130, fax 253-4210; Apdo. 236, 1002 San José) works towards conservation and sustainable development. Membership (US$30) brings a subscription to their magazine and a 10% discount at their store.
neotropica@apc.org
fneotrop@sol.racsa.co.cr

Publishers of the environmental monthly, **AECO**, The Costa Rican Ecology Association (☎/fax 233-3925; Apdo. 812-1000 San José) works with Indians and does research and projects on sustainable development.
aeco@sol.racsa.co.cr

The **National Association of Organic Farming** (ANAO; ☎ 441-2439) is a networking organization for those interested in organic farming.

ANAPAO (☎ 224-1770; the Güilombé Foundation) is The Association of Small Organic Farmers which works to organize organic farmers.

Working to protect the nation's aquatic resources such as dolphins endangered by tuna fishermen, **APROCA** (Asociación pro Conservación Ambiental; ☎ 255-3365) can be contacted at Apdo. 1863-1002.

The **Asociación de Amigos de Aves** (☎/fax 441-2658) is working to re-introduce macaws to the wild thorugh breeding. Send donations to Apdo. 32-4001, Rio Segundo de Alajuela or send a tax-deductible contribution (indicate the "Asociación de Amigos de Aves") to the International Wildlife Learning Center, 408 S 10th Av., Hattiesburg, MS 39401.

The **Irria Tsochok Foundation in Defense of the Earth** (☎ 234-1512, 225-5091, fax 253-6446; Apdo. 555, 2100 Guadelupe, San José) lobbies on behalf of La Amistad Biosphere Reserve.
firinia@sol.racsa.co.cr

Fundación Ambio (☎ 258-1212, fax 222-3182; Apdo. 1487, 1002 San José) is a coalition of lawyers, economists, and biologists who came up with the "ECO-OK" program which certifies sustainable agriculture.
ecook@sol.racsa.co.cr

WSPA (☎ 239-7158;Apdo. 526-3000, Heredia), the Costa Rican chapter of the World Society for the Protection of Animals, runs one of the few animal shelters found in the region and conducts an anti-cruelty program in local schools.

FECON (☎ 234-7938, fax 222-3182;

Apdo. 1948, 1002 Paseo de los Estudiantes), Costa Rica Federation of Environmental Groups, is a coalition of environmental organizations.
feconcr@sol.racsa.co.cr

The **Monteverde Conservation League** works to expand the Monteverde Biological Preserve, help implement Arenal National Park, and provide community education among other projects, T(fax 645-5104) accepts donations at Apdo. 10165, 1000 San José. You can also direct donations to them for the Children's Rainforest, or to The **Children's Rainforest**, PO Box 936, Lewiston, MA 04240. In Britain write Children's Tropical Forests, UK, The Old Rectory, Market Deeping, Peterborough PE6 8DA, England, UK.

The **Costa Rica Association for the Protection of Nature** (ASCONA, ☎ 222-2288/2296) is at Apdo. 8-3790, 1000 San José. One of the best-established organizations, they promote sustainable development. Tax-deductable donations may be made through the World Wildlife Fund.

APREFLORAS (☎ 240-6087; Apdo. 917, 2150 Moravia), the Association for the Preservation of Wild Flora and Fauna, is an invaluable watchdog group whose members patrol protected areas on weekends in search of illegal logging.

Working to protect Lomas Barbudal, the **Amigos de Lomas Barbudal** (☎ 415-526-4115) is at 691 Colusa Av., Berkeley, CA 94707.

ARBOLFILIA (Apdo. 512, 1100 Tibas; ☎/fax 240-7145) , the Association of Tree Protection, accepts a few volunteers for their work with tree planting.

The **Tsuli Tsuli, Audubon Society of Costa Rica** (☎ 240-8775; Apdo. 4910, San José) works on migratory bird habitat preservation, river restoration, and espouses environmentally friendly banana production.

Another worthy organization to support is the **Nature Conservancy** which buys land and sets it aside in debt-for-nature swaps. Send tax-deductible contributions to Costa Rica Program, The Nature Conservancy, 1785 Mass. Ave. NW, Washington, DC 20036.

An organization working to support the Carara reserve is **Fundación Gran Carara** (☎ 234-1867, fax 253-6338; Apdo. 469, 1011 San José.

Researching laws relevant to topics such as forestry, land use and tenure, urban air pollution, and marine and coastal resources, the **Centro de Derecho Ambiental y de los Recursos Naturales** (CEDARENA, ☎ 225-1019, fax 225-5111; Apdo. 134, 2050, San Pedro) is compiling an information bank which they hope will be used to make the environmentally-optimal developmental decisions.

SEJETKO (☎ 234-7115; Apdo. 1293-2150, Moravia) is an organization which defends indigenous reserves. They need volunteers for work with rural developement and other projects; a one-year minimum commitment is requested.

YISKI (☎ 297-0970, 236-3823, fax 235-8425; Apdo. 1038-2150 Moravia) sponsors groups of youth volunteers.

If you believe that elevating the quality of social and economic life is a positive step towards ensuring the continued protection of the rainforest, then you may wish to support **KuKula** (☎ 258-4058, 258-3085; Apdo. 463, 7300 Limón), a volunteer organization based in Limón, which attends to the needs of street kids. Projects include environmental and educational camping excursions, medical and dental referrals, attention to individual needs, and more.

ARCA (☎ 445-5490; Apdo. 172, San Ramón de Alajuela) is the San Ramón

Association for the Conservation of the Environment which organizes volunteers to fight against illegal logging, river pollution, and hunting.

If your interests run toward supporting local highbrow culture, you might wish to donate funds to the financially strapped Youth Symphony and other worthy projects. Write **Ars Musica** (☎ 233-9890), Apdo. 1035, San José.

GETTING MARRIED: The only officially sanctioned religious ceremony permitted in Costa Rica is a Catholic wedding. If you have any other type of wedding, you'll also need to have a civil ceremony, which can be performed by a local priest, notary, attorney, or provincial Governor. A Catholic wedding requires documents from the church(es) where you were baptized and confirmed. You must also take a course in marriage from a local church. Contact the San José diocese at 233-0198 for further information.

Be sure to bring your birth certificates as well as an affidavit from a US notary attesting to your single status. All of these must be authenticated by the nearest Costa Rican Consulate or Embassy. Likewise, if either partner has been divorced, you'll need a copy of the final judgment, which must also be authenticated.

STUDYING AND SPEAKING SPANISH: The more Spanish you speak the better! If you want to travel by bus around the country, negotiate meals in local (*comida típica*) restaurants, and stay in lower-priced accommodations you will need at least some basic command of Spanish. Even if you don't speak more than a few words, be sure to use them. The more you speak, the more you'll learn, and you won't learn unless you speak. If you regard the country as an intensive language laboratory, your Spanish will improve remarkably within a short time. But if you're going in without any language ability at all don't despair. Sign language is an effective means of communication when the situation arises; another possibility is a writing pad for numbers and prices. **note:** While Costa Rican Spanish is more in accord with that found in Spain than elsewhere in Latin America, its pronunication most resembles Guatemalan Spanish.

> **i** The ISLS (Insttiute for Spanish Language Studies) is a language school-broker who will help you find the school to suit your needs. Placement is free. It also offers a number of different services. In the US you should call 800-765-0025 or write 1011 E Washington Blvd., LA, CA 90021.
> **islscr@sol.racsa.co.cr**

STUDYING SPANISH: There are a number of language schools, but study here is much more expensive than in countries such as Guatemala. If you plan to study here, you'll need at least a few months to make any significant degree of progress. Costs run from US$3-$5 ph, and US$7 ph for private lessons.

LANGUAGE SCHOOLS: Most of these are in and around San José. However, the growth in tourism has meant that you can now study in locations such as Manuel Antonio and Tamarindo.

Featuring "Survival Spanish," a one-day, $50, six-hour class, **Mesomamerica Language Institute** (☎ 253-3195, ☎/fax 234-7682; Apdo. 300, San José) is run by the Institute for Central American Studies (ICAS, ☎ 224-8910). It also offers private study and private lessons. For 20 hrs. a week of study in a small class, they charge $110; you can stay and eat with a family for $85 additional. **mesoamer@sol.racsa.co.cr**

The **Kalexma Inn** (☎ 290-2634, ☎/fax 232-0115; Apdo. 6833, 1000 San José) combines budget accommodation with language study. It's across the highway from the Hotel Irazú. They offer homestays (as well as special hotel rates for Spanish students), and rates include continental breakfast.
www.goldnet.co.cr/kalexma
kalexma@ns.goldnet.co.cr

The Castilian House (☎/fax 441-4228/0334;) is a **language school** that also provides room and board. Facilities include breakfast buffet, board, Jacuzzi, videotheque, library, massage, and airport pickup/dropoff. Rates for a week are around US$340 pp.
www.castilian.co.cr
info@castilian.co.cr

The **Costa Rica Language Academy and Latin Dance School** (☎ 221-1624, fax 233-8670; Apdo. 336-2070, San José) offers homestays and private and group lessons; dance, cooking, and musical instrument lessons are also offered.
crlang@sol.racsa.co.cr

Running a Spanish program geared towards those concerned with social and environmental issues, **ICADS** (☎ 225-0508; PO Box 145450 Coral Gables, FL 33114 or Apdo. 3, 2070 Sabanilla, San José) discusses issues such as agriculture, social justice, and refugees. It is located near the college in Curridabat.
icads@netbox.com

Headquartered in Los Yoses to the E, with a branch in the center part of the city, the **Centro Cultural Costarricense Norteamericano** (☎ 225-9433., ext. 56; Apdo. 1489, 1000 San José) charges US$130 for classes lasting two months, two hours per day.
acccnort@sol.racsa.co.cr

Also running a study farm in Santa Ana to the W of San José, **Centro Linguistica Conversa** (☎ 221-7649, fax 233-2418; 800-354-5036; Apdo 17, 1007 Centro Colón) offers 6-15 hours of instruction per week.
www.conversa.co.cr
coversa@sol.racsa.co.cr

Based in San Pedro, **The Costa Rica Spanish Institute** (COSI, ☎ 258-2117) has a maximum of four students per class.
cosicr@sol.racsa.co.cr

Forester Institute Internacional (tel 225-3155, 225-0135; 619-792-5693; Apdo. 6945, 1000 San José) is set in Los Yoses and has classes ranging in length from a week to a month.
www.fores.com
forester@sol.racsa.co.cr

ILISA (Latin American Institute of Languages; ☎ 225-2495, fax 225-4665; 1-800-ILISA4U, ext. 1000; Dept. 1420, PO Box 25216, Miami, FL 33102-5216) offers two to four week intensive classes along with cultural activities and homestays. It is located in San Pedro and has 20 classrooms.
www.ilisa.com
spanish@ilisa.com

In Escazú, **ILERI** (Language and International Relations Institute; ☎/fax 228-1687; Apdo. 191, Escazú) offers small classes and immersion courses; it's 300 m W of the PO. It also has a branch in Panama.
Offering four to six hours pd, two- to four-week courses, **INTENSA** (call 24-6309) can be reached at Apdo. 8110, 1000 San José.
www.intensa.com
intensa@sol.racsa.co.cr

Instituto de Lengua Espanol (call 27-7366) has five-week courses beginning in Jan., June, and Sept. Write Apdo 100, 2350 San José.

Instituto Lingüistico (☎/fax 446-5952) is based in Athenas, in a large house on a working organic farm. Homestays are arranged. **inlinlat@sol.racsa.co.cr**

Offering two- to four-week programs along with a three-day mini-survival course (US$75), **Instituto Universal de Idiomas** (call 257-0441, 223-9662) is at Apdo. 219, 2120 San Francisco de Guadalupe.

Intercultura (☎ 260-8480, ☎/fax 260-9243) is in Heredia at Av. 4, C. 10.
intercul@sol.racsa.co.cr

The **Latin American Language Center** (☎ 916-447-0938, fax 916-428-9542) offers homestays and courses; it is based in Heredia. Dance and oooking classes are also available are volunteer projects.
lalc@madre.com

Offering special packages out at Cariari Country Club, **Lisatec** (☎ 239-2225, fax 293-2894) is at Apdo. 228, San Antonio de Belen. First opened in 1982, it now accepts boarders.
cciyesa@sol.racsa.co.cr

Preferring students who can commit themselves for four months, **Communicacion Transcontinental** (☎ 221-3364) is at Apdo. 8501, 1000 San José.

Offering both group and individual lessons, **IALC** (call 225-4313; Apdo. 200, 1001 San José) has a one-week minimum.

Based in San José, the **ICAI** (Central American Institute for International Affairs, ☎ 233-8571, fax 221-5238) limits groups to six. and offers courses ranging from nature photography to natural history. In the US call 916-432-7690 or fax 916-432-7615.
www.expresso.com/icai
icai@expresso.com

Instituto Británico (☎ 234-9054, fax 253-1894; Apdo. 8184-1000, San José) offers courses in San José and Liberia.
instbrit@sol.racsa.co.cr

Escuela Latina de Lenguas (☎ 261-5233, 237-5709; 520-776-7189) is set in the small town of Barva. It supplements language study with dance classes and other social activities.

In Tamarindo on the Nicoya Peninsula, **Instituto de Wayra Espanol** (☎/fax 653-0359) teaches Spanish as well as Latin dance.
www.spanish-wayra.co.cr
spanishw@sol.racsa.co.cr

In Dominical, the **La Escuelita de**

Costa Rican Colloquialisms	
Adios!	In the rural outback. (Only used as a farewell when leaving for a long time)
Bomba	Gas station
Buena nota	OK. Fine. Great
¿Hay campo?	Do you have space? (on a bus, taxi)
Cien metro	One block.
Maje	Close friend. (Used by young males)
Mi amor	My love. (Used by friends of both sexes as a form of address)
Porta mi!	I don't care
Pura vida	Far out, super. (Can be used as a greeting)
Salado	Tough luck. That's a shame.
Upe!	Is anyone home? (Used in the countryside in lieu of knocking)
Vos	Equivalent of "tu" in French, the intimate "you."

Dominical (☎/fax 771-1903) provides Spanish classes and arranges homestays.
La Escuela D'Amore (☎/fax 777-1143; Apdo. 67, Quepos), a "Spanish Immersion Center," is in Manuel Antonio. Call 414-781-3151 or 213-912-0600 in the US.
damore@sol.racsa.co.cr

STUDY SEMINARS: In order to give English-speaking persons first hand experience with and a better understanding of the people and issues of Central America, the **Institute for Central American Development Studies** (ICADS, ☎ 225-0508; fax 234-1337) offers semester abroad courses which have college credit.
www.icads.com
icads@netbox.com.

The **Monteverde Institute** (☎ 661-1253; MVI, Apdo. 10165, 1000 San José) hosts groups of university students during its summer programs in tropical biology. Call or write Tomás Guidon or Polly Morrison
Offering its students the opportunity to meet policymakers from all sides of the political spectrum during its course on Central America, the **Central American Institute for International Affairs** (ICAI, ☎ 255-0859; Apdo. 3316, San José) also has courses in Spanish, art, and Costa Rican education and society.
The **Organization for Tropical Studies** (OTS, ☎ 236-6696) conducts two-month courses at their research stations as well as logistical support for doctoral disserations. Write PO Box DM, Duke Station, Durham, NC 27706, ☎ (919) 684-5774, fax 919-684-5661.
www.ots.ac.cr
www.ots.duke.edu
reservas@ns.ots.ac.cr

Offering structured internships in Costa Rica or Nicaragua, the **Institute for Central American Development Studies** (ICADS, ☎ 225-0508) discusses issues such as agriculture, social justice, and refugees.
Work is also a form of study, and the **Council on International Exchange** (CIEE) sponsors a work-travel program. Call (212) 661-1414 or write 205 E. 42nd St., NY, NY 10017.
www.ciee.com
info@ciee.org

Outward Bound (☎ 777-1212, fax 77-1571 or 777-0279; 800-367-3230) operates a school in Quepos which combines adventure with Spanish study.
crrobs@sol.racsa.co.cr

Fundecor (☎ 240-2624, fax 297-1044; Apdo. 549, 2150 Moravia) is an NGO which brings many student groups to Costa Rica every year.
fundecor@sol.racsa.co.cr

UNIVERSITY STUDY: For longer term study, the **University for Peace** (☎ 249-1072/1511, fax 249-1929; Apdo. 199, 1250 San José) offers two-year Masters in Communications for Peace, Ecology and Natural Resources, and Human Rights degrees.
One innovative program is offered through Friends World College's **Latin American Regional Center** (☎ 240-7057; Apdo. 8946, 1000 San José). Working on their own, students are awarded credit for their journals. In the US, call (516) 283-4000 or write Friends World Program, Long Island University, Southampton, NY 11968.
The **State University of New York at Albany** offers one- and two-semester courses at the University of Costa Rica; groups; you must have a minimun of two years of college-level Spanish. Write Office of International Programs, L1-84,

Costa Rican Visitors' Dos and Donts

- *Don't* try to do too much in too short a time. Despite what you might think, Costa Rica is a large nation. It can take quite a bit of time to get from point A to point B, and there's no advantage to spending most of your time getting there and burning a lot of fossil fuel in transit. If you only have a week, spend time in one area. If you stay in Dominical, for example, try to get to know that area and feel comfortable there. *Don't* race down to Golfito or over to Cahuita. *Do* try to enjoy where you are as opposed to where you are going next.
- *Do* visit the national parks. *Don't* litter, disturb habitats unduly, or act as if they are a party-out zone. *Do* buy soft drinks and other beverages in returnable and not disposable bodies.
- *Do* purchase the work of local artisans. Don't buy any alligator skin or turtle shell items. These species are endangered and internationally protected. *Don't* buy any archaeological artifacts. The chances are that these are fakes. Even if they are not, you still don't want to purchase them. Such items are stolen goods and amount to pillaging the national heritage. Moreover, any item removed from an archaelogical site deprives researchers of valuable information which might add to our knowledge of the past.
- *Don't* give out gifts to children – whether it be sweets or pencils! This will turn them into dependent beggars with regrettable consequences for those who will follow in your footsteps. *Do* take their pictures, play with them, and use them as Spanish language teachers.
- If riding mountain bikes, *do* be considerate of hikers and other pedestrians. *Slow down* and don't go whizzing by them! *Don't* cause erosion on trails by riding on ones obviously unsuited for bike use. *Do* bike on the roads and hike in the wilderness. Nature is not something to be conquered but to be experienced in solitude and silence!
- *Do* patronize *sodas* and other local hotels and businesses whenever possible. *Do* try to practice your Spanish. *Don't* isolate yourself from the local culture.
- Costa Rica is a large nation. It can take quite a bit of time to get from point A to point B, and there's no advantage to spending most of your time getting there and burning a lot of fossil fuel in transit. If you only have a week, spend time in one area. If you stay in Dominical, for example, try to get to know that area and feel comfortable there. *Don't* race down to Golfito or over to Cahuita. *Do* try to enjoy where you are as opposed to where you are going next!

University at Albany, State University of New York, Albany, NY 12222.

Although it is primarily geared towards students attending several midwestern colleges, any student may apply to enter the **Associated Colleges of the Midwest** (ACM) program. While the fall semester focuses on language study and the social sciences, the spring deals with field research in the physical or social sciences. Write 18 S Michigan Ave., Ste. 1010, Chicago, IL 60603. In Costa Rica call 225-0725 or fax 253-5790.

Offering one- to three-semester courses, the **University of Kansas** welcomes students of sophomore level or higher at any US college or university. Write Office of Studies Abroad, 204 Lippincot Hall, Lawrence, KS 66045.

The **University of Costa Rica** (☎ 224-3660, fax 225-5822) offers "special student" status for foreigners who pay double the local rates. Auditors () are also welcome. Semesters run from March to the end of June and from July to Sept. During the winter break (Dec. to March) a number ofare offered for the price of a small registration fee. Contact Oficina de Asuntos Internacionales (☎ 224-3660, fax 225-5822), Apdo. 1455,

San Pedro, San José.
caiucr@cariari.ucr.uc.ac.cr

Offering two-year masters programs in Ecology and Peace and in International Relations, the **University for Peace** (☎ 249-1072/1511, fax 249-1929; Apdo. 138, Ciudad Colón) is set in Villa Colón to the Sw of San José. Write 199, 1250 Escazú. **upazcult@sol.racsa.co.cr**

NOTE: *For other types of "study," see the listing under "volunteering" above!*

Conduct

Currently, despite the straitened circumstances the average Tico lives with (low wages, high interest rates, high inflation), the nation is a comfortable place for visitors. Unlike countries such as Mexico, where open season has been declared upon turistas, here you will find yourself treated as a welcome guest. Help keep it that way by showing respect and courtesy in your dealings with locals and exercising a sense of fairness in your dealings. As Costa Ricans also consider themselves to be "Americans," it would be polite to refer to yourself as a "*norteamericano*" if you are a US citizen.

Remember that every visitor has an impact, and your behavior will make a difference. It's a sad fact but you'll see the worst American influences everywhere. Poor people will squander precious funds on overpriced, unhealthy meals at McDonalds, a sporty pair of Reebocks, or Levis — all in lieu of more moderate Costa Rican products. If you have the chance to steer them right, do it!

Sadly, you will meet many foreigners here — real estate salesmen, other budding entrepreneurs, *pensionados* turned into alcoholics and the like — who have no real affinity with the country and might well be happier residing somewhere else.

Keep in mind that Latin cultural mores prevail here. Men and women alike tend to dress conservatively. If you want to be accepted and respected—and avoid being called a *puta* — dress respectably. Although shorts are now widespread, skirts are appropriate attire for women in small, conservative villages. Bathing suits are unsuitable on main streets, as is revealing female attire. Unlike other Central American nations, skimpy bathing suits *are* OK on Costa Rican beaches.

And despite the general conservatism, it is definitely acceptable to kiss and cuddle in public, as any visitor to San José will note immediately.

Finally, if you want to be loved and respected by the police, you should carry your passport. In this "democracy," carrying of passports and ID cards is mandatory, and the police may stop you at any time and ask to see identification. If you don't have it on you, unless you look like you might be a wetback from the N or S, they probably won't bother you.

DRUGS: With the exception of alcohol, coffee, tobacco and their ilk, all drugs—from marijuana to cocaine—are treated as narcotics. Sentences of eight years or longer are not unusual.

DIRECTIONS: Never, no matter how fluent your Spanish is, believe all the directions you are given. Sometimes, in a misguided attempt to please, local people will tell you what they think you want to hear. It's better to ask a few people and get a consensus.

THEFT: Although Costa Rica is being marketed as a "peaceful paradise," any glance around at the painted steel bars, barbed wire, and the signs warning of attack dogs show that thievery is endemic. There's been a dramatic increase in violent crime and mugging. Although the Ticos will blame Nicaraguans or Panamanians for all of the thievery, this, of course, is nonsense. Still such crime has yet to reach the desperate level of Peru, where a camera, grabbed from around the neck of a tourist, represents a year's income.

Take precautions and you should not have any problems. The very best prevention is being aware that you might be a victim. By all means especially avoid the slum areas of San José, don't flash money or possessions around and, in general, keep a low profile. Avoid looking affluent. Keep track of your possessions. Things like expensive sunglasses are very popular. Don't leave anything unattended on the beach, and keep off the deserted beaches at night.

Avoid carrying anything in your back pockets. Women should carry purses that can be secured under your upper arm. Other things to avoid are: contact with drug dealers, getting drunk in public, or walking in a secluded area at night. Never, never leave anything in an unoccupied vehicle, not even in a trunk; there are reports of thieves cleaning out vehicles in broad daylight! Do not lose sight of your day bag, and do not keep valuables in it!

Locations like the front of major hotels and the area around the Museo Nacional are notorious for automotive break-ins.

> The latest scheme (which surfaced in 1998) is to spray tourists with a green slime. A "good samaritan" then invites the victims to go to a bar and clean off. His accomplice makes off with their things!

It's useful to photocopy your passport and keep it separately along with the numbers of your travelers' checks and any credit cards. A wise precaution is to secure any unnecessary valuables in the hotel safe; a more effective precaution is to leave them at home.

MODUS OPERANDI: "Holy" Week, which the *ladrones* do not regard as sacrosanct is the most dangerous time for thievery. Gangs have special tricks. One is to create a distraction and steal your bag. Another is to spill a bit of ice cream on your back and solicitously wipe it up while fleecing you at the same time. Refuse politely if offered candy or a soft drink on a bus; there have been cases of tourists being drugged and waking up hours later without their possessions.

Even if they see a theft or mugging happen, Costa Ricans are reluctant to get involved because of the complications that might result in a trial. Overly friendly Ticos (and foreigners as well) who hang out in tourist areas often may have an ulterior motive. Remember that locals who form sexual liaisons with foreigners often do so with pecuniary gain in mind. And, if you give one of them access to your hotel room, it can be a bit awkward if you later have to go to the police and make a charge! **note:** Tourists claimed in 1992 that they had been robbed by the police in San José. A new development on the crime scene are the *chapulines* ("grasshoppers"), gangs of youth who jump on unsuspecting pedestrians. They generally gather in the Parque Central, Parque Merced, and Plaza de la Cultura and operate in groups of four. One puts a stranglehold on the victim's neck while others pillage and plunder. Solo tourists are likely targets. Be sure to be careful and leave all valuables at your hotel!

WOMEN TRAVELING ALONE: Costa Rican men are not quite as chauvinist as their neighbors. But, perhaps because of their Spanish pedigree, the males are much more verbally aggressive and persistent than in, say, Guatemala. Some women maintain that they appear to be "always in heat." Their favorite activity in life appears to *piropear* (compliment) females, hopefully making a *conquista* of a *gringa*. Expect to be called *mi amor* (my love), *guapa* (cute), and other, sometimes less endearing, epithets.

Eclipsing even politics and soccer in popularity, flirting is the national sport. If you see a man staring at you intently, don't be alarmed, he's just practicing *dando cuerdo* (making eyes). Married or not, a Tico male will profess to love you with the greatest passion in mankind's history. Don't buy it! On the Caribbean coast, there are a number of "beach boys" available for rent should you be in the mood. But be warned that places like Cahuita, with one woman being replaced by another — over and over — are superb breeding grounds for AIDS, so proceed with caution."Remember,"one Tica advises, "the *best* attitude is one of confidence."

> **Mariah Wilderness Expeditions** (☎ 800-462-7424) organizes special trips for women including rafting expeditions.

MEN TRAVELING ALONE: Costa Rican women have been mythologized for their great beauty and their good standing as *chineadoras*, women who will take care of men as if they are babies. Of course, this is nonsense. But if you don't think that a number of *gringos* buy the myth, check the classified section of the *Tico Times*. Prostitution is legal in Costa Rica. Although it will not guarantee that a hooker does not have AIDS or some other disease, your chances of safety might be better if you insist on seeing their *carnet de salud*, a health card issued by the government which must be updated regularly.

Avoid being rolled in set-up situations, many of which take place around Parque Morazán, which might be better called Hooker Central. A favorite technique is for a tart to come up to you and give you a big bear hug while her accomplice grabs your wallet from your back pocket. If you see a young femme disrobing in the moonlight, be aware that she has two burly accomplices hidden in the bushes. Many other hookers have been known to roll their Johns while they sleep, or have an accomplice steal your wallet or anything else handy, so be careful during the *timo del amor*.

In addition, be advised that the government, despite the legal status of prostitution, is adamant that it is not promoting sex tourism. In Sept. 1994, then Tourism Minister Carlos Roesch commented that "under no circumstances will Costa Rica accept tourism based on exploitation of women or on totally unnatural acts such as homosexuality."

GAY AND LESBIAN TRAVEL: Although Costa Rica is friendlier than many other countries, it still has its puritan streak. In 1998, the popular protest by the religious establishment killed a "Gay and Lesbian Festival" scheduled to be held in Manuel Antonio. President Rodriguez denounced the festival: the government appears to unofficially equate gay tourism with sex tourism. Triangulo Rosa countered with a lawsuit against the Catholic Church. In October of that same year locals in the Guanacaste town

Handicapped Accesibility

While Costa Rica has made some inroads towards accommodating the disabled, it still has a long way to go. No curbs downtown (save those near the Gran Hotel Costa Rica) can be mounted by wheelchairs, buses can not be boarded, and hotels, restaurants, and tour companies alike are ill equipped to cope with the needs of the disabled. The only national park equipped to cope with wheelchairs is Póas. Very few hotels have handicapped-friendly bathrooms and only some are wheelchair accessible. It's best to contact your hotel ahead of time and ask. As buses have no special equipment, getting around by taxi is easiest. However, you should keep in mind it's best to call in advance for one.

An organization working to improve the situation is **Kosta Roda**, a foundation run by French Canadian Monique Chabot. For more information call or fax her at 771-7482, 297-2481, 225-9163, or write Apdo. 1312-1100, San José.

chabote@mail.tionet.co.cr

Vaya con Silla de Ruedas (☎ 225-8561, fax 253-0931) is a tour company which offers a van with wheelchair lifts and stations. They charge US$120 for a full day.

vayacon@sol.racsa.co.cr

of Sardinal de Carrillo blocked the access road to the Blue Bay Hotel mistakenly protesting what they believed to be a "Gay Congress."

Many hotels are gay-owned or gay-friendly. These include Villa De Cary in Arenal and the Colibri, Hotel California, Costa Verde, Makanda by the Sea, and Casa del Sol in the Manuel Antonio resort area. Casa Blanca (☎/fax 777-0253) in Manuel Antonio is a largely gay-only spot.

cblanca@sol.racsa.co.cr

In San José, Colours provides accommodation and the International Gay and Lesbian Association (☎ 234-2411) and the Asociación Triangulo Rosa (☎ 258-0214; Spanish only) provide info.

rastern@sol.racsa.co.cr

Run by the **ACES (*Asociación Creativa de Empresarios*), Gayness** (☎ 236-7446) is the local gay publication.

www.members.aol.com/gaycrica/guide.html

TRAVELING WITH CHILDREN: Costa Ricans love children, and the high health standards are a positive consideration. If you want to bring an infant with you, you should note that disposable diapers are very expensive and not readily available. The environmentally conscious, however, will wish to use cloth. Although many restaurants have high chairs and booster seats, car seats are unavailable, so if you plan on renting a vehicle, you'll either have to bring one along or do without. If your children are under 18 and stay more than 90 days, they'll require permission from the Patronato Office (C. 19, Av. 6) if you want them to leave with you! Both parents must be present in order to secure the permit. If you're a single parent traveling alone, you must have the permission of the other notarized by the nearest Costa Rican counsel prior to your arrival. Described in the travel section, the Parque Nacional de Diversiones is one way to please fickle children as are the Pueblo Antiguo and the Children's Museum and the Butterfly Farm and the Children's Museum.

Check the Friday edition of *La Nación*'s "Viva" section, which lists children's activities. Another way to entertain them is with *Let's Discover Costa Rica*, a coloring and activity book which is widely available.

Finally, the **Educational Resource Center** (☎/fax 282-9862) offers an "eco-camp" which operates in Jan., June, and

Clothing
socks and shoes
underwear
sandals, thongs, windsurfing sandals
T-shirts, shirts (or blouses)
skirts/pants, shorts
swimsuit
hat
light jacket/sweater

notes

Toiletries
soap
shampoo
towel, washcloth
toothpaste/toothbrush
comb/brush
prescription medicines
chapstick/other essential toiletries
insect repellent
suntan lotion/sunscreen
shaving kit
toilet paper
nail clippers
hand lotion
small mirror
glasses/contact lenses/sunglasses

July. It is run by local humanitarian services legend Gail Nystrom.
gnystrom@sol.racsa.co.cr

ENVIRONMENTAL CONDUCT: Respect the natural environment. Take nothing and remember that corals are easily broken. Exercise caution while snorkeling, scuba diving, or anchoring a boat. Dispose of plastics properly. Remember that six pack rings, plastic bags, and fishing lines can cause injury or prove fatal to sea turtles, fish, and birds. Unable to regurgitate anything they swallow, turtles may mistake plastic bags for jellyfish or choke on fishing lines. Birds may starve to death after becoming entangled in lines, nets, and plastic rings. Remember that the national parks were created to preserve the environment and refrain from carrying off plants, rocks, animals, or other materials. Finally, remember to treat nature with respect.

RIPTIDES: Especially because of the dearth of lifeguards, these are a major environmental hazard. If you are caught in one, yelling and waving your hands is the surest way to drown. Conserve your energy and try to swim in a parallel direc-

The Park Land Dilemna

Although you will see park boundaries defined on maps and Costa Rica is constantly referred to as a country which is saving its forests for posterity, much of the land in the parks remains unpurchased and faces harvest. In 1995 trees were cut on as-yet-unpurchased land at Manuel Antonio (see "Manuel Antonio National Park" in the Travel Section). A total of some 20% of land included in national parks by the government has not yet been purchased. And the land is legally exempt from governmental control as long as it remains unpurchased. The Supreme Court's Sala IV (which makes constitutional rulings) decreed in 1991 that land may be considered to be part of a protected area only after it has been paid for. And the Expropriation Law, passed in April 1995, states that land must be paid for before being expropriated.

Larger parks such as Braulio Carrillo, Tapantí, and Corcovado are under pressure to cut trees. Regrettably, the revenue pulled in from park admissions does not go back to the parks for maintenance and land purchase but, instead, 25% goes to the local municipality and the remainder goes to the National Parks Fund.

tion over to where the waves are breaking and ride them to shore. The best move is to avoid swimming at dangerous beaches; a good rule of thumb is the larger the wave, the stronger the rip. Some dangerous beaches are Puntarenas's Playa Barranca and Playa Doña Ana, sections of Jaco's beach, the beach outside Manuel Antonio National Park, Playa Espadilla Sur inside the same park, Limon's Playa Bonita, and the section of the beach near the entrance to Cahuita National Park.

WHAT TO TAKE: Bring as little as possible, i.e., bring what you need. It's easy just to wash clothes in the sink and thus save lugging around a week's laundry. Remember, simple is best. Set your priorities according to your needs. With a light pack or bag, you can breeze through from one region to another easily. Confining yourself to carry-on luggage also saves waiting at the airport. And, if a second bag of luggage gets lost, you at least have the essentials you need until it turns up. If you do pack a lot of clothes, you could leave things at your hotel and pick them up later. When packing it's preferable to take dark, loose clothing. If you're going to wear shorts, they should be long and loose.

PROTECTIVES: Avon's Skin-So-Soft bath oil, when diluted 50% with water, serves as an excellent sand flea repellent. Sunscreen should have an 8-15 protection level or greater. A flashlight is essential, and you might want to bring two, a larger one and one to fit in your handbag or daypack. Feminine hygiene items may be found outside of San José; but it doesn't hurt to bring an adequate supply. All prescription medicines, contraceptives, creams and ointments, and other such items should be brought with you.

OTHERS: Books are often twice US prices so you'll also probably want to stock up before arrival. It's a good idea to have toilet paper with you, as the least expensive hotels as well as park restrooms may not supply it. Film is very expensive so be sure to bring a good supply. Binoculars are invaluable for watching wildlife. The best models feature internal-focus roof prism designs and are waterproof; high light transmission and high magnification are desirable. Plastic trash bags and an assortment of sized baggies will also come in handy.

If you plan on in-depth rainforest explo-

Hiking Tips

- Plan your route ahead of time. Make sure that your physical condition is adequate for what you are attempting.
- If possible, hire a local guide.
- Let someone know your routing and your return time.
- Stay on the trail. Heading through the bush can be risky.
- Only hike during daylight hours.
- Should you get lost, find an area where you can be seen from the air or follow a river downstream (as long as it is not swelling). Relax and stay put. Don't waste your remaining resources.

ration, high-topped rubber boots (*botas de hule*) are a good investment (around US$8) after your arrival. If you have unusually large feet, though, it would be a good idea to bring your own. Batteries manufactured locally are not of the highest quality so you should bring a supply.

BUDGET TRAVEL: If you're a low-budget traveler, you'll want to bring along earplugs, some rope for a clothesline, towel and washcloth, toilet paper, cup, small mirror, a universal plug for the sink, and a cotton sheet. A smaller pack is preferable because a large one will not fit on the overhead rack above the bus seats and storage is available only in a small number of buses.

HIKERS AND BACKPACKERS: If nature is your focus, you'll want to bring a rain parka, walking shoes or hiking boots, a day pack, canteen, hat, binoculars, and insect repellent as well as a bird book or two. Loose cotton trousers are recommended; jeans take a long time to dry. Expect your clothing to get dirty, and there's not much sense in washing your rainforest gear until you get back to "civilization."

There's no perfect protection against rain. Parkas and raincoats are too hot. An unlined Goretex jacket is superior but still hot. And a poncho can restrict your movement. Umbrellas are useful in open areas, and you can still take pictures. One solution to eyeglass fogging is to use skin divers' anti-fog solution which you can buy at a dive shop. Standard hiking boots are fine for mountains and arid areas, but army surplus jungle boots are best; buy ones with light canvas uppers and a heavy-duty sole. You can also purchase rubber boots at home or in Costa Rica (see above).

CAMPING: If you are the average visitor, you will not be camping. However, the ideal setup for camping in the forest is to sleep in a jungle hammock with blanket which is protected from bugs by a mosquito net and from the rain by a fly. If you go this route, you might need to practice sleeping in a hammock—which takes a bit of adjustment—and you'll want to choose the trees where you hang your hammock with care. Smaller ones may be preferable, and try to find one with fewer ants. As a precaution, soak the cords with repellent. The problem with tents is that they rest on the ground, and the surface tends to be muddy. The most practical tent is likely to be one with plenty of screening, covered by a waterproof fly. Choose high ground and dig a trench.

Backpacking stoves are the way to go for meals; buy one which can burn gasoline or kerosene. Camping Gaz-type containers, while available, are hard to find, and it is illegal to carry them in on planes. If you have a headlamp-style flashlight, you can free your hands up while you cook or take a night hike. Don't forget to bring water purification tablets or boil your water. There is no safe water in the rainforest.

ANGLERS: Necessities include sleeved shirts and pants, a wide-brimmed hat, and effective sun protection. For the Caribbean coast-bound angler, raingear is necessary, even during the dry season. Although lodges can generally arrange rentals, it's better to bring your own equipment. Bring a 20 lb. or stronger line for saltwater fishing.

SNORKELING: Although you may be able to rent it on location, don't forget to bring your own equipment and test it in a tub. Those afflicted with nearsightedness, but who do not have a strong astigmatism, can have a mask fitted with prescription lenses at some dive shops for around $80; it's not cheap, but it's an invaluable investment if you're a serious snorkeler. You may be able to get by without fins, but it's better to have windsurfing sandals at least to protect your feet against injury. Remember, however, to avoid damaging the reef at all times!

Other Practicalities

MEASUREMENTS: The metric system is used, and gasoline and milk are both sold by the liter. While road distances are given in kilometers, road speed signs and car speedometers use miles per hour. Land elevations are expressed in meters. In addition to metric, traditional units are in use.

Traditional measurements include the *libra* (0.46 kg., 1.014 lbs), *arroba* (10.59 kg, 25.35 lbs), *quintal* (46 kg., 101.40 lbs), *fanega* (4 hectoliters, 11.35 bushels), *quartillo* (3.71 kg, 7 lbs), carga (816.4 kg, 1,800 lbs), *manzana* (2.82 hectares, 7 acres), and the *caballeria* (42.5 hectares, 111.68 acres). The *vara* (33 in.) is frequently used to describe distances.

Although Costa Rica operates on Central Standard Time, one can accurately say that time here is measured in ahoritas, the uncertain and uncharted span after which an official will return to his office or a bus will leave. Electric current is 110 volts AC.

CONVERSIONS: A meter is equal to three feet and three inches. A kilometer equals .62 miles (about 5/9 of a mile), a square km is equal to about 3/8 of a square mile.

> If you have a camera with the auto-focus feature, first focus on the lighter area. This will ensure that you do not leave the portrait area underexposed and therefore dark.

PHOTOGRAPHY: Film is expensive here so you might want to bring your own. Kodachrome KR 36, ASA 64, is the best all around slide film. For prints 100 or 200 ASA is preferred, while 1000 ASA is just the thing underwater. For underwater shots use a polarizing filter to cut down on glare; a flash should be used in deep water. Avoid photographs between 10 and 2 when there are harsh shadows. Photograph landscapes while keeping the sun to your rear. Set your camera a stop or a stop and a half down when photographing beaches in order to prevent overexposure from glare. A sunshade is a useful addition. Keep your camera and film out of the heat and protected from rain; silica gel packets are useful for staving off mildew. Replace your batteries before a trip or bring a spare set. Manual SLR (single lens reflex) cameras are preferable to automatics because they will still function without batteries and are not as subject to breakdowns. However, they are increasingly difficult to find. Inexpensive lenses may be more likely to develop mold than their otherwise nearly identical brand name equivalents. Finally, remember not to subject your exposed film of ASA 400 or greater to the X-ray machines at the airport: hand carry them through. Because local developing is very expensive and of generally poor quality, it's better to take your film home for developing. Likewise, avoid having camera equipment repaired here.

RAINFOREST PHOTOGRAPHY: Generally speaking, the bright tropical sun makes Costa Rica a photographer's paradise. However, the dark rainforest is a much more difficult environment. While high speed films can be used without a tripod, your shots will lack the sharpness of detail you get with lower exposure film. Tripods are too bulky to carry; one alternative is to set your camera on a tree stump or rock. If you do this, check your film packaging for information on any adjustments you must make. Amateur flash units are suitable only for close up photography. Whatever you do, don't wait for a sunny day. An overcast day is best for shooting because cameras are incapable of capturing the extreme contrasts between shadow and highlights.

Animal photography is an antsy proposition owing to distances and dense vegetation. You can't hesitate or the animal may be gone! If you're intending to shoot animals in their environments, the ideal would be to bring two camera bodies (loaded with ASA 64 and ASA 1000 film) along with 300 mm zoom and regular lenses.

VISITING THE NATIONAL PARKS: Many consider these treasures to be the nation's greatest attraction for visitors. A total of 11% of the land is with the National Park System, and nearly all volcanic summits are set within biological reserves or the 15 national parks. Although the Park Service should be the best-equipped government agency, it is actually the worst off. Some 350 employees must manage many hundreds of thousands of visitors on a budget that has been increased only minimally from year to year. No permission is now required to visit the parks and biological reserves unless you are planning to conduct research. Opening hours are generally 8-4 daily.

Radio communication with the other parks, reserves and refuges is available 24-hours a day, so you can contact them with regard to overnight space. Call 283-8004. Bilingual staff here can get you the latest scoop on road conditions, etc. At the parks themselves, personnel may only speak Spanish. As staff and space is limited, it is essential that they know when to expect visitors and what their needs will be in terms of meals, camping spaces, bunkrooms—some of which may or may not be available. The Park Service guide is in Spanish. For many of the parks, you'll have to bring your own food, and it may be difficult to get to others without a car. If you take a bus, you may be let off 10-15 km. from a park entrance. (The most accurate current transportation information is included in each park description). Wildlife checklists and maps are sold at the CIDA office at San José's national zoo. Another alternative may be to visit the

To read up on the origin of the parks check out David Rains Wallace's fine history of the parks, *The Quetzal and the Macaw.*

parks with a tour. (See "adventure tours" and the "getting there" sections of individual national parks for listings).

WILDLIFE REFUGES: For info on the call the Vida Silvestre at 233-8112 or 221-9533 or see the individual entries in this book.

SEEING WILDLIFE: Because their survival mechanisms are geared towards differing needs and circumstances, Costa Rica's wildlife differs dramatically with that found on East Africa's open plains. While the latter depend upon strength, speed, and size, Costa Rica's depend upon camouflage for survival, meaning that they are smaller and more difficult to see.

If you're visiting the reserve on your own, with a group or on a group tour, it is essential to maintain quiet. The quieter you are, the more you will see, and you will see what you deserve to see. Early morning and late afternoon are the best times for viewing wildlife. The best way to see wildlife, if you are really serious about it, is to camp. During the dry season, the animals come down to drink at waterholes during the early morning and late afternoon.

When you return, don't forget to tell every Tico you meet how much you think of the park system. The parks will only survive as long as Costa Ricans value their existence.

> *i* The National Park Service now has a toll-free **information number**: 192. It operates from Mon. to Fri. from 7:30-5.

San José

Costa Rica's capital city of San José was once a sleepy backwater. Today, it is today a mixture of boldly intruding billboards advertising Kentucky Fried and Coke, shanty houses on hillside *tugurios*, and ten-speed bicyclists in spandex, who roam the streets in the company of BMWs and Volvos.

Within a single generation San José has been transformed from a quiet town into a crowded, bustling metropolis, one which has already engulfed neighboring suburbs and threatens to swallow the nearby cities of Cartago, Alajuela, and Heredia, in the process creating one giant megapolis. Forecasts are that the greater San José metropolitan area will have over two million inhabitants by the end of this century. With some 660-700,000 people, 30% of the nation lives here.

Indeed, compared to the slow-paced provincial towns, San José's traffic-clogged streets appear overpoweringly tumultuous. Noisy and polluted, San José has few parks, and its traditional character has been lost in the new nondescript North American-style architecture. Fast food emporiums — such as Archi's Fried Chicken and Billy Boy Hamburgers — dot the mish-mash architectural landscape. Schizophrenia is the name of the game in big cities these days, and San José is no exception. In this is surprisingly eclectic city where you can expect the unexpected, from drive-through ice cream parlors, to wild after-hours dancing, to merengue at the Pizza Hut downtown.

Despite its size, San José does have its saving graces. It still retains some of the characteristics of its birth from a collection of villages. A city created by agriculture rather than industry, pastoral surroundings are still visible from many areas. It still has a small town core at its heart. Believe it or not, many *Joséfinos*, as residents of the capital are known, still shop at the neighborhood *pulpería*, hang out at *sodas* and bars, and greet each other by name. And it is a cool city; the daily temperature averages around

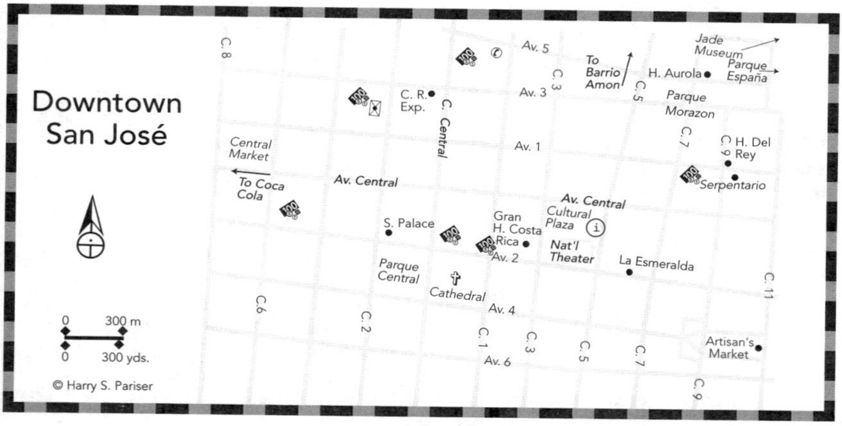

70°F (22°-25°C). There are a variety of cinemas, theaters, clubs, restaurants, bars, museums, and the whole gamut of services available.

HISTORY: Expanding from the initial settlement of Cartago, a group of farmers founded Villa Nueva del la Boca del Monte in 1737. Some time afterward, locals got tired of dealing with such a lengthy nomenclature, and the name was changed to San José, after the town's patron saint. The original settlement was founded largely by Spaniards and creole smugglers, the latter having been expelled from Cartago as punishment for dealing in contraband.

San José Transport

ARRIVING BY AIR: All flights enter the country through Juan Santamaría International Airport, 17 km W of San José. You may bring in up to US$100 in goods for friends. When you present your voter registration card or birth control certificate your passport will be stamped. If you intend to stay more than 90 days, you should have a passport, which is a prerequisite in order to apply for an extension.

The tourist information counter is just after Customs and before you mount the stairs. Although they may not go out of their way to help you, you should be able to find a number of brochures, a map, and perhaps a complimentary newspaper. There are banking facilities, and, should the banks be closed, there are also trustworthy moneychangers. A small shop sells powdered *café puro* as well as the current *Tico Times*, the *New York Times*, and other local papers. Other facilities include a post office and a duty-free shop. No baggage storage facilities are available.

NOTE: *This may change somewhat when the new terminal is ready (in 2000 or so).*

If you have limited luggage, the San José-Alajuela bus stop is just across from the entrance. It is about 50 cents (change given on the bus) to the terminal at Av. 2 and C. 12 via Paseo Colón. Not all buses go to San José; be sure to ask. A cab to the city will cost you about US$10 — twice as much as you might normally pay for a similar distance to and from a different location. A *colectivo*, if you can locate one, will run you about US$2.

FOR ESCAZÚ: If you're planning to drive to Escazú , take the highway SE towards San José. Then, at the fourth traffic light you come to (where the National Gymnasium, a round structure, should be on your R and McDonalds on your L), take a R onto the highway. exit R to Escazú and head downhill (with the McDonalds on your L and the Shell station to your R). From "El Cruce" head into Escazú and continue on to your hotel.

LAYOUT: Avenida Central divides the downtown area. A place to promenade and window shop, the wide variety of quality, expensive imported goods in its stores astonishes visitors arriving from

> When arriving, be sure to visit the small information kiosk which is just on your L before you board the short escalator to the street-level exit. Free copies of the *Tico Times* are dispensed here along with other useful information.
> If you can, bring in a bag full of used clothing and shoes, toys, and other items you don't need A volunteer will meet you at the airport and redistribute the goods to the impoverished Pacific coast community of Playa Palma. **cazoo21@hotmail.com**

other Central American nations. The section between C. Central/5 has been closed to traffic and is now a pedestrian mall. A continuation of Avenida Central, broad, bustling, and busy Paseo de Colón is another area of interest. What one might call the "Champs Elysees" of San José, this area has seen a number of its elegant houses disappear to be replaced with the likes of fast food emporiums and car dealerships. One traditional-style home, the Casa de Leones, vanished within a three-day interval. Trees have also been mysteriously poisoned along this stretch by injecting them with herbicide. The street terminates at La Sabana, the former site of the national airport. It has evolved into the nation's largest urban park and hosts the modern art museum.

Surrounding the city farther out are the *barrios* (neighborhoods) such as Bellavista, Sabana Norte, Sabana Sur; still further out, are the *Area Metropolitanas* (municipalities), which are extensions of the city.

GETTING AROUND: It's easy enough to do with a little practice. Equipped with turnstyles and quite often with wooden seats, slow but reasonably frequent city buses are priced from around ten cents on up. The fare is marked near the door, and they are identified in the front windshield both by number and destination; the driver will make change. Many either depart from or pass by the vicinity of Parque Central. Smaller (and therefore speedier) microbuses also run. Buses can be very crowded during peak hours (7-9 AM and 5-7 PM). Plan your travel for other times.

There are innumerable bus routes within the city. Two of the most convenient routes are the **Sabana Cemetario** and the **Cemetario Sabana** buses which run in parallel ellipses in opposite directions and on different streets around the Sabana and into town. Because of their circuitous and often confusing routing, however, it may be faster to walk.

The **Estadio Sabana** runs from the stadium to the Parque Central and back. All three of these provide an inexpensive city tour; expect to spend about 40 min. or so to get back to your starting point.

Heading to San Pedro via Los Yoses (departs Av. 2, C. 5/7), the San Pedro bus can drop you off right near the church and park in the center of the university area. The **C. Blanco bus** runs to the commercial shopping center of El Pueblo. The **El Carmen** (Parque de La Paz) and San Cayetano (the baseball stadium) buses run nearly overlapping routes from C. 8 at Av. 4 up along Av. 2 and then down C. 1. The return to the N is along C. Central. Also running to Parque de la Paz and passing by Plaza Viquez (from which buses to S suburbs depart) on C. 11, the **Barrio La Cruz** bus runs along C.

> *i* Kitcom Communications has come out with a useful **bus guide** which may be obtained from the tourist board at the airport upon arrival.
> **www.yellowcab.co.cr/crbuses.html**

Suburban Bus Destinations and Stops
Airport (domestic, Pavas) C. 20. Av.1)
Coronado C. 3/Av. 5/7
Curridabat C. 3, Av. 2/4
Escazú Av. 6, C. 12/14 (minibus), C. 16, Av. 1/3
Guadalupe Av. 3, C. Central/1
La Uruca Av. 3, C. 6/8
Moravia Av. 3, C 3/5
Pavas Av. 1, C. 16/18
Sabanilla Av. 2, C. 5/7
San Ramón de Tres Ríos Av. 2, C. 5/7
Santa Ana Coca Cola terminal
Villa Colón Coca Cola terminal

7, along Av. 3, down C. 10, and back via C. 2. If you wish to take a bus late at night (from Los Yoses to Parque Central for example), it's better to take the first bus that comes along, even if it is a suburban bus and you have to pay more. (Fares are determined by the length of the route). It's tough to find many buses before 6 AM or after 10 PM.

NOTE: *There is a plan to move the bus terminals to the edge of town and have the Sabana Cemetario run more frequently as a shuttle. This may be implemented in the 2000s.*

GETTING FARTHER OUT: Once the site of a now vanished Coca Cola bottling facility,"Coca Cola," as this rough neighborhood is still known, is the locus for buses to the suburbs (including Santa Ana and Villa Colón) and outlying towns. It's always preferable to board here than at the later stops, when it may be difficult or impossible to get a seat. Buses from here run to outlying towns like Ciudad Colón, Santa Ana, Escazú, Sarchí, and Naranjo, along with Orotina and Quepos. Buses for most destinations to the W (including Guanacaste) are nearby.

> Watch where you step in San José! Many of the sidewalks are punctuated by holes, large and small. Unfortunately, the government has had its head turned by the the Papagayo megaproject and has been ignoring infrastructural niceties.

ON FOOT: One might expect from looking at the map that San José is a large city. In actuality, it is rather like a metropolis compressed into Lilliputian format. It's easy to walk around the central part of the city. The blocks are small and you can cover a considerable amount of distance in 20 min. by foot. However, be extremely cautious when crossing streets. Drivers appear to regard their fellow humans as squishy things to be run over, and they actually seem to speed up when they see you coming! Watch the cars, not the stoplights because, as far as the drivers are concerned, traffic lights might as well be permanent Christmas decorations.

> Tour the historical areas of the city with **Caña Dulce Turismo Cultural** (☎ 258-3535, fax 222-0201), which charges 1,000 *colones* to survey the city's attractions in a one-hr. walking day tour. They also offer an unusual evening tour.
> **www.novanet.co.cr/dulce**
> **www.novanet.co.cr**
> **www.konfrenz.com/canadulce**

FINDING LOCATIONS: Laid out in a grid, *calles* (streets) run E to W and *avenidas* (avenues) run N to S. Numbering begins in all directions from Avenida Central. Even-numbered calles run to the W; odd-numbered calles run to the E. Odd-numbered avenidas run to the N of Avenida Central; even-numbered ones run to the S.

San José's **central downtown area** extends approximately .75 mi.(1. 3 km) from N to S and 1. 25 mi. (2. 1 km) from E to W. It can be roughly defined as being bounded by C. 20 on its W, Av. 9 on its N, C. 21 on its E, and Av. 20 on its S. You can usually find street numbers on the corners of buildings, but a new set of street signs (containing advertising) is being put into place in the tourist areas.

Many streets are still poorly marked. Buildings themselves, however, are not numbered and addresses are expressed in terms of 100 *varas* (slightly less than 100 yards) or, more frequently, in units of 100 meters (*cien meter*); either is the approximate equivalent of a block — an average block is actually shorter. An address given as "Av. 7, C. 9/11" indicates that the building faces either side of Avenida 7 on the block between Calles 9 and 11. Directions are also given from known landmarks, which can make things harder to find; businesses, restaurants, etc. are advertised in terms of meters from a famous landmark.

BY TAXI: An average trip costs around US$2 or less. Although the taxis theoretically have meters (called "Marías"), they are often either broken, or drivers maintain they are, so price negotiations may be required! Be aware that taxi drivers normally attempt to charge tourists from five to ten times the correct fare. One way to approximate your fare is to estimate it in terms of nine blocks per km and count the first km as around 60 US cents with 25 cents per km thereafter. You should note that there is a 20% surcharge after 10 PM. The fare for trips of 12 km or more must be negotiated. The bright red cabs are equipped with roof lights. It's difficult to find a taxi on weekend evenings so plan accordingly.

Downtown Sights

While there is not a great deal of spectacular interest here, the visitor will find it rewarding to spend at least half a day walking around town. The place to begin this is in the Parque Central, bounded by C. Central and 2 and Av. 2 and 4. The perfect place to escape from the surrounding hustle and bustle, this small park is great for hanging out during the day. It's also important as a bus terminal. A gift from Nicaraguan dictator Anastasio Somoza in the 1940s, the giant concrete kiosk in its center was scheduled to be razed as part of its 1993 renovation, but protests have saved it. A new fountain commemorates Costa Rica's first aqueduct. San José has a large number of museums, and most are worth visiting. Admission is free or minimal. The best place to begin seeing these is in the Plaza de la Cultura (see below).

CATEDRAL METROPOLITANA: Colored off-white and not particularly spectacular, the cathedral is more notable for the structure attached to its rear. The administration building represents a merger between 19th C. San José style and that of Europe; its stone-cased windows and pediments draw from the traditions of Renaissance Italy. The cathedral was recently restored.

At the corner of C. Central on the N side of the square, the **Teatro Melico Salazar** has fluted Corinthian columns, balconies, and pediments with stuccoed relief sculptures. It is a superb place to see theater or attend concerts.

TEATRO NACIONAL: One of the few buildings constructed before the beginning of this century, the Belgian-designed National Theater was financed by *cafetaleros* and finished in 1897. Often billed as a miniature version of either the Paris or Milan opera house, it replicates neither, and its rust-colored tin roof is typically Costa Rican. The impetus for its construction came after a European opera company, featuring the famed singer Angela Pelati, played in Guatemala in 1890 but turned down a San José date due to lack of a suitable venue. Planned by Belgian architects, its metal framework was the work of Belgian craftsmen.

Ornamented with baroque decorations and gilded with 22.5 karat gold, its Great Hall of Spectacles seats 1,040. The

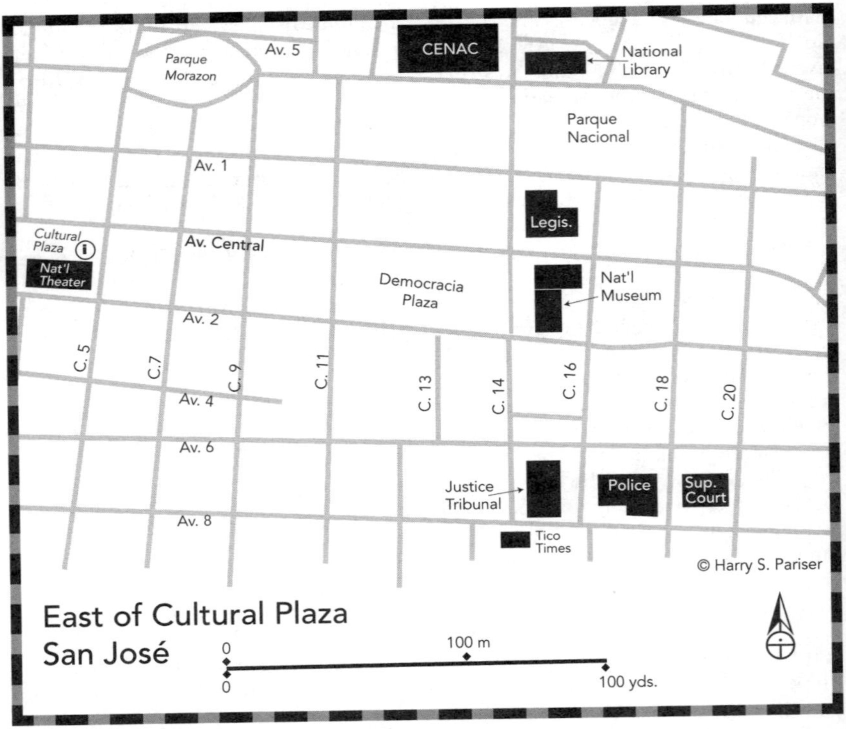

refreshment area has changing exhibits by local artists. Decorated in pink marble, the main lobby has two sculptures by Pietro Capurrore presenting comedy and tragedy."Heroes of Misery," the sculpture in the atrium, is the work of Costa Rican artist Juan Ramón Bonilla. The Carrara marble grand staircase leads upto the foyer, which has paintings along with a mural showing the nation's major exports. The ceiling fresco, painted by Italian Arturo Fontana and illuminated by an 85-light chandelier, depicts unclad celestial deities. Another of his paintings, in the Presidential Box which is set dead center in the balcony directly over the entrance, depicts Justice and the Nation. In its foyer, a three-part fresco by Vespasiano Bignami represents Dawn, Day, and Night. Replicas of the originals, the furniture in the room to the rear is fashioned from mahogany and has been gold leafed. Originally fashioned from European pine, the floor was replaced with a selection of the ten varieties of local hardwoods in 1940. One of the theater's unique features was the manual winch which once raised the floor to stage level — an operation performed by 12 men in just under an hour — allowing it to be used as a ballroom. Its Renaissance-style facade has statuary by Pietry Bulgarelli, which represents Music, Fame, and Dance. Statues by Adriatico Feoli of

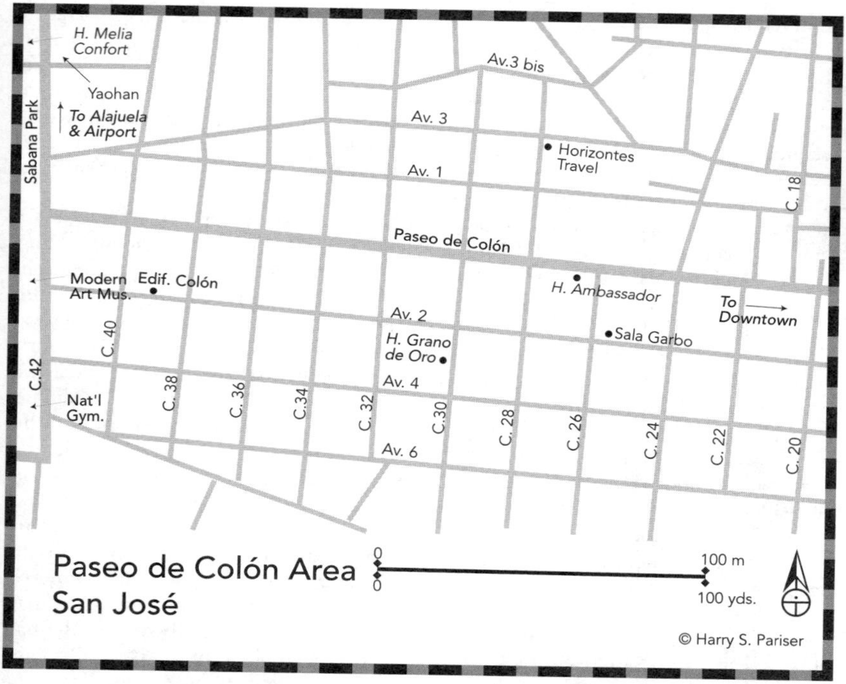

Beethoven and Calderón de la Barca, a 17th-C playright and poet, sit in niches on either side of the entrance. Restored after the 1991 earthquake and reinaugaurated in 1993, the building can be visited on your own, day or night (around US$1 admission), but if you have the chance, don't miss one of the performances, held here on a near-daily basis. It might well be one of the highlights of your trip. Outside the theater, the plays of the street progress as vendors flog their wares and an evangelical preacher thumps his bible against his head as he warns of the nasty events to come.

PLAZA DE LA CULTURA: Situated along Av. Central between C. 3 and C. 5 right beside the Teatro Nacional, this multilevel outdoor cultural plaza has underground exhibit halls. While you're here, be sure to head down the stairs and stop by the underground Instituto Costarricense de Turismo (ICT), the **tourist information center**, located near the corner of Av. Central and C. 5.

PLAZA DE LA CULTURA MUSEUMS: Right next door is the entrance to the two museums. First enter the **Museo Numismatica**. It has Native American artifacts, old coins, banknotes, and a 1,000-*colón* gold piece issued in 1970 — which gives you an idea of how far and how fast the currency has fallen. (Open Tues. to Sun., 10-5). Next door, a small exhibit hall displays works from the Central Bank's art collection.

Entered through thick vault doors set at the base of a beautiful winding marble staircase, the **Museo de Oro** has one of the world's finest collections of gold-crafted art — over 1, 600 pieces in all, weighing in at 24,000 troy ounces— making it the hemisphere's second largest collection. It's almost surrealistically spooky and quiet with beautiful displays and immaculately polished parquet floors. Gold pieces featuring animals, people, iguanas, quetzals, frogs, and jewelry and bells are displayed inside plexiglass cases. As you leave through the vault door at the end, you come upon what might well be a hydroponic garden used in an interstellar craft. Given the spiraling marble staircase, the roof high overhead composed of triangular concrete blocks, the mechanical whir of the a/c, and the occasional "bing" of the elevator, you could be on the set of a science fiction movie. Laser-gun-toting androids might come trotting down the stairs at any moment. If you need a quick escape from San José for whatever reason, this otherworldly environment is the place! It's open Tues to Sun. from 10-4:30. Admission (US$5 adults, US$1.50 students; US$.75 children) is charged.

MUSEO DE JADE: Misleadingly named, this small jewel of a museum is really a full-fledged introduction to the cultures of Costa Rica's indigenous peoples. There are musical instruments, bows and arrows, an aerial photo of the Guayabo archaeological site, ceramic ocarinas, flints, anthropomorphic *metales* (grinding stones) and others with elaborately carved undersides, a disk with Maya inscriptions, fantastic female ceramic figurines (from AD 700-1100), and a large two-piece incense burner with a marvelous *lagarto* (lizard) carved on the lid. The quality of both the imagery and the technique puts most contemporary art to shame. After some finely crafted carved jade pieces showing South American influences, there's a sitting room with a great view to the north. Give your feet, brain, and eyes a brief rest here because you'll need it for what's to come.

Next is a room displaying ceramic and gold objects. Then, the displays change with room after room of anthropomorphically-shaped jade scrapers and other objects from the Pacific coast, many of which show a Mayan influence. Works from the central and Atlantic areas are also on display. These jade pieces did not come from archaeological sites but rather were purchased from private collectors who bought them from looters. The last room shows some enormous clay phalluses along with phallic ocarinas, masturbating clay men, ceramic hermaphrodite and female fertility figures, and a group of wild-eyed, frantically clutching, copulating clay couples. Finally, out in the hall there's a replica of a 14th C. Tang Dynasty ceramic horse, a gift from the Chinese Embassy. Do you wonder where all of the objects in the museum came from? They were purchased from private collectors who bought them from looters. Very few items were excavated.

The museum (☎ 223-5800) is located on the 11th floor of the INS (Instituto Nacional de Seguros; Institute for National Security), C. 11, Av. 7. It's open Mon.-Fri., 8-4:30. Admission is US$2 for adults; children are free. After visiting the museum, head for **Café Mundo** at Av. 9, C. 15 (to the E) to dine or get caffeinated.

Be sure to check out the views before you leave; to the south is the **Edificio Metálico** (Metal Building), an incongrous green prefab building designed by French architect Victor Balatard.

VICINITY OF THE MUSEO DE JADE: Also known as the Parque de la Expresión, the atmosphere of the **Parque España** (next to the INS, between Av. 5 and 7 at C. 11) is accentuated by the transplanted tropical trees. Artists sell here on Sunday.

Across C. 11 is the Spanish-style **Casa Amarilla**, home of the nation's foreign ministry. Stroll through the traditional neighborhoods to the N where you'll find old tin-roofed homes of brick and wood.

PARQUE ZOOLÓGICO SIMÓN BOLIVAR: The national "zoo" is set at the N edge of the downtown area, off Av. 11. Conditions at the zoo have been improving, but it *still* leaves a lot to be desired. There's a new restaurant here, habitats for the animals are slowly being upgraded, plants are now identified, and it has a new entranceway and, unfortunately, a McDonalds. (Open. Tues. to Fri. 8:30-3:30; Sat., Sun., and holidays, 9-4:30. Admission is US$1.50 adults.

MUSEO NACIONAL: Housed in the Bellavista Fortress, a former army headquarters and barracks, the National Museum of Costa Rica displays pre-Columbian artifacts, period religious garb and dress, and other items from the colonial era. Visible bullet marks from the 1948 civil war on the building's exterior make it a living monument to recent history. The entrance has a small gift shop, a courtyard containing prehistoric basalt balls, and a cannon.

The *Sala Doris Stone's* exhibits includes a mastadon tooth, displays of Mesoamerican-style ceramics to the L and South American ones to the R, and anthropomorphic *metates*, as well as other beautiful artwork.

The *Sala Arqueologia* exhibits miniature brass and gold artifacts including jewelry. Other rooms show colonial furniture, presidential portraits and statuary, historical photos, and a collection of gigantic stick figures representing cultural groups who have added to the nation's ethnic fabric. There's also a fine collection of folk art, most of which was imported in colonial times from Mexico and Guatemala, as Costa Rica has always had a minimal number of artisans. The most engaging of these is a brightly colored Chinese-shrine-like cabinet creche from Guatemala, with a crowned Virgin in its center, and the devil — whose face indicates that he may vomit at any instant — lying in the bottom level.

The museum (☎ 222-1229, 221-0295) is at C. 17, Av. 2/Central, which is right on one edge of the Democracy Plaza (see below). It's open Tues. to Sun from 9-5. Students with ID and children under 10 are free.

VICINITY OF THE MUSEO NACIONAL: While you're in the area, you may wish to check out the **Plaza de la Democracia** (Plaza of Democracy) which cost US$1.5 billion to construct, and the Moorish-style, cream-colored legislature building. The plaza now boasts a bronze statue of former president José "Pepe" Figueres. The little girl with a violin and the boy with a book are intended to illustrate his concern for education.

Set to the N is the **Parque Nacional** which centers around an allegorical statue featuring the five Central American nations driving out William Walker (See "history" in the "Introduction"). Of the "parks" downtown, this is the only one which truly deserves the name. Its **National Monument** commemorates the struggle of the war against William Walker in 1856. The five females represent each of the five Central American nations, and the two men are Walker (who has a rifle) and one of his cohorts (who lies prostate on the ground). Costa Rica is represented by the flag-waving woman embracing a veiled Nicaragua. The bas reliefs on its base depict the Battle of Santa Rosa, the Battle of Rivas, the seizing of boats in the San Juan del Norte, and Walker's surrender. The staure was cast in bronze by French sculptor Lous Carreier and was installed in 1895. Scale the viewing platform to have a closer look.

In 1995, construction workers installing underground cables discovered a tunnel running under the park which appeared to once connect the former Casa Presidencial with the National Museum (formerly a fort). Apparently, it was intended to allow top officials to commute between the two in the event of a crisis.

Across from the park, the imposing **Biblioteca Nacional** (National Library) has a mural of the sun on the outside; **Galeria Nacional de Arte Contemporáneo** (GANAC), a branch of the modern art museum with rotating exhibits on the W side, is open Mon. to Fri. 10-5, closed 1-1:45 for lunch.

MUSEO DE LA CRIMINOLOGIA: Set inside the Hall of Justice at Av. 6, C. 17, this combination crime museum and museum of judicial history (open from 1-4 on Mon., Wed., and Fri.) displays weapons used in violent crimes, counterfeit lottery tickets and money (including US$), pictures of magic mushrooms, drug paraphernalia, photos of severed hands, and jars containing items like an embalmed hand severed with a machete, an illegally aborted fetus, and severed feet. Be sure to eat your lunch first.

OTHER SMALL MUSEUMS: A must for reptile (and particularly snake fans), the **Serpentario** (☎ 255-4210) (eye) hosts a wide variety of species, including poison dart frogs. It's at C. 9/11 on Av. 1, above the El Gran Chaparral restaurant. Admission (around US$4 for tourists) is charged; it's open Mon. to Sat. from 10-7.

Another imposing relic, a steam engine belonging to the now defunct Northern Railway stands on a spur in front of the closed Ferrocarril Atlantica station on Av. 3 at C. 21. The station has been converted into the **Costa Rican Railway Museum** which contains a display of railway memorabilia. It's open 9-4, Mon. to Thurs., and on Fri. from 9-3:30.

Artifacts from the life of the former president **Rafael Angel Calderón Guardia** are on display at the museum of the same name which is in Barrio Escalante at Av. 11, C. 25/27. (It's open Mon, to Fri., 10-4; US$1 admission; ☎ 255-1218).

You might also wish to visit the **Museum of Printing**, in the Imprenta Nacional in suburban La Uruca. (Open Mon. to Fri. from 9-3:30).

The **Children's Museum** (☎ 233-2734, 223-7003) is in the old Central Penitentiary (*Penitenciaria*) to the N of downtown San José on C. 4 to the N of Av. 9. The building dates from 1848, and it held as many as 4,000 prisoners as recently as 1989. Viewed from outside, it resembles a castle. Inside, you find 34 rooms, each with a different theme. Interactive educational exhibits are on the second level. Temporary exhibition spaces display paintings. A row of cells (*sans* prisoners) remain so you may imagine what the place was once like. It's open Wed. to Sun. 9-noon and 2-5; Ticos pay US$3; children of all nationalities under 12 and accompanied by an adult are free, but foreigner adults are fleeced for US$5 US$2.50 students).

The **Museo de Fotos** (☎ 222-4941), C. 7, Av. Central/1, displays photos from the 18th C. Presenting a portion of the 30,000 negatives taken by Manuel Gómez Miralles, the 175 prints cover Costa Rican history from 1910-1930 and include a shot of Irazú erupting in 1917.

The **Asociación Cultural Sejekto de Costa Rica (Voz del Indio)** in Sabanilla has a display of indigenous items and sells crafts. Items include traditional Bribri clothes, baskets, woven bags, flutes, drums, and even a violin. Call 234-7115 to make an appointment.

OTHER SIGHTS: Divided by C. 7 and Av. 3 into four individual gardens, compact **Parque Morazán** has a pseudo Japanese-style section in the NE. The "Temple of Music," which once hosted concerts, stands in the park's center. The entirety of this small park is now overshadowed by the immense Aurora Holiday Inn with its reflecting glass panes. On C. 2 and Av. 2/4, the **Post Office Museum** is open Mon. to Fri, 8-5.

The former National Liquor Factory has been converted into the **Museum of Contemporary Art and Design** which serves as a cultural center, museum, and performance space where the National Dance Company preforms and the National Theater Company puts on plays. Entrance is around US$2.50 for *gringos*. It's on the NW side of the Parque Nacional at Av. 5/7, C. 15.

Delineated by Av. 2 and 4 and Calles 12 and 14, **Parque Braulio Carrillo** has a pre-Columbian stone sphere from Palmar Sur which spans four ft. (1. 3 m) in diameter, along with a statue of the former president.

The city's newest plaza, the **Plaza de a Libertad** (C. 13, Av. 7/9) was dedicated n 1994. It features a chunk of the Berlin wall donated by the German govt. A plaque commemorates the date Nov. 9, 1989 which is when the wall came tumbling down. In the outlying suburb of **San Francisco de Dos Ríos**, there's a footbridge which resembles the Golden Gate Bridge in San Francisco.

Outlying Sights

PARQUE METROPOLITANO (LA SABANA): Set at the opposite end of the wealthy Paseo de Colón district is La Sabana, the city's largest park, which was formerly the site of the national airport. The lake here was drained for the airport era and then restored later. Sports facilities include a gym, pool, and stadium. Additions were made to the park in 1995 for the controversial Fiesta Internacional de Costa Rica (which never came off); lighting was improved and sand was trucked in to create a beach. On a typical Sunday afternoon, you'll find sports (soccer, softball, tennis, and basketball), picnickers, cyclists, and even a revivalist group. During 1995, the park's pond was mysteriously invaded by a crocodile who was witnessed dining on ducks. It was captured by the Wildilfe Dept. before it could expand its diet to toddlers and the like.

MUSEO DE ARTE COSTARRICENSE: Housed in what was formerly the airport control tower, the Costa Rican Museum of Art stands on C. 42, at the E side of La Sabana. This Spanish-style building has everything from pre-Columbian to modern art. Included in its collection are portraits, woodcuts, antique painted wooden sculptured busts, and antique ink drawings of the Gulf of Nicoya and a festival in Guanacaste. There's also the wooden sculpture,"Los Amantes" by

Juan Manuel Sanchez, paintings, woodcuts, a giant agricultural mural by Francisco Amighetti, the feminist portraits of Max Jiménez, and a sculptured wooden chair by Juan Luis Rodriguez. The museum is divided into sections such as *abstraccíon y figuracíon* and *nuevas tendencias*. The latter has works like Rafael Ottón Solis's "Homenaje a Monseñor Romero" and a batik on paper by Anabel Martén. Although the area is small, the robust collection is incredibly diverse, and the quality of its varied sculptures is outstanding: Be sure to visit the outdoor sculpture garden. (Open Tues. through Sun., 10-5; free on Sun.). Take any Sabana bus from Av. 3, C. Central/2, or from the Parque Central.

MUSEO DE CIENCIAS NATURALES: Opened in 1959, the Natural Sciences Museum (☎ 232-6427) is located in Collegio La Salle, a school set at the SW extremity of Sabana Park. You can either walk from the art museum or take the Estadio Sabana bus from near Parque Central. Stuffed animals are what you'll find here, with over 1,000 birds, as well as monkeys and other forest dwellers. Ring the buzzer at the R and the curator will come to the door, collect the small admission fee, and switch on all the lights for you. The first room to the R has a small archaeological collection. A pleasant place to sit and read, the courtyard has a whale skeleton. One room displays various bottles containing sea urchins, octupi, human fetuses, and bats. There are shells, shells, and more shells; rocks, rocks, and more rocks. Other rooms have dioramas which are so poorly done that they are almost comedic. Check out the chimp holding the plastic pineapple, and the spaced-out orangutan clutching his plastic pear. Then, there's the fierce looking mama opposum with the kiddies riding shotgun on top, and the Janus-faced, two-headed baby ox *mutacion*. Finally, the domestic rabbit has such a wild expression and tensely poised posture that he appears to have hopped straight from the pages of Richard Adams' novel, *Watership Down*. If you do come, you'll undoubtedly have fun trying to pick the most obscenely stuffed animal! (Open Tues. to Fri., 8-3, Sat. 8-12).

MUSEO DE ENTOMOLOGÍA: Located downstairs in the Facultade de Artes Musicales (music department) of the Universitas de Costa Rica in Sabanilla Montes de Oca, a suburb E of San José, Central America's sole collection of insects features a wonderful display of butterflies, including the turqoise-winged *Morpho amathonte*. There are also some dioramas, hercules and elephant beetles, and the totally cute *Megaloblatta rufiles*, a 4-in. (10-cm) cockroach. To get here take the *San Pedro* bus near the Teatro Nacional on Av. Central between Calles 7 and 9; get off when you see the park with the church on your L. Open weekdays, 1-4:45; researchers welcome anytime, ☎ 225-5555. Admission is 100 *colones* for Ticos and 300 *colones* for those not belonging to the chosen people.

While you're in the area you might want to visit the small, somewhat funky campus and the surrounding area which has a number of restaurants, including vegetarian-macrobiotic **La Mazorca** which has a bakery as well as a health food store. At the university check out the ledge to the R of the library. It's known as the "pretil," and is sure to have see-and-be-seen students galore.

ACUA MANÍA: Central America's largest water park, Acua Manía (☎ 293-2033) opened in Jan. 1995 in the suburb of Cariari to the W of San José. In addition to the extensive aquatic portion, it also has a go-kart course (with 20 karts), an 18-hole miniature golf course, a video arcade, and a fast food restaurant. A wave pool, a "lazy" river, soccer fields, and a tube slide which will weave through trees. Presently, a large pool has a volleyball net over one side and underwater caves with seats and piped-in music in the other; two short slides are behind the caverns, A smaller pool is calmer, and there is a children's pool with water guns, water slides, and sprinklers. There are more than a dozen lifeguards so your children will be safe here.

San José Accommodations

You can find any type of hotel in this the San José area. Accommodation rangesfrom fleabags to luxury suites. In general, you may get what you pay for, although this does not necessarily always apply. You have the option of staying directly downtown or basing yourself farther out and commuting. Downtown can be noisy, but it is decidedly more convenient. If you are sensitive to street noise, you'll want to have a quiet room. The least desirable places to stay are around the Coca-Cola terminal, but this is where many of the low-budget hotels are located.

HOMESTAYS: Bell's Home Hospitality (☎ 225-4752, fax 224-5884) will connect you with a homestay for US$45 d with shared bath and US$50 private bath; breakfast is included.

homestay@sol.racsa.co.cr

TurCasa (☎ 221-6161, 223-1165) is a group of Ticos who offer homestays; rooms are about the same as Bell's.

While *aparthotels* are convenient for longer stays, they tend to lack atmosphere.

LUXURY AND ULTRA-LUXURY ACCOMMODATION: These are defined as being over US$100 or over US$121 respectively for a single or double, including tax and services. As there are a number of hotels in this range at present, this list has been trimmed in favor of the smaller luxury hotels, and chains and the largest hotels have been eliminated.

Overlooking Parque Bolívar at C. 13, Av. 9/11, the service-oriented **Hotel L'Ambiance**'s rates include continental breakfast. Filled with antiques this six-room and one-suite hotel, set in a Spanish-style home, has a gourmet restaurant, a/c, and private TV. Call 222-6702, 223-1598; fax 223-0481; or write Apdo. 1040, 2050 San Pedro. Rates run from around US$90 d plus tax. In the US, write c/o Interlink, PO Box 526770, Miami, FL 33152.

The **Britannia Hotel** (☎ 223-6667, 800-263-2618; fax 223-6411, SJO 3264 Unit C-101, Box 025216, Miami, FL 33102-2618), C. 3, Av. 11, is the most luxurious of the hotels housed in restored buildings in Barrio Amón. It offers a restaurant, conference room, and rooms and suites. The rooms are in the original building as well as in the addition; the quietest rooms are in the back of the addition.

www.centralamerica.com/cr/hotel/britania.htm

britania@sol.racsa.co.cr

britania@sol.racsa.co.cr

D'Raya Vida Bed & Breakfast Villa (☎ 223-4168, fax 223-4147; C. 15, Av. 11/13) is another luxury B&B. The home has four rooms, each impeccably decorated in a different style. Most unusual is the mask room which has masks from all of the world. Rates run around US$65 s, US$85 d plus tax and include transport to and from airport, travel consulting, and a full breakfast.

bbb.or.cr/BedBreakfast/draya
draya@sol.racsa.co.cr

PASEO DE COLÓN LUXURY ACCOMMODATION: This quiet area has blossomed in terms of restaurants, night spots, and small hotels in the past few years.

At C. 30, Av. 2/4, No. 251, the 34-room **Grano de Oro** (☎ 255-3322, fax 221-2782; Box 025216, Miami, FL 33102-5216) is a well-located hotel set in a restored mansion. Rooms (smoking prohibited) have phones and cable TV, minibrs, brass fixtures with colonial tiles in baths, and hand-crafted ironwood furniture. Hundreds of tropical plants adorn the premises. On the premises are an acclaimed gourmet French restaurant in a courtyard (breakfast, light meals, and desserts served), a tropical sundeck terrace with two hot tubs; fax, photocopy, laundry/drycleaning and mail service; and secure parking. Prices are around US$75 for standard rooms, US$105 for deluxe, and US$150 for garden suites plus tax.
www.granodeoro.com
www.distinctivehotels.com
granoro@sol.racsa.co.cr

Also on Paseo de Colón, the **Rosa del Paseo** (☎ 257-3258, fax 223-2776; Apdo. 287, 1007 San José) is a beautifully restored old home which now operates as a small hotel. Rates are around US$55 d which includes a continental breakfast. If you have problems with noise, you should be sure to get one of the original rooms to the rear of the house.
rosadep@sol.racsa.co.cr

Billing itself as "the boutique hotel," **Palma Real** (☎ 290-5060, fax 290-4160, Apdo. 694-1005, Barrio México) is an ultramodern-style hotel geared towards the executive set. Facilities include Jacuzzi, gym, restaurant, and secretarial services. It is 200 m N of the ICE off Sabana Norte.
fiesta@sol.racsa.co.cr

IN SAN PEDRO: A restored home, the **Hotel Milvia** (☎ 225-4543, fax 225-7801; Apdo. 1660-2050 San Pedro) is one of the best places to stay in its price range in the San José area. Its attractively decorated rooms are each personalized with individual names and each has phone, TV, fan, and bath. Continental breakfasts (served as early as you need) and dinners (Italian, by request) are served in the small dining room; from the upstairs balcony you can see as far as Irazú on a clear morning. Coffee and tea are complimentary and always available; accompanying desserts are on sale. The hotel is 50 m E and 50 m N, and 200 m E of "Del Higueron" or turn L by the Muñoz y Nanne shopping plaza. Rates are around US$60 d.
hmilvia@sol.racsa.co.cr

OUTLYING LUXURY ACCOMMODATION: Near the Cariari and 1, 250 m E of the country club, **Hotel Vista de Golf** (☎ 239-4348, fax 239-4371) offers rooms ranging from standard doubles to suites. Write Apdo. 379, 4005 San Antonio de Belén. In the US call (800) 662-1656. Pool, spa, cable TV, fax are among the services.

The **Hotel Herradura** (☎ 239-0033, fax 239-2292) is off the main highway to the airport.
www.costasol.co.cr
hheradu@sol.racsa.co.cr

The **Meliá Carari** (☎239-0022, fax 239-2083; 800-33-MELIA) is another well established luxury hotel which is just down the road.
www.solmedia.es
cariari @sol.racsa.co.cr

Its sister establishment, the **Meliá Confort Corobicí** (☎ 800-33-MELIA is a

the E end of La Sabana.
www.solmedia.es
corobici @sol.racsa.co.cr

Spanish-style **Marriott Hotel and Resort** (☎ 298-0000, fax 298-0011, 800-228-9270) is in San Antonio de Belén.

The **Raddisson Europa Hotel and Conference Center** (☎/fax 800-333-3333) has a full-service business center with Internet access.
eurohot@sol.racsa.co.cr

EXPENSIVE ACCOMMODATION DOWNTOWN (US$61-100): Many new places have opened downtown, largely to the N of Parque Morazán. Owing to inflation, some of the more expensive of these may have moved into the luxury category by the time of your arrival.

The 104-room **Hotel del Rey** (☎ 221-7272,257-3130, fax 221-0096; Apdo. 6241, 1000 San José) is one of the most attractive and reasonably priced for the value offered in this price range. Rates start at US$55 s, US$68 d plus tax and range as high as US$125 for master suites; tax is added. It has a 24-hr. restaurant, casino, popular bar, travel agency, fishing and travel agencies, and offers room service. It's located right near Park Morazán and is at Av. 1 and C. 9.

Restored in 1994, the original building dates from the 1940s and is now painted pink and white. It largely attracts a white male fisherman crowd, and its location in the heart of the tourist's red light district makes it unsuitable for families and evangelical Christians alike.

A bed and breakfast set in a restored coffee plantation home constructed in 1910, the 20-room **Hotel Santo Tomás** (☎ 255-0448, fax 222-3950) is behind the Aurora Holiday Inn on Av. 7, C 3/5. It has French Provincial furniture produced in Costa Rica, Persian rugs, and 14-ft. vaulted ceilings. The floors are either handmade tile or pochote. English, German, French, Spanish, and Portugese are spoken. Each room has its own individual character and unique design. The breakfast (buffet-style coffee, pastries, and tropical fruit) in an open-air courtyard is another plus; complimentary coffee is available daily until 5. Rates run from around US$55/day on up.
www.hotels.co.cr/santomas.html
hotelst@sol.racsa.co.cr

An 11-room bed and breakfast, the **Casa Morazán** (☎ 257-4187, fax 257-4175) was designed by a famous Costa Rican architect during the 1930s; it offers rooms with cable TV and a/c; some have their own inside patio. Rates are around US$65 d.
anakeith @sol.racsa.co.cr

The 19-room **Fleur de Lys** (☎ 223-1206, 257-2621, fax 257-3637; Apdo. 10736, 1000 San José) is a renovated old home with artwork in its bedrooms; a gourmet restaurant is attached.
florlys @sol.racsa.co.cr

Set 50 m S of the Pizza Hut in Barrio California near the National Museum, intimate bed and breakfast **Ara Macao** (☎/fax 233-2742) offers free airport pickup.

A bed and breakfast in a light-green colored old home in Barrio Amón (C. 7, Av. 9), three-suite and five-room **La Casa Verde de Amón** (☎/fax 223-0969; Dept. 1701, Box 025216, Miami, FL 33102-5216) has a sauna; more expensive suites with cable TV are available. It received the restoration award from the Costa Rican branch of UNESCO in 1994. Features include stained glass, antiques, and a piano. Ask for a room away from the street. Rates run around US$75-130 d including breakast buffet.

casaverd@sol.racsa.co.cr

Still another choice in Barrio Amón (Av. 11/C. 3), **Taylor's Inn** (☎ 257-4333, fax 221-1475; Apdo. 531-1000) is a "bed & breakfast hotel" which has ten rooms with baths and cable TVs. The red-brick building dates from 1910. Rates are around US$60 d not including tax.
www.catours.co.cr
taylor@catours.co.cr

On Av. Central, C. 1/3, **La Gran Via** (☎ 222-7737, fax 222-7205) is another small hotel.

Formerly the Hotel Bougainvillea, the 80-room **Villa Tournón** (☎ 233-6622, fax 222-5211; Apdo. 6606, 1000 San José) has a restaurant, a/c, pool, Jacuzzi, and parking.

On C. Central between Av. 3/5, **Hotel Europa** (☎ 222-1222, fax 221-3976) has cable TV, pool and restaurant. Write Apdo. 72, San José or call (800) 223-6764 in the US.

Located on Av. Central between C. 7/9, the 120-room **Hotel Presidente** (☎ 222-3022, fax 221-1205; Apdo. 2922, 1000 San José) has restaurant, cable TV, a/c, casino, disco, and some kitchen-equipped suites.
hotpres@sol.racsa.co.cr

With a/c, cable TV, casino, and sauna, the businessman-oriented **Balmoral** (☎ 221-1919/5022, fax 221-7826) is at Av. Central, C. 7/9. Write Apdo. 3344, 1000 San José.

At C. 11, Av. 2/6 across from the Mercado Nacional Artesania, **Gran Hotel Doña Ines** (☎ 222-7443, fax 223-5426) is intimate and upscale; it's near the National Museum. Rooms come with phone, radio, and TV. Prices are around US$58 s, US$70 d.

LA SABANA/PASEO COLÓN: Located in a quiet neighborhood near La Sabana (C. 40, Av. 5 bis), **Sol Inn Torremolinos** (☎ 222-9129/5266, fax 255-3167) has suites and full suites with cable TV, pool, sauna, massage, and a/c (full suites only). Rates are around US$75-95 d, US$ 80 t.
torremolinos@sol.racsa.co.cr

Located on the SW side of la Sabana, the **Tennis Club** (☎ 232-1266, fax 232-3867; Apdo. 4964, San José) has a pool, tennis, sauna, gym, and skating rink.

LOS YOSES: Out in Los Yoses and quite popular with visitors, the 20-room villa-style **Hotel Don Fadrique** (☎ 225-8186, 224-7583/7947, fax 224-9746; Apdo. 1654-2050, San Pedro) is at C. 37 and Av. 8. The hotel is named after the owner's famous great-great uncle. Owner Oscar Urbina, a British-educated former World Bank agronomist, has work by over 60 Costa Rican artists on the walls. Simply but attractively-furnished rooms have cable TV, phone, and fan; some rooms have private gardens. There is a garden with fountain. Rates are around US$55 s, US$65 d plus tax for spacious and attractively furnished rooms; breakfast is included.
fadrique@centralamerica.com

At Av. 8, C. 35, the 18-room **Hotel Le Bergerac** (☎ 234-7850, fax 225-9103; Apdo. 1107-1002, San José) is set in two converted houses; the attractive, spacious executive suites have gardens or balconies, fans, cable TV (in English, French, Spanish, German), and phones. Defined as a French inn and named after the novelist, it's run by French Canadians and has a relaxed, serene, yet elegant atmosphere. Gourmet French dinners are served evenings in the hotel's gourmet **Ile'de France** restaurant. Rates run from around US$58 s, US$70 d including breakfast.
www.bergerac.co.cr
bergerac@sol.racsa.co.cr

Heading into its third decade of operation, **Apartotel Los Yoses** (☎ 225-0033, 255-0044, fax 225-5595; Apdo. 1597, 1000 San José) stands directly opposite the San Pedro Mall with its four cinemas. Its rooms are all different and some can hold up to five. Facilities include a/c, kitchenettes, and pool. Rates (US$50-100 s or d) include breakfast.
losyoses@sol.racsa.co.cr

NEAR THE AIRPORT: The Hampton Airport Inn (☎ 443-0043, fax 506-442-9532; 800-426-7866) is off the main highway.
www.hamptonhotel.co.cr
hampton@sol.racsa.co.cr

Other hotels in this price range, all of which have more character, are found near and in Alajuela. See this section for details.

MODERATE ACCOMMODATION (US$30-50): In Barrio Amón, **Kekoldi** (☎ 223-3244, fax 357-5476; Box 12150-1000, San José) is at Av. 9 and C. 3 bis in front of INVU. This lovely, colonial-style house has been transformed into a colorful ho☎ Its name is taken from the Bri Bri word meaning "holy tree of water," and each room has a Bribri name. It has a restaurant, and breakfast is served. It's run by a German-Tica couple. Prices range from around US$15-45. Reader R. M. relates it "was absolutely delightful and very unique."
www.kekoldi.com
kekoldi@sol.racsa.co.cr

At C. 9 and Av. 9, the 17-room **Hemingway Inn** (☎/fax 221-1804; Apdo. 1711-1002, San José) offers cable TV and continental breakfast. High season rates are around US$30 s, US$40 d, and US$50 t plus tax; subtract US$10 for low season rates.
heming@hotels.co.cr

The former home of President-Dictator Tomás Guardia (1870-82), **Hotel Don Carlos** (☎ 221-6707, fax 255-0828; Dept. 1686, PO Box 025216, Miami, FL 33102) is on C. 9 between Av. 7/9. It has a restaurant, gym, sun deck, cable TV, and complimentary breakfast. Rates are around US$70 d.
www.doncarlos.co.cr
hotel@doncarlos.co.cr

On C. 19, Av. 11/13, the family-run 23-room Caribbean-style **Hotel Aranjuez** (☎ 223-3559, fax 223-3528; Apdo. 457-2070, San José) has a garden, hammocks, courtyards and is actually two buildings connected together. Rooms are spacious and have hardwood floors. It serves a complimentary continental breakfast and offers Costa Rican-style hospitality. Prices start at around US$25 s with shared bath.

Next to Parque Morázan and directly across from the gargantuan Aurola (C. 5, Av. 3), Tico-owned and run **Diana's Inn** (☎/fax 223-6542) is a pleasure to stay at simply for its affable, helpful staff and relaxed atmosphere. Each room has a TV and some have a/c. Street noise can be a problem. A continental breakfast is served. Prices are around US$46 s and US$50 d.

One of the newer hotels, **La Gema** (☎/fax 222-1074) is on Av. 12, C. 9/11; breakfast is served, and it has its own restaurant and bar.

Centrally located at C. 9, Av. 10, the **Hotel Mansion Blanca Inn** (☎ 222-0423, 257-6198, fax 222-7947; Apdo. 85570, 1000 San José) is an 11-room bed and breakfast in an old mansion which is run by an affable Tico couple in their 50s. It has been recommended by a reader.

At C. 5 and Av. 11, the 27-rm. **Dunn Inn** (☎ 222-3232, 222-3246, fax 221-4596; Apdo. 6241, 1000 San José) includes continental breakfast in its rates. Located in a refurbished century-old mansion, it has one luxury suite with a Jacuzzi and other features. Rates are around US$65 d.

The attractive and distinctive Dutch-run **Apartotel El Sesteo** (☎ 296-1805, fax 296-1865; Apdo. 1246, 1007 San José) is 200 m S of La Sabana's McDonald's. It has 20 one- and two-bedroom units, 16 rooms, has a pool and Jacuzzi, and also shares some facilities with the nearby Costa Rica Tennis Club. Rates range from around US$50-80 d plus tax. Rates include continental breakfast.
www.hotels.co.cr/sesteo.html
sesteo@sol.racsa.co.cr

With some a/c rooms, the **Gran Via** (☎ 222-7737, fax 222-7205; Apdo. 1433, San José) is at Av. Central and C. 13. F

One of the nicest apartment hotels, the **Llama del Bosque** (☎ 225-5350, fax 224-0681) is located 100 m S and 50 m W of the Plaza del Sol, a shopping center in San Pedro. It has a pool, offers breakfast, and has kitchenettes.

The 25-room **Belmondo Hotel Bed & Breakfast** (☎ 222-9624) has a pool, bar, and restaurant. It's at C. 20, Av. 9 in Barrio Mexico. It also has dorm rooms.

Also on C. 20 and 250 m N of the Children's Hospital, the **Mesón del Angel** (☎ 223-7747, fax 223-2781) is a serene ten-bedroom hotel with a phone and cable TV in each room; rates are from around US$35 s to US$65 quad plus tax.

At Av. 7, C. 9, the **Rey Amón** (☎ 233-3819, fax 233-1769; Apdo. 7145-1000 San José) is a small, 13-room hotel set in a restored house. The high-ceilinged rooms have cable TV. Rates include breakfast; complimentary airport pickup with advance notification is available.

German-run 22-room **La Amistad** (☎ 221-1597) is a comfy bed and breakfast which is in Barrio Otoya at Av. 11/C. 15. Rooms have cable TV.
wolfgang@sol.racsa.co.cr

At Av. 6, C. 11/13 (50 m W of the Veterinaria Drs. Echandi), the **Villa Bonita Inn** (☎ 222-7075) is an *apartotel* which charges around US$50 s or d.

Cacts (☎ 221-2928, fax 221-8616; Av. 3 bis, No. 2845, C. 28/30; Apdo. 379, 1005, San José) has 36 rooms in a converted house. Rates are around US$50 d with breakfast. It has a sauna and Jacuzzi.
www.tourism.co.cr/hotels/cacts/cacts.htm
hcacts@sol.racsa.co.cr

Apartotel Castilla (☎ 222-2113, fax 221-2080;Apdo. 944, 1006 San José) is on C. 24, Av. 2/4, a location convenient to the Paseo Colón shopping area.

The **Cristina** (☎ 231-1618, 220-0453, fax 220-2096) is an attractive apartotel with sunny rooms and a garden. It charges around US$60 d with breakfast and has handicapped-accessible rooms available. One drawback here is that you lose privacy if your drapes are not drawn.
apacrit@sol.racsa.co.cr

At C. 29 and Av. Central/8, the **Apartotel Don Carlos** (☎ 221-6707, fax 255-0828) rents rooms on a weekly basis only.

On the Sabana, two-storey, colonial-style **Apartotel La Sabana** (☎ 220-2422, 296-0876, fax 231-7386; Apdo. 11400, 1000 San José) has a/c, cable TV, pool, and an arrangement with a nearby health club. Breakfast is included in the rates around US$40 d for rooms to US$80 for two- bedroom apartments.
lasabana@sol.racsa.co.cr

In Los Yoses, **Apartotel El Conquistador** (☎ 225-3022) can be contacted at Apdo. 303, 2050 San Pedro, and **Apartotel Lamm** (☎ 221-4290, fax 221-4720; C. 15, Av. 1) can be reached at Apdo. 2729, 1000 San José.

At. Av. 4, C. 8, the **Doral** (☎ 233-0665/5069, fax 233-4827) has clean and sunny rooms with phone.

Cloud Forest Sunset

Butterfly on Flower

Grasshopper on Flower

Basilisk or "Jesus Christ Lizard"
A splash and he's gone!

A White-Tailed Hawk holds court.

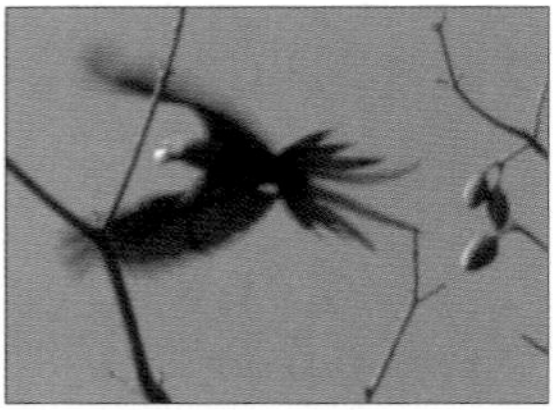

Feeding Scarlet Macaws
in Flight at Corcovado

The Keel-Billed Toucan is one of
Central America's most famed birds.

Nesting Cattle Egrets

Leaf Frog (Daryl Loth)

Poison Dart Frog

Bat captured from Corcovado's rainforest. Bats are extremely important for the rainforest ecosystem. They disperse seeds, fertilize plants, and help control the insect population.

Joined in a symbiotic relationship with the acacia tree, the acacia-ant wards off herbivores. The acacia tree supplies the ants with nectar, protein and and protection in return.

Blue Morphos collected as part of INbio's Biodiversity Project.

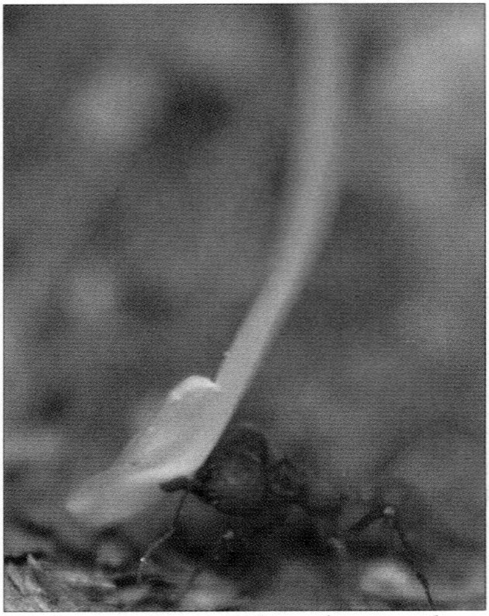

Leafcutter ants are the only animals besides man that farm.

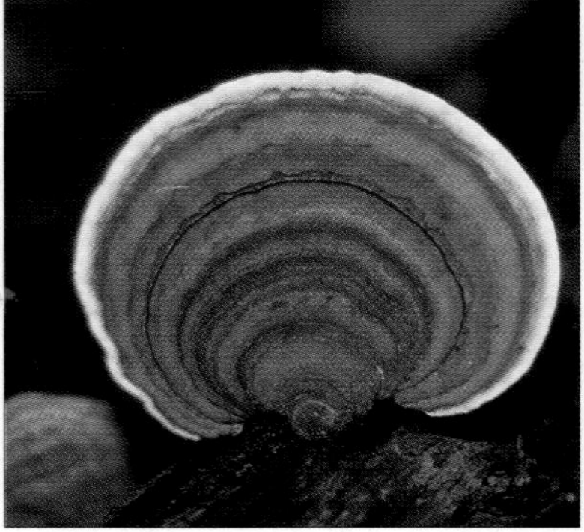

Fungi in La Amistad National Park

Ramgo (☎ 232-3823, fax 232-3111, Apdo. 1441, 1000 San José) is 100 m S of the Tennis Club at La Sabana.

INEXPENSIVE ACCOMMODATION (US$30-50): Set to the W of the Parque Nacional on Av. 1 at C. 11/15, **Pensión de la Cuesta** (☎ 255-2896, fax 2 57-2272) is a bed and breakfast run by artists. Baths are shared, as is the refrigerator and entire kitchen. Rates are less than US$30 d with breakfast.
www.arweb.com/lacuesta
ggmnbr@sol.racsa.co.cr

The 29-room **Hotel Diplomat** (221-8133, 221-8744, fax 233-7474; Apdo. 6606, 1000 San José) is located on C. 6 between Av. Central/2. It has small rooms with hot water for around US$30 d.

Located on C. 24, Paseo Colón/Av. 2, the **Petit Hotel** (☎ 233-0766, fax 233-1938) has rooms with both private and shared baths. Facilities include free coffee, communal TV, and kitchen privileges. (Note: one reader has written to complain about the cleanliness and size of the rooms here).

At C. 24, Av. 2 across from the Sala Garbo, the **Petit Victoria** (☎ 233-1812/1813, fax 233-1938) offers use of its kitchen as well as cable TV. Write Apdo. 357, 1007 Centro Colón.

A block away from the Mercado Central at C. 10, Av. 1/3, the 48-room **Bienvenido** (☎ 221-1872, fax 233-2161; Apdo. 389-2200, San José) is one of the better hotels in this range and is around US$25 d. Ask about their four rooms which hold four.

A cross between a bed and breakfast and a standard hotel, **La Amistad** (☎ 221-1597, fax 221-1409) is set in Barrio Otoya (Av. 11, C. 15) as is the attractively furnished 11-room **Hotel Edelweiss** (☎ 221-9702, fax 222-1241; Av. 9, C. 13/15) and the 20-room **Hotel Vesuvio** (☎ 221-7586/8325, Apdo. 477-1000, San José; Av. 11, C. 13-15) which has a restaurant.

Also in this area (V. 15, Av. 7/11bis) is the singular **Cinco Hormigas Rojas** (☎/fax 257-8581). "Five Red Ants" is nature-lover and artist Mayra Guell's special creation. The entire bed-and-breakfast is decorated with her artwork, right down to the painted toilet bowl lids. Enter via what Mayra calls her "little jungle." Mayra aspires to live in the country, but her sister will be running the place if she is not here. This is an unforgettable place to stay for down-to-earth types. Rates are around US$30 s, US$40 d with a discount for cash. Tell the taxi driver that it is "*doscientos metros oeste emergencias Calderón y setenta metros sur*)."
cincohormigasrojas@crtimes.com

In the Coca Cola area, the 52-rm. **Hotel Alameda** (☎ 221-3045/6333, fax 222-9673; Av. Central, C. 12/14; Apdo. 680, San José) is another formerly grand old hotel. It charges less than US$40 d for its sunny rooms. It has a restaurant.

The **Musoc** (☎ 222-9437), next to the Coca Cola terminal (at C. 16, Av. 1/30), is noisy but very popular. There have been reports of left luggage disappearing here.

Located on C. 6 between Av. Central and Av. 2, the centrally located **Diplomat** (☎ 221-8133) is popular, has a restaurant, and each floor has a sitting area.

The **Pensión and Hotel Ritz** (☎ 222-4103, fax 222-8849; C. Central, Av. 8/10) has a variety of rooms from single (US$ 20) through quad (US$40). Get a tour until you find one you like.

The **Hotel Fortuna** (☎ 223-5344, fax 223-2743; Apdo. 7-1570, San José); Av. 6, C. 2/4; has 30 rooms of varying quality for around US$30 d. It is right near the Parque Central; some rooms have TV sets.
fortuna@habitat.co.cr

You can also try the **Galilea** (☎ 233-6925, fax 223-1689; Av. Central, C. 11/13; around US$18 s, US$22 d), the **Pensión Centro Continental** (☎ 233-1731, fax 222-8849; Av. 8 y 10 and C. Central), and the **Astoria** (☎ 221-2174; Av. 7, C. 7/9; weekly discounts available).

The least expensive *aparthotel*, at around US$175/wk. and US$425/mo. is the **Scotland** (☎ 223-0833) in Barrio La California, an old residential area.

IN SAN PEDRO: Located on the N side of the University of Costa Rica in San Pedro, **D'Galah Hotel** (☎/fax234-1743; Apdo. 208-2350, San José) has a coffee shop, pool, sauna, and some rooms with kitchenettes. Rates run around US$50 d.

The **Maripaz** (☎ 253-8456) is a bed and breakfast with both shared and private baths.

LOW-BUDGET ACCOMMODATION (under US$30): It may be hard to stay cheaply at the beaches these days, but there's no dearth of cheap places to stay in town. The very cheapest can be well under US$10 a day.

BASIC PLACES: A very basic but hospitable place with lots of guests from the *gringo* trail, **Ticalinda** (☎ 233-0528, fax 257-2272) is at Av. 2, C. 5, #553; look carefully for the door right next to Esmeralda's.

In the same general area, **Pensión Palma** (☎ 233-3877) is at Av. 6, C 11/13.

The **Otoya** (☎ 221-3925; C. 1, Av. 3/5) has large rooms and offers a TV lounge as well as storage. Rates are around US$4 s, US$8 d, US$15 quad.

The **Principe** (☎ 222-7983, fax 223-1589; Av. 6, C. Central/2) is both cheap and very popular with travelers.

Another good place is **Pensión Americana** (☎ 221-4171/9799), C. 2, Av. Central/Av. 2.

The 11-room **Hotel América** (☎ 221-4116; Av. 7, C. 2/4) charges around US$6 but also caters to short timers.

Popular with Ticos and backpackers alike (the entrance can resemble a Grateful Dead concert), the **Gran Hotel Imperial** (☎ 222-7899), at C. 8, Av. Central/1, up the street from the Hotel Johnson, is one of the best values around US$4 s, US$8 d, US$12 t, US$14 quad. They will hold your luggage for a fee, offer a pay phone, and have a restaurant.

If this is too downscale for your tastes, the **Johnson** (☎ 223-7633, fax 222-3683; Apdo. 6638, 1000 San José, C. 8 and Av. Central/Av. 2 bis, is popular with Tico businessmen, the Lonely Planet travel guide author, and family groups. It charges around US$20 d and has a restaurant.

In a safer area of town, the **Galilea** (☎ 233-6925, fax 223-1689) is at C. 13 and Av. Central.

Hotel Rialto (☎ 221-7456; C. 2, Av. 5) has small rooms and shared but segregated common baths. Rates are around US$4 s, US$7 d.

The **Bellavista** (☎ 223-0095/5477, fax 223-8385; Av. Central, C. 19/21). is within 20 min. of the Plaza de la Cultura on foot. Also try the **Boruca** (☎ 223-0016, fax 232-0077); C. 14, Av. 1/3), the **Capital** (☎/fax 221-8497, C. 4, Av. 3/5; around US$20 d), **Central** (☎ 221-2767, Av. 3, C. 4/6), the **Cocorí** (☎ 233-0081, C. 16 Av. 3 near Hospital San Juan de Dios), **Marlyn** (☎ 233-3212, C. 4, Av. 7/9), the **Morazán** (☎ 221-9083; Av. 3, C. 11/15), the **Roma** (☎ 223-2179; C. 14, Av. 1), **Hotel Colón** (C. 4, Av. 1, #150 N), and **Gran Americo** (☎ 221-3362, Av. 2, C. 8).

BUDGET AND SPECIAL: A quiet and secluded oasis attractive to those who want access to the peace movement,

Casa Ridgeway (☎ 233-6168, fax 224-8910; Apdo. 1507, 1000 San José), in the Quaker-established Centro Por La Paz, is a great place to stay: US$8 pp in small dorm room, US$10 s, and US$16 d. There's an excellent lending library, kitchen privileges, hot water, and the central location (Av. 6 bis, C. 15) can't be beat. Although budget travelers can find better values price-wise elsewhere, it is highly recommended.

La Granja (☎ 225-1073, 234-8835, fax 234-1676) is a Tico home with shared kitchen. Expect to pay around US$15 pp; discounts available for youth hostel card holders. It's 50 m S of the Antiguo Higuerón in San Pedro.

Casa Leo (☎ 222-9725) offers dorm accommodation for around US$88 pp as well as slightly more expensive single and double rooms. This German-run homestay is at Av. 6 bis, C. 15; watch for the sign next to Acupunctura Kaminsky and across the street from Clinica Echandi.

The 19-rm. **Toruma Youth Hostel** (☎/fax 224-4085) stands on the N side of Av. Central in the eastern suburb of Los Yoses. Tell a taxi driver to let you off at *"Albergue Juvenil Toruma cerca de Pollos Fritos Kentucky,"* or you can take any of the various San Pedro-bound buses which also pass by. Its high-ceilinged dorms hold 6-20. It's open 24 hours, and you may stay as long as you wish. However, at around US$10 pp with breakfast (and youth hostel card) and US$12 pp (without card), it's definitely overpriced and quite a bit more than staying in a low-budget hotel on your own. You also have a shower schedule to contend with on top of the lack of privacy. (Two private rooms are available for US$26 s or d). One distinct advantage of staying here, however, is that you do get to meet a lot of people. And it is *clean* if you are fickle about such things.
reacjh@sol.racsa.co.cr

The **Kalexma Inn** (☎ 290-2634, ☎/fax 232-0115; Apdo. 6833, 1000 San José) combines budget accommodation with language study. It's across the highway from the Hotel Irazú. Rates are around US$20 s, US$30 d. They offer homestays (as well as special hotel rates for Spanish students), and rates include continental breakfast.
www.goldnet.co.cr/kalexma
kalexma@ns.goldnet.co.cr

D'Raya Vida Bed & Breakfast Villa (☎ 223-4168, fax 223-4147; C. 15, Av. 11/13) is another luxury B&B. The home has four rooms, each impeccably decorated in a different style. Most unusual is the mask room which has masks from all of the world. Rates run around US$65 s, US$85 d plus tax and include transport to and from airport, travel consulting, and a full breakfast.
bbb.or.cr/BedBreakfast/draya
draya@sol.racsa.co.cr

PASEO DE COLÓN LUXURY ACCOMMODATION: This quiet area has blossomed in terms of restaurants, night spots, and small hotels in the past few years.

At C. 30, Av. 2/4, No. 251, the 34-room **Grano de Oro** (☎ 255-3322, fax 221-2782; Box 025216, Miami, FL 33102-5216) is a well-located hotel set in a restored mansion. Rooms (smoking prohibited) have phones and cable TV, minibrs, brass fixtures with colonial tiles in baths, and hand-crafted ironwood furniture. Hundreds of tropical plants adorn the premises. On the premises are an acclaimed gourmet French restaurant in a courtyard (breakfast, light meals, and desserts served), a tropical sundeck terrace with two hot tubs; fax, photocopy, laundry/drycleaning and mail service;

and secure parking. Prices are around US$75 for standard rooms, US$105 for deluxe, and US$150 for garden suites plus tax.
www.granodeoro.com
www.distinctivehotels.com
granoro@sol.racsa.co.cr

Also on Paseo de Colón, the **Rosa del Paseo** (☎ 257-3258, fax 223-2776; Apdo. 287, 1007 San José) is a beautifully restored old home which now operates as a small hotel. Rates are around US$55 d which includes a continental breakfast. If you have problems with noise, you should be sure to get one of the original rooms to the rear of the house.
rosadep@sol.racsa.co.cr

Billing itself as "the boutique hotel," **Palma Real** (☎ 290-5060, fax 290-4160, Apdo. 694-1005, Barrio México) is ultra-modern-style and geared towards the executive set. Facilities include Jacuzzi, gym, restaurant, and secretarial services. It is 200 m N of the ICE off Sabana Norte.
fiesta@sol.racsa.co.cr

IN SAN PEDRO: A restored home, the **Hotel Milvia** (☎ 225-4543, fax 225-7801; Apdo. 1660-2050 San Pedro) is one of the best places to stay in its price range in the San José area. Its attractively decorated rooms are each personalized with individual names and each has phone, TV, fan, and bath. Continental breakfasts (served as early as you need) and dinners (Italian, by request) are served in the small dining room; from the upstairs balcony you can see as far as Irazú on a clear morning. Coffee and tea are complimentary and always available; accompanying desserts are on sale. The hotel is 50 m E and 50 m N, and 200 m E of "Del Higueron" or turn L by the Muñoz y Nanne shopping plaza. Rates are around US$60 d.
hmilvia@sol.racsa.co.cr

OUTLYING LUXURY ACCOMMODATION: Near the Cariari and 1, 250 m E of the country club, **Hotel Vista de Golf** (☎ 239-4348, fax 239-4371) offers rooms ranging from standard doubles to suites. Write Apdo. 379, 4005 San Antonio de Belén. In the US call (800) 662-1656. Pool, spa, cable TV, fax are among the services.

The **Hotel Herradura** (☎ 239-0033, fax 239-2292) is off the main highway to the airport.
www.costasol.co.cr
hheradu@sol.racsa.co.cr

The **Meliá Carari** (☎239-0022, fax 239-2083; 800-33-MELIA) is another well established luxury hotel which is just down the road.
www.solmedia.es
cariari @sol.racsa.co.cr

Its sister establishment, the **Melía Confort Corobicí** (☎ 800-33-MELIA is at the E end of La Sabana.
www.solmedia.es
corobici @sol.racsa.co.cr

Spanish-style **Marriott Hotel and Resort** (☎ 298-0000, fax 298-0011, 800-228-9270) is in San Antonio de Belén.

The **Raddisson Europa Hotel and Conference Center** (☎/fax 800-333-3333) has a full-service business center with Internet access.
eurohot@sol.racsa.co.cr

EXPENSIVE ACCOMMODATION DOWNTOWN (US$61-100): Many new places have opened downtown, largely to the N of Parque Morazán. Owing to inflation, some of the more expensive of these may have moved into the luxury category by the time of your arrival.

The 104-room **Hotel del Rey** (☎ 221-7272,257-3130, fax 221-0096; Apdo.

6241, 1000 San José) is one of the most attractive and reasonably priced for the value offered in this price range. Rates start at US$55 s, US$68 d plus tax and range as high as US$125 for master suites; tax is added. It has a 24-hr. restaurant, casino, popular bar, travel agency, fishing and travel agencies, and offers room service. It's located right near Park Morazán and is at Av. 1 and C. 9.

Restored in 1994, the original building dates from the 1940s and is now painted pink and white. It largely attracts a white male fisherman crowd, and its location in the heart of the tourist's red light district makes it unsuitable for families and evangelical Christians alike.

A bed and breakfast set in a restored coffee plantation home constructed in 1910, the 20-room **Hotel Santo Tomás** (☎ 255-0448, fax 222-3950) is behind the Aurora Holiday Inn on Av. 7, C 3/5. It has French Provincial furniture produced in Costa Rica, Persian rugs, and 14-ft. vaulted ceilings. The floors are either handmade tile or pochote. English, German, French, Spanish, and Portugese are spoken. Each room has its own individual character and unique design. The breakfast (buffet-style coffee, pastries, and tropical fruit) in an open-air courtyard is another plus; complimentary coffee is available daily until 5. Rates run from around US$55/day on up.
www.hotels.co.cr/santomas.html
hotelst@sol.racsa.co.cr

An 11-room bed and breakfast, the **Casa Morazán** (☎ 257-4187, fax 257-4175) was designed by a famous Costa Rican architect during the 1930s; it offers rooms with cable TV and a/c; some have their own inside patio. Rates are around US$65 d.
anakeith @sol.racsa.co.cr

The 19-room **Fleur de Lys** (☎ 223-1206, 257-2621, fax 257-3637; Apdo. 10736, 1000 San José) is a renovated old home with artwork in its bedrooms; a gourmet restaurant is attached.
florlys @sol.racsa.co.cr

Set 50 m S of the Pizza Hut in Barrio California near the National Museum, intimate bed and breakfast **Ara Macao** (☎/fax 233-2742) offers free airport pickup.

A bed and breakfast in a light-green colored old home in Barrio Amón (C. 7, Av. 9), three-suite and five-room **La Casa Verde de Amón** (☎/fax 223-0969; Dept. 1701, Box 025216, Miami, FL 33102-5216) has a sauna; more expensive suites with cable TV are available. It received the restoration award from the Costa Rican branch of UNESCO in 1994. Features include stained glass, antiques, and a piano. Ask for a room away from the street. Rates run around US$75-130 d including breakast buffet.
casaverd@sol.racsa.co.cr

Still another choice in Barrio Amón (Av. 11/C. 3), **Taylor's Inn** (☎ 257-4333, fax 221-1475; Apdo. 531-1000) is a "bed & breakfast hotel" which has ten rooms with baths and cable TVs. The red-brick building dates from 1910. Rates are around US$60 d not including tax.
www.catours.co.cr
taylor@catours.co.cr

On Av. Central, C. 1/3, **La Gran Via** (☎ 222-7737, fax 222-7205) is another small hotel.

Formerly the Hotel Bougainvillea, the 80-room **Villa Tournón** (☎ 233-6622, fax 222-5211; Apdo. 6606, 1000 San José) has a restaurant, a/c, pool, Jacuzzi, and parking.

On C. Central between Av. 3/5, **Hotel Europa** (☎ 222-1222, fax 221-3976) has cable TV, pool and restaurant. Write

Apdo. 72, San José or call (800) 223-6764 in the US.

Located on Av. Central between C. 7/9, the 120-room **Hotel Presidente** (☎ 222-3022, fax 221-1205; Apdo. 2922, 1000 San José) has restaurant, cable TV, a/c, casino, disco, and some kitchen-equipped suites. **hotpres@sol.racsa.co.cr**

With a/c, cable TV, casino, and sauna, the businessman-oriented **Balmoral** (☎ 221-1919/5022, fax 221-7826) is at Av. Central, C. 7/9. Write Apdo. 3344, 1000 San José.

At C. 11, Av. 2/6 across from the Mercado Nacional Artesania, **Gran Hotel Doña Ines** (☎ 222-7443, fax 223-5426) is intimate and upscale; it's near the National Museum. Rooms come with phone, radio, and TV. Prices are around US$58 s, US$70 d.

LA SABANA/PASEO COLÓN: Located in a quiet neighborhood near La Sabana (C. 40, Av. 5 bis), **Sol Inn Torremolinos** (☎ 222-9129/5266, fax 255-3167) has suites and full suites with cable TV, pool, sauna, massage, and a/c (full suites only). Rates are around US$75-95 d, US$ 80 t. **torremolinos@sol.racsa.co.cr**

Located on the SW side of la Sabana, the **Tennis Club** (☎ 232-1266, fax 232-3867; Apdo. 4964, San José) has a pool, tennis, sauna, gym, and skating rink.

LOS YOSES: Out in Los Yoses and quite popular with visitors, the 20-room villa-style **Hotel Don Fadrique** (☎ 225-8186, 224-7583/7947, fax 224-9746; Apdo. 1654-2050, San Pedro) is at C. 37 and Av. 8. The hotel is named after the owner's famous great-great uncle. Owner Oscar Urbina, a British-educated former World Bank agronomist, has work by over 60 Costa Rican artists on the walls. Simply but attractively-furnished rooms have cable TV, phone, and fan; some rooms have private gardens. There is a garden with fountain. Rates are around US$55 s, US$65 d plus tax for spacious and attractively furnished rooms; breakfast is included.
fadrique@centralamerica.com

At Av. 8, C. 35, the 18-room **Hotel Le Bergerac** (☎ 234-7850, fax 225-9103; Apdo. 1107-1002, San José) is set in two converted houses; the attractive, spacious executive suites have gardens or balconies, fans, cable TV (in English, French, Spanish, German), and phones. Defined as a French inn and named after the novelist, it's run by French Canadians and has a relaxed, serene, yet elegant atmosphere. Gourmet French dinners are served evenings in the hotel's gourmet **Ile'de France** restaurant. Rates run from around US$58 s, US$70 d including breakfast.
www.bergerac.co.cr
bergerac@sol.racsa.co.cr

Heading into its third decade of operation, **Apartotel Los Yoses** (☎ 225-0033, 255-0044, fax 225-5595; Apdo. 1597, 1000 San José) stands directly opposite the San Pedro Mall with its four cinemas. Its rooms are all different and some can hold up to five. Facilities include a/c, kitchenettes, and pool. Rates (US$50-100 s or d) include breakfast. **losyoses@sol.racsa.co.cr**

NEAR THE AIRPORT: The Hampton Airport Inn (☎ 443-0043, fax 506-442-9532; 800-426-7866) is off the main highway.
www.hamptonhotel.co.cr
hampton@sol.racsa.co.cr

Other hotels in this price range, all of which have more character, are found near and in Alajuela. See this section for details.

MODERATE ACCOMMODATION (US$30-50): In Barrio Amón, **Kekoldi** (☎ 223-3244, fax 357-5476; Box 12150-1000, San José) is at Av. 9 and C. 3 bis in front of INVU. This lovely, colonial-style house has been transformed into a colorful hotel. Its name is taken from the Bri Bri word meaning "holy tree of water," and each room has a Bribri name. It has a restaurant, and breakfast is served. It's run by a German-Tica couple. Prices range from around US$15-45. Reader R. M. relates it "was absolutely delightful and very unique."

www.kekoldi.com
kekoldi@sol.racsa.co.cr

At C. 9 and Av. 9, the 17-room **Hemingway Inn** (☎/fax 221-1804; Apdo. 1711-1002, San José) offers cable TV and continental breakfast. High season rates are around US$30 s, US$40 d, and US$50 t plus tax; subtract US$10 for low season rates.

heming@hotels.co.cr

The former home of President-Dictator Tomás Guardia (1870-82), **Hotel Don Carlos** (☎ 221-6707, fax 255-0828; Dept. 1686, PO Box 025216, Miami, FL 33102) is on C. 9 between Av. 7/9. It has a restaurant, gym, sun deck, cable TV, and complimentary breakfast. Rates are around US$70 d.

www.doncarlos.co.cr
hotel@doncarlos.co.cr

On C. 19, Av. 11/13, the family-run 23-room Caribbean-style **Hotel Aranjuez** (☎ 223-3559, fax 223-3528; Apdo. 457-2070, San José) has a garden, hammocks, courtyards and is actually two buildings connected together. Rooms are spacious and have hardwood floors. It serves a complimentary continental breakfast and offers Costa Rican-style hospitality. Prices start at around US$25 s with shared bath.

Next to Parque Morázan and directly across from the gargantuan Aurola (C. 5, Av. 3), Tico-owned and run **Diana's Inn** (☎/fax 223-6542) is a pleasure to stay at simply for its affable, helpful staff and relaxed atmosphere. Each room has a TV and some have a/c. Street noise can be a problem. A continental breakfast is served. Prices are around US$46 s and US$50 d

One of the newer hotels, **La Gema** (☎/fax 222-1074) is on Av. 12, C. 9/11; breakfast is served, and it has its own restaurant and bar.

Centrally located at C. 9, Av. 10, the **Hotel Mansion Blanca Inn** (☎ 222-0423, 257-6198, fax 222-7947; Apdo. 85570, 1000 San José) is an 11-room bed and breakfast in an old mansion which is run by an affable Tico couple in their 50s. It has been recommended by a reader.

At C. 5 and Av. 11, the 27-rm. **Dunn Inn** (☎ 222-3232, 222-3246, fax 221-4596; Apdo. 6241, 1000 San José) includes continental breakfast in its rates. Located in a refurbished century-old mansion, it has one luxury suite with a Jacuzzi and other features. Rates are around US$65 d.

The attractive and distinctive Dutch-run **Apartotel El Sesteo** (☎ 296-1805, fax 296-1865; Apdo. 1246, 1007 San José) is 200 m S of La Sabana's McDonald's. It has 20 one- and two-bedroom units, 16 rooms, has a pool and Jacuzzi, and also shares some facilities with the nearby Costa Rica Tennis Club. Rates range from around US$50-80 d plus tax. Rates include continental breakfast.

www.hotels.co.cr/sesteo.html
sesteo@sol.racsa.co.cr

With some a/c rooms, the **Gran Via** (☎ 222-7737, fax 222-7205; Apdo. 1433, San José) is at Av. Central and C. 13. F

One of the nicest apartment hotels, the **Llama del Bosque** (☎ 225-5350, fax 224-0681) is located 100 m S and 50 m W of the Plaza del Sol, a shopping center in San Pedro. It has a pool, offers breakfast, and has kitchenettes.

The 25-room **Belmondo Hotel Bed & Breakfast** (☎ 222-9624) has a pool, bar, and restaurant. It's at C. 20, Av. 9 in Barrio Mexico. It also has dorm rooms.

Also on C. 20 and 250 m N of the Children's Hospital, the **Mesón del Angel** (☎ 223-7747, fax 223-2781) is a serene ten-bedroom hotel with a phone and cable TV in each room; rates are from around US$35 s to US$65 quad plus tax.

At Av. 7, C. 9, the **Rey Amón** (☎ 233-3819, fax 233-1769; Apdo. 7145-1000 San José) is a small, 13-room hotel set in a restored house. The high-ceilinged rooms have cable TV. Rates include breakfast; complimentary airport pickup with advance notification is available.

German-run 22-room **La Amistad** (☎ 221-1597) is a comfy bed and breakfast which is in Barrio Otoya at Av. 11/C. 15. Rooms have cable TV.
wolfgang@sol.racsa.co.cr

At Av. 6, C. 11/13 (50 m W of the Veterinaria Drs. Echandi), the **Villa Bonita Inn** (☎ 222-7075) is an *apartotel* which charges around US$50 s or d.

Cacts (☎ 221-2928, fax 221-8616; Av. 3 bis, No. 2845, C. 28/30; Apdo. 379, 1005, San José) has 36 rooms in a converted house. Rates are around US$50 d with breakfast. It has a sauna and Jacuzzi.
www.tourism.co.cr/hotels/cacts/cacts.htm
hcacts@sol.racsa.co.cr

Apartotel Castilla (☎ 222-2113, fax 221-2080;Apdo. 944, 1006 San José) is on C. 24, Av. 2/4, a location convenient to the Paseo Colón shopping area.

The **Cristina** (☎ 231-1618, 220-0453, fax 220-2096) is an attractive apartotel with sunny rooms and a garden. It charges around US$60 d with breakfast and has handicapped-accessible rooms available. One drawback here is that you lose privacy if your drapes are not drawn.
apacrit@sol.racsa.co.cr

At C. 29 and Av. Central/8, the **Apartotel Don Carlos** (☎ 221-6707, fax 255-0828) rents rooms on a weekly basis only.

On the Sabana, two-storey, colonial-style **Apartotel La Sabana** (☎ 220-2422, 296-0876, fax 231-7386; Apdo. 11400, 1000 San José) has a/c, cable TV, pool, and an arrangement with a nearby health club. Breakfast is included in the rates around US$40 d for rooms to US$80 for two- bedroom apartments.
lasabana@sol.racsa.co.cr

In Los Yoses, **Apartotel El Conquistador** (☎ 225-3022) can be contacted at Apdo. 303, 2050 San Pedro, and **Apartotel Lamm** (☎ 221-4290, fax 221-4720; C. 15, Av. 1) can be reached at Apdo. 2729, 1000 San José.

At. Av. 4, C. 8, the **Doral** (☎ 233-0665/5069, fax 233-4827) has clean and sunny rooms with phone.

Ramgo (☎ 232-3823, fax 232-3111, Apdo. 1441, 1000 San José) is 100 m S of the Tennis Club at La Sabana.

INEXPENSIVE ACCOMMODATION (US$30-50): Set to the W of the Parque Nacional on Av. 1 at C. 11/15, **Pensión de la Cuesta** (☎ 255-2896, fax 2 57-2272) is a bed and breakfast run by artists. Baths are shared, as is the refrigerator and entire kitchen. Rates are less than US$30 d with breakfast.
www.arweb.com/lacuesta
ggmnbr@sol.racsa.co.cr

The 29-room **Hotel Diplomat** (221-8133, 221-8744, fax 233-7474; Apdo. 6606, 1000 San José) is located on C. 6 between Av. Central/2. It has small rooms with hot water for around US$30 d.

Located on C. 24, Paseo Colón/Av. 2, the **Petit Hotel** (☎ 233-0766, fax 233-1938) has rooms with both private and shared baths. Facilities include free coffee, communal TV, and kitchen privileges. (Note: one reader has written to complain about the cleanliness and size of the rooms here).

At C. 24, Av. 2 across from the Sala Garbo, the **Petit Victoria** (☎ 233-1812/1813, fax 233-1938) offers use of its kitchen as well as cable TV. Write Apdo. 357, 1007 Centro Colón.

A block away from the Mercado Central at C. 10, Av. 1/3, the 48-room **Bienvenido** (☎ 221-1872, fax 233-2161; Apdo. 389-2200, San José) is one of the better hotels in this range and is around US$25 d. Ask about their four rooms which hold four.

A cross between a bed and breakfast and a standard hotel, **La Amistad** (☎ 221-1597, fax 221-1409) is set in Barrio Otoya (Av. 11, C. 15) as is the attractively furnished 11-room **Hotel Edelweiss** (☎ 221-9702, fax 222-1241; Av. 9, C. 13/15) and the 20-room **Hotel Vesuvio** (☎ 221-7586/8325, Apdo. 477-1000, San José; Av. 11, C. 13-15) which has a restaurant.

Also in this area (V. 15, Av. 7/11bis) is the singular **Cinco Hormigas Rojas** (☎/fax 257-8581). "Five Red Ants" is nature-lover and artist Mayra Guell's special creation. The entire bed-and-breakfast is decorated with her artwork, right down to the painted toilet bowl lids. Enter via what Mayra calls her "little jungle." Mayra aspires to move to the country, but her sister will be running the place if she is not here. This is an unforgettable place to stay for down-to-earth types. Rates are around US$30 s, US$40 d with a discount for cash. Tell the taxi driver that it is *"doscientos metros oeste emergencias Calderón y setenta metros sur)."*
cincohormigasroajas@crtimes.com

In the Coca Cola area, the 52-rm. **Hotel Alameda** (☎ 221-3045/6333, fax 222-9673; Av. Central, C. 12/14; Apdo. 680, San José) is another formerly grand old hotel. It charges less than US$40 d for its sunny rooms. It has a restaurant.

The **Musoc** (☎ 222-9437), next to the Coca Cola terminal (at C. 16, Av. 1/30), is noisy but very popular. There have been reports of left luggage disappearing here.

Located on C. 6 between Av. Central and Av. 2, the centrally located **Diplomat** (☎ 221-8133) is popular, has a restaurant, and each floor has a sitting area.

The **Pensión and Hotel Ritz** (☎ 222-4103, fax 222-8849; C. Central, Av. 8/10) has a variety of rooms from single (US$ 20) through quad (US$40). Get a tour until you find one you like.

The **Hotel Fortuna** (☎ 223-5344, fax 223-2743; Apdo. 7-1570, San José); Av. 6, C. 2/4; has 30 rooms of varying quality for around US$30 d. It is right near the Parque Central; some rooms have TV sets.
fortuna@habitat.co.cr

You can also try the **Galilea** (☎ 233-6925, fax 223-1689; Av. Central, C. 11/13; around US$18 s, US$22 d), the **Pensión Centro Continental** (☎ 233-1731, fax 222-8849; Av. 8 y 10 and C. Central), and the **Astoria** (☎ 221-2174; Av. 7, C. 7/9; weekly discounts available).

The least expensive *aparthotel*, at around US$175/wk. and US$425/mo. is the **Scotland** (☎ 223-0833) in Barrio La California, an old residential area.

IN SAN PEDRO: Located on the N side of the University of Costa Rica in San Pedro, **D'Galah Hotel** (☎/fax234-1743; Apdo. 208-2350, San José) has a coffee shop, pool, sauna, and some rooms with kitchenettes. Rates run around US$50 d.

The **Maripaz** (☎ 253-8456) is a bed and breakfast with both shared and private baths.

LOW-BUDGET ACCOMMODATION (under US$30): It may be hard to stay cheaply at the beaches these days, but there's no dearth of cheap places to stay in town. The very cheapest can be well under US$10 a day.

BASIC PLACES: A very basic but hospitable place with lots of guests from the *gringo* trail, **Ticalinda** (☎ 233-0528, fax 257-2272) is at Av. 2, C. 5, #553; look carefully for the door right next to Esmeralda's.

In the same general area, **Pensión Palma** (☎ 233-3877) is at Av. 6, C 11/13.

The **Otoya** (☎ 221-3925; C. 1, Av. 3/5) has large rooms and offers a TV lounge as well as storage. Rates are around US$4 s, US$8 d, US$15 quad.

The **Principe** (☎ 222-7983, fax 223-1589; Av. 6, C. Central/2) is both cheap and very popular with travelers.

Another good place is **Pensión Americana** (☎ 221-4171/9799), C. 2, Av. Central/Av. 2.

The 11-room **Hotel América** (☎ 221-4116; Av. 7, C. 2/4) charges around US$6 but also caters to short timers.

Popular with Ticos and backpackers alike (the entrance can resemble a Grateful Dead concert), the **Gran Hotel Imperial** (☎ 222-7899), at C. 8, Av. Central/1, up the street from the Hotel Johnson, is one of the best values around US$4 s, US$8 d, US$12 t, US$14 quad. They will hold your luggage for a fee, offer a pay phone, and have a restaurant.

If this is too downscale for your tastes, the **Johnson** (☎ 223-7633, fax 222-3683; Apdo. 6638, 1000 San José, C. 8 and Av. Central/Av. 2 bis, is popular with Tico businessmen, the Lonely Planet travel guide author, and family groups. It charges around US$20 d and has a restaurant.

In a safer area of town, the **Galilea** (☎ 233-6925, fax 223-1689) is at C. 13 and Av. Central.

Hotel Rialto (☎ 221-7456; C. 2, Av. 5) has small rooms and shared but segregated common baths. Rates are around US$4 s, US$7 d.

The **Bellavista** (☎ 223-0095/5477, fax 223-8385; Av. Central, C. 19/21). is within 20 min. of the Plaza de la Cultura on foot. Also try the **Boruca** (☎ 223-0016, fax 232-0077); C. 14, Av. 1/3), the **Capital** (☎/fax 221-8497, C. 4, Av. 3/5; around US$20 d), **Central** (☎ 221-2767, Av. 3, C. 4/6), the **Cocorí** (☎ 233-0081, C. 16 Av. 3 near Hospital San Juan de Dios), **Marlyn** (☎ 233-3212, C. 4, Av. 7/9), the **Morazán** (☎ 221-9083; Av. 3, C. 11/15), the **Roma** (☎ 223-2179; C. 14, Av. 1), **Hotel Colón** (C. 4, Av. 1, #150 N), **Gran Americo** (☎ 221-3362, Av. 2, C. 8), and .

BUDGET AND SPECIAL: A quiet and secluded oasis attractive to those who want access to the peace movement, **Casa Ridgeway** (☎ 233-6168, fax 224-8910; Apdo. 1507, 1000 San José), in the Quaker-established Centro Por La Paz, is a great place to stay: US$8 pp in small dorm room, US$10 s, and US$16 d. There's an excellent lending library, kitchen privileges, hot water, and the central location (Av. 6 bis, C. 15) can't be beat. Although budget travelers can find better values price-wise elsewhere, it is highly recommended.

La Granja (☎ 225-1073, 234-8835, fax 234-1676) is a Tico home with shared kitchen. Expect to pay around US$15 pp; discounts available for youth hostel card holders. It's 50 m S of the Antiguo Higuerón in San Pedro.

Casa Leo (☎ 222-9725) offers dorm accommodation for around US$88 pp as well as slightly more expensive single and double rooms. This German-run homestay is at Av. 6 bis, C. 15; watch for the sign next to Acupunctura Kaminsky and across the street fro Clinica Echandi.

The 19-rm. **Toruma Youth Hostel** (☎/fax 224-4085) stands on the N side of Av. Central in the eastern suburb of Los Yoses. Tell a taxi driver to let you off at *"Albergue Juvenil Toruma cerca de Pollos Fritos Kentucky,"* or you can take any of the various San Pedro-bound buses which also pass by. Its high-ceilinged dorms hold 6-20. It's open 24 hours, and you may stay as long as you wish. However, at around US$10 pp with breakfast (and youth hostel card) and US$12 pp (without card), it's definitely overpriced and quite a bit more than staying in a low-budget hotel on your own. You also have a shower schedule to contend with on top of the lack of privacy. (Two private rooms are available for US$26 s or d). One distinct advantage of staying here, however, is that you do get to meet a lot of people. And it is *clean* if you are fickle about such things.
reacjh@sol.racsa.co.cr

The **Kalexma Inn** (☎ 290-2634, ☎/fax 232-0115; Apdo. 6833, 1000 San José) combines budget accommodation with language study. It's across the highway from the Hotel Irazú. Rates are around US$20 s, US$30 d. They offer homestays (as well as special hotel rates for Spanish students), and rates include continental breakfast.
www.goldnet.co.cr/kalexma
kalexma@ns.goldnet.co.cr

GAY ACCOMMODATION: Colours (☎ 296-1880, 232-3504, fax 296-1597) is a male-oriented homosexual guesthouse in Rohrmoser. They have fans, pool, and a restaurant and are owned by a Florida travel agency (800-934-5622, 305-9342, fax 305-534-0362).

The **Joluva Guesthouse** (☎ 223-7961, fax 257-7668; 800298-2418) charges less than US$50 d with bath. It is housed in an attractive old building; breakfast is served and included. It is located in historic Barrio Amon.
www.hotels.co.cr/joluva.html
joluva@sol.racsa.co.cr

> *i* Gay and lesbian travelers should contact the International Gay and Lesbian Association (☎ 234-2411) and the Asociación Triangulo Rosa (☎ 258-0214; Spanish only) for information on the local scene.

RENTING A ROOM: If you wish to economize and plan on spending a great deal of time in the city, this is the way to go! However, you will need a command of Spanish to find a room. The best approach is to check the classified sections of the newspapers. You can also look for signs at the university campus.

> Bells' Home Hospitality (☎ 225-4752, fax 224-5834; Apdo. 185, 1000 San José) will provide you with the opportunity to stay with a Costa Rican family and get more of an inside view of the society and culture. Vernon Bell has a few rooms at home, and he also arranges accommodations with others. Charges are US$30 s, US$45 d; airport pickups (US$10 pp) and dinners (US$5 pp) are also available. Vernon will meet you at the airport and give you one of his famous tours. (He's also the author of a pocket-sized guide to San José). In the US, write Dept. 1432, PO Box 02516, Miami, FL 33102-5216.

You can find either lodging alone or lodging that includes food and laundry. Two specialists that connect you with rooms are Soledad Zamora (☎ 224-7937) and her sister Virginia.

OTHER ACCOMMODATION NEAR SAN JOSÉ: If you wish to avoid the hustle of the urban areas you might stay at any of the outlying lodging suggested under the towns in the "Meseta Central" section. here are some other suggestions. The singlemost popular location is Escazú, a hilly suburb of San José which is actually a collection of mountain villages; it has its own section below,

Pavas has the **Hotel Miravalles** (☎ 231-6186, fax 231-4319) which is near the US Embassy, shops, and restaurants. It has babysitting service and a complimentary shuttle service to downtown. Rates are around US$35-50 plus tax but including a full breakfast.

Located in the suburb of Tibás, **Roxana's** (☎/fax 235-4440; Apdo. 1086-1100, Tibás) is an inexpensive bed and breakfast which welcomes neither smokers nor children. Rates are around US$25-35 d including full breakfast and tax.

Curridabat has **Casa Zamia** (☎/fax 225-9474), a bed-and-breakfast which is around US$70 d. It is run by naturalist Sergio León, who has been director of some national parks. It is 100 m S and 100 m W of the Plaza del Sol.
cazamia@sol.racsa.co.cr

In Rohrmoser, a W suburb of San José, the French country-style **Majestic Inn** (☎/fax 232-9028) is an attractive bed and breakfast which has an expresso bar. Also here is **Carrie's** (☎ 232-9028), a bed and breakfast in a four-storey home which charges from US$35 d and up.

In San Antonio de Belén, the **Villa Belén** (☎ 239-0740, fax 239-2040) is an elegant Spanish colonial estate which has gardens, pool, sauna, TV lounge/library, and has weekly and monthly rates. Rates are around US$70-80 d plus tax and include a continental breakfast.

MORAVIA: In Moravia, moderate-to-expensive bed and breakfast **El Verolis** (☎ 236-0662) offers rooms with both private and shared bath. Write Apdo. 597, 2150 San José. You can also try **Casa Margarita** (☎ 285-0525, around US$35 d with breakfast) and **Chalet Costa Rica Vista** (☎ 285-0512, around US$60 d with breakfast), an attractive mountain home with gardens, waterfalls, and a fireplace.

A final choice is **Casa Rosa Inn** (☎/fax 235-9743) which has rooms for around US$80 d. It's in a plush neighborhood and in fronto of the Club La Guaria.
mail@vanweb.com

IN SANTA ANA: The 12-room **Hotel Posada Canal Grande** (☎ 282-4089/4101/4103, fax 282-5733; Apdo. 84-6150, Santa Ana) has a sauna, pool, and restaurant; breakfast is included. It's near Santa Ana, and the bus runs here. Rates run around US$60 s, US$70 d not including taxes; off-season discounts are available.

Near Santa Ana in Pozos de Santa Ana, **Paraiso Canadiense** (☎/fax 282-5870; Apdo. 68-6151, Santa Ana 2000) offers one- and two-bedroom apartments with pool and laundry for around US$50 pn, US$225 pw, and US$550 pm and up.

Set on the old road between San José and Tres Ríos enroute to Cartago, the **Casa de Finca 1926** (☎ 225-6169) is a German owned restored art deco mansion which offers 11 attractive rooms for around US$75 d. The home has antiques, plants, and a fountain.

In the town of San Ramón de Trés Ríos, a half-hour by bus to the E of San José, the **Bello Monte** (☎/fax 234-3879) is a moderately-priced bed and breakfast.

Near Rancho Redondo, expensive 19-room **Hotel Hacienda San Miguel** (☎ 229-5058, fax 229-1097; Apdo. 6897, 1000 San José) is a dairy farm and reforestation project. It has a cloud forest tour on horseback, heated swimming pool, Jacuzzi, steambath, game rooms, and live music. Rates run from around US$60 d (with breakfast) and up.

LA GARITA/ATENAS AREA: This former ox-cart checkpoint is now a center for tourist attractions, and a number of hotels have sprung up here. Accommodation in the quiet town of Atenas — said to have the nation's best climate — has been slower in coming but is gradually growing. This area is around 20 min. from the airport.

Opened in 1999, 34-rm. **Hotel Martino** (☎ 433-8382, fax 433-9052) is in La Garita. Named after the resident Italian hotelier of the same name, its landscaped grounds have a pool, hand-carved doors, local reporoductions of classic European furniture, small spa and gym, phone and cable TV. Graeco-Roman styles mix with Pre Columbian. Service is personal. It is 125 m E of Zoo Ave.
www.orbitcostarica.com/hotel maritimo.htm maritimo@sol.racsa.co.cr

Villa Tranquilidad (☎ 460-5460; Apdo. 28, 4013 Alajuela), set on an organic coffee farm, is a bed and breakfast featuring a pool and a nearby waterfall. It's located two km from the attractive fruit- growing town of Atenas along a country road: turn R at the phone booth before the town. Weekly rates here are around US$200; monthly US$700.

One km to the L of La Fiesta de Maíz in La Garita, **Chatelle** (☎ 487-7050, fax 487-7095; Apdo. 755, Centro Colón) is an expensive set of nine *cabinas*. Each is named after a volcano and contains furniture from Sarchí and a kitchenette. It offers restaurant (different menu daily), pool, cable TV, jogging paths, free airport pickup, and other services. Rates are around US$60-90 with breakfast.

IN ATENAS: **El Cafetal Inn** (☎ 446-5785, fax 446-7028; Apdo. 105, Atenas) is a 10-bedroom bed and breakfast set in a modern building on a coffee plantayion. Atenas itself is famous for its climate, and the facilities allow you to take full advantage of this. You may lounge in a hammock, bathe in the pool, or walk down to the river. Dinner is served upon request, and tours are offered. Rates are around US$65-85; monthly rates are available.
www.cafetal.com
cafetal@sol.racsa.co.cr

Apartamentos Atenas (☎/fax 446-5792) is on the main road to Jacó at the edge of Atenas.
apatenas@sol.racsa.co.cr

Hotel Colinas del Sol (☎ 446-6847, fax 446-7582) is on the edge of town but withing walking distance. It has a pool and cabins for around US$50 s or d with breakfast. Weekly and monthly rates are available.

STUDYING SPANISH: **Instituto Lingüistico** (☎/fax 446-5952) is based in Athenas, in a large house on a working organic farm. Homestays are arranged.
inlinlat@sol.racsa.co.cr

IN CASCAJAL: Near Orotina, the luxury **Dundee Ranch Hotel** (☎ 267-6222, 428-8776, fax 267-6229) which is a working ranch with secondary tropical dry forest reserve. There are two pools on the property as well as a restaurant with Tico and international fare. Horseback riding, boat tours of the estuary, and tractor-tram rides are available. Rates are around US$80 d with breakfast. It's related to the **Chalet Tirol**. Finally, don't overlook the hotels near Alajuela, Heredia, Póas, and Cartago which are listed later on.

ESCAZÚ ACCOMMODATION: A mountainous set of small villages popular with both Ticos and wealthy foreigners, Escazú has expanded its range of accommodation in recent years.

IN SAN RAFAEL: Close and convenient, the **Tapezco Inn** (☎ 228-1084, fax 289-7026) is 50 m S of the church. A blue-and-white colonial-style structure, it has 15 rooms (with TVs and fans), a Tico-style restaurant commanding great views, and pool, Jacuzzi, and sauna. Service is personalized, and rates run around US$50 s (with breakfast) and US$50 d (without breakfast).
camtapez@sol.racsa.co.cr

Also in San Rafael de Escazú, the 30-room attractive and distinctive **Hotel Sangildar** (☎ 289-8843, 228-6451-2, fax 228-6454) is 250 m W of the NE corner of the Costa Rica Country Club. Its restaurant, **La Terraza del Sol**, offers a champagne brunch on Sun. Rooms run around US$100 d including breakfast.
pentacor@sol.racsa.co.cr

Set on the S side of the Costa Rica Country Club, the **Apartotel Villas del Río** (☎ 289-8833, fax 289-8835) offers one-, two-, and three bedroom apartments, suites, and penthouses. All have a/c, cable TV/VCR, kitchen, and other amenities. On the grounds are also sauna, pool, and guarded parking. Rates run from US$180 pd. Ask bout long-term rates.

Casa de las Tías (☎/fax 228-5517, fax 289-7353) is a popular five-room, quiet bed and breakfast run by foreign service retirees. Rooms each represent a different Latin American nation, and there are spacious gardens as well as a TV/lounge area. Airport pickup can be arranged. Rates are around US$65 d.

Complete with washing machine, cable TV, a/c, pool, sauna, and restaurant, **Apartotel María Alexandra** (☎ 228-1507, fax 228-5192; Apdo. 3756, 1000 San José) is also in this area. They have a tour company and Harley rental service.
www.arweb.com/crpages/hotels/marial
matour@sol.racsa.co.cr

IN SAN ANTONIO: Modeled after a US Civil War era mansion and billed as the ultimate in luxury, the **Tara** (☎ 228-6992, fax 228-9651; Interlink 345, PO Box 02-5635, Miami, FL 33152) is surrounded by 38,000 sq ft. (12,000 sq m) of grounds. It has swimming pool, tennis court, and health club. A curving wooden staircase leads up to the 12 rooms; each is given a name such as "Scarlett" in order to reflect the theme. Opened in 1995, the new and fully equipped spa has its own aerobics trainer.Rates are around US$135-300d depending upon your choice.
www.cmn.com/tara
taraspa@sol.racsa.co.cr

The inexpensive-moderate 55-room **Pico Blanco** (☎ 228-3197, 289-6197, fax 289-5189; Apdo. 900, Escazú) is a mountain getaway. An attractive, white colonial-style structure with brick archways and stone patios, this recently renovated hotel is run by an Englishman expatriate and his Tico family. It has a pool, a couple of *cabinas* (around US$60), and an outdoor pavilion with occasional performances. Rooms have balconies and some have refrigerators. You should have a four-wheel-drive vehicle if staying here. In the US call 816-862-1170 or fax 916-862-1187.

IN ESCAZÚ WEST: One of the more unforgettable places to stay is the **Hotel California** (☎ 289-7486). Owned by Philadelphian Bruce Cohen, this small hotel provides reasonable but spartan digs. Bruce is a real character and is great for active, single guys who like to go out and party (as does Bruce). It's 700 m W of the Banco Nacional and 150 m N of the Escuela Corazón de Jesús. Geriatrics, yuppies, and fundamentalist Christians would find it an uncomfortable experience to stay here. It's possible to bargain with Bruce, and he may be hanging around the airport when you arrive. Rates are around US$15 pp on up, and it should be possible to strike some sort of bargain if you'll be staying around for a while.

Near the Escazú Country Club, the **Villa Escazú** (☎/fax 228-9566), a bed and breakfast set in an alpine-style home, charges around US$60 d. Its porch is perfect for birdwatching or gazing at the lovely panorama presented.
www.yelloweb.co.cr
villasescazu@yelloweb.co.cr

IN BELLO HORIZONTE: Many of these listed can hook you up with the pool and tennis courts at the Bello Horizonte Country Club.

Named after the Spanish literary hero, Spanish colonial-style **Posada El Quijote** (☎ 289-8401, fax 289-8729) is set high in the hills. It offers large rooms with cable TV, phones, and large baths. Personalized service is offered by owners Gordon and Lucy Finwall.It has a full library and artwork by the likes of Chagall, Picasso, and Lichtenstein. Rates are around US$50-70 s, US$60-80 d including breakfast. Discount offered for extended stays.
quijote.co.cr
quijote@quijote.co.cr

The homey bed and breakfast **La Posada del Bosque** (☎ 228-1164, fax 228-2006; Apdo. 669, 1250 Escazú) is surrounded by gardens; it charges from around US$40-55 plus tax and including a full breakfast. It offers Tico-style hospitality and cooking (including a *típico* breakfast and homecooked dinners). It's also right near Bello Horizonte Country Club. Rates are around US$35-45 d plus tax. Airport pickup is US$12 extra.

OTHERS: Set between Escazú and Santa Ana, the luxurious **Alta** (☎ 282-4160, fax 282-4162, 888-388-ALTA) has 16 rooms and four suites, a full-service health spa, and **La Luz**, a gourmet restaurant. Rates are around US$144 s, US$168 d. plus tax.
hotlalta@sol.racsa.co.cr

San José Dining and Food

HOTEL DINING: Most hotels have good restaurants. The Hotel Balmoral's **Restaurante Altamira** serves Spanish cuisine. **Hotel L'Ambiance** (☎ 222-6702) offers gourmet dining in an elegant atmosphere by reservation.

The Hotel Britannia offers acclaimed gourmet dishes in its **The Cellar** (☎ 233-6667) which is handicapped accessible.

Out in the Paseo de Colón area, the **Grano de Oro**, C. 30, Av. 2/4, No. 251, offers gourmet French dishes and is quite popular.

Between Escaú and Santa Ana and set in the Hotel Alta, the luxurious **La Luz**, (☎ 282-4160) offers "California-Costa Rican" cuisine featuring delights such as fiery sauteed garlic prawns and hand formed feta cheese tart.

BUDGET DINING: San José can be quite a cheap place to eat if you stick to where the poorer locals dine. **Churrería Manolo Chocolateria** (Av. Central, C. 2) is good for breakfast; **Bella Vista** (Av. Central, C. 19/21) specializes in Limón-style fare.

Vegetarian restaurants (given their own listing below) are generally competitive in price with the cheaper establishments. *Sodas* are the way to go both for price and local color. One of the best is **Soda Palace** (C. 2, Av. 2), where money changers are found; it has good coffee, an entertaining milieu, and a kiosk serving fresh baguettes 24 hrs. per day.

Just around the corner, The attractive **El Iman** is a pub which serves a wide variety of beers as well as traditional Costa Rican dishes.

Costa del Sol (☎ 223-1335) is run by friendly Italians and serves reasonably priced pizza and pasta dishes; Av. Central, C. 9/11 and across from Cine Capri.

The **Café Wanchope** is set next to the Gran Hotel has daily specials and prepares Caribbean dishes on Fri. and Sat.

Fu Su Ku (C. 2, Av. 2), serves Korean food; **Chicharronera Nacional** is at Av. 1, C. 3/5.

For attractive outoor cafeteria-syle dining, try **Recesos** (Av. 2 and 4 on C. 21), just near the Museo Nacional. **Soda Tico** near Parque Morazán has a cheap breakfast along with a US$2 lunch .

If you just want a sandwich, **La Casa de Sanwich** (Av. 2, C. 11) is open 24 hrs and has an amazing variety. Specializing in wood-roasted chicken, **Restaurante Campesino** (C. 7, Av. 2/4) also has *palmito* salad. Another reasonably priced place is **Soda Amón**, near the Hotel Aurora in Barrio Amón. Featuring a good variety of *refrescos* and a *casado* at lunch, **Soda La Casita** is at Av. 1, C. Central/1. Known for its mariachi music late at night, centrally located **La Esmeralda** (Av. 2, C. 5/7) has a range of Tico food. Also try **El Escorial** (Av. 1, C. 5/7), **Finistere Food World** (Av. Central/C. 7), and **Soda Central** (Av. 1, C. 3/5), which has a good selection at reasonable prices. Set at the E corner of the Supreme Court Bldg. (Av. 6, C. 21), **La Cocina de Bordolino** specializes in beef and chicken *empanadas* prepared as they are in Tierra del Fuego, Argentina. Located on Sabana Sur, **Bar/Restaurante La Foresita** serves *típico* food.

Set across from the E side of La Sabana, large **Soda Tapia** serves reasonably priced local food on tables both inside and out on the street.

For real low-budget dining try the **Mercado Central**, the market, an excellent place to sample low-cost traditional Tico food, especially *ceviche*.

IN-TOWN GOURMET EUROPEAN CUISINE: Very attractive **Café Mundo** (☎ 222-6190) is at Av. 9, C. 15; they have great pastries and offer tasty lunches (salads, sandwiches, soups) and international cuisine gourmet dinners as well. US expat Ray Johnson is one of the owners here and his influence shows. This place has real atmosphere!

For French food, expensive **L'Ile de France** (☎ 222-4241, C. 7, Av. Central/2) has high quality food and service.

A longstanding popular restaurant, **El Balcon de Europa** (☎ 221-4841; C. 9, Av. Central/1) has Italian and international cuisine.

Fleur de Lys (☎ 223-1206) is a gourmet restaurant offering seafood and other entrees; it's at C. 13, Av. 2/6.

La Bastille (☎ 255-4994; Paseo Colón, C. 20/22) serves gourmet-quality continental cuisine.

For Italian food, try **Miro's Bistro** (☎ 253-4242) which is in Barrio Escalante, a short walk from downtown.

Zermatt (☎ 222-0604), C. 23, Av. 11 bis; near the Iglesia Santa Teresita; offers Swiss specialties including fondue.

With an elegantly expensive colonial-style atmosphere, **La Masía de Triquell** (☎ 296-3528; C. 40, Av. 2) serves Spanish food. It is 175 m N and 175 m W of the Nissan dealership on Paseo de Colón.

Middle Eastern: Across from the Mercedes Benz dealership, **Lubnan** (☎ 257-6071) is at Paseo Colón, C. 22/24.

CHINESE AND ASIAN FOOD: There are too many to list all of them here! **Tin-Jo** (☎ 221-7605; C. 11, Av. 6/8) offers Thai dishes as well as Indonesian *gado-gado*); neighboring **Don Wang** (☎ 233-6484), C. 11, Av. 6/8, serves Cantonese dishes including delectable dim sum ("touch the heart" appetizer-sized) dishes.

Others include San Pedro's **Nueva China** (across from Banco Popular) and **Ave Fénix** (200 m W of the San Pedro Church); both of these serve Mandarin dishes.

Definitely for those with weighty wallets, the **Sakura**, out at the Sheraton Herradura, specializes in Japanese cuisine.

The medium-priced and popular Korean restaurant **Arirang** in Edifico Colón (☎ 223-2838; Paseo Colón, C. 24/26) also serves Japanese dishes including a *sushi* platter.

SEAFOOD: The medium-priced **Fuente de los Mariscos** is well known and has branches near Hotel Irazú in the San José 2000 shopping center and at Plaza del Sol shopping center.

Another famous seafood restaurant is **Rias Bajas** in El Pueblo.

With a blue-and-white marquee and plenty of parking, **Marisqueria La Princesa Marina** (open 10:30-11:30 daily on the W side of the Sabana) offers reasonably priced seafood.

Set 300 m E of the McDonalds along the Sabana, **Mariqsuerias Al Tamar** (☎ 256-4067) is a budget seafood place with good service and daily specials.

PERUVIAN SEAFOOD: The **Machu Pichu** (C. 32, Av. 1/3), an extremely popular Peruvian restaurant which is often packed at lunch; a variety of spicey appetizers and main dishes are available. It's behind Kentucky Fried Cadavers on Paseo de Colón.

VEGETARIAN DINING: There are a growing number of vegetarian restaurants, and ones open and close all of the time. Most of the vegetarian restaurants feature simple but good fare with brown rice used as a base. They usually offer soyburgers, fruit and vegetable salads, and set meals (around US$2.50) which are good value. All are singularly disappointing in their seasonings which, as is typical in Costa Rica, are not used. Ask for tabasco to spice things up a bit.

The author's favorite for the food, atmosphere, and price is **Shakti** (☎ 222-9096, open 11-6:30) on C. 13 at Av. 8. Besides the daily specials (around US$2.50), it has a wide variety of dishes including salad, *bistec vegetariano*, herbal teas, granola, and five kinds of spaghetti.

Naturama Uno (☎ 257-0907) is a quality place which is across from the Omni cinema on Av. 1, C. 3/5.

Soda Vegetariana (☎ 221-5885) is on. C. 5 next to the Hotel Europa.

Centrally located, attractive **Tangara** (☎ 221-3115) is on Av. 1, C 1/3.

Although not exclusively vegetarian, **Pipo's** (Av. Central, C. 9/11) offers soyburgers and a vegetarian plate (less than US$2).

Open Mon. to Fri. from 8-4, **Don Sol** is 50 m E of the Casa Amarilla, the Foreign Ministry, on Av. 7. This is a convenient place to eat either before or after visiting the Jade Museum in the INS building which, in turn, is 50 m W of the Casa Amarilla.

There are also a number of others; new ones are opening and closing all the time.

For other restaurants check under "San Pedro" below.

OTHER SAN JOSÉ DINING: One of the best places to try classic Tico food, **La Cocina de Leña** at El Pueblo has local specialties such as mondongo, *olla de carne*, and banana and *palmito ceviche*.

In Sabana Norte and 500 m to the W of ICE, **Las Tunas** (☎ 231-1802) serves lunch and dinners with Mexican and other fare including seafood.

FAST FOOD: Expensive compared to the healthier meals you can find in any soda, fast food appears to be the city's specialty; in San José representations of Ronald McDonald are so omnipresent that one might think that he is president! You will find a veritable who's who in American fast food. There are innumerable clones — such as Archi's and Woopy's about. Don't find them; they'll find you. In any event, there are much better and healthier places to eat.

CAFÉS AND BAKED GOODS: A popular outdoor café for people watching, **Parisien Café** is on the ground floor of the Gran Hotel Costa Rica (C. 3, Av. 2). It also serves reasonably priced meals.

The National Theater's **Café Ruiseñor del Teatro** across the way has artwork, marble tabletops, and classical chamber music. This is undoubtedly the plushest place in the country to sip coffee. Intimate and set to the N of the Parque Morazán, **La Esquina del Café** is at Av. 9/C. 3B. Great espressos, cakes, and unique souvenirs are on sale.

La Flor del Café, relatively nearby on Av. Central, C. 7/9) is another good coffee shop which also offers dishes ranging from lasagna to salads.

Another good coffee shop is the **Coffee Station-Expresso Bar** at Av. 5/C. 1.

Other small, good coffee shops include **Las Cuartetas** (C. 2, Av. 3/5), **Manolo's** (Av. Central, C. Central/1 and Av. Central, C. 9/11), and **Spoon** (Av. Central, C. 5/7).

One of the best bakeries is **Giacomín** on C. 2. **Repositería Fina Coppelia** along Paseo de Colón offers hamburgers, fruit salad and baked goods.

Out in San Pedro, **Café Maga** (☎ 290-9361) is about the hippest place around to imbibe some java (ask for a "Picasso") or have a salad with tuna and heart of palm (ask for a "Borges"). Located 100 m W and 100 m S of La Hispanidad, it doubles as a cultural center and art space. If you visit only one place in San Pedro, this should be it! It's open daily, 11 AM - 1 PM.

NOTE: The **Pereficós** supermarket chain also has a bakery in each of its stores. Soda Palace (across the street from Parque Central) also has a bakery kiosk with fresh bread baked constantly.

LOS YOSES FOOD: Good coffee shops here include **Azafrán**, **Spoon**, **Giacomín**, and **Café Ruisenor**, which also offers quiche, soups, and a salad bar.

Set 175 m E of the Automercado on the R-hand side as one heads to San Pedro, **Choices** (☎ 225-5230) has a great salad bar, crepes, and luscious desserts. It's not open for dinner.

On Av. Central, **Le Café des Artistes** is perfect for hanging out. Dine at **Restaurant**

Some Gourmet Restaurants in the San José Area

Restaurant	Cuisine	Locale	Phone
Bijahua	*Nouvelle* Costa Rican	Near Centro Commerical Calle Real	225-0613
Bougainvillea Santo Domingo	European	Santo Domingo de Heredia	240-8822
Café Mundo	International	Av. 9, C. 11/13	222-6190
Chalet Tirol	French	Near Heredia	267-7371
El Balcon de Europa	Italian and international	C. 9, Av. Central	221-4841
Grano de Oro	French	C. 30, Av. 2/4 No. 251	255-3322
L'Ile de France	French	Hotel Bergerac	234-7850
La Galería	European	San Pedro	234-0850
Le Chandelier	French	San Pedro	225-3980
Machu Pichu	Peruvian	C. 32, Av. 1/3	222-7384
Oceanos	International	Between Cariari and Herradura hotels	293-0622 293-0622

La Galería (☎ 34-0850) or **Paprika** (☎ 225-8971, Av. Central, C. 29/33). Located in the shopping center next to Cancún, reasonably-priced **Valerio's** (☎ 225-0838) has pizza, lasagna, and desserts.

Popular with *los plasTicos*, **Río** (Av. 2/C. 39) serves typical food including good *casados*. Open weekdays, **Che Pato** is an inexpensive health-food restaurant with lunch specials which is in the lobby of the Teatro Carpo which is next to KFC in Los Yoses.

Set 100 m N of the Iglesia de Fatima in Los Yoses,, **Café 1900** (☎ 225-0819) offers Peruvian as well as international dishes. Valerio's is a reasonably priced Italian restaurant which is set in the shopping center next to Cancún.

SAN PEDRO DINING AND FOOD: This lively student-oriented area offers a wide range of reasonable restaurants. A favorite of college students, **El Pomodoro** pizza is next to the church at the university. Also specializing in pizza, **La Mazorca** (☎ 224-8069) is perhaps the nation's best known vegetarian restaurant; its cosy café atmosphere makes you feel as if you could be in Cambridge, MA or Berkeley, CA. It's 100 m N and 200 m E of the church. It has its own food market across the street. A competing restaurant is the **Vegetarian Restaurant San Pedro** which is 200 m N of the church. A third is **Ditso**, a macrobiotic joint set 200 m N of the church and near the RR tracks.

Located in Centro Commercial de la C. Real, **Ambrosia** serves a mixture of vegetarian and non-vegetarian cuisine.

La Villa has a swinging bamboo curtain and great bohemian atmosphere. It's 20 m E and 100 m S from the church.

El Jardín del Pulpo serves Mexican food, and **Chily's**, in the Centro Comerical Real 75 m E of Banco Popular, serves Tex Mex. **Omar Khayam** has Arab and other dishes. **El Jorongo** serves Mexican food in an unpretentious environment. **Barabarella** is another Italian restaurant. Set 75 m to the S of the Banco Popular, **El Corrocio Verde** serves French crepes and has a salad bar.

For those suffering bagel withdrawal symptoms, a fix is at hand at **Boston Bagel** which is in Plaza Calle Real and next to Rosti-Pollo.

SAN PEDRO GOURMET/CONTINENTAL: For high-class dining, try expensive **La Petite Provence** (☎ 255-1559; Av. Central, C. 27).

The nation's classiest French restaurant is highly expensive gourmet **Chandelier** (☎ 225-3980). It's one block to the L of the ICE building and 100 m to the S.

Set 200 m W and 25 m N of the Iglesia San Pedro, **Il Ponte Vecchio** (☎ 225-9339) offers good Italian food prepared by a chef from NYC at moderate rates.

Just 75 m E of Banco Popular, Centro Commercial Calle Real), **Restaurant Marbella** (☎ 224-9452) specializes in Paella Valencia; it has a flamenco show on weekend evenings.

Set 125 m W of the ICE building in San Pedro, **La Galería** serves European food in a classical-music atmosphere. The **Villa Franken**, nearby, offers German food.

Opened in 1995, the attractively designed **Bijahua** (☎ 225-0613) offers *nouvelle* Costa Rican cuisine including dishes such as *lomito* on eggplant toast with shrimp and zucchini *fricasée* and red snapper stuffed with green plantains. To get here turn R at the Centro Commerical Calle Real just before the Mas X Menos and head one block further; it's two blocks S on C. 13 which is fronted by the Galería Miró.

La Leyenda is 700 m S of the Shell Station near El Cruce and offers classy Mexican food. The **Euro Café** is nearby.

> ☛ While in Curridabat, be sure to check out the K&S Restaurant and Brewery (☎ 283-7583). Check out their executive lunch. It is owned and operated by a former foreign minister (1982-86) who has hired a German *brewmeister*.

IN SANTA ANA: Set in a 130-year-old adobe house, **Casa Quitirrisí** (☎ 282-5441) serves a 20-item buffet on Sun. afternoons for around US$10. It serves traditional carnivore-geared Tico dishes evenings and has live music on Fri. and Sat. nights.

ESCAZÚ DINING AND FOOD: For cheap eats, try **Restaurante Pollos Yakky** (or other *sodas*) near the main square and church.

Bookstore **Rincón de la Calle Real** (☎ 289-5112) offers lunch in a garden setting. It's near the Pomodoro Restaurant (50 m W and 100 m S of the US Ambassador's residence on the old Santa Ana Road).

The **Café del Sol** (☎ 228-1645) is 275 m E of the church.

Chango (☎ 228-1173) offer a full menu and specialize in fresh fish. There's live music every Wed and Thurs.

The Central Restaurant and Bar (☎ 289-4594) has homemade food with a large selection at breakfast, lunch and dinner. Great bocas. Open 7 AM to 2 AM. It is across from the church; watch for the large mural of flags from the U.S.,Canada and Costa Rica.

The Rib Shack (☎ 381-5370) serves exclusively delicious smoked fish and other such items. Open 12 AM to 9 PM. It's located 100 m S of the church. (Watch for sign on left-hand side 600 m south from the church).

The **Euro-Café** (☎ 289-5206) serves gourmet cuisine and homemade pastries and breads. Open everyday except Mon. It is 300 m S of "El Cruce" in San Rafael, Escazu.

Open daily from 1-8 PM, **American Legion Post 10** (☎ 228-1740) serves the best US Southern style seafood in the country.

Set four km above San Rafael, **Añoranzas** (☎ 267-7406) offers *típico* food and has play equipment for children.

On the old road to Escazú — approximately halfway betwen Los Anaonos Bridge and Parque la Sabana, **Peperoni** (☎ 232-5119) offers Italian food including a salad bar, smoked fish, and desserts. The atmosphere is informal.

Another Italian restaurant is **Sale e Pepe** which serves pizza, pasta, and a salad bar as well as low-budget lunchtime specials. It's on the Escazú main road, in the Centro Comerical del Valle just to the rear of Pops.

Yet another Italian restaurant is **Capriccio Italiano** (☎ 228-9332) which is in San Rafael Escazú 100 m E and 150 m S from McDonalds.

Vivaldi (☎ 228-6045) bases its cuisine on items made with pastry dough (such as quiche) and also sells sandwiches, and delicious desserts. It's 150 m s of Centro Comercial Blvd. in Santa Rosa de Escazú.

Mexican food is served at **Órale** (☎ 228-6437) in Centro Comerical Trejos Montealegre.

Quite popular, **Muy** (☎ 254-6281) is open for dinner daily, and is open for lunch on weekends. It specializes in Tex-Mex BBQ supplemented by Tico entrees and is just above the Pico Blanco Hotel in San Antoinio de Escazú.

GOURMET: Offering personalized gourmet dining in a classy private-home-style atmosphere, **Il Tulá** (☎ 228-0053) offers five antipasta dishes and more than a dozen entrees; it's 200 m and 50 m S of the Los Anonos Periférico market in San Rafael.

The **Tara** (☎ 228-6992) offers the "Atlanta Dining Gallery." Quite popular with affluent Ticos who come for the view as well as the food, it offers a variety of gourmet dishes including seafood and vegetarian entrees.

In the María Alexandra Apartotel (some 100 m N of Tega in San Rafael de Escazú), there is a branch of the gourmet bistro **La Galeria Finale**.

Hostaria Cerutti (☎ 228-4511) is at La Cruce and offers gourmet Italian. A traveler relates: "Excellent menu and OK winel list. Salads, rissottos, pastas, fish, and great desserts. Excellent service and ambience in cool white rooms. About US$50 including tax for two."

The **Cascado** is a Tico-style upscale eatery. One visitor writes: "Best sea bass had in Costa Rica. About US$25-30 for two" It is located on the R fork leaving El Cruce from Escazú, approximately 500 m on the L behind the gas station.

Rancho Macho in the hills offers mariachi entertainment in the evenings.

San José Entertainment

There's always something to do here!

CLASSICAL MUSIC: The **National Symphony Orchestra** performs most weekends from April to Nov. at the National Theater. Featuring chamber music, the "Una Hora de Musica" performances are also held here once or twice a month during the same time period. Located near the Villa Tournón, **Chavetas Tavern** has a classical music variety program every Mon. night. Many of the cultural centers also feature concerts.

DANCE: The **Compañía Nacional de Danza** holds between two and four per-

San José Festivals and Events

JANUARY: The **Copa del Café**, a week-long tennis tournament, draws an international collection of talented teenagers.

In the **Carrera de la Paz**, a footrace held in March, around a thousand people run from San José's National Gymnasium to the campus of the University for Peace in Villa Colón.

MARCH: Featuring 500-plus species, the **National Orchid Show**, a weekend-long festival, takes place in the Colegio de Medicos y Cirujanos headquarters in Sabana Sur every March.

Taking place on the second Sunday in March, **National Oxcart Day** celebrates the *boyero* (oxcart driver) and the *carreta* (the wooden-wheeled painted cart); the locus for the celebration is in San Antonio de Escazú outside of San José.

The nation's cattlemen assemble at the Bonanza Fairgrounds, on the airport highway, for the Bonanza Cattle Show every March. Featured are prize bulls, bullfights, rodeos, horseraces, and mechanical bulls.

Taking place the same month, the **Crafts Fair** on the Plaza de la Cultura has 150-200 local artisans exhibiting their wares.

APRIL: In San Jose's Plaza de la Democracia, an annual three-day **Festival of Native American Handicrafts** in April is followed by the celebration of Earth Day.

Many events are held in and around San José during **Easter Holy Week** (*Semana Santa*) from Wed. noon through Sun. During **University Week**, taking place around the beginning of May, University of Costa Rica students crown a queen, and participate in sports events and a parade. Many local bands also perform on campus. This is a great time to investigate what college life is like here.

MAY: On May 15, the **Día del Boyero** ("Day of the Oxcart Driver") is held in San Antonio de Escazú near San José. Activities include parades featuring brighly colored oxcarts, as well as blessing of animals and crops by the local priest.

On San Juan Day, May 17, around 1, 500 run the **Carrera de San Juan**, 22.5 km from El Alto de Ochomongo (near Cartago) to San Juan de Tibás, N of San José.

AUGUST: Celebrating International Black People's Day and taking place in San José every August, the cultural week **Semana Afro-Costarricense**'s highlights are lectures, panel discussions, and displays.

SEPT: At 6 PM on Sept. 15, the nation's **Independence Day** (which is also that of all of Central America), the Freedom Torch, relayed by a chain of student runners stretching all the way from Guatemala, arrives in San José, and Ticos join in singing the national anthem. That evening schoolchildren march in *farole* (lantern) parades, carrying handmade lanterns along the route.

NOV.: Sponsored by the Asociación Canófila Costarricense every Nov., the **International Dog Show** has a splendid assortment of dogs.

DEC: YEAR'S END FIESTAS: Commencing with the distribution of the *aguinaldo*, the annual bonus given to salaried workers, the city's liveliest time is during the month of Dec. Sidewalks are crowded with *chinamos* stalls which sell toys, nativity creche paraphernalia, and fruit such as apples and grapes. Merchants are open for extended hours, and the streets get wilder and wilder as the month progresses. During the last week of Dec. and extending through the beginning of January, bullfights are held at the Zapote ring daily; the *topé*, a procession of horses, departs from Paseo Colón, proceeds along Av. Central and ends at Plaza Viquez. Finally, a dance in Parque Central welcomes the New Year.

formances per year. College troupes of reknown are the **Danza Una** of the National University and the UCR's **Danza Universitaria**. The **Instituto Technical** also has a folkloric dance troupe. Other groups include **Cedanza**, **Codanza**, **Danza Contemporanea**, **Danza Libre**, and **Diquis Tiquis**. Composed of teenagers, **San Luis Gonzaga Amateur Troupe** is one of the oldest performing companies. **Danacart** is out in neighboring Cartago.

THEATER: In addition to the papers, check the listings on the board in front of the Teatro Nacional. Don't miss a performance at the **National Theater** if you can help it.

Even though most of the plays are presented in Spanish, no language ability is necessary to enjoy performances by the opera, symphony, and dance (Compania Nacional de Danza) companies.

Another outstanding venue is **Teatro Melico Salazar** (Av. 2, C. Central/2); you can see just fine from the cheapest seats here, and they allow you to peer right into the orchestra pit and watch the players. Most plays are, of course, in Spanish with the exception of those presented by the Little Theater Group at the American Cultural Center. The National Theater Company often takes a satirical view in their performances.

Performances are listed in *La Nación*

> San José is becoming increasingly dangerous at night. Take appropriate precautions. Visitors should be aware that the red light district begins to the W of C. 8. Also avoid the area around Cine Libano, Av. 7, C. 10-14, and the three-to-four-block area S of Av. 4 at C. 4. On May 1, 1995, a Florida tourist was stabbed to death near C. 6 and Av. 7 after he resisted during a robbery attempt.

and here are the addresses: **Teatro de la Aduana** (C. 25, Av. 3/5); **Teatro del Angel** (Av. Central, C13/15); **Teatro Bellas Artes** (E side of the UCR campus at San Pedro), **Teatro La Comedia** (next to Mas X Menos supermarket on Av. Central across from the Plaza de la Democracía), **Teatro Carpa** (Av. Central, C. 29; next to Kentucky Fried in San Pedro); **Sala de la Calle 15** (Av. 2, C. 15), **Teatro Chaplin** (Av. 9, C 1/3), **Teatro Laurence Olivier** (Av. 2, C. 28), **Teatro La Mascara** (C. 13, Av. 2/4), **Teatro Arlequin** (C. 13, Av. Central /2), **Teatro Tespis** (100 m W of Cine Magaly); **Teatro Calle 15** (Av. 2, S side of Plaza de la Democracia), and **Teatro J. J. Vargas Calvo** (C. 3/5, Av. 2).

AROUND EL PUEBLO: Popular with *"los plasticos,"* the area around this imitation Spanish-style shopping center is one of the nation's liveliest. **Cocoloco** has two dance floors, one small *salsa* disco and one darker, playing more intimate music. Live bands play here mid-week.

More conventional **La Plaza** is an attractive disco and *salsa/merengue* club. Dark and steamy **Infinito** has three different discos (rock, Latin, and *salsa*). Other bars include **Amaretta** and **Bar Boquitas** which has an intimate atmosphere. **Jerry Morgan's Piano Bar** has a glittery interior. **Salón Musical de Lety** has cabaret entertainment. **Momentos** is romantic. **Taina's** has an Argentinian vocalist singing ballads on Fri. and Sat. nights.

OTHER VENUES: Located in the Letras Bldg., a new open-air theater in the **University of Costa Rica in San Pedro** offers a variety of performances. For information call 225-5711 and 253-5323, ext. 5433. More regular entertainment is found at **Café Maga** in San Pedro. A cultural center (films, dance workshops, and graffiti art getogethers) and art exhibition space.

OTHER DISCOS: Located around the middle of Paseo Colón, **Club Copacabana** is a large disco. Hot and sweaty **Disco Salsa 54** (C. 3. Av. 1/3) plays a lot of romantic music; couples cuddle as they dance. **El Tunel de Tiempo** (Av. Central, C. 11/13) comes with a head-spinning, light-spiralling entrance. **O Key** is another disco at C. 4, Av. 6/8. **Members** is in Centro Colón on Paseo Colón.

One of the best around, **Dynasty Discoteque**, located at Centro Comercial del Sur which is about 10 blocks S of the Teatro Nacional, plays a lot of reggae, calypso, rap, funk, and soul. Featuring disco and *salsa*, **Partenon** is also here. Take the Desamparados bus from the N side of the Parque Central. **Disco Las Tunas** (☎ 231-1802) is in Sabana Norte.

The place to hang in San Pedro is at **La Bodega** which has a spacious dance floor. It is opposite the car park belonging to Antojitos Restaurant and is S of Mall San Pedro.

Gambling

If the word "gambling" brings to mind row upon row of slot machines along with cavernous casinos, you'll be disappointed with Costa Rica's gaming scene. Most casinos only open their doors in late afternoon or early evening. And terminology and practices are both a bit different. Ticos term **blackjack** "*rommy.*" The difference here is that the ace and ten card combo only pays even money. If you receive three of a kind in your first three cards, however, you'll win three-to-one! Although a straight flush pays the same, it will pay out a four-to-one if it adds up to more than 21. Three sevens pay five-to-one.

Craps is "Domino China" here, and dice are replaced with domino-lookalike tiles. You turn over two tiles at every turn. Tute resembles poker. You receive one card up and four down. Pairs pay even, and there are no draws. Two pairs pay two-to-one, three pairs three-to-one, and so on. A royal flush will pay 100-to-one!

Canasta is the Costa Rican version of **roulette** in which a basket filled with red and black balls replaces the roulette wheel.

Casino locations include the Del Rey, Cariari, Aurola Holiday Inn, Irazú, and Balmoral Hotels. Another popular spot is Club Colónial, on Av. 1 at C. 9.

GAY AND LESBIAN CLUBS: Although the nation's gays attempt to keep things low key, there are a few hangouts. **La Avispa** (☎ 223-5343; C. 1, Av. 8/10) is a popular lesbian bar which features salsa and merengue music. On C. 7 off Av. 1, **La Torre Tonite** is a mostly-gay high-energy disco as is **Deja-Vu** at C. 2, Av. 14/16 (which was subject to a shocking raid executed by the homophobic police in July 1994.

Buenas Vibraciones and **Bochinoche** are on Paseo de las Estudiantes; **La Tertulia**, **Faces**, and **Bambú** are in San Pedro; and **Boy Bar International** is in Tibás.

> ☛ If you can speak some Spanish, you'll find that seeing a play may be cheaper than seeing a movie, and it may provide you with a unique window into Costa Rican life.

BARS: The **Blue Marlin Bar** in the Hotel del Rey is the place to go for fishing yarns and available female hookers. The **Charleston** (C. 9, Av. 2/4) is a video bar which attempts to create a Charleston-like atmosphere. American-owned yuppie bar, **Risa's**, is at C. 1, Av. Central. **Los Murales** (Gran Hotel) and **Las Palmas**

(Aurola Holiday Inn) are other alternatives. Open 24 hours a day on a daily basis, **Chelles** (Av. Central, C. 9) is a landmark — a great spot for people watching. A version with booths, **Chelles Taberna** is around the corner.

Out in the Paseo de Colón area at C. 28 and Av. 2 next to the Sala Garbo, the **Shakespeare Bar** provides a classy atmosphere and is a good place to take a date after a movie at the theater.

Relatively nearby (diagonal to the supermarket on Paseo de Colón), the **Cabeza Grande Brew Pub** is the nation's one and only. It has a Japanese brewmaster to boot!

In Escazú, **Mac's American Bar** is the place to go for TV sports and boisterous *gringo* jocks. (At press time it was searching for a new location).

CLUBS: Soda Blues (☎ 221-8368) features live blues and Caribbean music. It's on C. 11, Av. 10/12 and is 200 m S of Cine Real.

Set behind the Casa Amarilla in Barrio Amón, the **Villa Borghese** (☎ 233-3838; C. 11/13, Av. 9) is a piano bar which presents "the best jazz and blues performed live in a '50s atmosphere." Set across from Kentucky Fried Chicken on Av. Central, **El Tablado** has jazz on Mon. and Latin and *Nueva Canción* (progressive folk music).

El Cuartel de la Boca del Monte, with white walls and prints is attractive and one of the classiest places around; it has live music and is near the Cine Magaly which in turn is near the Toruma YH.

IN SAN PEDRO: San Pedro's **Bar Rock** showcases heavy metal. **Café Banana** is a popular weekend hotspot. It's 200 m E from Muñoz y Nanne.

MARIACHI: This has become such a national institution that many Ticos believe they invented it! Centrally located **La Esmeralda** (Av. 2, C. 5/7) is lively and open 24 hours except on Sun. Next to the Barrio México church, **Bar México** also features mariachis. As it's in a bad neighborhood, take a bus (C. 6, Av. Central) or hop a cab.

LOWLIFE: Located in a century-old converted sea captain's house which has

San José Cinemas	
Bellavista Av. Central, C. 17/19	221-0909
California C. 23, Av. 1	221-4738
Capri Av. Central, C. 9/11	223-0264
Colón Paseo de Colón/C. 38	221-4517
Colonial Plaza Colonial (Escazú)	289-9000
Laurence Olivier Av. 2, C. 28	223-1960
Magaly Barrio La California	223-0085
Metropolitan C. 28, Av. Central/1	222-1249
Omni C. 3, Av. Central/1	221-7903
Rex Av. 4, C. Central/Av. 2	221-0041
Sala Garbo Av. 2, C. 28	222-1034
Universal Paseo de Colón, C. 26/28	221-5241
Variedades Av. Central/C. 5	222-6108

i The ICT has its **information offices** in the underground portion of the Cultural Plaza at C. 5 (☎ 222-1090) and at the airport. From any touchtone phone, information is available at 257-4667. The best sources of what's going on are the *Tico Times* and the weekend section of *La Nación*.

Important San José Phone Nos.	
American	257-1266
American Express	223-3644
Aviateca	255-4949
Clínica Americana	222-1010
Clínica Bíblica	257-0466
Clínica Católica	225-5055
Clínica Jerusalem	285-0202
Continental	223-0266
Coopetaxi Garage *(car trouble)*	235-9966
Copa	223-7033, 221-5596
Costa Rica Exped.	257-0766, 222-0333
Delta	257-4141
Emergencies *(ambulance, fire, police)*	911
Grupo Taca Horizontes	222-2022
Hospital San Juan de Díos	222-0166
Lacsa	232-3555-7
Parques Nacionales	257-0922
Personalized Travel	257-0507
Sansa	221-9414
SIRCA bus (Nicaragua)	222-5541
Taca	222-1790
TICA bus	221-8954
Travelair	220-3054
US Embassy	220-3939
TRACOPA bus	221-4214 223-7685

also served as a conservatory of music, **Key Largo**, the city's most notorious bar (US$2.25 admission; C. 9, Av. 3), teems with craftily winking hookers (first price US$100; US$200 with no condom!) who aspire to being high class. There's a live band, caged toucans. and a back-room restaurant.

Similar but less classy bars like **Happy Days**, **New York** and **Nashville South** are nearby. It's always amusing if somewhat pathetic to walk through and watch the grey-haired, paunch-bellied *gringos* having a whirl with wispy, seductive teenage hookers.

Beatle Bar (C. 9, Av. Central/1) does not appear to be a hooker bar, but some US males told me that some women they met there were on the hustle.

YOU CAN LEAVE YOUR HAT ON: One of many classy-wannabe stripper joints is **Theatre Josephine** (Av. 9, C. 2/4; ☎ 257–2269), which invites you to "envision a scenery traveling through different place through time and space under the most diverse special effects and the most beautiful women in Costa Rica." Several others — almost equally pretentious, overpriced, and uninteresting— are in the vicinity. Some of the city's strip joints are located in the area centering around C. 2, Av. 8. Be careful around here! For those upright souls righteously incensed by the local scene, Club 700, the local branch of the fundamentalist 700 Club, is on C. 1.

CINEMA: First-run films cost around US$2-4 in mostly-comfortable theaters. Theaters include the **Magaly** (Av. Central, C. 23), the **Colón 1 and 2** (Centro Colón on Paseo de Colón), **California** (C. 23, Av. 1), **Capri 1 and 2** (Av. Central, C. 9), **Cine Omni** (C. 3, Av. Central and 1), and **Cinema Real** (C. 11, Av. 6 and 8).

Art films are shown at the **Sala Garbo**, a highly recommended elegant cinema set next to **Teatro Laurence Olivier**, Av. 2, C. 28, near Paseo Colón. In case you arrive early, it has a pleasant if pricey coffee shop adjoining, or have dinner in a nearby restaurant. To get here walk 25 min. from downtown or take the *Sabana Cementerio* bus (C. 7, Av. Central/2), get off by the Pizza Hut and walk a block to the S. Check the ads in *La Nación* for times.

Other San José Practicalities

ORGANIZATIONS AND CLUBS: There are innumerable clubs in San José. The US citizens in **Costa Rica for Peace** (☎ 233-6168), off C. 15 on Av. 6B, meet Mon. eves. **Hash House Harriers** (☎ 228-0769) run on Mon. at 5 PM. Promoting partnership between Costa Rica and Oregon, **Partners of the Americas** (☎ 259-4326) is at Apdo. 219, 2400 San José. Located 400 m N and 100 m W of the Parque Morazán's pavilion, the **Krishnamurti Information Center** (☎ 484-4172, 224-3360) holds bi-weekly meetings on Wed.

ASSOCIATIONS: The **American Chamber of Commerce of Costa Rica** (☎ 233-2133, fax 223-2349) can be contacted at Apdo. 4946, 1000 San José. The **Asociación de Pensionados y Rentistas de Costa Rica** is located next to the Jubilados office on the ground floor of the ICT building (☎ 233-8068, fax 222-7862; write Apdo. 700-1011, San José).

EMBASSIES: The **US Embassy** (☎ 222-5566) is out in the W suburb of Pavas.

The **Canadian High Commission** (☎ 296-4149, fax 296-4270; Apdo. 351-1007, Centro Colón) is is on the third floor of Bldg. 5 at the Oficentro Ejecutivo La Sabana which is behind the Comptroller General's Office on the S side of La Sabana.

The **U. K.**'s address is Edificio Centro Colón 110, ☎ 221-5566. The **German Embassy** (☎ 221-5811) is at C. 36, Av. 3A. The **Swiss Consulate** (☎ 221-4829) is at 4th F, Centro Colón, Paseo Colón. For others consult the telephone directory's yellow pages under "Embajadas y Consulados."

HEALTH: English-speaking doctors and 24-hour service can be found at **Clínica Americana** (☎ 222-1010), Av. 14, Calles Central/1, at the **Clínica Bíblica** (☎ 257 0466), C. 1, Av. 14/16, at **Clínica Católica** (☎ 225-5055) in San Antonio de Guadalupe, and at **Clínica Jerusalem** (☎ 285-0202) in El Alto de Guadalupe.

The 105-room **Hospital San José** (☎ 231-0111) opened in 1999. It is 125 M S of the Channel 7 Building on La Sabana.

The **Medical Center Cariari** (☎ 293-4363) is near the hotel of the same name. It has two bilingual doctors available on weekdays.

Clinica San Miguel (☎ 228-4600) is in downtown Escazú and across from the San Miguel church.

Clinica La Paz (☎ 234-7659) is a "holistic" clinic which is 20 m N of the Fátima chuch in Los Yoses. Aromatherapy, acupuncture, homeopathy, and rent-a-friend (psychotherapy) are among services offered.

Since charges are uniform if you are not covered by the social security system, it is better to go to the private hospitals where the care is superior. While US insurance coverage isn't accepted, credit cards are, and you can have your company reimburse you later.

In case of an emergency, go to any public hospital; the nearest one to downtown is **Hospital San Juan de Díos** (☎ 222-0166), Av. Central and C. 16.

To call a Red Cross ambulance, phone 221-5818.

SHOPPING: Apropox (C. 3, Av. Central/1) manufactures quality clothing. What they don't have in stock, they will make to order.

Arte Libros Regalos, next to Dankha Boutique (Av. 5, C. 3), sells second-hand goods plus inexpensive used English books.

Centrally located, **Galerías Plaza de Cultura** is a general department store at

Av. Central, C. 5/7. Others are to the W along Av. Central.

A good place for high-quality leatherwork is at the chain **Artesanías Melety**, the most centrally located of which is at Av. 1, C. 1/3. Other depots for leather include **Galería del Cuero** (Av. 1, C. 5) and **Del Río**, C. 9. Lower quality but more affordable goods are found at **Industrias Pesapop**, C. 3, Av. 1/3.

For silver ornaments, try **La Casa del Indio**, Av. 2, C. 5/7.

CRAFTS AND SOUVENIRS: The **National Museum's shop** sometimes has examples of indigenous weaving. Another outdoor vending area is at the stalls on the E side of C. Central, just N of Av. Central.

Local **artisans** sell daily at C.5, Av. 4 where you may find goods sold by indigneous people from the Bribri, Chorotega, and Guaymi as well as items from Africa and Russia; the goods are sold directly from the artisans who made them; no middlemen or merchants are permitted.

Opened in 1998, **Galería Namú** is on C. 7 directly behind the Holiday Inn and combines *campesina* paintings with as well as indigenous crafts.
befrench@sol.racsa.co.cr

Selling finely crafted but steeply priced wooden bowls among other items, **La Galeria** is at C. 1, Av Central/1. Other stores in the same price range are **Suraska** (C. 5, Av. 3) and **Atmósfera** (C. 5, Av. 1).

Mercado Nacional de Artesanías, the National Handicraft Market (C. 11, Av. 2/4), offers souvenirs similar to those found in hotel stores, as does **CANAPI**, an artisans' guild at C. 11, Av. 2b.

Specializing in crafts such as pottery and gourds carved by Indians, **ANDA** is on Av. Central between C. 5/7. Set next to the Melico Salazar Theater on Av. 2 between C. Central/2, **Arterica** has an unusual assortment of craft items.

On C. 9 at Av. 9, the **Hotel Don Carlos** also has a gift shop with a good selection. **Magia** is at C. 5 between Av. 1/3, and **La Casona** (which has a selection of Central American handicrafts) is on C. Central between Av. Central/1.

Sol Maya (across from the Hospital San Juan de Dios on Paseo Colón) also sells them; Guatemalan textiles are also sold at C. 3, Av. 3/5.

Located behind Iglesia La Soledad, **Casa del Artesano** (C. 11, Av. 4/6) is another craft center.

A set of stalls grouped under a single roof, the **International Arts and Crafts Market** sells Costa Rican crafts exclusively. It has restaurants, craft demonstrations, and music and dance performances. It's in Curridabat, a suburb to the E of San José, and is open Tues. to Thurs. and on Sun. from 9-6 and on Fri. and Sat. from 9-9. It's closed on Mon.

Moravia, a NE suburb, is well known for its leather crafts including belts, wallets, briefcases, and purses. **Sarchí** is famous for its *carretas*, painted ox carts, and other souvenirs.

SHOPPING CENTERS: Centro Comercial El Pueblo is a shopping center set up as an imitation colonial village. It's complete with tile roofs, walls of stucco and whitewashed brick, wrought iron lamps, and narrow streets. The nighttime is the right time for boogeying here. Take the *C. Blancos bus* (Av. 5, C. 1/3), a cab, or walk.

SHOPPING MALLS: Many have opened in and near San José

Mall San Pedro San Pedro near the Los Yoses roundabout. Has 260 stores and 35 restaurants. Opened in 1995.

Metrocentro Near Cartago's central market. Has 40 stores, supermarket, and a restaurant.

Multiplaza Across from the Camino Real Hotel in Escazú. Has some 100 stores and ten restaurants as well as a supermarket

Novacentro Set in Guadalupe at the intersection for Moravia. It has some 30 stores and a supermarket.

Plaza del Sol Set on the E side of town on the way to Curridabat. It has some 50 stores as well as supermarket and restaurants.

Plaza Mayor In suburb of Rohmoser. Has some 20 stores including bookstore and supermarket.

CAMPING SUPPLIES: The major store is **Centro de Aventuras** (☎ 55-0618) on Paseo Colón (C. 22/24) which also rents snorkeling, kayaking, or camping equipment. Another store, **Aro Ltd.** (Av. 8, C. 11/13), sells camping gaz refillable cartridges. **Ferretería El Clavo** (C. 6, Av. 8) has *gasolina blanca* (kerosene). Other stores with outdoor gear include **Carlos Luis** (Av. Central, C. 2/4) and **Palacio del Deporte** (C. 2, Av. 2/4).

FISHING EQUIPMENT: The two major outlets are **La Casa del Pescador** (C. 2, Av. 18/20) and **Deportes Keko** (C. 20, Av. 4/6). Tide tables are also available here.

SURFING SUPPLIES: Set 80 ft. (75 m) W of the Banco Popular in San Pedro, the **Mango Surf Shop** is one of two alternatives here. The other is the **Keola Surf and Ding Shop** (☎ 225-6280, Apdo. 6280, San José) which is 100 m E and S of the aforesaid bank. The latter provides board repair, information, and guides. Also try the **Tsunami** in Los Yoses.

MARKETS: The **Mercado Central** is at C. 6., Av. 1. Here you can buy fresh spices (sold in 10 and 25 gm bags), fruits and vegetables, and there's also a stall selling honey and natural herbs. Herbs are also available in bulk at **La Avena Hierba**, Paseo de los Estudiantes (C. 9). A block N, at C. 8 between Av. 3 and 5, is the **Borbón** which specializes in vegetables. Another market is at the Coca Cola bus terminal at C. 16, between Av. 1 and 3. For hardware items try **Ferretería Glazman**, Av. 5, C. 6/8.

> For gourmet coffee beans (from all over the nation) which are roasted on the premises, try ***La Esquina del Café*** at Av. 9/C. 3B. Another good location to buy beans is at ***Café Trebol*** which is on C. 8, Av. Central/1.

FOOD SHOPPING: In addition to the above-mentioned markets, there are a number of places to buy food items. King of the supermarkets is **Mas x Menos** chain; there's a branch on Paseo Colón across from the Ambassador Hotel between C. 24/28; others are across from the Plaza de la Democracia (C. 3/5) and in the suburbs.

Its chief competitor is the **Automercado** chain (closed Suns.) which is at C. 3/5 at Av. 3, in Barrio Mexico and Los Yoses, and in Plaza del Sol and Plaza Mayor.

Set at the end of Paseo Colón on C. 42, **Yaohan** offers a wide selection, but prices are high. The place is huge and has commando-mentality security guards with walkie talkies patrolling.

Café Moka sells coffee beans along with peanuts along Av. Central near C. 10; many other such shops are in the vicinity.

Boston Bagels (☎ 232-2991) is located on a side street, across fro the "La Artistica" furniture store along he main road to Pavas.

DRUGSTORES: Located at Av. 4 between C. Central and 1, **Clinica Biblica**'s dispensary is open 24 hrs. per day. The **Farmacía Cartin** is located on the east side of the Central Market. The **Farmacía del Este** is across from Banco Popular in San Pedro. The **Farmacía del Oeste** is across from the US Embassy.

MAIL: Also known as **Coretel** (Correos y Telégrafos), the main post office (Correo Central) is on C. 2, Av. 1/3. Window service runs from 7 to 6 weekdays and from 7 to 2 on Sat. You can have mail sent via *Lista de Correos* (Post Restante) here. Accepting mail directed to its traveler's check and card holders, **American Express** is at 4 F, T. A. M. Travel, C. 1, Av. Central/1.

BANKING: Banks are open from 9 to 3. Certain branches may be open until six. Most banks will also sell you *colones* if you have a major credit card. A money changing operation run by Banco Mercantil is on Av. 2 (C. Central/2). It's open 9-noon and 1-5:45 weekdays. For banking on Sat. AM try the bank across from the Amstel Hotel on Av. 1, C. 7. Canadian dollars can be changed at Banco San José (C. Central, Av. 3/5), Banex (C. Central, Av. 1), BCT (C. Central, Av. 1/3), and Lyon (C. 2. Av. Central/1). You can also change money in the larger hotels.

MONEYCHANGERS: At all cost, avoid moneychangers on the street. However, there are a number of trustworthy moneychangers who operate from kiosks or markets. These are preferable to the banks because you cut out the red tape. One good place to change money is at the Villalobos Brothers (☎ 233-0090/3127), No. 204 on the second floor of the Schyfter Bldg., which is on C. 2, Av. Central/1 near the GPO.

PHONES: Although it may not be hard to find a pay phone in the city, it can be exasperating to try and find one which both works and for which you have the correct coinage. Try hotel lobbies or outside the ICE building at C. 1, Av. 2. Card phones are identified by the "CHIP" sign on their sides. These are readily found around town these days.

INTERNET ACCESS: Access is limited to a few hotels and several Internet cafes.

In the second floor of the OTEC building (25 m S of C. 3/Av. 3), **KitCom** (☎ 258-0303) is open Mon.-Fri. 8:30-8, Sat, Sun., 9:30-5. It offers e-mail access and faxing. **www.yellowweb.co.cr**

On the second floor of the Las Arcadas (next to the Gran Hotel in the Plaza de Cultura, **CyberCafe** (☎ 258-1751) offers Internet access and e-mail. It is open Mon.-Sat. 8-6.

Out in San Pedro, the German-run **Internet Cafe** offers surfing for free provided that free web surfing to anyone who spends C500 per hour on food and/or drinks. It has 24 computers (with more on the way) and provides a speedy 128 kb connection direct to RACSA. It is open 24-hours-per-day and is open daily throughout the year **www.internetcafecr.com**

For **laundry and dry cleaning** there is a service on Paseo de Colón near Restaurante Bastille (to the W of downtown); Lavantia Doña Ana (closed Sun.) is 400 ft. (125 m) to the E of Plaza Gonzales near the Ministry of Public Transport to the SE; and yet another is in the Centro Commercial on the N side of the San Pedro road to the E of Los Yoses. To get here take the San Pedro bus on Av. 2 and ask the driver to let you off.

BABYSITTING: Ask at your hotel or contact Viajes Colón (☎ 221-3778, 225-2500).

AIRLINES: *Continental* (☎ 233-0266, fax 233-7146) has its offices at C. 19/Av. 2.

American Airlines (☎ 255-1607, 255-1911) is in the Centro Cars Building, Sabana Este, the enormous reflecting glass VW car sales building next to Yaohan.

Lacsa/TACA (☎ 231-0093) is across from the Melía Comfort Hotel on the Sabana.

United (☎ 220-4844) is behind the Contraloria bldg. in Sabana Sur.

Aviateca (☎ 233-8390, 255-4949) has is 100 m N of the Banco de Costa Rica in Paseo Colón.

PLANNING YOUR ITINERARY: If you've arrived without an itinerary and are confused, there are a number of places in San José where you can get help.

Horizontes (☎ 222-2022; Apdo. 1780, San José 1002) is a local agency which is popular with many visitors and offers good planning. **www.horizontes.com**

Costa Rica Expeditions (☎ 257-0766, 222-0333, fax 257-1665)will help you plan visits to their lodges as well as a number of reputable hotels.
costa-rica@expeditions.co.cr
www.expeditions.co.cr

If you're looking for something a bit more personal and informative, **Personalized Tours** (☎ 257-0507: 24 hrs.) are definitely recommended. This father-and-son operation can provide everything from trips to Manuel Antonio to quetzal tours to trips to Curú Wildlife Refuge. This is a great chance for you to meet with Ticos as friends instead of as servants and to have a chance to ask a number of questions. Even if they aren't going with you, they can still hook you up with trips and book hotels. This is an ideal place to go for small family groups.
perstour@sol.racsa.co.cr
www.intercentro.net/personalizedtours

Ocarina Expeditions (tel. 253-4579; Apdo. 1265-2050, San José) offers some great tours including trips to Chirrip and Corcovado.
www.ocarinaexpeditions.com
ocarina@sol.racsa.co.cr

LIBRARIES AND CULTURAL CENTERS: Best for periodicals and books in English is the US-sponsored **Centro Cultural Costarricense Norteamericano** (Costa Rican-American Cultural Center, ☎ 225-9433, ext. 223, 214, 252; 253-5783, fax 224-1480) which is located in eastern San José on C. Negritos. You'll have to pay a membership fee if you wish to borrow books. You may also watch CNN here. Its Mark Twain Information Center and Library also boasts access to data bases including CD-ROM, card catalog, US Congress "Legislate," and "Phonefiche." It's open Mon to Fri., 8:30-6:30 and Sat. from 8 to noon.

On C. 21 just off Av. Central on the E side of the Parque Nacional, the **Centro Cultural de Mexico** (open Mon. to Fri., 3-5), has a small library.

Another library is at the **Biblioteca Nacional** (Av. 3 at C. 15) which has a newspaper room featuring foreign journals such as *The People's Korea*. Another is the one at the **University of Costa Rica** in San Pedro.

Alianza Franco Costarricense, Av. 7, C. 5, has French newspapers and shows films every Thurs. evening. The **Instituto Goethe** highlights German culture and also has a reading room; the San Pedro bus passes right by.

MAPS AND BOOKSTORES: Most of the bookstores mentioned here carry the

Tico Times as well as imported newspapers. **7th Street Books** (☎ 256-8251, fax 258-3302) offer a wide variety of books at reasonable prices. It's on C. 7, Av. Central/C. 1.
marroca@sol.racsa.co.cr

Librería Lehmann, Av. Central, C. 1/3 and **Librería Universal**, Av. Central, C. Central/1, have good map sections (topographics) as well as a fine selection of books.

Located in the Arcadas Mall at Av. 1, Calles Central/2, **Librería Quijote** has a smaller selection of English books including some used ones.

Shakespeare and Co. (☎ 233-4995) is 350 m to the N of the Gran Hotel Costa Rica.

In the Pizza Hut on Av. 1 near the Plaza Cultural, **Mora Books** (☎ 383-8385) which offers a great selection of used books (including travel books) at very reasonable prices.

Another place to buy is at **Gambit** which is across from the bowling alley, down the way from the Centro Cultural Costarricense Norteamericano in Barrio Dent.

Near the center of Escazú and the Pomodoro Restaurant (50 m W and 100 on the old Santa Ana Road), **Rincón de la Calle Real** (☎ 289-5112) is the nation's most unusual bookstore. In addition to a fine selection of books, it offers lunch in a garden setting, poetry readings, and jazz and classical music concerts.

DANCE LESSONS: There are a large number of inexpensive dance schools in San José. If you're going to be staying a while, it's well worth checking them out.

With two schools (one on the E side of the US Embassy in Rohmoser and another 50 m W and 100 m S of the Banco Popular in San Pedro), the **Centro de Enseñanza e Investigación del Baile Popular** (Merecumbé Research and Training Center of Popular Dance; ☎ 224-3531/1548) offers training in a variety of steps ranging from *bolero* to *merengue*. They have a special program for tourists.

Set 75 m S of the "Antiguo Higueron" in San Pedro, **Danza Viva** teaches everything from modern dance to tango to *soca*.

San José Itinerary

One Day

There's no need to leave San José! Visit your choice of museums, shop, and take in the nightlife.

Two Days

Take an excursion to somewhere in the Central Valley. Recommended are Poas, Irazú, and Orosi. You can also go whitewater rafting.

Three Days

Take a day trip or spend a day walking around Heredia or Alajuela, savoring the atmosphere.

Four Days or More

Take in locations such as Grecia and head further north or south. Don't worry about getting lost: It's part of the fun!

Costa Rica may also be used as a staging ground for a trip to **Cuba**. LACSA has three weekly flights, and the flight (including airfare) costs around US$350-500 for four to seven nights including meals. US citizens will not have their passport stamped and can pay for everything in Cuba using the preferred currency: the sacred greenback!

Contact a travel agent or EASA (☎ 256-5458/256-7830; Av. 5, C. 3 y 5, San José. When departing by air, be sure to keep US$18 handy for the airport tax and an additional US$15 for the Cuban tourist visa.

Set 175 m E of the Plaza de la Democracia next to Apartotel San José, **Academia de Baile Popular Malecón** (☎ 222-3214) teaches everything from *danzon* to reggae to *mambo*.

On Av. Central between C. 25B and 27 on the way to San Pedro, the **Academy de Bailes Latinos** (Academy of Latin Dances; ☎ 221-1624, 233-8938) teaches dance techniques in calypso, *cumbia*, *salsa*, and the like. They also have Spanish classes (free dance lessons for students), intensive courses, and private lessons. An added advantage is that there is no enrollment fee.

From San José

Using the city as a base, many different day excursions are possible. Good day trips include visits to Volcán Poás, Orosi Valley, San Antonio de Escazú, Alajuela, Volcán Irazú, Ojo de Agua, Cartago, Lankester Gardens, Heredia, the Reventazón river for white water rafting, and many others.

BY BUS: Especially during weekends and holidays, it's preferable to buy your ticket the day before and arrive an hour before departure. **Check the times in the travel section, and recheck the times, if possible.**

FOR THE CARIBBEAN COAST: Opened in late 1997, the US$2.1-million Gran Terminal del Caribe (☎ 256-4248; C. Central near Av. 11) is the nation's first modern bus terminal. Buses for Limón (approx. three hrs.) depart on the half-hr. from 5 AM-7PM. Try to board a direct bus.

For the best views take the 10:30 AM double-decker bus. (It returns at 4:30 PM).

Buses for Cahuita (approx. four hrs.) depart at 10, 1:30, and 4 from the Gran Terminal del Caribe (☎ 256-4248; C. Central near Av. 11).

Direct buses to Sixaola (bypassing Limón) leave from at 6 and 3:30, passing both park entrances. Sixaola is about 25 min. farther down the road.

From Limón, buses (one hr.) leave from Av. 4, C. 3/4 at 5, 8, 10, 1, and 4. If you get a 7 AM bus from San José, there should be no problem meeting the 10 AM bus out of Limón.

BY AIR: Government-owned and subsidized, *SANSA* (☎ 221-9414, 233-0397, 233-3258, fax 255-2176) flies daily or several times weekly between San José and Tamarindo, Nosara, Samara, Quepos, Golfito, and Coto 47 near the border with Panama. SANSA operates shuttle buses to and from the airport. (For more information on SANSA, see their mention in the "Introduction.")

Their competitors are privately owned *Travelair* (☎ reservations: 220-3054, sales: 296-1102, fax 296-2316; SJO 788, PO Box 025216, Miami, FL 33102-5216) which flies from San José to Barra del Colorado, Quepos, Golfito, Puerto Jiménez, Tambor, Palmar Sur, Limón, Nosara, Tamarindo, Punta Islita, and Carrillo. Like SANSA, it leaves from Pavas. While its flights are two or three times as expensive as SANSA's, they are markedly more reliable. In addition, they fly on Sun. to and from Tamarindo, Carrillo, Palmar Sur, Quepos, and Golfito. To get a copy of their latest schedule, check with a travel agent or fax them at 220-0413.

Vicinity of San José

HORSEBACK RIDING: Many excursions are available from San José. Average cost runs around US$60-US$80. All provide transport both ways. At Rancho

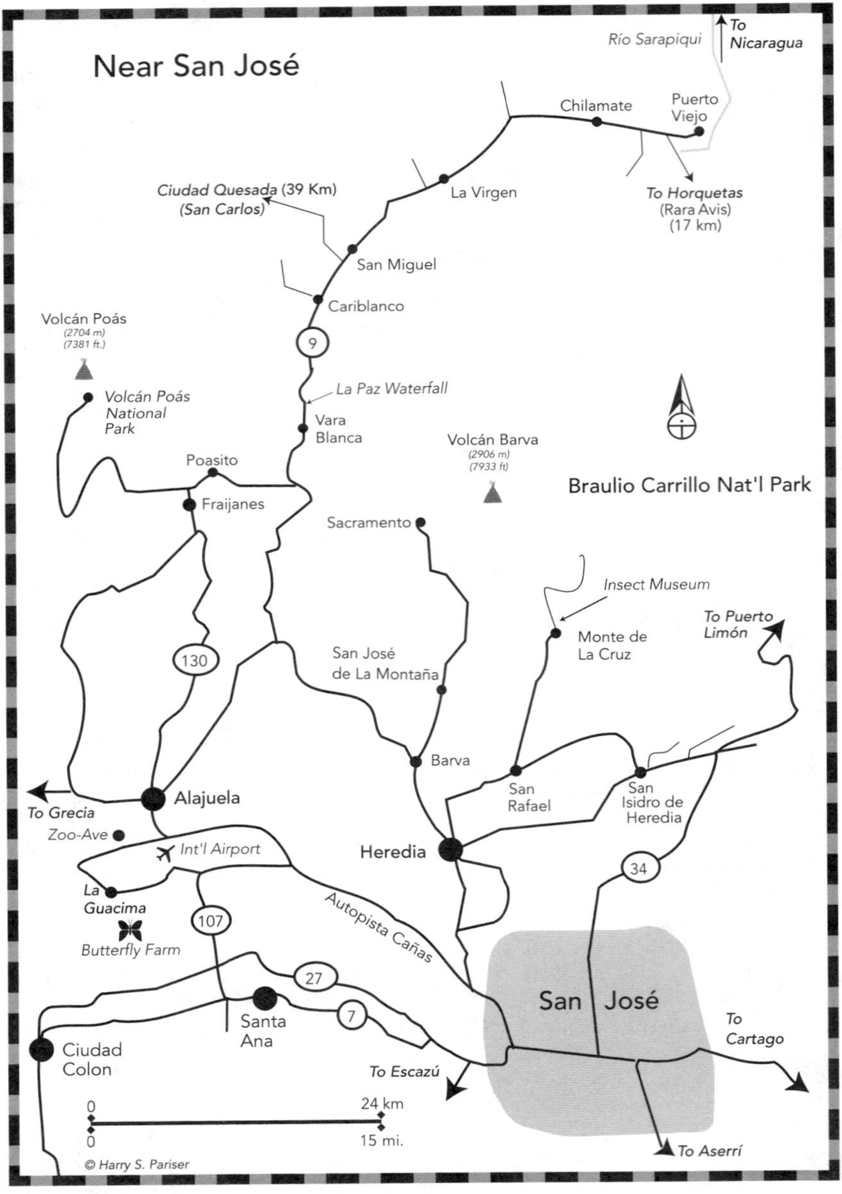

Near San José
Río Sarapiquí
To Nicaragua
Chilamate
Puerto Viejo
La Virgen
To Horquetas
(Rara Avis)
(17 km)
Ciudad Quesada (39 Km)
(San Carlos)
San Miguel
Cariblanco
9
Volcán Poás
(2704 m)
(7381 ft.)
La Paz Waterfall
Volcán Poás National Park
Vara Blanca
Volcán Barva
(2906 m)
(7933 ft)
Poasito
Braulio Carrillo Nat'l Park
Fraijanes
Sacramento
Insect Museum
To Puerto Limón
Monte de La Cruz
San José de La Montaña
130
Barva
San Rafael
San Isidro de Heredia
To Grecia
Alajuela
Zoo-Ave
Int'l Airport
Heredia
34
La Guacima
Butterfly Farm
107
Autopista Cañas
27
San José
7
Santa Ana
To Cartago
Ciudad Colon
To Escazú
0
24 km
0
15 mi.
To Aserrí
© Harry S. Pariser

Redondo, 30 min. E of the city, **Hotel-Hacienda San Miguel** (☎ 229-1094, fax 221-3871) gives a cloud forest tour; lunch is served. Breakfast and lunch are included.

Offering a trip through pasture and along the beach, **L.A. Tours** (☎ 221-4501) visits a farm near Orotina. Breakfast and lunch are included.

Magic Trails (☎ 253-8146/8160) offers a trip to Hacienda Reyes with two routes — along the pasture or through steep Prusia reserve and up to Irazú. Lunch and a snack are included.

With rides to Jacó or into the forest, **Rainbow Tours** (☎ 233-8228) has a trip to Rancho Nuevo which includes breakfast, lunch, and refreshments.

On a farm at Sacramento, bordering Parque Nacional Braulio Carrillo, **Robles Tours** (☎ 237-2116, fax 237-1976) takes you on a ride with panoramic vistas. An oxcart trip is also available.

Running up Cerro de la Muerte, **Tipical Tours** (☎ 233-8466) offers a quetzal search (sightings not guaranteed) through cloud forest terrain.

BUNGEE JUMPING: This rather unusual pastime appeals to those who wish to get their adrenalin up and roaring. After being strapped into a harness, you dive 280 ft. (86 m) off the top of a bridge (the Puente Negro) into a tropical jungle canyon. You fly until you hit the end of the cord, then rebound, and fall again and again. After the rebounds stop, you find yourself hanging suspended over the canyon. Depending upon the company, either a line is lowered and you hook yourself on to it to be hauled up or you are lowered to the river, unharnessed, and then climb up a rocky slope to return. There are two systems: European and US. Under the US system, the line consists of three to four elastic cords which were originally designed by the US military to parachute tanks or jeeps from planes. The European system consists of a specially made elastic cord which is attached to a thick rope. The harnesses differ in design as well. Contact **Tropical Bungee** (☎ 233-6455), or **ASP** (☎ 222-4547). Depending upon the company, residents pay about US$30-US$40 for a jump; tourists pay US$40-55. Spectators pay US$4-US$5 RT. If you are pregnant and/or have back or neck problems, avoid bungee jumping.

Exploring the Central Valley

Here are just a few things you might choose to do while in the area.

- Visit Irazú or Poás volcanes
- Take the Café Britt tour
- Visit Cartago with its cathedral
- Take a stroll around Alajuela or Heredia
- Visit the Orosi Valley, Lankaster Gardens, and/or Tapanti National Park
- See the snake milking at the Instituto Clormido Picando
- Visit the Jewels of the Humid Tropics collection
- Climb Turrialba volcano
- Go whitewater rafting

Paraue Nacional de Diversiones/Pueblo Antiguo

Ideal either for children or the child in you, this amusement park (☎ 296-2212) has a variety of rides. Food here is mostly fast (i. e. greasy) so bring your own nibbles. Pueblo Antiguo, the recreated-village theme-park portion of the park, offers a chance to visit a sugar mill, a country store, and a coffee factory as well as ride through a replica of the famous canals leading to Tortuguero. Its three areas are labeled "the City," "the

Country," and "The Coast." Each attempts to recreate the atmosphere of the years from 1880-1930. It also has a recreated indigenous settlement, a fish aquarium housed in a Spanish galleon, and a cocoa plant which shows the steps in processing. Professional actors provide ambiance, and there is folkloric dancing. It is a few km W of Hospital Mexico. You should leave the main highway there and take an access road running parallel to the main highway. Catch a bus from Av. 6, C. 10/12 to get here. It is only open on weekends. Admission for foreigners is around US$7, and admission to all shows and rides is around US$30.

Festival of San Isidro Labrador

Celebrated on May 15, the patron saint day of San Isidro Labrador is marked by blessing – blessing everything, that is! (A native of Spain, Saint Isidro, patron saint of farmers, was an impoverished yet generous farmer). Priests bless people and their belongings (including bicycles, cars, trucks, and pets) with holy water. The most famous of these ceremonies is held at the gothic-style church in San Isidro de Coronado.

note: The blessing may be moved to a Sunday should May 15 fall on a weekday in order that that the community might attend.

Parque del Este

Situated in the hills above San Pedro in San Rafael de Montes de Oca, this park has a jogging and exercise trail, pool, soccer field, basketball courts, playgrounds, picnic tables, a nature trail, and great views. It's open daily except Mon. until 4. Admission is around US$.50 Take the *San Ramón de Tres Ríos* bus from Av. 2, C. 5/7.

Moravia

Named after Juan Rafael Mora and 7 km NE of San José, the shops in this slow-paced small town feature everything from furniture to leather work. Its most famous shop is **Caballo Blanco**, set on one corner of the plaza. Others include **La Rueda** and **El Potro**.

Eat at **Soda San Martín**. **Rincón Europeo** (☎ 235-8678) is for the gourmet set and offers Hungarian food. Hotels here are listed under "outlying accommodation" in the San José accommodation section.

GETTING HERE: Take the bus from Av. 3, C. 3/5 or the microbus from Av. 7, C. 6 and disembark at the main stop, two blocks before the main square. From the town, it's about 10 km to San Jerónimo de Moravia, which is another 10 km from the boundaries of Parque Nacional Braulio Carrillo.

Coronado

Actually a collection of three villages—San Antonio, Dulce Nombre, and San Isidro, this country town has a Gothic-style church and good views of San José. **Club Mediterráneo** (☎ 229-0661) is the local gourmet restaurant. They celebrate their *fiestas patronales* each Feb. 15. If you're coming by car, you can head seven km E to Las Nubes which has **Cronopios** (☎ 229-6283; call for times) which serves soups, salads, and apple pie in an attractive atmosphere.

SNAKE MILKING: Undoubtedly one of the most unusual places to visit in the Americas, the **Insituto Clodomiro Picado** (☎ 229-0344/0335, fax 292-0485) which is situated one km before the town on the R hand side in the village of Dulce Nombre de Coronado. It is named for its anti-venom researcher Dr. Clodomiro Picando Twight (1887-1944). Opened in 1972, it researches snakes and processes venom into antivenom serum.

The "milking" demonstration – held every Fri. afternoon from 1:30 to 3:30 – is something no serpent lover will choose to miss. It begins with the milking: *terciopelos* are pinned down with a hook, then picked up firmly but gingerly. After prying open its jaws, the snake's fangs are pressed against the netting of the venom collection cannister. After the pale milk is expelled, the process is repeated again and again. A small *terciopelo* is also fed to a *zopilota*, which is immune to its venom, and which slowly crushes and then eats it.

One of the smallest but certainly the most frightening snake is the *culebra del mar*, found on the Pacific coast from California to Chile, for which there is no serum available. Fortunately, only ten people have been bitten by it during the past ten years. The *biblo la diablo* and the *lora* are small, green-colored poisonous snakes. Found in Guanacaste, the cascabel rattler is less aggressive than the *terciopelo*. The coral snake has a distinctive red, yellow, and black coloring; its mimic, the false coral, alternates red, black, and yellow; a boa constrictor which hisses and snaps; the aggressive bushmaster or *matabuey* is also on hand.

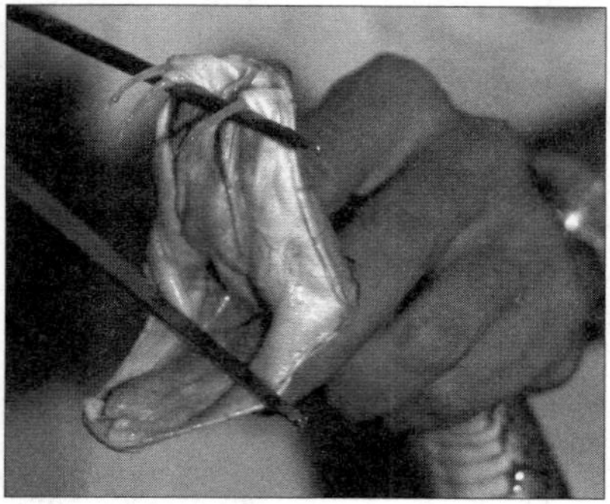

Milking a fer-de-lance

The afternoon's apex comes with the display of the two Asiatic cobras. Mice are crushed to death with giant tweezers and fed to the snakes. Then, in case you came late, there's another display of milking. The booklet *Aspetos Básicos sobre las Serpientes de Costa Rica* offers a thorough (albeit Spanish-only) introduction to the nation's snakes.

To get here take a bus from Moravia or from Av. 5, C. 3/5. On the way back, it's a pleasant stroll down to Moravia, less than an hour away. Open 8-noon, 1-4, Mon. to Fri.

Aserrí

Situated 10 km past the working-class suburbs of Desamparados and San Rafael, Aserrí — with its clean country atmosphere and white-washed church with a broken clock — provides a welcome break from the polluted urban environment. Take a bus here from C. 2, Av. 6/8. Check out the large religious statuary by the church altar.

Set to the SW, **La Piedra de Aserrí** (Rock of Aserrí) is a precariously balanced, 90-ft. (30-m) boulder which has a cave at its base. According to local legend, the witch Na Zárate lived here and would walk the slopes to guard her hidden treasure.

Chicharronera Cacique Acserí (☎ 230-3088) offers menus carved on pieces of wood shaped like a smiling pig. Bands play on weekends.

El Rodeo

One of the largest expanses of rainforest still extant on the Meseta Central, this area is just outside of Ciudad Colón, a 30-minute bus ride (from Coca Cola) to the W of San José. Disembark in Ciudad

Colón, 300 m before the Plaza Central, and walk three km N (heading to the R). Watch out for the *cementerio* which is some 500 m from the main road; ask any local for assistance. Take the road to the R from the cemetery which will head E about a km before starting the descent to El Rodeo. On the way, you'll pass Finca Obla-Di-Obla-Da on the R before reaching the basin, where you cross a stream.

Of the well-trodden trails here, one leads up to the **University of Peace**. This unusual university offers a four month study program in "international indigenous studies" which brings together indigenous people from all over the Americas. Tours of **Radio For Peace International** (☎ 249-1821 for times) are also offered. There are restaurants in Ciudad Colón.

Reserva Guayabo

To get to this Indian reserve, take the *Santiago Puriscal* bus from Coca Cola, C. 16, Av. 1/3. Leaving approximately every 45 min. and taking about an hour, the trip proceeds through rolling countryside, climbing up with hairpin turns and spectacular drops. Located at Km 30, this chilly reserve is home of the Quitirrsí Native Americans who are noted for their basketweaving ability. Puriscal, at the end of the line, is mainly of note for its seismic activity: It was the epicenter for thousands of tremors during 1990. Its name derives from *purisco*, the time that the beans begin to blossom. If driving during the dry season, an attractive return route is via Acosta (San Ignacio), an unpaved road.

Arbofilia

Operating in the Puriscal area, **Arbofilia** (☎ 235-5470; Apdo. 312, Tibas) is involved with "ecological regeneration"— replanting formerly forested land with native species in an attempt to mimic natural patterns. Biologists work together with *campesinos*. The latter donate labor while the former provide seeds and train them in grafting, greenhouse use, and in tree planting techniques. **Jungle Trails** (☎ 255-3486) offers tours.

San Antonio de Escazú

Brightly painted oxcarts ply the streets of this Mediterranean-flavored mountain town which has a church, colorful adobe houses with outdoor ovens, and views of Volcán Barva and San José. Eat at **Hotel Mirador**, **Pico Blanco** or **Tiquicía**, all with legendary views. Take a bus from C. 16, Av. Central/1. If you only want to go to the preceeding town of Escazú, noted for its expatriate community, board a bus at Av. 1, C. 16/18.

> ☛ If you are staying in (or visiting) Escazú, the **Trapiche de Tito Hidalgo** is an old-fashioned cane mill which is 200 m W and 100 m S of San Antonio's church.

Pico Blanco

This reserve protects the surrounding water supply of Escazú. From San Antonio (above), walk from the Parque Central uphill; all roads converge on the reserve. After passing a goat farm and continuing on for several hundred m, the road winds around the mountain, and you lose sight of San José. To the R, you'll see the rainforest. Either head straight up through the large expanse of pasture or continue along the road which wends its way up the mountain. You'll gain sight of the city again. Pico Alajuelita can be recognized by the cross which adorns its top. The trails are not

Escazú's Witches

Escazú is popularly known as *La Tierra de Brujas* ("Land of the Witches"). It is still believed that witches reside here. San Miguel was selected as the patron saint because he allegedly drove Satan from Heaven and would thus afford protection. To be doubly sure, the color scheme of blue and white is applied, a combination believed to repel witches.

You might see the witch Zárate who lives atop Pico Blanco. She gets her jollies by appearing as fog, a howling wind, or the sound of a river. More attractive is *La Segua*, a gorgeous babe who will alter herself into a horse as a suitor approaches.

The *Cadejos* is a chain-dragging brute of a black dog who has been known to harass late-night drunks. And the *Mico Malo* is an evil monkey that may block your path. You may keep and ear out at night for the *Carreta sin Bueyes*, the oxless ox cart driven by *El Diablo*.

clearly marked. Avoid the side trails which go nowhere. Go early to avoid the afternoon fog. Watch for mythical creatures believed to inhabit the area.

Los Juncos

This cloud forest reserve is less than an hour from San José. Tours will take you to the reserve's farmhouse for breakfast, around a trail, back for lunch, around another trail, and back to San José. It's also possible to overnight here. Call **Green Tropical Tours** (☎/fax 255-2859) or write Dept. 252, PO Box 0252216, Miami, FL 33102.
greentp@sol.racsa.co.cr

Grecia

This pineapple cultivation and sugar processing center has a church roofed in dark red painted metal. Be sure to visit the workshop of **Paul Smith** (☎ 444-6990), an instrument maker who was one of Monteverde's first settlers.

ACCOMMODATION: You may stay at **Cabaña Los Cipreses, Cabinas Los Trapiches**, or low-budget **Pensión Quirós.**

La Posada de Grecia (☎ 494-2000, fax 494-4660) is a bed and breakfast which is in the town center across from the park. Rates are around US$30 including tax and a continental breakfast.

The **Healthy Day Inn** (☎/fax 444-5903) is an *apartotel* with pool, Jacuzzi, tennis, massage, horseback riding, and restaurant. It's on the road to Sarchí and charges around US$30 pp including breakfast.

NEAR GRECIA: Formerly Posada Las Palomas, **Vista del Valle Plantation Inn** (☎/fax 451-1165, 450-0800, 450-0900.) is an attractive bed and breakfast set on a coffee plantation and fruit farm. It has a "nouvelle Tico" restaurant, pool, Jacuzzi, and horseback riding and lessons. Its small nature reserve has a trail with waterfall. Botanical gardens are on the premises, and it borders the Río Grande Canyon Preserve. It's in the hamlet of Rosario which is situated between the Grecia and Naranjo exits on the Interamerican. Rooms and cabins are available; rates are in the luxury range.
www.vistadelvalle.com
mibrejo@sol.racsa.co.cr

Posada Mimosa (☎ 494-5868) is a small bed-and-breakfast which offers great views and rooms with fans and private baths. It has a pool.
cmimosa@sol.racsa.co.cr

Sarchí

In the nation's most famous crafts center, family-run workshops make painted oxcarts using traditional designs, which have been passed on for generations. The

The Ox Cart

Popularized during the late 1800s, thousands of ox carts (*carretas*) once traversed a muddy road between the Central Valley and Puntarenas, hauling the nation's coffee bean harvest to port for export. Today, the ones produced for tourists bear little resemblance to the comparatively crude originals. The cart wheels came to be decorated with flowers and geometric designs, and each cart was designed to produce its individual sound, a result of a metal ring striking the wheel's hubnut; this was intended to allow the owner to keep track of his workers.

compulsion to paint controls the residents here to the point that even the bus stops and garbage cans are decorated! In addition to the real McCoy, souvenirs—including napkin holders, salad bowls, and jewelry — are also made for the tourist market. Visit the **Joaquín Chaverri** factory and sales outlet. Before leaving town, be sure to note the bi-towered, multi-windowed **church**.

SIGHTS: Ox carts are displayed in the **Ox Cart Museum**, an old adobe-style house in Salitral de Desamparados which is open 10-4. The **Butterfly Valley** (☎ 454-4050) offers tours daily from 8:30-4; US$6 entrance.

GETTING HERE: To get here take the hourly Grecia bus from Coca Cola and connect there with the *Alajuela-Sarchí* bus. In terms of time, this is better than going to Alajuela and then changing. By car, take the Grecia exit and then turn L behind the church, circle it to the L, and then go three blocks to the R where a road branches off diagonally for Sarchí. If heading for Naranjo from Sarchí, follow old and scenic Carr. 1.

ACCOMMODATION: The one place to stay in town here is the **Villas Sarchí Albergue** (☎ 454-4644, fax 454-4006; Apdo 34, Sarchí Norte) in Sarchí Norte which charges around US$40 d including breakfast. Rooms have cable TV and hot water, and are decorated with local handicrafts. The *albergue* has a pool and offers tours of the area as well as Spanish language classes.

Cabañas San Miguel Rancho Mirador (☎ 451-1302, fax 451-1301) is in San Miguel de Naranjo. Set on a hilltop, it has a pool, and each room has a balcony with a view.

Los Trapiches

If you would like to see how *tapa dulce* (hardened brown sugar) is made, this is the place. The antique cane press (of Scottish vintage) is waterwheel-driven, and the runoff cane juice is collected and heated before being poured into molds. There's also a restaurant (☎ 444-6656), pools, and a small lake with rental boats. It's popular on weekends with Ticos and closed on Wed. Call 44-6656 to make sure the press is operating before you go. From Grecia, you should drive three blocks past the church, turn L onto Carr. 13, and then follow the signs. Admission is less than US$1.

Los Chorros

A rough but short trail leads from the road to these falls which are popular on weekends. From Tacáres, to the W of Alajuela, turn R at the church and head L for two km until the road ends. Ignore the sign prohibiting entrance and follow the path downhill. When you reach the quarry, turn L and then follow the path to the L.

Ojo de Agua

Meaning literally "Eye of Water," 200 liters of water per second (6,000 gallons per minute) gush out here, filling three big swimming pools. Bordering are tennis courts and a lake with rowboats. New additions, including a mini-gymnasium, five new picnic shelters, and multi-purpose playing courts, were inaugurated in 1993, and an ampitheater and natural garden of waterfalls is planned. You'll have plenty of chances to meet locals here on weekends. Entrance is around US$1.

A few km S of Alajuela and to the SE of the airport, Ojo de Agua can be reached by bus from Alajuela, Heredia, or from near Coca Cola at Av. 1, C. 20/22 in San José. Buses run about every half-hour on weekdays and every 15 min. on weekends.

Butterfly Farm

One of the more recent attractions on San José's outskirts, this farm — second largest of its kind in the world — exports butterflies to Europe. You will witness all stages of the butterfly lifecycle — from egglaying to chrysalis formation. A highlight of the tour is a ride in a specially-designed nine-passenger ox cart pulled by oxen "Precious" and "Darling."

Entry includes a 2-hr. guided tour; admission is US$14 for adults and US$7 for children (US$20 and US$14 respectively with transit included); locals and residents pay considerably less. A restaurant serves Tico and US-style fare.

GETTING HERE: Set SW of the airport in La Guácima; you have to take a bus at 11 from Av. 1, C. 20/22 (marked as "San Antonio/Ojo de Agua") and get off at the terminal. From that point follow signs to the farm which is about 1,000 ft. (300 m) away. The trip takes one hr. and the return bus leaves at 3:15. The direct bus makes three trips daily from the major hotels. For info about buses from Alajuela or Santa Ana, phone 438-0400 or pick up a brochure.

www.butterflyfarm.co.cr
tbf@butterflyfarm.co.cr

Rancho San Miguel

Rancho San Miguel (☎ 220-4060, 232-2048, fax 221-2231, 220-2828) offers a horse fancier's dream performance each weekend. Performances include quadrilles, long reins, and other traditions you are unlikely to see elsewhere. The owner is a horse lover, and it shows! If you love horses, this is a must.The finale features traditional folkloric dances. A buffet lunch or dinner is included. Rates are US$85 pp; transport is US$6 extra.

horsepre@sol.racsa.co.cr

La Garita and Environs

This area is becoming increasingly popular as its attractions continue to grow. For La Garita, proceed to Alajuela and then take the La Garita bus. If you're driving, get off at the Atenas turnoff on the Cañas hwy. Accommodation in this area is listed under the "San José Accommodation" section.

Bosque Encantado (Enchanted Forest, ☎ 487-7050) — a lake surrounded by a castle and storybook characters — is just 20 min. from San José. The nation's closest approximation of Disneyland! As the playground and other facilities deteriorated, it's now visited chiefly for its pool which is generally crowded. It is set 1.5 km to the L of the Fiesta de Maíz (see below).

About 3.5 km to the R after the Atenas turnoff (follow the billboards), **Zoo Ave** (☎ 433-8989, fax 433-9140) an exotic bird collection (60-odd species) which has deer, monkeys and other wildlife on hand. It is attempting to breed and reintroduce a variety of native species (such as the endangered macaw and the great currasow) to the wild. The zoo is not for profit and the money is put back into wildlife protection. However, it has yet to release any animals back into the wild. It is the project of Dennis and Susan Janik, a Canadian couple. (Open daily 9-4:30; US$7 admission; US$2.50 for nationals; US$1 for children). **zooave@sol.racsa.co.cr**

FOOD: The La Garita area has a number of dining alternatives. Highly commercial **Las Delicias de Maíz** offers the entire range of native maize dishes — from corn stew to cheese *tortillas*. Free samples are offered. It's open Fri. to Sun. and is about 2.5 km on the L after the Atenas turnoff.

Also in the area is **La Llorita/The Green Parrot** (☎ 487-7846) — an attractively decorated restaurant which offering wood-roasted meat dishes (sorry, no parrots!) as well as salads, sandwiches, and fruit drinks. Take the hourly Atenas bus from Coca Cola to get here. **Chatelle Country Resort** (☎ 487-7781) offers dishes from a different nation daily.

Finally, the **Mi Quinta** is a restaurant which also has two pools, dance floor, basketball and volleyball courts, and TVs. A modest admission is charged.

Commercio Alternativo (☎ 232-2643) is a **natural foods outlet** which operates in the San José suburb of San Pedro. It is at the Restaurante Vegetariano, 50 m S of the Catholic Church and near the entrance to the University of Costa Rica. It sells more than 60 products. It is open on Sat. from 9-1, but some goods are for sale at other times.

Destinations by Bus A to Z

*Departure is from San José unless otherwise noted in parenthesis. Although generally consistent, **times and departure points are subject to change**. If there are only a few departures per day, you don't want to miss one!*

Destination Name/phone	location	times (after hours)	duration
Airport			
TUASA ☎ 222-5325	Av. 2, C. 12/14	Every 10 min. (4:20 AM-10 PM)	
☎ 222-4650		Every 10 min. 10 PM-midnight	
	Av. 2, C. 2	midnight-4:30 10 PM-midnight	
Alajuela			
TUASA ☎ 222-5325 Every 10 min.	Av. 2, C. 12/14		45min.
		(4:20 AM-10 PM) (5 AM-11 PM) (5:30 AM-10 PM)	35 min.
☎ 222-4650		Av. 2, C. 12/14 Every 5 min.	
Arenal			
Garage Barquero ☎ 232-5660 ☎ 222-4650	C. 16, Av. 1/3 Av. 2, C. 2 Av. 2, C. 12/14	8:40 AM and 11:30 AM midnight-4:30 Every 5 min.	
Brasilito			
Tralapa ☎ 221-7202	C. 20, Av. 1/3	Daily: 8, 10, 3:30	4 hrs.
Braulio Carrillo			
Coopetragua ☎ 223-1276	Term. Atlántico N, *C. 14, Av. 9*	Daily: every 30 min., 5:30 AM-7 PM	
Butterfly Farm			
	C. 20/22, Av. (11, 2) (Guácima Abaja sta. in Alajuela)	Tues.-Fri. (6:20, 9 11, 1)	1 hr.
Cahuita			
Trans. Mepe ☎257-81296	Term. Atlántico, *C. 14, Av. 9*	Daily Express: 6: 30 AM, 3:30 PM Regular: 10 1:30, 4	4 hrs.
Trans. Mepe ☎ 257-8129	C. Central/1, Av. 11 (Limon)	Daily 10, 4 5, 8, 10, 1, 4, 6	
Cañas			
Transportes la Cañera ☎ 222-3006, 669-0145	C. 16, Av. 3/5	Daily: 8:30, 10:30, 1:20, 2:30	3 hrs.
Carara			
Transportes Morales ☎ 223-1109, 641-3135	C. 16, Av. Av. 1/3	Daily:7:30, 10:30, 3:30	

Destination Name/phone	location	times (after hours)	duration
Cartago			
Sacsa ☎ 233-5350	C. 5, Av. 18	Daily: every 10-15 min. (4:45-12 midnight)	30-60 min.
Ciudad Quesada (San Carlos)			
Auto Trans. Ciu. Quesada ☎ 255-4318	C. 16, Av. 1/3	hourly (via Zarcero) 5AM-7:30 PM	3 hrs.
Coco			
Pulmitan ☎ 222-1650, 666-0458	C. 14, Av. 1/3	Daily: 8 AM, 2 PM	5 hrs.
Dominical (from Quepos)			
Transportes Blanco ☎ 771-2550	Merc. Mun.de Quepos	Daily: 5:30-1 PM	1.5 hr.
Dominical (from San Isidro)			
Transportes Blanco ☎ 771-2550	125 m E of Catholic Church	Daily: 8-4	
Dominical (via Quepos)			
Transportes Delio Morales ☎ 223-5567, 777-	C. 16, Av. 1/3 (Coca Cola) 0101	Mon. to Fri.: 3 PM	
Flamingo			
Tralapa ☎ 221-7202	C. 20, Av. 1/3	Daily: 8, 10, 3:30	4 hrs.
Fortuna			
Garage Barquero ☎ 232-5660	Term. Atl. *C. 14, Av. 9*	6:40, 8:40, 11:30 AM	4.5 hrs.
Golfito			
Tracopa-Alfaro ☎ 221-4214, 223-7685, 222-2666, 222-2051	Av. 18, C. 2/4	Daily, regular: 7; Express: 3	
Guápiles (via B. Car. Nat. Pk.)			
Empresarios Guapilenos ☎ 222-0610. (to Limón) .	Term. Atl. *C. 14, Av. 9*	Half-hr: 5 AM-11 PM	5 hrs
Coopetragua ☎ 223-1276	C. 12, Av. 7/9	Half-hr. , 5:30 AM-7 PM	
Guayabo (Turrialba)			
Hrm. Rivera ☎ 556-0583	100 m S of bus station	Sat. 11, Sun., 9:30 AM	1 hr.
Heredia			
Microbuses Rapidos ☎ 233-8392	C. 1, Av. 7/9 Av. 2, C. 10/12	Daily: 5 min. 5:25 AM -12 PM, then hourly minibuses every 15 min. midnight – 6: every30 min.	30 min.
Hermosa (beach) (via Liberia)			
Esquivel ☎ 666-1249		Daily: 7:30, 11:30, 3 ,3:30, 5:30, 7 PM	

Destination Name/phone	location	times (after hours)	duration
Hermosa (beach)			
Esquivel ☎ 666-1249	C. 12., Av. 5/7) (front of Los Rodriguez	Daily: 3:20 PM	5 hrs.
Irazú Volcano			
☎ 272-0651	Sat., Sun., hol.,8 AM	C. 1/3, Av. 2 (front of Gran H. Costa Rica)	2 hrs.
Jacó Beach			
Transportes Morales ☎223-1109, 641-3135	C. 16, Av. Av. 1/3	Daily: 7:30, 10:30, 3:30	3 hrs.
Junquillal			
Tralapa ☎ 221-7202, 680-0392	C. 20, Av. 3/5	Daily: 2 PM	5 hrs.
La Cruz			
Carsol ☎ 224-1968	C. 14, Av. 3/5	Daily: 5, 7:45, 1:20, 4:10 Express: 4:30, 7 AM	6 hrs. (4.5 hrs.)
Laguna de Fraijanes			
3 bl. W of Cent. Mkt Coopetransasi % 449-5141 .	Tues.-Fri. (9, noon,	4:15, 6:15,7:30) Sat., Sun. (hourly, 9-5)	50 min.
Lankester Gardens			
Coopepar ☎ 574-6127	(Cartago) Paraiso bus S side of "ruins" park	Daily 5AM-10:30 PM	
Liberia			
Pulmitan ☎ 222-1650, 666-0458	C. 14, Av. 1/3	Daily, hourly: 6 AM-8 PM; Express: 3, 5	
Limón			
Coopelimon ☎ 223-7811	Terminal Atlántico Norte C. 14, Av. 9	Hourly, daily: 5 AM-7 PM	
Los Chiles (Caño Negro)			
Autotransportes ☎ 460-5032	C. 12, Av. 9	Daily: 5:30 AM, 3:30 PM	2 hrs.
Manuel Antonio			
Transportes Delio Morales ☎ 223-5567, 777-0101	C. 16, Av. 1/3 (Coca Cola)	Express: 6, noon, 6. Regular: 10, 2, 3, 4, 5	4.5 hrs
Matapalo			
Tralapa ☎ 221-7202	C. 20, Av. 1/3	Daily: 7:30, 10:30, 2, 4, 6	
Monteverde			
Transportes Tilarán ☎ 222-3854	Terminal Atlántico Norte *C. 14, Av. 9*	Daily exp.: 6:30 AM, 2, 2:30 PM	4 hrs.
Nicoya			
Empresa Alfaro ☎ 222-2666	Av. 3/5, C. 14	Daily (via ferry): 6, 8 AM, 2 PM Daily (via Liberia) 6:30, 10, 1:30, 3, 5	5 hrs.

Destination Name/phone	location	times (after hours)	duration
Nosara			
Empresa Alfaro ☎ 222-2666	C. 14, Av. 3/5	Daily: 6 AM	6 hrs.
Orosi Valley *(Cartago)*			
Auto Transportes MataSW ☎ 551-6810	corner of ruins park	Mon.-Fri.: 30 min. Sat., Sun.: 45 min.	30 min.
Palmar Norte			
Tracopa-Alfaro ☎ 221-4214, 223-7685, 222-2666, 222-2051	C. 2/4, Av. 18	Daily: 5, 7, 8:30, 10, 1, 2:30, 6	
Panama *(beach) (Liberia)*			
Esquivel ☎ 666-1249		Daily: 7:30, 11:30, 33:30, 5:30, 7 PM	
Panama *(beach)*			
Esquivel ☎ 666-1249	C. 12., Av. 5/7 (front of Los Rodriguez	Daily: 3:20 PM	5 hrs.
Panama *(beach)*			
Esquivel ☎ 666-1249	C. 12., Av. 5/7 (fr. Los Rodriguez	Daily: 3:20- PM	5 hrs.
Paso Canoas			
Tracopa ☎ 221-4214, 223-7685	Av. 3/5 C. 14	Daily: 5, 7:30, 11, 1, 1, 4:30, 6	8 hrs.
Peñas Blancas			
C. 14, Av. 3/5 Carsol ☎ 224-1968	Daily: 5, 7:45, 1:20, 4:10	Express: 4:30, 7 AM	6 hrs. (4.5 hrs.)
Portrero			
Tralapa ☎ 221-7202	C. 20, Av. 1/3	Daily: 8, 10, 3:30	4 hrs.
Puerto Jimenéz			
Transportes Blanco ☎ 771-2550	C. 12, Av. 7/9	Daily: 6, noon	
Puerto Viejo (Sarapiquí)			
Autotransportes ☎ 259-8571, 255-4318	Av. 9, C. 12	Daily *via Zurquí Tun.:* 11:30 AM, 1:30, 3:30, 4:30, PM *Via Vara Blanca*: 8, noon, 3, 8, 10,	4 hrs.
Puerto Viejo (Talamanca)			
Transportes Mepe (Limón) ☎ 257-8129		Daily 10, 4 5, 8, 10, 1, 4, 6	
Puntarenas			
Trans. Puntarenas ☎ 221-5749, 223-2612	C. 16, Av. 10/12	Daily: every 30 min., 6 AM-9 PM	2 hrs.

Destination Name/phone	*location*	*times (after hours)*	*duration*
Quepos			
Transportes Delio Mor. ☎ 223-5567, 777-0101	C. 16, Av. 1/3 (Coca Cola)	Express: 6, noon, 6. Regular: 10, 2, 3, 4, 5	4.5 hrs.
Sámara			
Empresa Alfaro ☎ 222-2666	C. 14, Av. 3/5	Daily: 12:30 PM	4 hrs.
San Ignacio de Acosta			
	C. 8, Av. 12	Ev. 1.5 hrs. dly.	1 hr. 15 m.
San Isidro (from Quepos			
Transportes Blanco ☎ 771-2550	Mercado Municipal de Quepos	Daily: 5:30-1 PM	2 hrs.
San Isidro de El General			
Musoc ☎ 222-2422	C. 16, Av. 1/3	Daily, hourly: 5:30 AM-5 PM	
San Ramón			
Empresarios Unidos ☎ 221-5749, 233-2610		Daily: every 30 min 6 AM-10:30 PM	1 hr.
San Vito			
Tracopa ☎ 222-2750	C. 14, Av. 3/5 11:30, 2:45	Daily: 5:45,8:15	
Santa Cruz			
Tralapa ☎ 221-7202	C. 20, Av. 1/3	Daily: 7-1, 2, 4, 6	5 hrs.
Santa Elena (Monteverde)			
Transportes Tilarán ☎ 222-3854	Terminal Atl. N *C. 14, Av. 9*	Daily exp.: 6:30 AM 2, 2:30 PM	4 hrs.
Santa María de Dota (Los Santos)			
Empresa Los Santos ☎ 223-1002	Av. 16, C. 19-2	Daily: 6, 7:15, 11:30, 12:30, 3, 5, 7:30	2 hrs.
Santa Rosa (entrance)			
Carsol ☎ 224-1968	C. 14, Av. 3/5	Daily: 5, 7:45, 1:20, 4:10 Express: 4:30, 7 AM	
Sarchí			
Tuan ☎ 441-3781 (Alajuela)	C. 16, Av. 1/3 C. 8, Av. Central/1 Daily	12:15, 5:30 (daily express) Every 25 min. 1 hr. 15 min.	
Siquirres			
Coopelimon ☎ 223-7811	Term. Atl. N, *C. 14, Av. 9*	Daily, hourly (to Limón): 6:30, 8:30-6:30	
Tamarindo			
Alfaro ☎ 222-2750, 223-8229	C. 14, Av. 3/5	Daily: 3:30	6.5 hrs.

Destination Name/phone	location	times (after hours)	duration
Turrialba			
Transtusa ☎ 556-0073	C. 13, Av. 6/8	Daily, hourly 5:30 AM-10 PM	1.5 hrs.
Uvita (from San Isidro)			
Transportes Blanco ☎ 771-2550	125 m E of Catholic Church	Daily: 8-4	
Uvita (via Quepos)			
Transportes Delio Morales ☎ 223-5567, 777-0101	C. 16, Av. 1/3 (Coca Cola)	Mon. to Fri: 3 PM	

The Meseta Central

The Meseta Central — the nation's principal area — is to Costa Rica what the Japan's Tokai (Tokyo, Yokohama, Kawasaki) region is to the Japanese or the Boston-Washington corridor is to the Eastern US. Although densely populated and containing the nation's capital, every other dimension — size, industrialization, and degree of pollution — is on a considerably smaller scale.

This 20-by-50-mile (32-by-80-km) "plateau" — really more a series of valleys intersected by rolling hills — still retains its agricultural base. Much of the land has been shaped by the innumerable volcanic eruptions which, over the eons, have also given the soil its fertility. In addition to San José, it also includes the towns of Heredia, Alajuela, Cartago, and Turrialba, as well as many smaller villages.

Although it is sometimes referred to as the "Switzerland of Central America," the area is Swiss only in its orderliness. There is nothing Swiss about either its poverty or its climate. Verdant and shimmering fields of sugarcane grow in the E. Elsewhere the ever-present coffee colors the landscape in shades that vary from shiny green to red according to the season. Acres of plastic-covered houseplants and flowers are another feature on the landscape; these are for export. Factories are interspersed with pastures and coffee-plant-covered hills. You'll see the occasional sugar processing plant, macadamia plantations, a man hacking sugar cane, and teams of men and women picking coffee. However, not all is pastoral paradise. During the rainy season dark grey clouds loom menacingly over hills, and deforestation is always appallingly evident, with treeless plots edging up to the tops of hills.

note: For organizational convenience, areas on the periphery (but not geographically part of) the Meseta Central are also included in this section.

EXPLORING: As local wags have it, outside of San José there is a nation called Costa Rica. And the Meseta Central region is one of the best places to begin seeing it. Here are three charming provincial capitals (Alajuela, Cartago, and Heredia), dramatic volcanos, winding roads and rivers, hot springs, old churches, and much more. If you have only time to do a few things you'll have to choose carefully. Buses are generally plentiful, and the area is perfect for day or overnight trips. The more adventurous you are here, the more substantive your experience will be, and the more memories you'll have to take back home with you.

Alajuela

This pleasant town (pop. 35,000) is located near the airport, just 17 mi.(23 km, a 20-min. ride) W of the capital. Founded in 1790, Alajuela is a center for sugar processing, cattle marketing, and small industry. As in other towns, every part is accessible on foot.

GETTING HERE: Take a microbus from San José's Av. 2, C. 12/14; they leave every 15 min. until midnight and then hourly on the hour. To get here by car, take "la pista" (the Cañas highway) and get off at the turnoff near the airport.

HISTORY: Originally named La Lajuela in 1657, the town's name was changed to

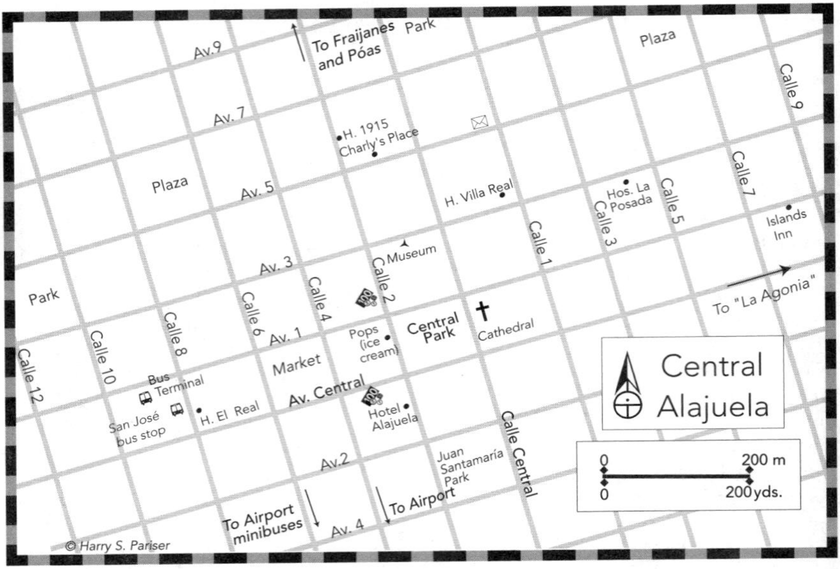

Villa Hermosa, then to San Juan de Nepomucena, before becoming Alajuela (pronounced ah-lah-HWEL-lah) in 1825. Today, it is the capital of the province of the same name.

SIGHTS: A number of three-toed sloths reside in the charming bandstand-equipped **plaza** or, more accurately, in its trees. The park's nickname is *"El Parque de los Palomas Muertas"* (The Park of the Dead Doves) and it resembles a cross between a garden and a forest. *Palomas* also refers to the male sexual organ in Panamanian slang, and some contend the name derives from the physical capacities (or lack thereof) of the park's occupants: retirees who come to stare at lovely young things as they pass by. (Perhaps it may yet be re-christened Parque Viagra).

The number of solidly constructed buildings on its borders date from the era when coffee dominated the local economy. The teacher's training college which shares the building with the **Museo de Juan Santamaría** (open Tues.-Sun. 10-6; free admission) which deals with the war against William Walker. A remodeled colonial-style *carcel* (jail) dating from 1874, the museum is more of interest for its ambiance than its content, and it's a pleasant place to sit.

With a dome-shaped roof covered with bright red corrugated metal, the white-columned **cathedral** stands in front of the park. With an interior more ornate and spacious than those in other towns, it has large religious statuary — including a very realistic Jesus nailed to the cross and bleeding which is to the L of the altar sitting in the center of the cupola. There's also an image of the Black Virgin along with a small, wall-mounted cabinet filled with arms, legs, and other body parts in the event you missed the displays in the cathedral in

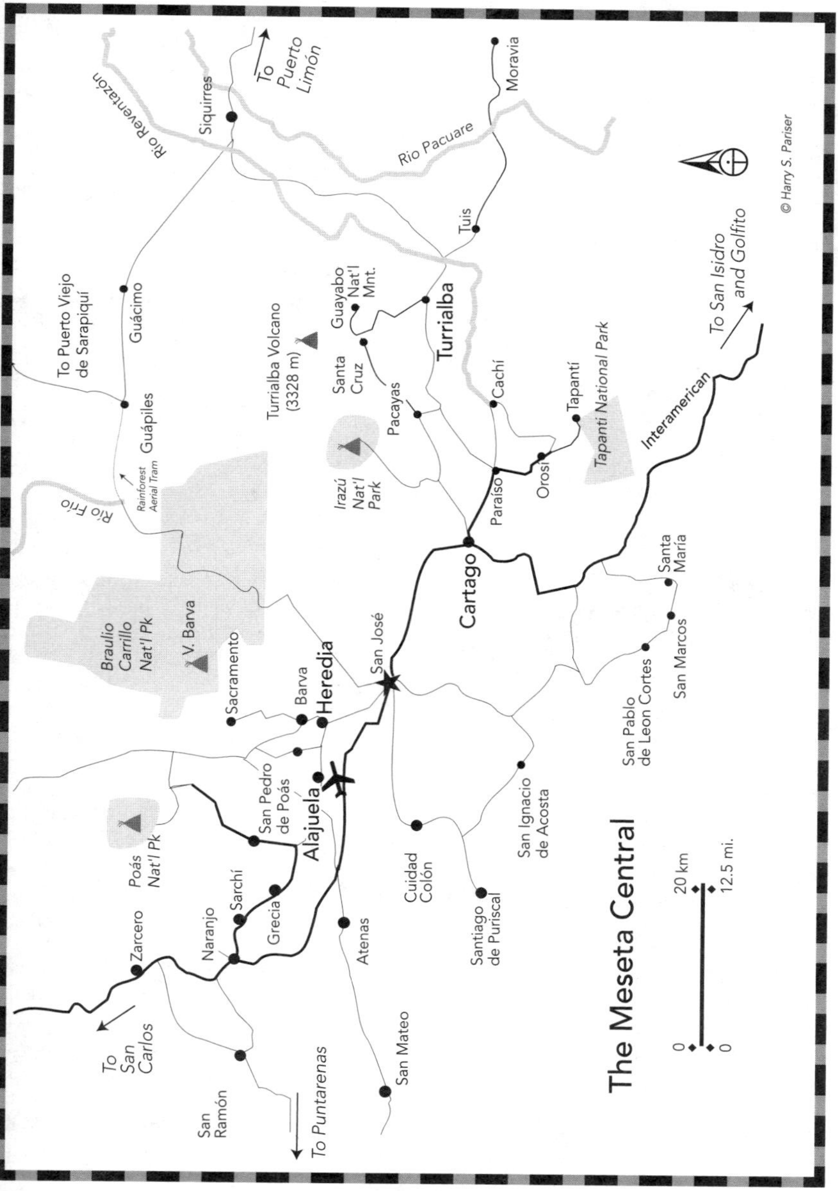

The Meseta Central
To Puerto Limón
Moravia
Siquirres
Rio Reventazón
Rio Pacuare
Tuis
Turrialba
Guayabo Nat'l Mnt.
Santa Cruz
Pacayas
Turrialba Volcano (3328 m)
To Puerto Viejo de Sarapiquí
Guácimo
Guápiles
Rainforest Aerial Tram
Rio Frio
Irazú Nat'l Park
Cachí
Tapantí
Tapantí National Park
Paraíso
Orosi
To San Isidro and Golfito
Interamerican
Cartago
Santa María
San Marcos
San Pablo de Leon Cortes
Braulio Carrillo Nat'l Pk
V. Barva
Sacramento
Barva
Heredia
San José
San Ignacio de Acosta
Alajuela
San Pedro de Poás
Poás Nat'l Pk
Sarchí
Grecia
Zarcero
Naranjo
Atenas
Cuidad Colón
Santiago de Puriscal
To San Carlos
San Ramón
To Puntarenas
San Mateo
20 km
12.5 mi.
0
0
© Harry S. Pariser

Statue of Juan Santamaría, Alajuela

Cartago. Although it doesn't show it now, its cupola, which has its balconies and curtains painted on, cracked in half during the March 1990 quake. Some of the town's other buildings suffered fissures.

To get to **Iglesia La Agonia**, walk along the edge of the square, passing the circular red corrugated roof cupola of the church which contrasts sharply with the ultra-modern reflective glass bank directly across the street. Continue down until you see the immense structure on the R. If it's closed ask at the shop to get in.

There's a Renaissance-like portrait of Our Mother of Perpetual Sorrow, a brown Christ suspended above the altar, and a number of large murals. One statue depicts a priest holding a cross with a miniature Jesus on it with a skull and flowers resting at his feet.

The town's other park, a block to the N at C. 2, Av. 3, is named after Juan Santamaría, and his statue is across the way.

FESTIVALS AND EVENTS: Held in Alajeula in April, the **Día de Juan Santamaría** commemorates Juan Santamaría, Costa Rica's only national hero and the town's pride and joy, with a parade complete with marching bands and majorettes.

The highlight of Alajuela's year, July's **Mango Festival**, offers nine days of parades, music, outdoor food markets, and arts and crafts fairs.

ACCOMMODATIONS: From a town with only one respectable hotel just a few years ago, Alajuela has attracted a hotel boom. Near the plaza, inexpensively-priced **Hotel Alajuela** (☎ 441-1241, fax 441-7912) is very popular; they also have a few furnished apartments. The rooms in the old portion of the building are the least expensive.

Positioned in the town center, just a few blocks from the Parque Central, **Hotel 1915** (☎/fax 441-0495) has rooms with cable TV and your choice of a/c or fan.This cosy hotel is furnished with antiques.

The eight-room **Islands Inn** (☎ 442-0573) is set five blocks E of the main square. Rates are around US$25 s, US$40 d, and breakfast is included. The owner, David Quesada, is a young US-educated Tico who enjoys collecting frogs and raising orchids.

An inexpensive bed and breakfast with weekly and monthly rates, **Hospedaje La Posada** (☎ 442-9738) is set 100 m N and

75 m E from the Red Cross (Cruz Roja), which is three blocks E from the park. Rates are around US$8 pp.

Hotel Villa Real (☎ 441-4856; call after 4 PM) is an old home which has inexpensive rooms; it's 100 m N and 100 m E of the Parque Central.

Miraflores Apartments (☎/fax 442-6527) are 150 m E, 50 S, and 50 E from McDonalds.

Set 700 m N of Parque Central on the way to Tuetal, **Paraíso Tropical Hotel** (☎/fax 441-4882) offers rooms (around US$40 d) and apartments (around US$65) in a garden setting.

Less expensive but low-class hotels include **El Real** (C. 8, Av. 1/Central), **Moderno** (down the street across the RR tracks), and **El Tucano** (☎ 487-7192) at Turrucales.

OUTLYING ACCOMMODATIONS: If you are looking for a peaceful haven to base yourself at while in the San José area, there are a number of excellent choices right near Alajuala and the airport.

Situated on eight acres of land set three km N of Alajuela, Canadian-run **Tuetal Lodge** (☎ 442-1804; Apdo. 1346-4050, Alajuela) is in Tuetal Norte two km from Alajuela and has cabins, treehouses, pool, and camping. Water is solar heated and organic fruits and vegetables are grown in the garden. Camping costs around US$5 s, US$7 d; treehouses rent for around US$9 s, US$12 d, and cabins start from around US$30 s, US$35 d; more expensive ones have kitchenettes. Tents are also available for rent.

tuetal@sol.racsa.co.cr
www.islandnet.com/~tuetal

Outside of town and enroute to the town of Poás, attractive **Orquideas Inn** (☎ 433-9346, fax 433-9740; Apdo. 394, Alajuela), set in a converted *hacienda* house, offers expensive rooms (around US$70 d) which include breakfast. Geodesic dome bungalows are planned, and there is a good gift shop. It also has a pool and offers excursions. Call (800) 525-0280 in the US or (800) 231-0856 internationally.

www.hotels.co.cr/orquideas.html
orchid@sol.racsa.co.cr

Located just two km from the airport, **Hilda's Bed & Breakfast** (☎ 433-0614, fax 443-2018) is a homey Tica-run place which offers airport transportation, breakfast, and rooms with fans and hot water for US$25 s, US$40 d; US$500 monthly.

hilda@arweb.com

Set in the Plias de San Isidro area, the luxury priced **Hotel Buena Vista** (☎/fax 442-8701, 442-8595, 442-8701; 800-506-2304) is set amidst a coffee plantation. Carpeted rooms have cable TV sets and balconies. It has a gourmet restaurant, pool and offers tremendous views. Rates are from around US$ 65 s, US$70 d plus taxes. It is owned and managed by a hospitable "retired" American couple and is a great place to stay if you want to be in the vicinity of the airport but don't want to stay at a chain hotel.

bvista@sol.racsa.co.cr

Set two km from the airport and five blocks from the bus station, expensive **Apartotel El Erizo** (☎/fax 441-2840; Apdo. 61-4050) offers cable TV, one- or two-bedroom apartments, and babysitters. Good for families and groups.

apterizo@sol.racsa.co.cr

El Colibrí (☎/fax 441-4228) is a set of houses near the Zeta free trade zone which is W of the airport. Facilities include pool, and tennis and basketball courts. Rates are around US$50 d with breakfast and US$1,000 pm for a house which holds up to eight.

Set a few km from Alajuela town, the **Xandari Plantation** (☎ 443-2020, fax 442-4847;) is a highly luxurious and attractive place to stay. It offers 16 private villas with terraces, library, mini-fitness center, horseback riding, massages, and fabulous sunset views. Many of the rooms feature stained glass windows, and the villas' designs (by owner-architect Sherrill Broudy) are unforgettable. Artwork is by Broudy's wife Charlene.

Vegetarian meals are served in the dining room. Breakfast is included and may be served on your patio; two-way airport transport is provided as well. Well maintained trails lead to cascades and several waterfalls and pass by bamboo groves. The coffee plantation is on the way towards being organic.

Rates are around US$130 prima and US$170 ultra. Children In the US call 800-686-7879 or 805-684-7879 or fax 805-684-4295). Ask about their "Honeymoon Escape."

www.xandari.com
paradise@xandari.com

Set seven km from the airport, seven-rm. **Villa Dolce Hotel & Villas** (☎/fax 433-8932) is in the village of Coyol near Alajuela. It has an Italian restaurant, pool, garden, and offers a full range of services. Rates run around US$40 s, US$50 d with breakfast.

Also don't overlook the relatively nearby Cariari and Herradura ultra-luxury hotels mentioned in the "San José Accomodations" section.

FOOD AND SHOPPING: One of the best restaurants is the **Cencerro**, upstairs on Av. Central across from the plaza.

Restaurant El Primer Sabor serves international and Chinese dishes in an attractive atmosphere. **La Jarra**, at C. 2 and Av. 2, upstairs and a block S from the square is less expensive and has salads, fish, and shrimp. With country music and rock, **Joey's** serves *norteamericano* and Tico dishes. It's on the S side of the park. **La Cocina de Leña** has traditional Tico dishes with a good selection of seafood.

You can also try **Bar Marisquería Evelyn**, to the R of the *museo* and down towards the square, and **La Troja**, across the street from the *museo* and down, which has a sophisticated art and jazz atmosphere; a good place to bring a hot date. Live music is also featured here frequently.

Right at the park, **Las Américas** (☎ 441-5691) is an "American Bar & Restaurant" which boasts no less than six TVs plus video projection and holds an annual Superbowl party.

Near the park, **Ilean's Cafe** has very reasonable prices and offers a US$2 lunch special.

Asami (☎ 442-7646) is an authentic Japanese restaurant which serves *sashimi*, *sushi*, and combination platters. It's 75 m N of Pops near the old church.

Plaza Garabaldi offers open-air Mexican dining with traditional dishes.

Specializing in seafood, **La Esquina de los Mariscos** is also open-air and has goodies such as octopus and paella. The specialty of **Marisqueria La Sirenita** is its seafood soup.

Open daily, the **Mercado Central** (central market) is a fascinating place to explore as well as to eat. There's also a giant outdoor market every Sat. AM. Although it's considered a farmer's market, it's actually run by the ubiquitous middlemen, the bane of Costa Rica's marketplace economy. Every type of vegetable and fruit imaginable is for sale.

Huge trucks at the rear unload and vend bananas, enormous Japanese-style pumpkins are sawed up, and young boys sell bundles of garlic with all of the enthusiasm of country preachers. Most of the produce is sold in one long row of stalls, each of which is topped with multicolored, beach ball-like umbrellas.

A block and a half W of the plaza on Av. Central, **ItalPan** is one of many bakeries. There's not much to buy in town (save for some remarkably tacky souvenirs), but if you're in the market for a casket, there's a great place just 100 ft. (30 m) L of the *museo*.

Just outside of town on the road to Grecia, **Rancho Las Tinajitas** is a good restaurant which has meat and seafood dishes at a reasonable price.

Located in Tambor on the way to Poás, the **Russian Tea Terrace** (☎/fax 433-9257) features dishes such as spicy eggplant, hot borschst, and Russian strudel.

EVENTS AND FESTIVALS: Soccer games are held most Sundays at the stadium. **La Guácima** (☎ 233-3166) has car and motorcycle races every weekend.

SERVICES: The **Welcome Center** (☎/fax 441-1141; Av. 2, C. 2/4) provides information; it is twinned with the Alajuela Travel Agency next door. It also contains **Central Valley Services**, which offers property management, financial services, and sells real estate. The ICT (☎ 233-1733) has a branch office at Av. 4, C. 1/3. **Farmacía Unica** is at the NW corner of the Mercado Central. A former country club, **Campestre del Sol** (☎ 442-0077) has swimming pools, gymnasium, dance hall; open Tues. through Sun., 8-4.

FROM ALAJUELA: Alajuela makes an excellent base for exploring the Meseta Central. A special bus leaves for Poás at 8 AM on Sun. from the S side of the church. Attractions at **La Garita** are described under "Vicinity of San José."

Paraue Nacional Volcán Poás (Poás Volcano)

Poás, the world's largest geyser-type crater, has been protected in a national park. Its name derives from the thorny bush which grows on its upper slopes. Along with Irazú, Poás is probably one of the world's most popular volcanoes.

Located 23 mi. (37 km) from Alajuela and 37 mi.(59 km) from San José, it last erupted in 1978, but its crater still boils and steams. As you progress toward its 8,871-ft. (2,704-m) summit, the weather becomes cloudier and cooler as coffee plantations give way to pastures filled with dairy cattle and terraced potato patches.

> When visiting Irazú or Póas volcanoes, be sure to get an early start! Clouds move in early, and it may be impossible to see anything after 10 AM. On the other hand, if you wait a while, the clouds may shift and portions of the crater may come into view.

GETTING HERE: A bus runs from the SE corner of Parque Braulio Carrillo (formerly known as Parque Merced) in San José at 8:30 on Sun. and holidays; be there by 7:30 to assure a seat. The ride, in an exquisitely funky "Bluebird" brand bus, takes 2.5 hrs. (including a 20-min. rest stop where you can breakfast briefly). The bus arrives at 11 and returns at 2:30. Another bus leaves at 9 AM from the SE corner of the plaza in Alajuela.

An alternative is to take an hourly bus

from Alajuela's Parque de Cemetario to San Pedro de Poás, and then take a taxi (about US$20 RT) from there, or go by bus to Poasita, 10 km (6 miles) from the crater. Along with some snacks or a box lunch, you should bring a sweater or jacket and rain gear all year round. If you're driving, take the expressway to Alajuela and then proceed via San Pedro de Poás and Poasito; another route is to go through Heredia, Barva, Los Cartagos, and Poasito. Admission is charged at the going rate for *gringos* (US$6); no more than 1,800 people are permitted in the park at any one time.

ORIENTATION: The first thing you find at the crater is the visitor's center which has a slide show in Spanish about the National Parks, **Cafetería Botos**, and the Neotropical Foundation's **Nature Store** which sells books and crafts.

A road leads up to the two lookout points over the volcano. If you've never seen an active volcano before, you're in for an amazing sight. The crater is approximately 2.4 mi. (1.5 km) wide and 1,000 ft. (300 m) deep; the lake on the bottom has somewhat muddy waters which change colors depending upon the degree of volcanic activity. If you're lucky, you might see a small eruption of sulphur dioxide and mud, and you might spot bubbling pools of molten sulphur if the water level is low enough.

From the road leading to the crater a short trail leads to Botos Lake, highlighted by a number of *sombrilla de pobre* (poor people's umbrella) plants and dwarf trees. Out of a total of five craters formed, Lake Botos was number three in the line; the present active crater was number five. Once believed to have a whirlpool which would suck unwary swimmers through a passage into the active crater, this lake is fed entirely by rainwater, and hosts algae, shrimp, and various species of frogs and toads. Its greenish color is due to the presence of sulfur in colloidal suspension. There is no access down to the lake, and there is only one other trail: the *Sendero Escalonia* runs from the picnic tables past wooden trail markers inscribed with poetic paeans to the environs.

HISTORY: Although the first European, Mata Guevara, reached the crater at an unknown date, its first mention in a written document was in 1783, and a priest named Arias, arriving in 1815 from Alajuela, baptized it with the name Juan de Dios. The other names, Poás and Votos or Botos, by which the crater has been known, are thought to be the names of indigenous tribes that lived in the area. Curiously, a tourist hotel was built a km from the crater in 1915; it closed in 1924, and no trace remains today. Eruptions have occurred 20 times since 1834 — notably in 1888, 1904, 1905, 1910 (when it shot a fountain of water four km into the air) and from 1952 to 1954.

After things settled down, a cone of ash and debris had formed at the site of the lake which had refilled with water by 1967 and hasn't changed much since. Comprising 13,138 acres (5,317 ha), the Parque Nacional Volcán Poás was established on Jan. 30, 1971.

Since 1989, the crater has again become increasingly active, and the sulfur gas and steam ejected have caused acid rain, resulting in the destruction of 75% of Grecia's 1989 coffee crop and causing skin and respiratory problems. Problems accelerated during 1994 when 400 tourists had to be evacuated one day, and many farmers in the area had from 80-

100% of their crops destroyed. In addition, some 173 head of cattle suffered from diarrhea and appeared to be intoxicated.

FESTIVALS AND EVENTS: Held March 15, the nationwide celebration of **Farmer's Day** is headquartered in Tierra Blanca (whose farmers celebrate deliverance from a plague of locusts in 1877). It is a day devoted to the farmer's patron saint, San Isidro, a humble 12th C. Spanish farmer. On **San José Day**, Mar. 19, local families traditionally visit Volcán Poás for a hike and picnic.

ACCOMMODATIONS: Closest to the crater at five km from the entrance, low-budget **Lo Que Tú Quieras** (☎ 448-5213) comprises *cabinas* and a restaurant.

Restaurant Las Fresas has two two-bedroom *cabinas* for rent for about US$40 pn.

Billed as a "bed and breakfast" and accomodating up to 15 people, expensive **Poás Volcano Lodge** (☎/fax 482-2194; Apdo.5723-1000, San José) was originally built by an English family, and incorporates elements of Welsh farmhouses, English cottages, and American architecture into its design. You'll find brick and stone walls as well as fireplaces. There are areas of protected forest within the farm. It's set next to the farm El Cortijo at Vara Blanca up in the hills at 6,000 ft. (1,900 m). Rates are around US$70 d.

The **Albergue Ecológico La Providencia** (cell. ☎ 380-6315, fax 290-0289) offers a a restaurant and accommodation. Its entrance is marked by a dirt two-km road leading off to the L of the green entrance gate to the park. Guests are offered a complimentary tour which features a three-hr. tour that terminates at a waterfall; day visitors can go on this for US$25. Rates are around US$65 d.

The haunting expanse of Volcán Poás's caldera

Set 2.5 km before the entrance, **Lagunillas Lodge** (☎ 448-5506) is a converted dairy farm which affords an excellent opportunity to enter the lives of a local family. Rates are around US$30 d. Costa Rican meals are prepared, and horseback trips and guided hiking (and birding) through the forested property are available. The steep one-km access road is suitable for a regular car.

Other accommodation is listed under "Alajuela."

FOOD: It's best to bring your own as there's usually little or nothing for sale at the crater. About 10 mi.(16 km) above Alajuela, **Chubascos** has tables set amidst an outdoor garden. Specialties include large casados, strawberry and blackberry shakes, and cheesecake.

Other eateries in the Poás vicinity include Italian **Las Fresas** (☎ 448-5567; call ahead for pizza baked in a wood-fired oven) which has an Italian chef, but a German owner; the bamboo-designed **Churrascos Steak House** (in Poasito); **Los Jualares** (3 km from Fraijanes which frequently has live music on Fri. and Sat. nights); **El Recreo**, and **Restaurant Volcán Poás**.

Restaurant Vara Blanca is at, you guessed it, Vara Blanca which is at the intersection of the eastern road leading to Póas and the Heredia Sarapiquí road; it's also near Poás Vocano Lodge.

Another restaurant, mentioned under "accommodations," is **Lo Que Tú Quieras**, which offers great views and traditional so-so food.

VICINITY OF POÁS: Open 9-3:30, Tues. to Sun., the **Fraijanes Lake Recreation Park**, about a half-hour down the road from the summit, has paths through cypress and pine groves, a lagoon, an exercise course, basketball courts, a soccer field, trails, and horses for rent (around US$1.50/hr.). Admission is inexpensive.

Famous **Cascada de La Paz** (Peace Falls) are five km past Vara Blanca just after Poás turnoff. A charming wooden bridge runs right by it, and a caged Jesus is to one side.

Featuring "Jurassic rain/cloud forest" and three other falls, the **La Paz Waterfall Gardens** (☎ 221-1378, fax 257-2772) is nearby. It has a restaurant, and butterfly, orchid and hummingbird gardens. Admission is US$15 pp.
wgardens@sol.racsa.co.cr

The "La Angel" food processing plant, which makes jelly, is farther on.

Farther still and well off in the distance to the R is the **Caida del Angel**, a magnificent waterfall; a path leads down to it. Another few km to the R is the entrance to **Colonia Virgen del Socorro**, reached by a rough dirt road which runs for several km further. The surrounding area is a fine birding spot. The toll booth collects a voluntary toll which is used for the protection of this beautiful area. The contributions also function as a lottery; there's a monthly drawing.

Heredia

Another in the line of provincial capitals, Heredia sits at the foot of extinct Volcán Barva, seven mi. (11 km) from San José. It is the nation's fourth largest city. This university town and coffee growing center of 65,000 is one of the most peaceful and relaxing towns in the nation. Founded in 1706 as La Villa de la Immaculada Concepción de Cubujuqui de Heredia, its nickname is "La Ciudad de las Flores," Heredia

GETTING HERE: Take one of the frequent red-and-yellow buses operated by

Buestas Heredianas from Av. 2, C. 10/12 (via La Uruca), take Microbuses Rápidos Heredianos from C. 1, Av. 7/9 (via Tibás and Santo Domingo), or from the terminal in Alajuela.

SIGHTS: Dating from 1797, the squat, solid, and imposing **Cathedral of the Immaculate Conception** appears to ruminate about days of yore from its spot on the plaza; its low contours were designed to resist earthquake damage. The bells in this old church were brought from Cuzco, Peru in the colonial era. Inside there are numerous large statues, inluding one to the L of the altar which has the Virgin Mary standing on a white neon crescent moon and surrounded by white neon stars of David. There's also a full length statue of Jesus who's brown-skinned, dreadlocked, clothed in a velvet gown, and penned-in (presumably) for protection. Supplicants gather in the morning to pray.

In addition to several other old colonial-style buildings, **El Fortín**, a Spanish-style fort tower that has become the town's emblem, borders the central plaza to its L. The province's governor, a former military man, ordered its construction in 1876, but it has never had to face invading forces. Permission to climb the tower may be obtained at the municipal office below.

On the N side of the park is the **Casa de la Cultura** (☎ 260-2588) which has art exhibits. It is housed in the home of former President Alfredo González (1914-1917) who resided here until his death in 1962

ACCOMMODATION: **Hotel América** (☎ 290-9292, fax 260-9293) is a modern hotel which has TVs, and a 24-hr. restaurant/bar. It is at Av. Central, C. 2/4.

The 8-unit **Apartotel Vargas** (☎ 237-8526, fax 238-4698) is 750 m N of the Colegio Santa Cecilia. It charges around US$35 d.

The **Apartotel Roma** (☎ 260-0127, 238-3705, fax 260-6339) is set in a residencial area, the Jardines de Flores which is near the university. It offers furnished two-bedroom suites with kitchen, Cable TV, phone, living/dining room, tour service, business services (including fax and e-mail), secure parking, and a restaurant. Inexpensive rates are negotiable for longer stays; units hold up to five. **www.arweb.com/roma** **romasuit@sol.racsa.co.cr**

Hotel Valladolid (☎ 260-2905, fax 260-2912; Apdo. 93, 3000 Heredia) is at C. 7/Av. 7. It has a sun deck with a Jacuzzi on its roof, a restaurant, and a travel agency. Rates are around US$60 d plus tax, and rooms include amenities such as hair dryer, cable TV, and phone. They offer packages in cooperation with other lodges such as Rara Avis.

Camping is permitted at **Bosque de la Hoja**, three mi.(five km) from San Rafael de Heredia.

LOW BUDGET: Right in town stay at **El Parqueto** (☎ 238-2882, Av. 6/8, C. 4) which charges around US$4 pp, has an 11 PM curfew, and has simple rooms with shared, cold-water baths. The same owners have **Hotel Las Flores** (☎ 338-2882; 200 m S and 50 m E from the hospital) which charges US$6s and US$8d.

Near the Parqueto, low-budget **Hotel Verano** (☎ 237-1616, C. 4, Av. 6) has shared baths, midnight curfew, and charges around US$6 s, US$8 d. A final alternative is the **Colonial** (Av. 4, C. 4/6).

OUTSIDE TOWN: A Canadian-run bed and breakfast in a housing development in

Santa Lucia de Heredia, moderate **Los Jardines** (☎ 260-1904) can be reached easily by bus from Heredia. Airport pickup is around US$6 extra.

Debbie King's Country Inn (☎/fax 268-8284; SFO 381, PO Box 025216, Miami, FL 33102-5216) is set on a three-acre fruit and coffee plantation. A pink, two-storey house, it has three bedrooms and two cabinas with kitchenettes. Rates run from US$30 s to US$50 d (for the cabinas) with breakfast.
debbiek@sol.racsa.co.cr

Set 1.3 km N from the bridge at San Isidro de Heredia, moderate-expensive the German-run **La Posada de la Montaña** (☎/fax 268-8096; Apdo. 1-3017 San Isidro de Heredia) provides lodging in its main house as well as in more expensive cabins which have private bath, kitchen, and fireplace. Rates (including full breakfast) start at US$35 s, US$40 d plus tax for rooms in the main house with shared bath; packages are available, and there's a 20% discount from May-Dec.In the US, call 800-632-3892. It's a good place for birders.
cwatzo@sol.racsa.co.cr

A full 12 mi.(20 km) N of San José, the village of San José de la Montaña has **Hotel Cypresal** (☎ 237-4466, 223-1717, fax 221-6244) . It offers volleyball, conference rooms, pool, fireplace-equipped lounge, horseback riding, and other facilities. Its restaurant serves an international menu and functional cabins (around US$60) have TVs, phones, balconies, and fireplaces.

Also in the cool hills of San José de la Montaña, **Las Ardillas Resort** (☎/fax 260-2172) is a health spa with accommodation in 15 ivy-covered, fireplace-equipped cabins. Facilities include restaurant, spa with Jacuzzi and wraps, and sauna.
verasol@sol.racsa.co.cr

Inexpensive and tasteful **El Pórtico** (☎ 237-6022, fax 260-6002), up the road, has heated rooms along with pool, Jacuzzi, and restaurant.

Located in Parque Residencial del Monte, Monte de la Cruz, Heredia, **Hotel Chalet Tirol** (☎ 267-6222, fax 267-6228; Apdo. 7812, 1000 San José) has ten two-storey Swiss-style chalets and trout fishing, conference rooms, French cuisine, as well as a surrounding cloud forest with waterfalls. It also has a new entymology museum, the **Bioplanet Institute**. (See next section). Airport pickup is available. Rates are around US$85 d with breakfast.
www.chalet-tirol.com
info@chalet-tirol.com

Located 800 m off the road from Barva to Alajuela and a total of 1.4 km from the town of Santa Barbara de Heredia, ultra-luxury **La Rosa Blanca/Finca Rosa Country Inn** (☎ 269-9392, fax 269-9555) is set at 4,265 ft. (1,300 m). The main building's interior sports murals and features a collection of indigenous art. It has four suites and one master suite, each with its own design theme, as well as two two- bedroom villas (sleep 6-8) which have murals, living rooms, and decks. The hotel offers a complete range of services — zall supplemented by a pool, nature trails, and organic gardens with fruit trees. Gourmet meals (around US$25 pp) are prepared using herbs grown on the property.In the US, call 800-327-9854 or write SJO 1201 PO Box 025216, Miami, FL 33102-5216.
www.finca-rblanca.co.cr
rblanca@sol.racsa.co.cr

The **Bougainvillea Santo Domingo** (☎ 240-8822, fax 240-8484), is set on a ten-acre estate in Santo Domingo de Heredia, about nine km (15 min. by car) from San José. Its facilities include

restaurant, satellite TV, tennis, pool, jogging trail, and shuttle bus.
bougain@sol.racsa.co.cr

FOOD AND ENTERTAINMENT: Lying 450 m E of Pop's ice cream on the plaza, **Café Plaza** has cuisine as diverse as lasagna, pastries, espresso coffee, and stuffed croissants. **Mercado Florense** is 300 m S and and 50 m W of the Church; it has an inexpensive restaurant inside. **Fresas** is set one block from the university. Offering vegetarian recipes and pastries, **Natura** is nearby. For vegetarian food you can also try **Yerba Buena**.

Other restaurants are in the vicinity of the Mercado Central. Restaurante El Nido, on the S side of the plaza, serves some veggie dishes.

Student bars near the university include **El Bulevar** and **La Choza**. Also near the univerity, **Le Petit Paris** (☎ 238-1721) offers traditional French dishes such as *ratatouille crepe* as well as sandwiches and salads. Named after the owner's cat, **Bar Barucho** is a throwback to the US 1960s scene; it's 300 m W of the Heredia Stadium.

Out near Monte de la Cruz (see below), **Le Barbizon** is a gourmet French restaurant. Another French restaurant is in **Hotel Chalet Tirol** (☎ 267-6222). The **Stein Biergarten** (open weekends) is near Bosque del Río de la Hoja. Four km above San Rafael, **Añoranzas** offers Tico food and a playground for your children.

Refugio (☎ 380-6100) is a charming restaurant on the road between Barva and San José de la Montaña.

INFORMATION: There is a branch of the ICT (☎ 223-1733) at Av. 4, C. 5/7.

SHOPPING: The Plaza Real Cariari shopping center is just outside town. At the same location since 1889, the Mercado Municipal (C. 2/4, Av. 6-10) offers a pleasant and more personal shopping experience.

Book Swappers is diagonally across from McDonald's on Av. 4 and is marked by a yellow sign.

Vicinity of Heredia

This is an interesting area to explore. The **Attiro coffee mill**, on the outskirts of town, is one of several beneficios nearby. On the outskirts of **San Pedro de Barva**, the **Centro de Investigaciones de Cafe** (☎ 237-1915) has a small coffee museum with coffee production antiquities including a display of grinders and carved wooden statues of coffee workers in action. It's open weekdays 7-3. Take the *Santa Bárbara por Barrio Jesús* bus from Av. 1, C. 1/3 in Heredia. If you're driving, turn L in front of the square in Barva and head two km onward to San Pedro and keep to the R.

Up on the street just past El Fortín to the L (C. 1, Av. 1/3) is the stop for **Barva**. Situated a few km to the N, Barva's grassy plaza has low, thick-walled buildings with red tiled roofs and a baroque-style 19th C. church; it has been declared the nation's first historic town. From here you can also continue on by bus to San Pedro de Barva and the coffee museum. When you return to Heredia, be sure to note the house shaped like a miniature castle just before town on the R.

MUSEO DE LA CULTURA: Opened in 1994, the Museo de La Cultura (☎ 260-1619) is near Santa Lucía de Barva. Any Barva bus passes by, but you must walk 1.5 km up a hill to reach it. This century-old home once belonged to President Aflredo González Flores; it was donated to the project in 1989 by the now-bankrupt Banco Anglo. It presents a portrait of rural life during the era when coffee was king. The home is constructed with a pre-Columbian technique known as barbareque in which layers of wood, wild cane and wild cane sap, stones, bricks, dung, and mud are used to build walls which resemble adobe but are thinner. Rooms are furnished with antiques appropriate to the era. Popular Ticos pay 50 cents; foreigners, US$1.50. Also on the premises is the **La Fonda** restaurant. A museum dedicated to Costa Rican peasant culture is in the works.

THE ARK HERB FARM: Set in the hills above Santa Barbara de Heredia, **The Ark Herb Farm** (☎ 269-9683, fax 239-2233) is the home of Tommy Thomas and Patricia Riley. It grows organic herbs for export. Tours are available by reservation, and donations are requested. To get here from Santa Barbara take the road N past the main church and turn L onto the dirt road found where the previous road flattens out.
arkherb@sol.racsa.co.cr

CAFÉ BRITT'S COFFEE TOUR: One of the most popular tours, the Coffee Tour (☎ 260-2748, fax 238-1848; 800-GO-BRITT) takes place three times daily at the Café Britt installation at Barva. It was presented with a 1995 Award for Tourism Excellence by American Sightseeing International, an international network of tour operators. The theatrical portion of the presentation combines music with comedy to relate the history of coffee cultivation in Costa Rica. If you make a suggestion to improve the tour which is then utilized, you will receive a free bag of coffee. The presentation takes place at 9, 11, and 3; those attending the 9 AM performance are also shuttled to the Butterfly Farm while those attending the 3 PM performance are also taken to the Santa Lucía coffee mill. Prices run around US$19 for foreigners and US$12 for Costa Ricans. If you get there on your own, the price is US$14 and US$7 respectively.
www.cafebritt.com
info@cafebritt.com

An alternative to the Café Britt tour is the **Orosi Coffee Adventure** (☎ 533-3030, fax 533-3212) which takes visitors to the Esquivel family plantation. However, you must have a large group to book.

INBIO: In Santo Barbara de Heredia, **INBio**, the Instituto Nacional de Bioversidad (☎ 244-4730, fax 244-4790) offers fascinating tours by appointment. You will see how specimens are processed, how they are mounted, and be able to see many of the unique specimens from the nation's natural treasure chest.

Their latest project is **InBioparque**, a theme park for biodiversity. It recreates different forest habitats and provides a valuable learning experience. Rates vary but entrance is US$18 plus transfer (US$10) and lunch (US$20). A guide is US$3 pp extra. Rates for a family of four is around US$75 including transfers but not lunch.
www.inbio.ac.cr/inbioparque

Monte de La Cruz

One of the most traditional areas in the Meseta Central, **Monte De La Cruz** offers a number of dining and recreational facilities near and on the way to it.

Pizza La Finca (☎ 268-8635) is an attractively set mountain-style restaurant which offers homemade pizzzas, salads, and special meals on Fridays. It's open on Thurs. from 5-11 PM and on Fri., Sat., and Sun. from noon-11. To get here take the road to San Rafael de Heredia (by turning R at the end of Heredia's main street), then pass the church and plaza and swing N until you see a sign for the La Troja Bar where you turn R. Then keep going for another km.

Bar-Restaurant Monte de la Cruz is at the sight of the **Paradero Monte de la Cruz**. Here, you'll find the remains of a small chapel (dismembered following incidences of vandalism during the 1970s) and picnic areas.

Five km from San Rafael de Heredia, **Bosque del Río de la Hoja** is two km down a forest road. There's not much in the way of facilities except for the **Bar las Chorreras,** but the hiking trails traverse forests and meadows, and you may camp here.

The **Stein Biergarten** (☎ 267-7021) serves the food one associates with Germany; it's open Wed. to Fri. for dinner and on Sat. and Sun. for lunch and dinner.

Back on the main road, **El Castillo** is a stately country club. The US$5 admission entitles you to use the pool, gym, ice-skating rink, BBQ pits, and to ride on the go-carts and the miniature train. Look for it on the R, a few hundred m after the sign for Residencia El Castillo. The turnoff for Monte de la Cruz is another km.

It's best to avoid parking near the *miradores* (lookout points) along the main highway. Visitors were robbed by men with guns in 1992, and break-ins along the roadside are numerous and commonplace. It's also better to hesitate before going into the park on your own: one member of a family from Missouri was robbed and beaten by two armed thieves after the group had entered the park in March 1995 to birdwatch. If you are going to visit, you should leave your vehicle by the ranger station or take a bus. Bring little in the way of money or material possessions with you. Let the ranger know where you are going.

To the L is **Hotel Chalet Tirol** (gourmet French food; see description above) which has several great hiking trails in their private cloud forest reserve, including one with a grove of waterfalls.

Formerly the Whitten Gallery and Jewels of the Humid Tropics, the **Bioplanet Institute** (☎ 267-6222, fax 267-6228) is housed in a new building at Chalet Tirol. Here you'll find the Whitten Arthropod collection which contains more than 50,000 insect species. half-domes in the center of each room closely replicate butterfly and orthopod habitats. Other exhibits detail biodiversity, parasitism, mimicry, and camouflage. The collection was brought to Costa Rica in 1992 by biologist Richard Whitten. Tours are offered.
www.mimosa.co.cr./whitten.html
insect@sol.racsa.co.cr

GETTING HERE: A bus runs hourly until 4 PM from Av. 10, C. 2 in Heredia; it stops two km before Monte de la Cruz except on weekends when it continues on to the top. By car take the San Isidro exit to the L approximately 14 km down the Guápiles highway and continue until you reach San Isidro, where you turn R in front of the church and continue two km to Concepción and then on to San Rafael. There you turn R at the church.

Parque Nacional Braulio Carrillo
(Braulio Carrillo National Park)

The only national park near San José, Braulio Carrillo begins seven mi.(12 km) from San José en route to Guápiles. It encompasses elevations ranging from eastern lowlands (1,500 ft., 500 m) up to the summit of 9,534-ft. (2,906-m) Volcán Barva.

If you are going to the Atlantic Coast, it is virtually inevitable that you will pass through this park, the only national park divided by a highway. The surrounding greenery is often enveloped in mist which brings to mind Chinese landscape paintings. The park's most unusual feature must be the sickeningly orange-colored water of the **Río Sucio** (Dirty River). It's coloration is due to sulfuric deposits on Volcán Irazú. Watch for it below the bridge located towards the end of the park in the direction of Limón. Rainfall averages 110-115 in. (2,800-3,800 mm) annually, and it rains almost daily between March and October; the park's E slope is generally overcast when it isn't raining.

HISTORY: The story of this park is of people attending to the lessons of history, a historically significant occurrence in and of itself. After the idea of a highway surfaced in 1973, environmentalists, fearing a repeat of the indiscriminate deforestation which had followed the opening of other new roads in the past, argued for the establishment of this park. It was inaugurated in April 1978, and the Limón highway opened to traffic in 1987. Under the US AID-funded Foresta project, the park has received funds for more trails and viewpoints and a visitor's center.

FLORA AND FAUNA: Comprising 108,969 acres (44,099 ha), 84% of the park's surface is primeval forest, 11% is used for ranching and farming, and 5% is secondary forest. There are over 500 species of birds; the magnificent quetzal and the black-faced solitaire reside on Volcán Barva as well as on other high peaks.

GETTING HERE: Take the hourly *Guápiles*-bound bus from C. 12, Av. 9. An impressive way to enter the park is by Volcán Barva through the road leading to Sacaramento de San José de la Montaña. The bus to Paso Llano (Volcán Barva) leaves from Heredia at 6:30, 11, and 4 and returns at 7:30, 1, and 5 from Mon. to Sat. On Sun. it runs at 11 and 4. In addition to the ranger stations at either Zurquí or Quebrada Gonzales, it's possible to enter the park near La Virgen off the road to Puerto Viejo de la Sarapiquí if you are packing a four-wheel drive.

TOURS: Jungle Trails (☎ 255-3486, fax 255-2782) operates hiking tours here as do others.

HIKING: Inquire at the ranger station (where you pay admission) concerning trails and current conditions. There are two trails accessible from the highway. One, before the tunnel, is sheer and arduous; the other, the *Sendero Botello*, 17 km (11 miles) after the tunnel and 2.5 km (1.5 miles) before the Quebrada Gonzales station at the park's far end, is less difficult. Both are muddy, and snakes may be a danger. You're most likely to spot birds along these trails. There's also a four-day hike from Barva to Puerto Viejo de Sarapiquí with shelters available along the way. En route you descend from 2,900 m (9,514 ft.) to 34 m (112 ft.).

CLIMBING BARVA: From Heredia take the 6:30 AM *San José de la Montaña-Paso Llano* bus (Mon. to Sat.) from behind Heredia's Mercado Central. (On Sun., you must first travel to San José de la Montaña and then take a 7:10 *Paso Llano* bus). Watch for signs at Paso Llano (Porrosati) leading to the entrance, four mi.(6.4 km) to the L. Sacramento is four mi.(seven km) farther, and from there it is approximately two mi.(three km) to the top of Volcán Barva (9,534 ft., 2,906 m) Its main lake is 600 ft. (200 m) in diame ter. The Danta, another lake, is nearby.

Be sure to bring a compass, rubber boots, warm clothing and food— no matter how nice the weather is! Although they were planning only a day hike around the crater, three German hikers were lost in rain and fog for 11 days here. Plan to make it back in time for the 5 PM bus (4 PM on Sun.). If traveling by car, you should note that the road after Sacramento is not generally navigable in the rainy season. Expect afternoon rains any time of the year and plan accorodingly. Accommodation is available at the park entrance. Bottled water, sodas, and coffee and tea are for sale here. It costs C300 to camp or stay in one of the small bungalows. More upscale digs may be found at the Sacramento Lodge (☎ 381-0367) which also offers horseback tours. No restaurant but they will cook your food for you. Other area farmers will also put you up. Food is available at the **Restaurante Sacramento**. If you like, you may also purchase cheese and *natilla* from the dairy farms in the area.

Set 3.5 km above Paso Llano, **Restaurante La Campesina** serves *comida típica*. A half km farther up, **Restaurante Sacramento** offers similar food. Both have basic rooms for sleeping and are good bases to use to explore Barva.

The **Los Robles de Sacramento** (☎ 237-2116/2441, fax 237-1976) offers the "finest ecological horseback tour." Its lodge is a converted old dairy, and tours up Barva are offered. Rates are around US$50 s, US$100 d.

San Jerónimo Lodge (☎ 292-3612, ☎/fax 292-3243) has nine rooms and is 800 m E of the church in San Jerónimo de Moravia, 18 km from San José. It is farm which offers great horseback riding and birding. Activities include a horseback ride up the "banana highway" (see following), hiking, waterfalls, and birding (quetzals are present in their private reserve, a stiff hike away). Rates are around US$ 80-140 d.
jeronimo@sol.racsa.co.cr

La Danta Salvaje (☎/fax 750-0012) translates as "The Wild Tapir." This adventurous lodge offers four-day, three-night excursions. This 1,000-acre reserve has an abundance of wildlife and numerous waterfalls. You must hike for three hours from the end of the four-wheel-drive road to reach the lodge which is set next to a waterfall. Trips are scheduled about every three weeks.
atecmail@sol.racsa.co.cr

THE BANANA HIGHWAY: As the RR to Limón ran only as far as Carrillo, 41 km from San José, capitalist entrepreneur extraordinaire Minor Keith built a highway through here in 1881 to connect the capital with the terminal. Fallen into disrepair since completion of the railway line, it now makes a wonderful day hike. Take a bus (Av. 3, C. 3/5) to San Jerónimo de Moravia and then a road to the N; in less than an hour, at the "Alto de Palma" area, you'll come to the old stone pavement which you can follow along for about nine km until you reach the park boundary; entrance is prohibited here.

From Braulio Carrillo to Guapiles

RAINFOREST AERIAL TRAM: The **Rainforest Aerial Tram** (Teleferico del Bosque Lluvioso) brings the rainforest canopy — formerly accessible only to daredevil arbolists — within the reach of the ordinary visitor. If you aren't into the comparatively vigorous outdoor activity needed to access the canopy otherwise, aren't into strenuous hiking, and have the money to pay to get in, this serves as one of the best introductions to the rainforest around. While visiting the project, be sure to note the cables used to secure plants out of harm's way. Admirably, the tramway was designed in order to minimize environmental impact.

As you glide pleasantly through the treetops, you will have the opportunity to witness first hand primary forest in its natural splendor, the difference the effect that cutting the forest has had, and the contrasts between prima]ry and secondary forest.

HISTORY: The tram project was initiated by biologist Don Perry, one of the pioneers of treetop canopy exploration and research. It is a one-of-a-kind-project, not only in its design but also in the way it is attempting to train locals to be guides and bring them into the project. The project was financed by 60 investors who purchased some US$2 million worth of shares. The administration first sought out a Russian pilot and his helicopter in Columbia where they were available for charter. Unfortunately, the helicopter broke down, and the Sandinistas came to provide the second choice. after the chief of the Sandinista Air Force granted permission to use a helicopter. Removing the machine guns from its Russian-built M1-17 helicopter, the Sandinista Air Force helped install the tram's towers. At first, the towers swung back and forth, so the tether had to be shortened in order to rectify the problem. It took an entire week, along with a cool US$50,000, to finish the project of implanting all 12 towers. It opened in 1994.

THE TOUR: At the main road you must first register at the guard's booth. A bus (actually a truck with seats) then picks you up and transports you to the first river where you generally cross via a bridge and then wait for a second truck-bus to pick you up. Depending upon the numbers of visitors present, you will either take a hike or go on the tram. On the hike, your guide will give you an orientation and then take you around. You might see any from among some 300 bird species ranging from a toucan to a woodpecker. Or you might come upon a snake swallowing a frog. The guide provides informative narrative details through both the terrestrial and aerial segments. (If the guide is a local, his parlance may not be quite up to par; please bear with him).

The tram will transport you in one of its 20 comfortable, smooth-running green-painted cars through the canopy via its 1.3 km of cableway. It's exceptionately pleasant to pass over the river with its giant tree ferns. Much of the forest is disturbed, but around 60% remains primary. Don't expect to see much in the way of wildlife. Many animals are nocturnal, some are intimidated by the tram, and there has also been hunting in this area in the past. As with rum or wine, the tram should improve with age as the vegetation grows and the guides gain in experience.

PRACTICALITIES AND ACCOMODATION: Be sure to bring binoculars, insect repellent, hat, and rain gear when you come to visit. There's a somewhat pricey restaurant with a limited menu; the *soda* on the road is cheaper, or you might want to bring your own bag lunch. Note that you can take the tram more than once if things aren't busy. Keep in mind that, as already noted above, you probably won't see many animals: be aware that the best possible time for sightings runs from 6:30-9 AM and plan your visit accordingly. For current information call 257-5961 or fax

257-6053.
www.rainforest.co.cr
dosela@sol.racsa.co.cr

HAPPY RANA LODGE: This lodge (cell ☎ 385-1167; US ☎ 520-743-8254) offers comfortable elevated screened cabins along the Río Blanco for around US$60 with breakfast. They offer tubing, waterfall hikes, and a swimming hole. A good place to relax and get away!

LAS CUSINGAS BOTANICAL GARDEN: Las Cusingas Botanical Garden (☎ 710-7114 for appointments) covers 25 acres (20 ha). Owners Ulises Blanco and Jane Segleau cultivate medicinal plants along with plants considered to be rare and endangered — more than 60 in all. The couple have a cabin which accommodates four; meals are available or you may self-cater on your woodburning stove.

Set near the village of Buenos Aires (and accessible by taxi from Buenos Aires or Guápiles), they are some 3.5 km from the main highway. To get here, look for the large gas station which is on your L at the third entrance to Guápiles (Soda Buenos Aires will be on your R). Take a R and then continue until your see the gates. A donation is requested.

COSTA FLORES: Spread across 300 acres, this flower plantation (☎ 220-1311, ☎/fax 717-5457) specializes in heliconias. On the farm are waterfalls, fountains, and ponds as well as some 20 species of birds including an abundance of hummingbirds. To get here, head L at Guacimo and follow the signs to Costa Flores. Expect to spend around US$15 for tours, less if in a group.

GUÁPILES: This small town doesn't really have a lot to offer, but it is a good place to stock up on supplies while you're in the area. There are a couple of low budget and other hotels which might be used as a base to explore the area. The **Cabinas Car** (☎ 710-6523) is clean and inexpensive. There are a few *sodas* in the town. Taxis leave from the main square.

The expensive **Hotel Suerre** (☎ 710-7551, fax 710-6376) is in front of the Colegio Tecnico. It is done up in a sort of colonial style with terracotta floors and an entrance marked by pillars. Rooms have a/c and cable TV.

HOTEL RÍO PALMAS/E. A. R. T. H.: E. A. R. T. H. Agricutural School (☎ 255-2000, fax 255-2726 for advance tour reservations) which has a forest reserve and also passes on sustainable agricultural techniques.

Situated across the road in Pocora from the school, the **Hotel Río Palmas** (☎ 760-0305, fax 760-0296; Apdo. 6944, 1000 San José) is a 22-room establishment which has a pool and a reserve with trails. Its restaurant serves Costa Rican food, and a number of activities (including horseback riding and kayaking) and day trips (Pocora Falls, and other nearby attractions) are offered.

Cartago

This once-impoverished village was founded in 1523. Located 14 mi (23 km) E of San José in the Valle de Guarco, Cartago is the nation's oldest settlement. Since the 1800s Cartago has also been known as *La Ciudad de las Brumas*, the "city of fog." A former nickname is *La Ciudad del Lodo*, the city of mud. If you arrive on a rainy day, you'll soon see why. A nickname for the inhabitants is *pateros* (potato people), probably because potatoes are such an important crop in this province.

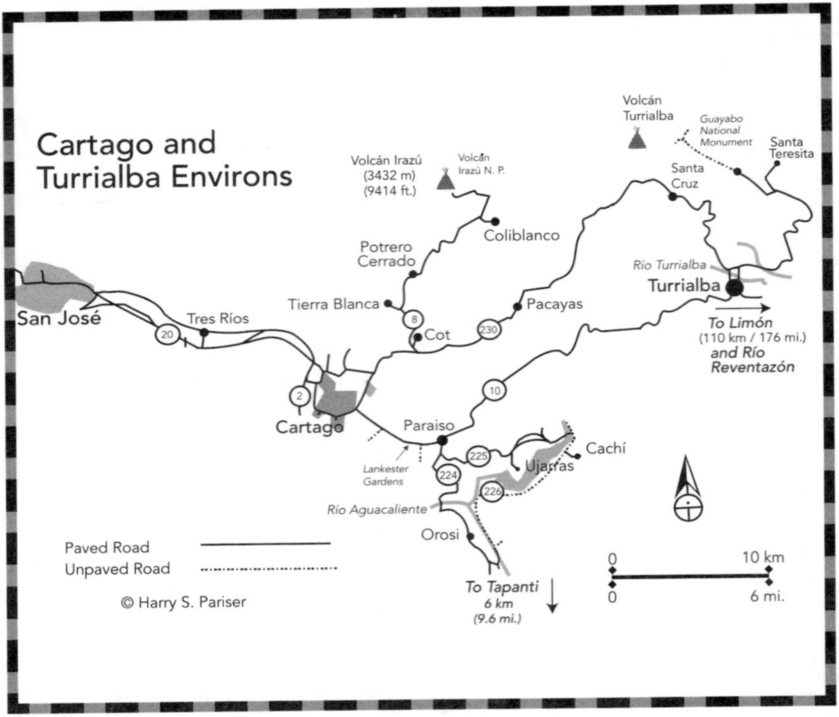

GETTING HERE: Buses run from San José about every 20 mins. They leave from C. 13, Av. Central/2, near the Plaza de la Democracia. Be sure to get the *directo* bus. If driving, head out to San Pedro via Av. Central and then get on the *autopista*.

SIGHTS: Cartago does not have as many old buildings nor the atmosphere one might expect in a city of its age, largely because earthquakes (in 1841 and 1910), along with raining ash and debris from Volcán Irazú, have destroyed most of its old buildings.

If you are coming by bus, you might want to get out at the town's center where you'll see **Las Ruinas**. Iglesia de Convento, the parish church of La Parroquia, the first parroquial church dedicated to St. Santiago, was severely damaged by earthquakes. After the 1910 quake — perhaps owing to the legend that the Creator had cursed the church for its priest's murder of his brother — it was deemed not worth rebuilding. Today, it's a walled park complete with trees, a pond, shrubs, and benches — all of which combine to afford a more attractive park than any found in San José. The plaza built in front has a statue of the opera tenor Manuel Salazar Zuniga. A great place to relax and do some birdwatching.

A few blocks away to the E is the town's main attraction: the cathedral. An example of what some call Byzantine style and others call an architectural mishmash, the **Basilica de Nuestra Señora de Los Angeles** (Basilica of Our Lady of the Angels, named after the nation's patron saint) houses a statuette of the Black Virgin holding the infant Christ. Legend has it that on Aug. 2, 1635 a young girl named Juana Periera found a small statuette of the Virgin Mary perched on a rock beside a stream while she was strolling in a forest. Taking the statuette home, she placed it in her collection. Passing the same point the next afternoon, she discovered another identical statuette at the same location. Returning home, she found that the first statuette had vanished, and she placed the new one where it had stood. After this happened three days in a row, she went to the priest who, after having the identical experience, decided to build a shrine at the site.

Today, the rock is found in the church's basement, and thousands credit the stream's water with miraculous powers to heal injuries, handicaps, and even enable supplicants to survive surgery. Arriving supplicants have donated miniature trinkets resembling the body parts requiring healing, and today there are fingers, arms, hearts, stomachs, eyes, legs, livers, lungs, and feet in cases all over the church; many of them are silver medallions. You could spend hours gazing at the collection. Trophies are the gift of grateful sports teams who allegedly owed their victories to the Virgin's intervention, and there are photos of children next to written testimony extolling the Virgin's healing powers; there's even a geisha doll and a pair of carved wooden oxen being led by a *campesino*. Statuary abounds, and there are also some beautiful confession booths. At the rear to the L of the altar is a collection of life-sized statues, some of which have most unhappy faces.

Downstairs, reduced and weathered by years of attention and chiseling, is the original stone, topped with a replica of the Virgin which is all done up in an elaborate gold case. The original statue, crudely fashioned from a granite-like stone, is rarely removed from its cabinet set above the altar. Stolen several times, it has always been returned. Holy water, from the stream which still runs alongside, is available in a shed at the back; you must pay for a container. Across the street in a diagonal from the R of the cathedral's entrance, you'll see a shop ("Venta de Objetos Religiosos") which sells hands, feet, eyes. and other paraphernalia at reasonable prices.

Open from 9-4, the **Elias Leiva Museum of Ethnography** (Av. 3/5, C. 3/5) houses colonial-era furniture, pre-Colombian artifacts, and other items. Finally, if you have time, you may want to see the art exhibits at the **Casa de la Ciudad** in Edificio Pirie.

PRACTICALITIES: The **Hotel Cartago/Posada Guesthouse** (☎ 551-1531, fax 552-0875) is a recently-constructed place in Cartago which has rooms (around US$35 d) and suites (US$75 d).
lodging@therealestate.net

Also acceptable is the **Los Angeles Lodge** (☎ 551-0957, Av. 4, C. 14/16) which is next to the basilica. Rates are around US$25 s, US$40 d, US$50 t. Breakfast is included.

If all you want is an inexpensive place to sleep so that you can head up to the top of Irazú the next morning, that can be found near the railway station and the market. Try the **Casa Blanca** in Barrio Asia, and less expensive **Pensión El Brumoso** (☎ 551-4351; Av. 6/8, C. 5) and the **Valencia**. Most of the others rent rooms by the hour for obvious purposes, so if you don't mind creaking springs and frantic gasps coming from the room next door.

FOOD: Bars and restaurants cluster around the basilica. **Pizza y Hamburguesas Maui** is on the N side of the park in front of the Cathedral; a large restaurante is behind it. One of the most attractive places to dine is **Salón París**, which has Venetian and bullfight scenes, and is opposite one corner of the market on the main street. Located near the bus station, the large and bustling market, with yet another replica of the Virgin on display, has lunch counters galore. Watch the mother and daughter team in one shop making tortillas. You also might find any type of odd souvenir in its innumerable shops. **Metrocentro** is the town's shopping mall.

FESIVALS AND EVENTS: The **Virgin of Los Angeles**, held on August 1, is Cartago's largest festival; thousands arrive for this.

Vicinity of Cartago

Cartago's most famous outlying attraction is the Irazú volcano which is covered in a separate section below. Set five mi.(seven km) to the SE of Cartago, **Jardín Lankester**, the Lankester Gardens, named after British expatriate Dr. Charles Lankester who founded them in the 1940s, possesses one of the nation's finest orchid collections. Although the over 800 species found here bloom throughout the year, the blossoms are at their peak in March. Also featured are fruit trees, groves of bamboo, aloe, hardwoods, bromeliads and other species. Unfortunately, they're identified only in Latin, so unless you're a botanist it might as well be Greek to you. Guided tours are offered on the half-hour from 8:30 to 3:30 daily. Although you can come through on your own, an employee will tag along behind you to make sure you keep to the route and don't pick anything.

Cartago's famous cathedral

To get there, take the *Paraíso* bus from the Cartago terminal and get off at the Ricalit factory and the distinctive and unforgettable dog training school sign, then walk over a quarter-mile (.5 km) down the side road to the S, which leads to the entrance.

Admission is around US$.50 for locals and US$3 for foreigners. If you want to head outwards and onwards after your visit take a bus marked "Orosi." (See Valle de Orosi section below). If you're driving, you'll want to check out the spectacular view from the mirador (lookout point) a few km past Paraíso en route to the S.

Also near Paraiso is the **Autovivero del Río**, a combined greenhouse and miniature zoo which sells colored volcanic stones, plants, and rabbits. In Paraíso, eat at the **Bar Restaurant Continental**. Finally, on the way back to San José, the **Nuestra Señora de Pilar Religious Art Museum** is on the S side of the Church of Tres Ríos.

Route of the Saints

This road to the S takes one along to semi-remote villages like Santa María de Dota, San Marcos de Tarrazú, San Pablo de León Cortés, and San Cristobal Sur. In the vicinity is also La Lucha where Don Pepe Figueres had his famous farm.

At **Cañon del Guarco**, Km 58 on the Interamerican Highway, a road leads seven km downhill to Copey where you will find **El Toucanet Lodge** (☎/fax 541-1435) has cabins (around US$50 with breakfast) and a restaurant. It also has a stone Jacuzzi.

It is then another seven down to Santa María, where there are some low-budget hotels including **Hotel Santa María** (☎ 541-1193) and the **Hotel Dota** (☎ 541-1026). You may eat at **Las Tejas** which is open Fri. and Sat. evenings as well as noon-11 on Suns. From Santa María buses return at 6, 9, 2, and 4. This makes a great day trip.

Also in the area, the **El Manatial** (☎ 771-0255) has rooms around US$120 with board. Facilities include steam, hydro massage, "healing magnetic rocks" (yes, *healing* magnetic rocks!), and organic food. Veggie food is also offered as is (upon advance request) trout for the unconverted and red meat for the truly heathen. A 60-km trail leads to Hacienda Barú near Dominical, and a guided three-day tour (stopping at eco-resorts along the way) is offered. Rates are around US$50 pp with three meals and US$35 pp for dorm beds.

Back between Copey and on the way to Providencia, the two-cabin **Finca El Edén** (☎ 541-1299: message only) may be reached by taxi from Santa María or by car from the highway. Each cabin here has a kitchen with wood stove; bring your own food. The owners will sell you cheese and milk. Activities include birding, horseback riding, hiking, and tennis.

Set on a farm with 190 acres of cloud forest, the **Cloud Forest Hideaway** (☎ 541-1485, fax 541-1437) offers several one-bedroom cottages with kitchens for around US$55 or US$365 pw; the cabins can hold a couple and two children. French, English, and Spanish is psoken, and guests may pick as many fruits and vegetables as they wish. **fintluni@sol.racsa.co.cr**

Out on the main highway, you can also stay at deceptively-named and inexpensive-to-luxury-priced **Albergue de Montaña Tapantí** (☎ 232-0436, 233-0133, fax 233-0778; 800-334-8582; Apdo. 26, 1017 San José). It offers activities such as trout fishing and hiking. as well as horseback riding and a visit to its namesake.

From Santa María, you can also continue on six km to **San Marcos** which has spartan accommodation. From here, a 40-km four-wheel-drive-only road descends to the Pacific highway.

TRANSPORT: *Los Santos* buses (two hrs.) run to Santa María (two hrs.) from C. 21, Av. 16 bis (☎ 223-1002) in San José at 6, 9, 12:30, 3, and 5. Return buses leave from the main square. For Copey, take the bus from the square here. Or take a *San Isidro* bus from C. 16, Av. 1/3, to Cañon del Guarco at Km. 58 and walk or hitch the remaining seven km.

San Gerardo de Dota

The entrance to this village is quite a bit farther S at Km 80 on the Interamerican Highway,. The interior of these cloud forests has been acclaimed as the best place in the nation to see a quetzal. To get here take any San Isidro bus and tell the driver you wish to get off at the *"entrada a San Gerardo."*

The Chacón family's **Albergue de Montaña Savegre** (☎/fax 771-1732) charges around US$65 pp) with meals and hot showers The 15 spacious rooms are in bungalows with small porches; there's a bar and restaurant where visitors can enjoy views of surrounding gardens and the boulder-strewn Savegre.

Septentaguarian Efrain, his wife and eleven children, have 790 acres (320 ha) of peach and apple orchards surrounded by 494 acres (200 ha) of primary forest. Trout ponds on the property provide fishing; you pay for only what you catch. A naturalist guide will take you along a trail up to Cerro de Muerte, and a range of day trips are available upon request. Horseback riding, trout fishing, and other activities are also offered as is pickup from the highway entrance to the village. **ciprotour@sol.racsa.co.cr**

Rolando Chacón (☎ 771-2376), their cousin, has two *cabinas* for around US$30 pp including meals.

Luxury **El Trogon** (☎ 222-5463, fax 255-4039) is a set of *cabinas* which are owned by the same people who run Mawamba Lodge in Tortuguero. Three-day packages run around US$250 pp. Horseback riding and trout fishing are also offered.

Another alternative is the **Finca Mirador de Quetzales** (☎ 381-8456) which is at Km 70. Recommended for birders, they have a 43-ha cloud forest reserve and spectacular views (from 2,600 m, 8,530 ft.) when it is not fogged in. Built with milled fallen trees, the lodge provides simple rooms with shared bath, and a set of cabins is also on the farm. US$30 pp, pd buys lodging, breakfast and dinner, and tours.

ACTIVITIES: The nearby **Río Savegre** is filled with introduced rainbow trout. The trail to a dramatic **waterfall** starts near the Bar La Deportiva. **Whitewater rafting** is also popular here; contact *Rios Tropicales* (☎ 777-0674; tropical@sol.racsa.co.cr), Adventuras Naturales (☎ 224-0889; www.toenjoynature.com), or any of the numerous other companies for details. Transportation from the junction (nine km on a bad road) is available for around US$12 RT if you stay at the Chacón's place. Reservations are advisable for all of these places, and you should prepare for some chilly nights.

San Pablo

The area around El Abejonal Mountain in San Pablo de León Cortes has two family-run lodges which offer tranquility and a cool climate. To get here turn R from El Empalme along the Pan American and drive 28 km (5 km past the town). The **Refugio Silvestre El Coyote** (☎ 546-6487) provides lodging in two comfy two-story cypress cabins which rent for around US$25 pd with discounts for longer stays. Camping is also available

The 15-cabin Area **Silvestre El Abejonal**

(☎ 546-7479) has units renting for around US$36-50 pd. It has a restaurant (open on weekends), hiking trails, tennis and volleyball courts, and even a motocross racetrack!)

Genesis II

Steve and Paula Friedman's private reserve is situated at 7,500 ft. (2,360 m). It lies just over the ridge of the Talamancas on the nation's Atlantic side, some 35 mi.(58 km) S of San José and near the Dota valley. Approximately 12 mi.(20 km) of trails run through the 95-acre property. Rainfall here averages about 90 in. (2,300 cm). Most mornings are bright and clear, but rain generally falls in the afternoon. The Friedmans are engaged in recreating cloud forest on deforested land and have a nursery which is experimenting with alternative methods of propogation.

GETTING HERE: Transportation to and from the airport is included in the rates. If you are coming here on your own, take a San Isidro de El General-bound bus from the Coca Cola depot in San José (C. 16, Av. 1/3). Have the driver let you off at Km 58 across from the Genesis II sign. From there it's four km on foot to the lodge. If driving, you can take a four-wheel drive all the way to their gate; otherwise park at the third sign (not including the one at the bus stop) where your vehicle will be safe.

FLORA AND FAUNA: There are some 20 species of trees here including palmettos and tree ferns. The 200 species of birds include 50 endemic ones such as the resplendent quetzal, emerald toucanets, tropical warblers, collared trogons, and a wide variety of hummingbirds. Sloths and armadillos may also be seen.

PRACTICALITIES: There's no set program here. Visitors generally rise at dawn, drink coffee and have a snack, then leave the house to find birds, returning in time for breakfast. Most of the meals feature garden-fresh food, and any dietary regimen can be catered to. In the main house, there are four bedrooms with two single beds in each; there are two other cabins. All guests share toilet and hot water shower facilities in the main house's two bathrooms. Electricity is available. Rates vary depending upon the length of stay and number in your party and include all meals (except alcohol), laundry (for guests staying five days or more), and guides. Tips, phone calls, and transport are not included.

Rates are around US$85 pp, pn. There are also special rates (US$45 pn) for students and academics. Volunteers pay a weekly rate for room and board, stay in spartan facilities, and spend five hrs. per day constructing nature trails. Campers can be accommodated on a tent platform, but you must bring your own tent.

Rates are high for the standard of accommodation offered, but meals are hearty, and you are paying to help Steve and Paula continue their work. Day visits are US$ 10 pp (US$5 pp for students). For more information (and current rates and policies). Write Steve and Paula Friedman, SJO 2031, 1601 NW 97th Ave., Unit C-101, PO Box 025216, Miami, FL 33102-5216. In Costa Rica call 381-0739 which is a cellular phone or fax 551-0070.
www.yelloweb.co.cr/genesis
genesis@yellowweb.co.cr

Avalon Private Reserve

Set three km from Divisi6n (Km 107) and off a side road, **Avalon** (☎ 380-2107, ☎/fax 771-7226, cellular: 380-2107; Apdo. 846-8000, San Isidro de El

General) is an alternative to Monteverde for those who wish to experience the cloud forest environment. Avalon offers some 375 acres of cloud forest along with horseback riding, guided birding (US$60 pd for a group), and mountain biking. Day use is US$3 pp, camping is US$6 pp, dorm rooms with shared bath are US$9 pp, rooms with private baths are US$22 d, and private cabins with baths are around US$35-45, camping, and other rooms (around US$45). There is a US$99 pw special for "backpackers," and a US$39 pw special for those who are willing to chip in three hrs. pd to help with the reserve.
smiller@sol.racsa.co.cr

Irazú Volcano (Parque Nacional Volcán Irazú)

Rising to 11, 260 ft. (3,432 m), Irazú's prime distinction is that it is one of the world's few volcanoes that can be viewed up close with ease. And, should the day be clear, both the Atlantic and Pacific are visible from its summit. A lumbering menace that has devastated Cartago on more than one occasion, its presence has also had a beneficial effect: the very ash that wreaks devastation is also responsible for the soil's fecundity.

ORIENTATION: This mountain is the birthplace of the Chirripó, Reventación, Sarapiquí, and Grande de Tárcoles rivers. It has shot billows of steam up as high as 1,640 ft. (500 m) and volcanic debris up to 984 ft. (300 m). With a rusty, mineral-colored lake at its bottom, Diego de la Haya crater is approximately 2,270 ft. (690 m) wide and 328 ft. (100 m) deep; its NW slope has active fumaroles. Measuring 3,445 ft. (1,050 m) in diame-

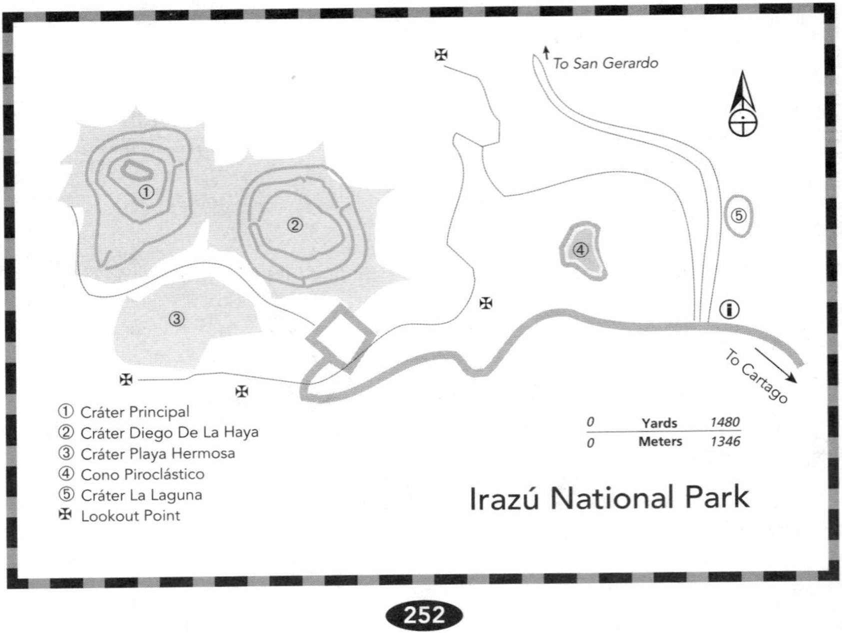

ter, the principal crater is 820-984 ft. (250-300 m) deep.

FLORA AND FAUNA: The vegetation is adapted to high altitude and low temperatures. Wildlife here is scarce but there are forest cats, porcupines, coyotes, and a variety of birds including the mountain robin and the volcano junco, a chunky sparrow.

HISTORY: Although there are many possible explanations for the volcano's name, the most likely one is that it derives from Iztarú, an Indian word meaning "mountain of tremors and thunder." Although it has various names, it has been known solely as Irazú since 1854. Its first recorded eruption occurred in 1723 when it formed the present-day Diego de la Haya. It has erupted some 15 times since then. The next eruption was in 1775, and it also erupted in 1822, perhaps in celebration of Costa Rica's independence that year. The area was established as a 5,700-acre (2,309-ha) park in 1955.

From 1963-65, the eruptions traumatized the region, affecting farming in San José, Alajuela, and Heredia provinces. In 1963, 300 houses were destroyed, and the following year, another eruption poured five in. (127 mm) of ash on San José. An estimated 250 million *colones* in agricultural revenues were lost as a consequence. During this period the crater widened from 656 to 1,722 ft. (200 m to 525 m).

GETTING HERE: On Sat., Sun., and holidays, a bus runs from the front of the Gran Hotel at the Plaza de la Cultura (C. 1/3, Av. 2) in San José. It passes by the Ruinas in Cartago at 8:30 and returns at 12:15. For more information call 272-0651/2948 or 551-9795. Otherwise. the closest you can get is Tierra Blanca or Linda Vista, from where you must hike, hitch, or grab a taxi. The bus to *Linda Vista* (8.5 miles, 13.7km, from the crater) leaves Mon. and Thurs at 5:45 AM from Cartago, arriving at 8, and returns at 12:45 to arrive back in Cartago at 2. Ask in Cartago about buses as far as *Tierra Blanca*.

From San José, buses straight to the top leave at 8 from Av. 2 across from the Gran Hotel Costa Rica on Wed., Sat., Sun., and holidays; the return trip is at 12:15. Another alternative is to take a taxi from Cartago, about US$15 RT after bargaining. It's preferable to visit in the dry season, and it would be a good idea to bring food with you. Many companies offer half- or full-day tours which stop here. Admission is at the prevailing special *gringo* rate of US$6; no more than 950 people are permitted in the park at any one time.

> Although the crater walls may appear to be safe, a descent to either crater's bottom is dangerous and not recommended.

SIGHTS EN ROUTE: On the way from Cartago, you will pass many dairy farms, potato patches, and the immaculate towns of **Potrero Cerrado** and **Tierra Blanca**,"White Land"— so named either because of the ash or because of the soil's fecundity . After the town of Cot, you come next to Potrero Cerrado ("Closed Field'), then you pass a TB sanatorium converted into a juvenile reform school. **Prusia** was destroyed by an eruption, and the surrounding area has been reforested by the Guardia Civil. Now known as **Area Recreativa Jiménez Oreamuno**, it's reached by a short but steep hike; there are picnic tables and trails.

ACCOMMODATION: If stuck or something, you may stay at the inexpensive (but less than wonderful) **Hotel de Montaña Gestoria Irazú** (☎ 253-0827), 12.4 mi.(20 km) from Cartago and 7.5 mi.(12 km) from the crater. Another alternative is to overnight in Cartago. The only place to eat, aside from the none-too-good hotel just mentioned, is at the **Linda Vista**, a somewhat pricey (by local standards) but basic restaurant featuring an incredible display of name cards, *cedulas*, and foreign banknotes.

Valle de Orosi (Orosi Valley)

This spectacularly scenic area makes a great day trip from San José, providing a good opportunity for escape from the urban sprawl into the countryside by car or bus. Among its attractions are scenic outlooks, old churches, a wildlife reserve, and a waterfall. To go by bus, take a Cachí bus to Cartago and then ask to be let off at Ujarrás. You can then walk half an hour to Charrara. (On Sundays., the bus goes all the way at 8, 11, and 12).

TOURS: A number of operators run here, and — if you're on a tight schedule and want to see everything — a tour is advised. Otherwise, you can have fun with the buses.

FESTIVALS AND EVENTS: Held mid-March, the **Ujarras pilgrimage**, a procession from Paraíso to the ruined church in Ujarras, commemorates the rescue of Ujarras by the Virgin from floods. Her graven image returns along with the crowd for the occasion.

***MIRADORES*:** There are two scenic overlooks in the region. Featuring a garden-like setting, **Mirador de Orosi**, a facility constructed by the ICT, has some of the most magnificent views in the nation. Take the path to your L; Irazú and Turrialba peaks will be directly in front and, as you continue along, you'll see Orosi on the side with coffee plantations in the foreground. Dammed at its lower end by the Cachí Dam, the Río Reventazón wends its way down the valley.

NEARBY PRACTICALITIES: Near the *mirador* is the **Lost in Paradise Café** (☎ 574-6047), a Canadian-run snack bar with homemade goodies and a gift shop. It's well worth the stop. Other places include **Soda Luz** and **Soda el Nido**.

Also near the *mirador* is relaxed **Hacienda del Rio** (☎/fax 533-3308; Apdo. 46, 7100 Paraiso de Cartago), an attractive house which was once designed as a country club— a plan which was later abandoned. It is now open for guests. It has a restaurant, pool, Jacuzzi, hiking, horseback riding, and numerous hammocks. Tours can be arranged. They will pick you up if you can get to Paraiso and phone. Rates are around US$50-70 d including breakfast.
hacderio@sol.racsa.co.cr

In Paraíso, the **Sanchirí Mirador and Lodge** (☎/fax 533-3210) has five spartan *cabinas* (around US$30 d) with balconies commanding splendid views. It has a restaurant as well as horseback riding.

The Swiss owned-and -operated **Peña Blanca Bed and Brunch** (☎ 551-9701) has ten *cabinas* (with stoves and refrigerators) which hold up to four and rent for around US$65. Views are great. Facilities include hiking, restaurant, and tours.

A bed and breakfast, five-room **Cabinas Los Rápidos** (☎ 225-3506, fax 574-6074) is well to the E of Cachí in the village of Tucurrique right by the Río Reventazon.

It has a restaurant and arranges tours. Rates are around US$25 d.

SIGHTS IN OROSI AND VICINITY: With the nation's oldest active church, Orosi, a village in which Indians were once forcibly resettled, is a pleasant, well-manicured town. It has several *balnearios* (public pools), public baths, and hot springs.

Be sure to visit the restored **church** next to the soccer field. Built in 1743-86, it has whitewashed walls of sun-dried bricks, paved brick floors, a red tile roof supported by eight square cedar columns set on stone, and religious statuary thought to be the work of Mexican and Guatemalan artists.

The monastery next door has been converted into a **museum** housing a collection of religious art. You'll find a Christ in a coffin, elaborate candelabras, clerical robes, and a bleeding wooden Christ, in the company of other statuary. (Open daily, 1-6, small admission charged).

Near town, **Beneficiadora Renex** may be visited with *Orosi Coffee Adventure Tours* (☎ 533-3030, fax 533-3212)

The church in Orosi at Ujarrás

NEARBY PRACTICALITIES: Inexpensive **Albergue Montaña Orosi** (☎ 533-3032, fax 228-1256) is a house transformed into a ho☎ The owners also run **Restaurant Coto** on the main square. You may also ask about their cabins.

Near Tapantí, the **Monte Sky Ecological Mirador** (☎ 232-0884, 382-7502, fax 231-

The woodcarvings found at El Casa de Soñador are one of the Orosi Valley's attractions.

3536) offers the change to stay in an old house (around US$12 pn with breakfast), stay in a jungle cabin, or camp. Tours (for both individuals and groups) are available. There's a majestic waterfall, and you can see up to 260 or more species of birds. Trails are steep but sweet. Owner "Billy" Montero tries to introduce Costa Ricans to the wonders of nature. Most cooking is done on a wood stove, and candles are favored over electric power.
montesky@sol.racsa.co.cr

> "We want people to learn to treasure the forest for its power over the human spirit. We want them to have an intimate experience with the natural world, to love it with utmost respect and leave it undamaged by nature" — Monte Sky owner Billy Montero as quoted in the *Tico Times*.

Also near Tapantí, **Kiri Lodge** (☎ 533-3040, 284-2024) has a restaurant (trout dishes are a specialty), organiclly-grown fruit groves, and a private reserve. You may hike here from Orosi or charter a taxi. Rates are around US$20 s, US$35 d, US$40 t, and US$45 quad.

WATER FACILITIES: Two thermal pools are in town. **Balneario Termal Orosi** is to the W of town; it's open from 7:30-4 daily and charges around US$1 admission. Another is **Los Patios** which charges a bit more and is open from 8-4 from Tues. to Sun. On the lake's N side, another ICT facility offers a swimming pool, picnic area, restaurant, playing fields, boat launching area, and campground.

Parque Nacional Tapantí (Tapantl National Park)

The side road to the Río Macho hydroelectric plant, two km after Orosi, leads 12 km to the 12,577-acre (5,090-ha) Tapantí National Park. A reserve now reclassified as a park, Tapantí offers nature trails, a good stream for trout fishing (with a permit), and a lookout point. No bus is available; a taxi will cost about US$4 OW. It's open 6-4, and birders should get an early start. Inside, you might see quetzals, olingos, or kinkajous. Jaguars and ocelots are also found here.

It rains a tremendous amount in this area, especially between May and October, so you'll want to be well prepared. As a compensation for the weather, there are approximately 150 streams and rivers running through. Fishing is permitted in designated areas. There's a small exhibit room at the entrance and nearby trails, including a *mirador* overlooking a waterfall.

To enter the park from its S extremity, which is known as the **Reserva Forestal Río Macho**, get information from the *pulpería* owner in La Trinidad de Dota, 1.5 hrs. S of San José on the Interamerican Highway. Las Chesperitos is next to the ranger station there, and you can stay at inexpensive **La Georgina**, a half-hour away. This entrance is also open from 6-4 daily. There're a number of small waterfalls here including Salto and Palmitos. The *Sendero Oropendola* leads to a swiming hole and picnic tables. If you leave the reserve and find no taxi available, the best procedure is to walk four km to Río Macho. From here you should be able to get a cab or else hitch a ride with a local. **note:** Accommodation near Tapantí is listed under Orosi above.

Palomo

This is accessible by either a footbridge from Orosi (which exacts a maintenance toll on Sundays) or a sturdier suspension bridge two km farther on. The chief feature here is the inexpensive **Motel Río** (☎ 533-3128, 533-3057) with a swimming pool and restaurant specializing in fresh fish. Some of the units are equipped with kitchenettes. Most buses end their routes here so if you wish to visit Cachí dam eight km away, you must either walk, hitch, or backtrack to Cartago where you catch a bus via Ujarrás.

La Casa del Soñador

Built by master woodcarver and retired university professor, Macedonio Quesada Volorin (1925-1995), this primitive yet ornate wooden "House of the Dreamer," built late in 1989, rises on boulders by the side of the road right next to the Río Naranjo. The carved female silhouettes gazing out from the windows as you approach represent gossiping women. The shutters pull down to match the outline when the window is closed.

Macedonio's work evokes not only Costa Rica and Latin America but also seems influenced by native American art along with Dayak and Japanese Buddhist woodcarvings. On one side is a carving of the Last Supper and on the back is a representation of the "Children's Last Supper." The carved door immediately adjacent shows a dog, mother, and child. Inside are carved nativity creches and other woodwork, much of which is made from coffee roots, *tirra*, *cerro royal*, and *pilon* woods.

Macedonio was awarded the National Prize for Popular Culture in 1995. The late Macedonio's one small bedroom and other workspace is upstairs. He taught disadvantaged locals to carve. His son Hermes continues his work, and his assistants are constantly chiseling away downstairs.

Cachí Dam, just down the road, was constructed during the mid-1960s for 182 million *colones*. In the marsh across the road you may be able to spot waterbirds.

Ujarrás

This settlement lies past Cachí Dam 1.5 km to the W down a side road. Now a historic shrine, the ruins of **Ujarrás church** are set amidst beautifully maintained grounds with flowers, birds, and a stand of bamboo. Coffee plantations and a reforested pine grove border the grounds. It was built in 1681-93 and was abandoned in 1833 after a flood forced the village to relocate on higher ground. The ruins are currently endangered by the encroaching river.

The cross on the grounds was found in a nearby canyon. According to legend, a Huetar Indian found a wooden box in a river which he brought to Ujarrás. From there it could be moved no farther. When opened, it was found to contain a statue of the Virgin, and a church was built right on the spot. This very statue was credited with repelling an invasion by the pirate Henry Morgan and his brigands who were turned back in 1666 from their attempt to sack Cartago by an outnumbered band of colonial militia. Today she resides in Paraíso, where all of the inhabitants of the time relocated, and the statue is now known as Virgen de Candelaria. A fiesta is still held here in mid-March.

PRACTICALITIES: Eat at **Restaurante Típico Ujarrás** or the popular **La Casona del Cafetal** (☎ 533-3280) which has a Sunday buffet and also markets its own labeled brand of coffee. It's one block past the town of Cachí and overlooking the lake. There's dancing on Sat. nights, rental boats are available as are mountain bikes, and horseback riding is also offered.

NEARBY SIGHTS: The **Lacustre Charrara** recreation area is two km off the main road down a spur from the Ujarrás road. On weekends and holidays the bus goes all the way instead of dropping you at the turnoff. It features a pool, basketball courts, a boat tour of the lake, picnic tables, and a restaurant. It's closed on Mon.

The **Ujarrás lookout point** is located six km from the Charrara turnoff towards Paraíso. Nearby is the **Veil de la Novio (Bridal Veil) waterfall**. According to legend, a group of family and friends arrived here to celebrate a wedding. The horse went berserk and jumped, taking the bride and her long trailing veil over the cliff

Reader's Password and Update Access

Remember that your special site access **user name** ("manati") and **password** ("bluesea") work at:
www.savethemanatee.com/innersoul

You will find free updates for this book as well as information on a $3 discount if you purchase the Palm Pilot version of **Explore Costa Rica**.

(Regular price: $14.95)

Information on the PDF (Adobe Acrobat Reader) version of this book is here as well!

The Turrialba Area

The name Turrialba (originally "Torrealba") means "white tower" in archaic Spanish. It has its origins in the enormous columns of white smoke which were constantly expelled from the then-active volcano. As the number of visitors to Costa Rica continues to grow, this area — because of its great scenic beauty, attractions, and proximity to San José — has come under increased attention.

Turrialba

This agriculturally-based town of 30,000 lies 64 km from San José, set at 2,050 ft. (625 m) up the slopes of the Turrialba volcano. There's little to pique the interest of a visitor here, but its proximity to the Río Reventazón (whose name means "bursting") has made it a major area for kayaking and white water rafting. Its size and its climate make it ideal for relaxation. The town makes a good base for low-budget travelers planning to climb Volcán Turrialba, visit Guayabo reserve, or check out the surrounding area. Kayakers sometimes come all the way from Canada and rent houses here. Turrialba is also noted for its baseball factory where workers are paid a pittance for a six-day week.

GETTING HERE: A bus runs hourly (7 AM-9 PM) from San José, departing from Av. Central, C. 13. The 65-km trip takes under two hours. A *directo* takes 1.5 hrs. Buses also run from Siquirres (around every two hrs.; 1.5 hrs.). En route the bus traverses a narrow mountain road past villages such as Tres Equis. Overcast hills are off in the distance, and coffee plants grow on steep hillsides. You can see CATIE on the R past Turrialtico and then you descend into the town. If you're coming by car, you can also come via San Isidro de Coronado and Rancho Redondo to Santa Cruz where you turn for Turrialba.

FACILITIES AND TOURS: Just outside of town, **Balneario Las Américas** (US$.75 admission) has two large pools and a restaurant-bar. It sometimes has a disco and dances.

Parque La Dominica is to the W of town; it has swings and basketball court. It's next to the river which the follies of mankind have rendered fit for looking at only.

For those wishing to tour the area, the **COSANA travel agency** (☎ 556-1513) operates tours. **La Calzada** (☎ 551-3677, 556-0465) also offers tours to a local cheese factory, small ponds, and to a sugar cane plant. **Hector Lezama** at the Turrialtico restaurant (☎ 556-1111) will also arrange tours, including one to the top of Turrialba, but sufficent advance notice is required.

WATERFALLS: The **San Antonio waterfalls** are near Santa Rosa and the **Zapote waterfalls** are also nearby. Ask directions in town.

CLIMBING VOLCÁN TURRIALBA: From San José or Cartago one can go by bus to the village of Pacayas to reach the top of this semi-active 3,339-m (10,995-ft.) volcano on horseback or with a four-wheel drive. Another place to start your climb is from the village of Santa Cruz to the N. Although there's a four-wheel-drive road that winds up the mountain, it's too rough to drive more than two-thirds of the 21 km to the top. To hike, proceed from Santa Cruz along the main road for three km where you'll find the Bar Canada.

After turning R here, you'll find the sign marking the route after 600-800 ft. (200-300 m). Here, you turn R again and ascend. When you come to a fork (about every few km) take the trail which goes up; the other route usually goes to a farm. After about 7.5 mi.(12 km) of this, you'll come to a group of houses. Here, ascend via the R fork, and you'll reach a metal gate. After another km or so, you reach a fork where you go R and then go through a barbed wire gate (which may be rolled open). Pass by the cow barn and through another wire gate to its L. A few hundred yards (100-200 m) thereafter is the last spot to obtain water en route to the summit. The summit is another km or so up. There's a great camping area on top, and there are plenty of paths to explore.

ACCOMMODATIONS: Inexpensively-priced **Hotel Wagelia** (☎ 556-1566/1596, fax 556-1596) is the most attractive in-town choice. Their a/c rooms are in the moderate range (around US$65 pp); its **Hotel Wagelia Annex** (☎ 556-1142, fax 556-1596) is a converted old house set about a km from town which has a pool, restaurant, and basketball court. It charges around US$55 d; more expensive rooms have refrigerators and TVs.

The **Wittingham Hotel** (☎ 556-8822, 556-0013) is low-budget, i.e. caters to backpackers.

Also in town are the low-budget **Hotel Central, Hotel Chamanga, Hotel/ Pensión Primavera**, and **Interamericano** (☎ 556-0142, low-budget with shared bath). The **Pensión Chelita** (☎ 556-0214) and the **Hotel La Roche** (☎ 556-1627) are other alternatives.

About 15 min. SE of Turrialba by car, luxury 12-room and four-suite **Casa Turire** (☎ 531-1111, fax 531-1075) is set amidst a sugarcane, coffee, and macadamia nut plantation. It is one of Costa Rica's most famous luxury hotels. There's a restaurant, five-hole golf course, pool, and gardens. Rooms have refrigerators, satellite TV, and phone. Added touches in the room are floor tiles with floral designs, handpainted wardrobes, and flower arrangements in the bathroom. Horseback riding and mountain biking are also available. Rates start at around US$100 s or d. The hotel will have a "lake" next to it after 1999 or so when a dam is expected to have been completed. **turire@sol.racsa.co.cr**

If you wish to be near Guayabo, stay at low-budget **Hotel La Calzada** (message ☎ 573-3677, 556-0465, fax 556-0427), named after the indigenous trail that passes through the property. Meals are coooked over a wood-burning stove and geese and ducks reside on the property. Discounts are available here for YH members and students.

To the S of town, seven km along the road to Limón, **Albergue Mirador Turrialtico** (☎ 556-1111, see description below under "food") offers two inexpensive rooms for rent with private bath; breakfast is included.

A few km farther, **Albergue de Montaña Ponchotel** (☎ 556-0111, fax 556-6222) offers two inexpensive two-room *cabinas* with private bath. You can also camp here.

Set some 19 km from Guayabo, **Guayabo Lodge** (☎/fax 556-0133) is a small home set on a dairy farm owned by the Figueres family of presidential fame. It sports green and white decor — the colors of the Liberation Party.

Packages (around US$70 pp, pd) are available and include San José pickup.

Naturalists and horse lovers might choose to stay in the expensive 10-room **Albergue de Montaña Rancho Naturalista** (☎ 267-7138), up a dirt road from the village of Tuis to the SE. Laundry service and horse rental are included; there are nature trails and guided birdwatching. They provide an extensive birdlist which describes birds such as the green-backed heron, rufous-tailed hummingbird, tropical kingbird, and the golden-hooded tanager as being abundant here. Guided tours to Carara and other areas are offered. Accommodation is in the seven-bedroom main lodge and five cabins with private baths. Expect to spend about US$800/wk. Write Apdo. 364, 1002 San José or Dept. 1425, Box 025216, Miami, FL 33102-5216 for more information.

Also out of town is the 20-unit **Esperanza Reserva** (☎ 223-7074, fax 225-3095) which has cabins, pools, restaurant, and — of course — a reserve. Activities featured include kayaking, fishing, and hiking. Rates are around US$110 d plus tax; an all-inclusive package is available. In the US call 800-213-0051 or fax 401-453-3966.

Enroute to Guayabo and to the W of Pacayas, rustic yet homey **Campo Silvestre Proyecto Ecológico** (☎ 591-0800, 534-4357) charges around US$40 d with breakfast. It has a reforestation project and offers tours of nearby farms.

The eight-room **Albergue Volcán Turrialba** (☎ 273-4335; Apdo. 1632-2050) is an attractive lodge set just five km from the crater. It's off a side road located between Hacienda la Esperanza and Finca la Central. Meals are cooked on a wooden stove. Facilities include horseback rides (including one to the peak), carriage and ox cart tours, and bicycle tours and rentals. It's accessible only by four-wheel-drive. Rates are around US$65 pp including three meals and tax.

NOTE: *Accommodation in the direction of Orosi is listed under that section.*

FOOD: There are a large number of good places to eat in town. One of the best places in terms of value is **Restaurante El Caribeño**; try their *casado corriente* with fish. A convenient place to hang out, **Soda Valencia** is at one corner of the park. Inexpensive **La Garza** is right by the park and offers seafood. Popular with teenyboppers, **Pizza Julian** is just down the street and also facing the park. **Soda Bar Tico Chino** is one of several Chinese restaurants. There are also a number of supermarkets and a small market. **Café, Mani, Condimentos Turrialba** is across the street from **Faro Disco** and has health food items.

About 10 km E of town, **Ponchotel** offers Tico cuisine. They have a device which will bring your order up to the top of the observation tower. Located just four km from CATIE (the huge agricultural research facility — see below) and two km from Pochotel, **Restaurante Turrialtico** offers spectacular views, coffee-root sculptures by famed primitivists Benjamin Paniagua and Victor Barahona, and traditional-style food cooked over wood stoves. Specializing in Jamaican fare, **Restaurant Kingston** is right outside town. Another good place to eat is at **La Calzada** on the way to Guayabo.

Posada de la Luna is W of the church in Cervantes, halfway between Cartago and Turrialba. This restaurant is nearly as extra-terrestrial as its name implies. Certainly, it is unique to this planet. Housed in an unassuming red and yellow concrete building and under a corrugated roof with peeling red paint, this restaurant houses one of the nation's most spec-

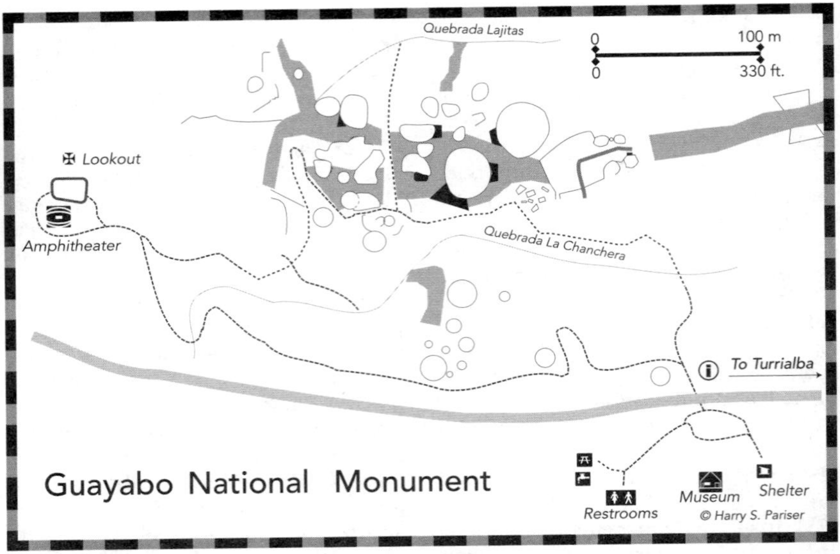

tacular museums. Among the items on display, some of which are housed in glass cabinets, are a sheathed sword inscribed in Arabic, rusty irons, old smashed-up radios, indigenous artifacts, a wooden Buddha, old newspapers (one headline reads "RENDICION TOTAL NAZI"), and a ceramic frog sitting in a brass chair. Packets of *chile jalapeno* are for sale. This is also one of the best places to try *típico* food. The *gallo pinto* and *tortilla de queso* here are legendary.

NIGHTLIFE: There's not much to do. The most exciting place is the frequently packed disco, **El Faro**. There are also three movie theaters; **La America** is in the main square. Bars with unusual ambience include **Bar la Cueva** in Santa Rosa, and (difficult to find) **Bar David** in La Suiza.

SERVICES: Codetel is up one block from a corner of the park.

Monument Nacional Guayabo (Guayabo National Monument)

Located 12 mi.(19 km) NE of Turrialba. **Guayabo** may be the nation's most famous archaeological site. It is, however, worth a visit more for its natural surroundings and overall ambience than for its ruins. While similar sites are found in Ciudad Cutris in the San Carlos region and in the Barranca de San Miguel de San Ramón, only Guayabo has been placed under protection. There's a nature trail with two branches, one of which drops down to the river, and there are a variety of mammals and more than 80 varieties of orchids. The archaeological site here is still under exploration, and it is open daily from 8-4. Free and quite informative guided tours are available, but they are in Spanish.

GETTING HERE: Get here from Turrialba by taking the *Santa Teresita* bus (daily at around 10:30 and 1:30); it terminates at the beginning of an uphill gravel road four km away. The bus returns from the crossroads at 12:45.

Another alternative is to take the bus which leaves from Turrialba at 5:15 PM and arrives at around 6:30 PM; it stays overnight and then returns at 5:40 AM. On Mon. and Fri. a bus leaves Turrialba for Guayabo at 11:15 and arrives at 12:45 PM. A bus on Sun. leaves at 9 and returns at 4. You can also take a taxi from Turrialba or hitch.

TOURS: Contact **Green Tropical Tours** (☎/fax 255-2859)
greentp@sol.racsa.co.cr

HISTORY: The settlement here once housed as many as 10,000 and covered an estimated 37 acres (15 ha). It is thought to have originated around 1,000 BC, thrived between 800 and 1300 AD, and declined thereafter and was abandoned about 1400 AD. The site's stone pedestals were thought to have been built between 800 and 1000 AD. Declared a national monument in 1973, it is the nation's only archaeological park. In order to protect the surrounding premontane rainforest, the Guayabo River Canyon area was added in 1980; its 539 acres (218 ha) now protect the only extant primary forest in Cartago Province. Begun in Aug. 1989, a five-year restoration plan will increase the excavated area to 50 acres (20 ha).

SIGHTS: The circular mounds (*montículos*) here once supported large buildings. Some of the stones in the walkways (*calzadas*) are decorated with petroglyphs, and there's also a large boulder carved with representations of the crocodile and the jaguar, both indigenous deities. Although the meaning of the petroglyphs found at the site is unknown, it is commonly thought that they were carved to invoke supernatural protection. There's a system of aqueducts, and what may be the nation's oldest bridge: a broken black rock which crosses an aqueduct. There are great views from the *mirador* which has sets of wooden benches placed in rows, giving it a resemblance to an outdoor theater. At the base of the ruins near the exit is a partial reconstruction of a four-km walkway. Unfortunately, the rest of the land remains in private hands so there is no likelihood of it being restored.

While the trail to the L leads past the ruins, the one to the R is a loop trail which heads through secondary forest. Across the road from the entrance are the picnic area and toilets. A small exhibition hall with some zoomorphic figures and ceramics and another room with an archaeological reconstruction of the site are nearby.

PRACTICALITIES: Camping is permitted. Nearby accommodations are listed under "Turrialba" above. In addition to the aforementioned **La Calzada**, there are a number of places to eat here. **Soda La Palma** is closest to the reserve's entrance. **Soda La Orquídea** is in the Colonia Guayabo which you pass on the way up.

Other Attractions Near Turrialba

Whitewater Rafting

One of the most popular activities for visitors to Costa Rica, even those who are not particularly athletic, is rafting on the Río Reventazón, the "foaming" river. The Class II rapids on this river serve as an excellent introduction to rafting for the inexperienced, and rafting is one way to discover that a river has a life and personality all its own.

Of the many companies rafting on the river, **Costa Rica Expeditions** (☎ 257-0776, 222-0333 fax 257-1665; costa-rica@expeditions.co.cr; www.expeditions.co.cr) is the longest established. Its owner-managers first opened the river up for rafting in 1979. After a hotel pick-up and a stop for a Costa Rican-style morning feed, you'll be bused through Turrialba to the river, where the rafts and equipment are assembled. You'll be given safety instructions and perform a trial run before departure. Going down the river, you can expect to spin around backwards — one of the thrills! You'll pass oropéndola nests, giant ferns, hanging epiphytes, sloths in the treetops, and perhaps some agricultural workers; you may even spot a crocodile or toucan. There might be a place where you have to disembark and then reboard because of dangerous riptides, and you'll stop briefly for swimming. Lunch is served in a tent off the river bank. After passing through some more rapids (and traversing a kayak endurance course), you'll come to the end of the run. The rubber rafts are hauled up. Then, it's back to San José.

The other companies, such as **Ríos Tropicales** (☎ 233-6455, fax 255-4354; www.riostro.com; info@riostro.com) and **Adventuras Naturales** (☎ 225-3939; www.toenjoynature.com; avenat@sol.racsa.co.cr), differ in small details such as lunch sites. Expect to pay around US$65 for the day. In the area contact **Tico River Adventures** (☎ 556-1231), **Dos Ríos** (☎ 556-1575, 556-1111), or **Rios Aventuras** (☎ 556-9617; www.costaricarios.com).

One good local company is **Locos Tropical Rafting Tours** (☎ 556-6035).

NOTE: Rafting on the river will come to an end after a dam is completed in the early 2010s. So send a written protest to the government!

CATIE

Located four km E of Turrialba on the road to Limón, the Centro Agronomico Tropical de Investigación y Enseñanza, a 27,500-acre agricultural research station, provides assistance to the small farmer. Established in the 1930s, it is one of the world's five major centers for tropical agricultural research. Supported partly by overseas governments, research here is devoted to producing high-yielding disease-resistant varieties of bananas, coffee, and cacao.

Other research projects include studies on improving palms, plantains and on breeding livestock which will thrive on pasture alone without supplemental feed. New species are replicated in a tissue culture lab and packed for shipment worldwide. Tropical agricultural instructors from all over the world gather here for study. The world's largest collection of papers and books on tropical agriculture is here. There's also a collection of hundreds of species of palms. Visiting birdwatchers should be aware that, in addition to a lagoon, there's also a trail from behind the administration building to Río Reventazón.

VISITING: If you wish to tour the grounds with an English-speaking guide, call 556-6431, 556-0755, or fax 556-7948 three days ahead of time to arrange an appointment. The tour includes a visit to the seed lab and bank, the meat and dairy farm, orchids, coffee, cacao, and other research facilities. There is also a birdwatching trail. Organized groups are preferred. Ask in town concerning buses.

Parque Viborana

Set in the village of Pavones, a 20-min. drive from downtown, snake expert Minor Camacho operates a great serpentarium. You may walk right in the cage and see the boa constrictors. The deadlies are safely ensconsed behind glass. Admission to the farm and displays (cell.☎ 381-4781) is around US$4 for adults.

Puerto Viejo de la Sarapiquí Region

This wet but wonderfully scenic area is set on the slopes above the Caribbean coast to the N and NE of Braulio Carrillo Park and also bordering La Selva. Depending on which of the two routes you take getting here, you may pass pejibaye palm plantations, two of the nation's most beautiful waterfalls, banana plantations, lush bamboo thickets, and some superb scenic outlooks.

GETTING HERE: Buses (4.5 hrs.) depart six times daily from Av. 11, C. Central/1. One at 9 follows the Carr. Guápiles via Braulio Carrillo before turning N towards Horquetas and La Selva, then terminates at Puerto Viejo. The bus at 1 runs back through to San José. The one at 4 goes the same way but stops in La Virgen. The buses at 6:30, noon, and 3 take the route above Heredia. A *San Carlos-Río Frio bus* (two hrs.) also runs.

> When taking a bus to this area, be sure to get a bus to the correct Puerto Viejo, as it may be easy to confuse this one with its Caribbean Coast namesake.

Rara Avis

Established as a corporation in 1983, Rara Avis S. A., comprising 1,500 acres (600 ha), is the only place of its kind in the world. Biologist-entrepreneur Amos Bien's philosophy is that development and conservation can be compatible and mutually reinforcing. His hope is to set an example which the local people will follow. One way is through tourism: the reserve is already the largest employer in Horquetas. Another is through utilizing the rainforest commercially without destroying it. Future projects planned include the commercial production of tree ferns, wicker, and wood, all to be done in an ecologically sustainable fashion. At present butterflies are being exported in cocoon form to Europe. If you only have time to visit one private nature preserve, this is the one to see! Jan., Feb., and March are busiest here.

Rara Avis (☎ 764-3131; fax 764-4187; Apdo. 8105, 1000 San José) is set 2,000 ft. (700 m) above the often-inclement Caribbean coast so you have a 75% chance of being rained on if you come for a short visit. So don't plan your schedule too tightly. May is both rainy and is "horsefly month"; Oct. is a good month to visit. It is constantly booked so reservations are a must.

GETTING HERE: This is the fun part! When you reserve, Amos will instruct you when and how to meet the tractor near Las Horquetas; it pulls a green canvas-covered cart with seats. The normal transit point is the "casa de Roberto Villalobos," (☎ 764-4187), where the Rara Avis office is located. A "Jungle Train" truly worthy of the name, this infamous "tractor from Hell" takes you on a bumping and jarring ride, traversing only nine km in the interim. Much improved from earlier times, it now takes four hrs. in the rain and 2.5 hrs. under sunny skies.

Fording two rivers en route, you pass slowly-moving panoramas of local life, past rolling hill after rolling hill of sadly deforested terrain, most of it cut down by local farmers who eke out a living by using it for pasture. As an additional bonus, as you ride along you learn how clothes feel while they're in the dryer. Finally, you arrive at El Plástico, a former prison colony site. The name relates to the fact that prisoners slept on the ground outside under plastic tarps. The renovated lodge here formerly housed administrators. Surrounded by volcanoes Barva, Turrialba, Irazú, and Cacho Negro, the Caribbean coast is also visible from here. Check out the framed portrait of the Patron Saint of the Jungle upstairs.

El Plastico and the surrounding 1,400 acres (572 ha) are owned by Selva Tica (☎ 253-0844). In the dry season, you will have lunch here before proceeding; in the wet season, you'll likely continue on to the waterfall lodge where you'll dine and recuperate. The last stretch of the road has been improved and is now accessible by tractor and on horseback.

SIGHTS: The chief attraction is the spectacular two-tiered Catarata Rara Avis which has a swimming hole at its base; an alarm — installed after three Canadian students drowned in a freak avalanche of water — warns of flash floods coming from above. There is also an orchidarium with some 100 species of orchids.

OTHER ATTRACTIONS: A birdwatcher's paradise, Rara Avis has had confirmed sightings of 335 species. Check out the hummingbird feeder as well as the area by the bridge. Other things to revel in include the spectacular collection of butterflies, the beautiful sunsets, the amazing night noises in the forest, and you can see the lights of the banana plantations off in the distance on a clear evening.

PRACTICALITIES: Albergue El Plastico charges around US$45 pp (US$22.50 for student groups). There are four rooms with a total of 10 lower bunks and nine upper bunks, and shared hot showers and flush toilets.

The eight-room **Waterfall Lodge** (US$80 s, US$75 pp d) can hold up to 32. Each room is equipped with a double bed, a single, and two fold-down bunks. There are hammocks for lounging outside and a reading area upstairs where a pressure lamp attracts an incredibly diverse flying entomology museum every evening. A thatched *rancho* provides a place for groups to gather. There's a two-night minimum stay. Although large groups may leave at any time, departures for small groups are scheduled for every Tues., Fri., and Sunday. Aside from the meals, nothing else is available for sale so anything (including candy or any other snacks) that you might require should be brought with you. The beer, soft drink, and phone concessions belong to the cook. While Rara Avis has a large supply of rubber boots, essential for exploring the reserve, there is no guarantee that a pair will fit you, so you might consider bringing your own.

www.intelog.com/~rainfrst
www.rara-avis.com
raraavis@sol.racsa.co.cr

La Selva Biological Reserve

La Selva is second only to Monteverde as the nation's most well-known privately-run natural reserve. With more than 100 species of mammals, 400 species of birds, thousands of species of insects, and 2,000 plant species, La Selva could never bore a true naturalist. Located near the confluence of the Puerto Viejo and Sarapiquí rivers, this 3,707-acre (1,500-ha) tract is owned and operated by the Organization for Tropical Studies (OTS), and its main function is as a research station for visiting biologists.

In the 1950s tropical biologist Dr. Leslie Holdridge began an experimental farm (*cacao, pejibaye*, and laurel) on the present-day site. In 1960, he sold the farm and the surrounding old growth to the OTS. Today, it has a large number of lowland tropical forest trails. On a walk, you might see anything from poison dart frogs to sloths to *caimáns*.

The site of a small field of *cacao* with a rich overstory of shade trees, the 8.7-acre (3.5-ha) **Holdridge Arboretum** contains more than 240 species, more than two-thirds of the native tree species at La Selva; its openness makes it easy to view the tree crowns.

PRACTICALITIES: Reservations are essential. A day visit is around US$18 which includes lunch. Three meals in the cafeteria and a night in the "rustic" quarters (bunkrooms with shared hot water bathrooms) cost around US$90. The hefty fees help support ongoing research. Contact OTS (☎ 240-6696, fax 240-6783; Apdo. 676, 2050 San Pedro) about overnight stays. For day visits call La Selva directly at 710-6897. Ask about their bus that runs three times a week. **www.ots.ac.cr laselva@ns.ots.ac.cr**

Selva Verde River Lodge

Located in Chilamate, five min. W of Puerto Viejo, this attractively designed lodge (☎ 710-6077, fax 766-6011) has a 600-acre (243-ha) forest reserve across the river. This large establishment is popular with those who want a more comfortable experience than at Rara Avis and is especially popular with Elderhostel There's the river lodge trail, a self-guiding 45-min. nature trail right on the premises (with a several-century-old *gavilán* tree numbering among the giants), the river (good birdwatching) is readily accessible, and a butterfly garden is across the road. To visit the reserve you head out to the main road, turn R, then turn R again and cross the bridge. Get a map from the reception and follow any of the trails through the secondary forest which has patches of old growth. You may see white-faced monkeys.

GETTING HERE: Selva Verde will provide transportation from San José by prearrangement. Otherwise, the bus will drop you by the entrance if you let the driver know. Another option is to take a taxi from Puerto Viejo. If you're driving, it's conveniently located right off the highway.

PRACTICALITIES: This large lodge is divided into two portions, each of which are on opposite sides of the highway. The main portion is a series of attractive structures accessed by a beautiful covered boardwalk. Enroute to your room you pass by a stream with turtles basking in the sun. You might see an armadillo dart across a path or a hummingbird flit by. Each room is equipped with hot water shower, fan, and dresser. Hammocks are on the balconies. Across the road and well back along a slope, a set of five bungalows are aligned along a black-painted wooden walkway. There are four beds (two bunk beds) in each room plus a fan, walk-in closet, and bath. Prepared with fresh vegetables, meals are served buffet-style in the spacious dining room above the bar and gift shop. A library is also here. Activities include nature walks, rafting, bike tours, canoe trips, a river boat tour, guided trail walks, and a butterfly garden tour. The premises are non-smoking, with several smoking areas provided. Rates start at around US$75 pp, single occupancy, and

The Virgin of Sarapiqui

As the start of the next milennium nears, Virgin Mary sightings and the like are on the increase. One such sighting took place in the hills above San Vincente de Miguel, 120 km N of San José, where then 15-year-old Jorge Arturo first spotted her in Jan. 1993 near a weathered tree trunk amidst a pejibaye plantation. Since that date, Arturo has become a celebrity and regularly communicates with the spirit. He says she speaks to him in Spanish and changes her robe each time she appears. A statue has been erected in the "Holy Forest" where she appeared, but he claims that the apparition is much more beautiful than the statue. Jorge now plans to become a priest.

Pilgrims still flock to the spot. Its creek has become contaminated with fecal matter so visitors collect purified water dispensed from a pump near the statue (designed to match Jorge's description); cement walkways have been put in along with restrooms and parking spaces. An ambulance is on the scene on "apparition" days, but a radio campaign has educated attendees about the dangers of staring straight into the sun so cases of sun damaged vision have decreased. A booth in the parking area sells transcripts of monthly messages and religious paraphernalia in return for an unspecified donation. The money collected is slated to be used to erect a church. The only hitch is that the Church does not recognize the site, and *La Nación* has published an admonition from the Bishop of San José which warns Catholics not to visit the sight until the apparitions have been officially recognized. Few people lay claim to having actually seen the Virgin, but some claim to have seen cloud formations resembling Jesus, the sun changing colors, and even attendees surrounded by halos. Meetings — attracting believers from as far away as the US and Italy — are held on the first of every month and are led in devotion by a priest. Jorge stands near the altar at 2PM: the Virgin transmits her message, and he lets everyone in on it.

US$65 pp, double occupancy, including meals but not tax. Bungalows rent for from US$35 pd for student groups and US$46 for four and up. Write Costa Rican Lodges, Ltd., 3540 NW 13th St., Gainesville, FL 32609 or call (800) 451-7118 or, in FL, (800) 345-7111.
www.holbrooktravel.com
travel@holbrooktravel.com

La Quinta De Sarapiquí

This Tico-run lodge (☎/fax 761-1052) is set by the side of the Río Sardinal between La Virgen and Puerto Viejo. Each of the ten rooms (around US$50 d) have fans and porches. It has a restaurant, game room, and there is a reforested tract. Activities include hiking, swimming, mountain biking, horseback riding, and birding.

Centro Neotrópico Sarapiquí

The brand new **Centro Neotrópica** (☎/fax 761-1004; San José: 239-2738), a public museum built using pre-Columbian architectural techniques. It opened during the summer of 1999 and features "the story of the rainforest." Also on the property are a 24-unit lodge, a research station, and a restaurant overlooking the Sarapiquí. The impressive *museo* is the gateway to the Reserva Jirimbina across the river. A visit costs a steep US$25 (US$12.50, children under 12), but it includes a guided tour of the museum, reserve, gardens, and canopy walk. Allow 4-6 hrs. Rates are around US$72 s, US$85 d; children are half price. Vegetarian food is an alternative offered in the restaurant.
magistra@sol.racsa.co.cr

Other Puerto Viejo Area Attractions

El Gavilán Lodge

Covering 432 acres (175 ha) and lying 90 km from San José by the Río Sarapiquí in Río Frio, this private reserve opened in 1989.

PRACTICALITIES: One-day to one-week packages (including San José pickup for US$20 pp; four-person minimum) are available. There are 12 rooms with private bath, hot water, and fan. German/Spanish cuisine is served. Vegetarians can be catered to. Although there's a BYOB policy in effect with respect to alcohol, delicious tropical fruit drinks are served. One-day excursions from San José, including a boat trip on the Sarapiquí or horseback riding, are also available, as are river trips to Barra Colorado and white-water kayaking on the Sarapiquí. Write Apdo. 445-Zapote, 2010 San José, fax 253-6556, or call 253-9507.

costarica.tourism.co.cr/hotels/gavilan
gavilan @sol.racsa.co.cr

Oro Verde Station

Nestled between the Sarapiquí and the Sucio rivers, this spartan but expensive lodge is set amidst a large garden within a former cattle ranch. Three-day packages (around US$200 pp) are offered. Call 233-7479 or fax 223-7479.

Puerto Viejo De La Sarapiqui

Once an important and bustling trade settlement in the long departed days of river travel, the town is chiefly of note for its low-budget hotels: **Cabinas Restaurant Monte Verde** (☎ 766-6236), **Hospedaje Santa Marta**, **Hotel Gonar** (☎/fax 766-6196), **Hotel Santa María**, and **Restaurant Cabinas La Paz**. More expensive is **Mi Lindo Sarapiquí** (☎ 766-6281) which offers attractive rooms above its restaurant for around US$20 d.

Hospitable **Hotel Bambú** (☎ 766-6005, fax 766-6132) offers modern rooms with TVs for around US$50 d including breakfast.

Andrea Cristina Bed and Breakfast (☎/fax 776-6265) has rooms with fans and a small pool. The owner is an environmental activist.

Cabinas Manglares are to the L before town. There are also a number of inexpensive places to eat. The *soda* by the water is a good place to hang out; Don Justo here can help you with transport.

Set four km from town on the Chilamate road, **Cabinas Yacaré** (☎ 766-6691) offers attractive low-budget rooms; the Cristo Rey bus passes by.

La Virgen

The area in and around this village offers a number of options. At about US$4 pp and right in the village, **Cabinas el Río** is one of the only truly low-budget places to stay. It's near a *comedor* and next to a store. Behind it, you can follow a black bridge past attacking geese (the charge of the white brigade) to a really nice covered patio complete with hammocks — a perfect spot to relax.

Set at the end of the village on the way to Selva Verde, **Rancho Leona**, a restaurant run by Leona and Ken, has a library and art studio. **Kayak Jungle Tours** (☎/fax 761-1019; La Virgen de Sarapiquí, Heredia) is headquartered here. Seed jewelry and tee shirts are on sale. Trips—from beginning to advanced — run around US$75 pp. for a day; longer trips (to Caño Negro and Tortuguero) are more expensive. Kayakers lodge at the Rancho for two nights. Trips (US$250 pp) on the Río Bongo in Nicoya are also offered from Sept.-Nov. They also have a

rainforest dome (holds up to 11) and now offer treks there. They serve everything from salads to eggplant parmesan and banana splits.
rleona@sol.racsa.co.cr

You can also eat at **El Rancho de Doña Rosa** near La Selva.

The 34-room **Islas del Río**, a moderate to expensive hotel (☎ 710-6898, 233-0366, fax 233-9671) is six km W of Puerto Viejo. Also set up as a "youth hostel," it's unfortunately not very impressive for the price.

Rancho Turisticos Los Venados is set near La Virgen and has meals, a pool, and hiking; live music is featured nightly; it's open 7AM-11PM daily.

MUSA: On the R in the village of La Tigre as you approach Puerto Viejo from Horquetas, this female-run cooperative sells local herbs. You can tour their farm and learn about natural remedies. Unfortunately, due to petty squabbling, it is not as enchanting as it used to be.

TRAVELING UP THE SARAPIQUÍ: Many lodges offer trips up here. One of the most unusual is the Río Colorado Lodge's trip up the Río Sarapiquí from Puerto Viejo. (See the "Barra del Colorado" section for details). Heading up as far as Río San Juan, a public launch also departs from the pier between 10 and noon, returning at 5 the next morning.

FROM PUERTO VIEJO: There are two routes. The more scenic is toward Chilamate and down. The other is on gravel roads through the heart of the banana plantations and past bamboo groves— an equally fascinating excursion in its own right. Watch for the aerial tramways which transport the bananas.

Monteverde/Arenal Area

Over the past few years, this area has become one of the most popular areas for visitors. Centrally located, it can easily be visited enroute to Guanacaste. The main attractions in this area include the cloud forest reserve (described in the following section), the other sights near Monteverde, and the active Arenal volcano and its nearby artificial lake of the same name.

EXPLORING: This area would be ideal to travel around in a rental vehicle with because public transportation tends to be poor. You can get around by bus, but you must be patient. Road conditions between Arenal and Monteverde are poor. March and April are the best times to visit Monteverde because you are most likely to see a quetzal then.

Reserva Biológica Del Bosque Nuboso Monteverde (Monteverde Biological Reserve)

If you have somehow managed not to have heard the name "Monteverde" prior to your arrival in Costa Rica, you certainly will have before long! Although Costa Rica has any number of cloud forests, Monteverde— despite its dusty, winding road— remains both the most accessible and the most developed. The combination of the Quaker colony, the reserve, and years of hype have transformed the area into a major tourist destination and big business. An incredible 50,000 visitors enter the reserve annually! Don't be under the illusion that Monteverde is a town. It isn't! Monteverde is a community of Quakers who originally came here to live apart from American "civilization." It is ironic that, in doing just that and in seeking to preserve the cloud forest, they have attracted unwanted attention and loosed the devil of development upon themselves.

ITINERARY: Plan on spending at least one full day (i.e., two nights) in Monteverde in order to fully appreciate the reserve. If you are intent on visiting both reserves and the surrounding area, then more then three days or more are necessary.

APPAREL: Keep in mind that it rains a lot: have your umbrella in hand at during May to Nov. and a poncho between Dec. and April (when a strong wind blows). Be sure to have warm clothes handy on the way up and be ready to take off your sweater as you descend to sweltering lowland Guanacaste on the return stretch. Rubber boots are not a necessity, but the reserve does rent them.

> Look for quetzals near *aguacatillio* trees. Their fleshy, black-colored fruit is a favorite with the birds.

FLORA AND FAUNA: Vegetation is profuse and, despite the 300 species of orchids, very green. The 2,500 plant species include 200 types of ferns. Many of the canopy plants take their nutrients directly from the mist and dust suffusing the air. The reserve is not all cloud forest: there are relatively dry areas, swamps, and dwarf trees. There are a wealth of other reptiles and amphibians, some 490 species of butterflies, and

The Golden Toad

Aside from the quetzal, the nation's most famous living creature is the golden toad, so far sighted only in Monteverde's rainforest preserve. In 1983, University of Miami researcher Marc Hayes spotted hundreds; none have been spotted since 1987. This is part of a worldwide decline of amphibians (also encompassing glass frogs and rain frogs), and no one knows what the cause is. Some think that acid rain and airborne pesticides may be to blame. Some scientists maintain that amphibians may be a canary in a coalmine, a portent boding of coming ecological disaster. Others connect this depletion with a concomitant increase in lawyers, politicians, and advertising account executives. frogs book! For a the story of the discovery of the golden toad and its subsequent disappearance, as well as an informed account of the disappearance of frogs all over the world, check out the superb book, *Tracking the Vanishing Frogs* by Kathryn Phillips.

some 100 species of mammals. In addition to the quetzal, other birds to watch out for include the ornate hawk-eagle, bare-necked umbrella bird and the three-wattled bellbird, as well as 50 varieties of hummingbirds.

SIGHTING A QUETZAL: If you really want to see one, you're likely to be disappointed! One way to ensure a sighting is to visit in the wee morning hours, especially in the nesting months (March-June), when they are most conspicuous. Painted picture signs along the trail demarcate Quetzal Country. (For more information about the quetzal, see the description in the Introduction).

HISTORY: Founded in 1951 by Quakers from Alabama seeking a better spot to live after some had been imprisoned for refusing the draft, the Monteverde farming community came in, purchased land, and struggled to establish itself. It soon discovered cheese-making, which now provides its principal income as well as that of the area's numerous Tico dairy farmers. Over the years the colony has grown, and many non-Quakers have settled here as well.

The cloud forest reserve was initiated by George and Harriet Powell in March, 1972. Originally, 6,200 acres (2,500 ha) of land were set aside as a reserve; another 24,700 (10,000 ha) have been added.

Tourism has grown to become the area's major "industry" during the past decade or so; as recently as 1974 Monteverde received only some 400 visitors per year. However, the financial benefits of "ecotourism" remain outside of the community as much of the money stays parked in San José or in the States. Intelligently, the area's long established cooperative loans its funds for what it views as long-term sustainable investments: handicrafts, coffee cultivation, and dairy farming. The area's population has now grown to around 3,500— a 25% increase in the past five years or so.

GETTING HERE: Buses depart daily at 6:30 AM and 2 and 2:30 PM from the *Terminal Atlántico Norte, C. 14, Av. 9,* ☎ 222-3854; C. 12, Av. 9/11) in San José. Costa Rica Expeditions also has a bus which runs to its hotel, and most hotels can arrange van transportation from San José. Be sure to ask the driver to stop in front of your hotel.

BY CAR: Take the Interamerican Highway (Carr. 1), to the junction at Km 149 (look for the iron bridge crossing the Río Lagarto; it's easily missed) and then proceed another 20 mi.(32 km) along a steep and dusty dirt road; it may be impassable without a four-wheel drive during portions of the rainy season. The best photos will be from the R-hand side of your vehicle.

FROM PUNTARENAS: This route is convenient if you're coming from Montezuma, Manuel Antonio, or if you are unable to take a direct bus from San José. A daily bus runs at 2:15 PM from the bus shelter along the oceanfront and a block away from the Puntarenas-San José bus station. To meet this bus if you are coming from San José you must leave San José by 11 AM. If you don't go through Puntarenas, you can take the 12:45 PM *San José-Tilarán* bus (☎ 222-3854, C. 12, Av. 9/11) and transfer at the Lagarto junction on the Interamerican. Your hotel will send a taxi to meet you in Santa Elena if you have made reservations in advance.

FROM LA FORTUNA/TILARÁN: From La Fortuna (Arenal area) you need to take a bus to Tilarán at 8 AM (three hrs.). Then take a bus to Santa Elena at 12:30 PM (3.5 hrs.). It may not come all the way in the rainy season so plan on walking for around an hour.

FROM THE NORTH: Take any bus along the Interamerican. Get off at the Lagarto junction and take the first arriving bus up the hill.

BY CAR: The road from the Lagarto junction off of the Interamerican leads to Santa Elena and Monteverde. A shortcut from San José is to take the Sardinal turnoff (look for it some 20 km before Puntarenas), head L from the town central square, and then continue on to Guacimal where you join with the regular road. A third option is to head from Tilarán to Quebrada Grande and Cabeceras and then head either up Turín or Las Nubes (the L). Allow around three hrs., and don't attempt this route during the wet.

ORIENTATION: From the junction at Lagarto, your bus climbs two hours along a winding, dusty road, passes thoroughly deforested terrain, and then enters the village of Santa Elena. It stops in town and then heads up the hill towards Monteverde. If taking the afternoon bus from San José, you may have to stop and switch into a smaller bus which appears to have been designed for midgets: woe to those with long legs! The bus usually also stops at a slightly overpriced basic restaurant.

From the town, two badly rutted roads lead towards the cloud forest reserve and then eventually merge. (A separate road heads out in the direction of the Santa Elena reserve). The N road passes by the clinic, and the S road passes by Costa Rica Expeditions' Monteverde Lodge. After the merger, the first landmark is El Sapo Dorado to the L. Up the hill, you pass the Heliconia, Monteverde Inn, Manakin, Cabinas Los Piños, and the Monteverde Conservation League.

The road veers off to the L, with the gas station and nearby souvenir stand, which leads to Hotel Belmar, the El Bosque, the Co-op, the Lecheria, Pensión Flor Mar, the Friend's Meetinghouse and School, the Fonda Vela, the taxi and telephone service, and then, onward and upward, past Villa Verde, past the estate of legendary nature photographers the Fogdens, to the reserve entrance.

Monteverde Sights

There are a growing number of things to do in this area. Suggestions are detailed below and in the Santa Elena section. For an overview of the area, hike up to the TV towers from behind the Hotel

Belmar. On a clear day, you can see as far as Nicoya. Aside from visiting the two reserves, one of the butterfly gardens, and/or going horseback riding, you can also hike down (and up!) to the waterfalls in San Luis.

MONTEVERDE CLOUD FOREST PRESERVE: Straddling the low continental divide in the Cordillera de Tilarán at the junction of Alajuela, Guanacaste, and Puntarenas provinces, the reserve (or "preserve" depending on your prediliction) ranges from 4,000 to 5,800 ft. (1,200-1,800 m) in elevation. Here, you are about to enter cloud forest country, one of the most luxurious found in all of the Americas. From May through Oct. it rains almost daily.

VISITING THE RESERVE: Stop in the visitor's center (☎ 645-5122, fax 645-5034; open 7-4) where you pay, ask your questions, and receive a detailed trail map of the reserve. Entrance fee is around US$8 for adults. There is a discount for students (US$4), residents and nationals (US$1); children under 15 are free. Weekly passes are available. In addition to the entrance

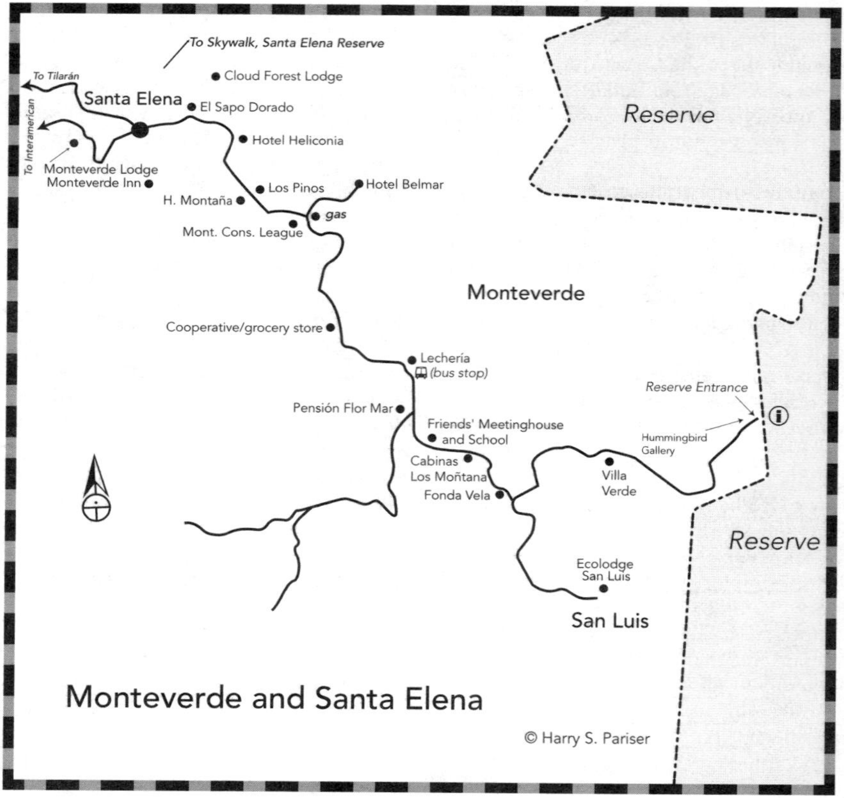

Monteverde Music Festival

A series of high-quality concerts are presented at 5 PM daily at the Fonda Vela Hotel during the dry season. Latin American, jazz, and classical concerts are presented. Buses will meet you at your hotel. From the beginning of Jan. to mid-Feb. annually For information call 645-5125/5119 or fax 257-1413 or 257-1416.

fee, tour groups are now required to pay a user's fee of US$10 for each visitor they bring in. (All of this brings in revenues of some US$850,000 annually!)

Only 100 visitors are allowed in the reserve at one time, so — if planning an early hike during tourist season (mid-Dec.-April) — you might wish to buy your admission ticket the previous day to avoid disappointment. Guided, four-hour nature walks (US$24 including admission) are conducted every morning; proceeds go towards an Environmental Education Fund. Night hikes (you might see phosphorescent mushrooms or an olingo) are also offered in season. Inside the reserve, the steps in some areas are fashioned from logs with a covering of netting to prevent slippage. As you go farther out, the trails become less "civilized" and, therefore, less traveled. It's safe to refill your canteen at either of the two waterfalls.

SUGGESTED ROUTING: This depends on your disposition and time requirements. You might go out on the *Sendero Nubose*, then go down the *Sendero Brillante* to Marker No. 28 where there's a view at the *"ventana"* (window), with rainforest stretching off into the distance. Then hike back up the *Sendero Pantanoso* and either along the *Sendero Río* (with a stop at the gorgeous, two-tiered waterfall) and then back. Two side trails, the *Sendero Bosque Eterno* and the *Sendero George Powell*, connect the *Sendero Río* with the Chomongo.
www.cct.or.cr
montever@sol.racsa.co.cr

MONTEVERDE CONSERVATION LEAGUE: To prevent Monteverde from becoming a green, isolated island in a sea of deforestation, this organization (☎ 645-5003, fax 645-5104) is endeavoring to expand the reserve by the end of the century to 30,000 acres (12,141 ha). They have a small gift shop.

Their *Sendero Bajo del Tigre* is a two-mi.-long trail which is past the CASEM store; it's open 7-5 daily. US$5 admission.
acmmcl@sol.racsa.co.cr

BUTTERFLY GARDEN: One of the nation's best, this garden exhibits some 40 species of butterflies in a forest that has been covered with a fine screen. It's open 9:30-4:30 daily; US$5 admission. The entrance is marked by a path commencing at the Hotel Heliconia. Follow the butterfly-shaped signs.

OTHERS: Other attractions in the area include the **Parque Ecológico** (US$5 admission, open 9-5 and for night tours) which feeds wild animals and the **Serpentario Santa Elena** (☎ 645-5243; US$3 admission) which offers guided tours.

The El Sapo Dorado (☎ 645-5010) arranges 3-4 hr. tours of **Sendero Tranquilo**, a private reserve.

The **Original Canopy Tour** (☎ 645-5243, ☎/fax 257-5149) charges around US$45 (student discount available) to zoom up the canopy. Their office is in Cerro Plano which is near Johnny's Pizzeria.
www.canopytour.co.cr
canopy @sol.racsa.co.cr

SKY WALK: A set of suspension bridged running above rainforest canopy, the **Sky Walk** (☎ 645-5238, fax 645-5796) offers a very special way to visit the forest's upper realm. The 1.8 km trail runs in a loop through cloud forest in a set of five suspension bridges. Admission is US$8 for *gringos*, US$6 for *gringo* students, and US$4 for the citizens of *Pura Vida*. It is open 7-4, and special arrangments may be made for groups who wish to visit earlier or later. It is set 3.5 km N of Santa Elena on the way to the Santa Elena Reserve.
www.skywalk.com
info@skywalk.com

> Unless, you have a rental car be sure to factor in the cost of a taxi back and forth from the reserve when you calculate your room rates. It is impractical to walk there from many of them!

SANTA ELENA RAIN FOREST RESERVE (RESERVA SANTA ELENA): Set five km NE of Santa Elena, this 900-acre (364-ha) reserve has around 10 km of trails and is open from 7-5. You can see Volcán Arenal. You need a four-wheel drive to get here. The reserve was created by the local high school in cooperation with Youth Challenge International, a Canadian organization. Admission is about US$5. Some local guides, trained in 1993, can show you around. It's quite a bit less developed (an less crowded) than the Monteverde reserve and has mostly secondary growth forest. Many birds seen here are not found in the Monteverde reserve. Call 645-5390 or fax 645-5014 to arrange a guided tour.
forestse@sol.racsa.co.cr

> The nearest place to the reserve to stay is Cabinas El Gran Mirador in San Gerardo (see mention under Santa Elena later in this chapter).

PARQUE DE AVES: This reserve is in the village of Cerro Plano which is halfway between Santa Elena and Monteverde. It's open daily until 4 PM, and admission is around US$5 pp. The property includes banana groves, coffee fields, and secondary forests. Coming here with a guide would be preferable.

BEN: Begun in 1988 and already extending over 17,000 acres (7,000 ha), El Bosque Eterno de los Niños (BEN, the Children's Rainforest), is perhaps the world's most singular rainforest conservation project, and it is the product of a single farsighted individual. Teaching in Fagerveig, Sweden, Sharon Kinsman (originally from the State of Maine in the US) was showing slides about the cloud forest to her class when a student volunteered his pocket money to help save rainforest land. The class had soon accumulated funds sufficient to purchase 16 ha; students from the US, UK, and Germany also pitched in, and the preserve continues to grow. Fifty dollars buys an acre, so you can earmark any collection and send it in care of the Monteverde Conservation League, the Nature Conservancy, or the World Wildlife Fund. In return, you'll receive a letter showing how many acres you've saved.

Monteverde Practicalities

MONTEVERDE ACCOMMODATION: New hotels here are sprouting faster than mushrooms after a spring shower, many of them quite attractive and tasteful. While you probably won't require reservations off-season, they are mandatory during the dry season. Christmas and Easter are booked months in advance.

First out of Santa Elena enroute to the preserve, the **Finca Valverde** (☎/fax 645-5157) is a coffee plantation with five cabins for around US$45 d; there're some short trails, a restaurant, and horseback riding.

Expensive **Monteverde Lodge** (☎ 645-5057, fax 645-5126) is run by Costa Rica Expeditions. It has private bus service from San José, a Jacuzzi, conference room, gardens, and some short trails. Rates are around US$ 115 d including tax. Meals are expensive but gourmet.
www.expeditions.co.cr
costa-rica@expeditions.co.cr

Run by a friendly and informative couple, **El Sapo Dorado** (☎/fax 645-5010, fax 645-5180; Apdo. 9-5655, Monteverde; a bar and international restaurant outside of Santa Elena, has 20 attractive cabin suites for around US$55 s, US$ 65 d plus tax.. They offer hiking and occasional live music.
www.coolco.cr/usr/sapodorado
elsapo@sol.racsa.co.cr

The attractive and secluded **Pensión Monteverde Inn** (☎ 645-5156) offers eight rooms with private bath and two with shared; rates are around US$15; packages with food are available; they will cater to vegetarians. It has friendly and helpful owners, a private 28-acre (11-ha) preserve, horseback riding, and other amenities. It is about one km off the road to the R near the butterfly garden.

The Spanish-style **Hotel Heliconia** (☎ 645-5109, fax 645-5205) is another of the hotels closest to Santa Elena. It has bathtubs, a Jacuzzi, private reserve, and conference rooms. Its international restaurant is reserved only for guests. Rates are around US$70 d.
heliconi@sol.racsa.co.cr

Next door, moderate **El Establo** (☎/fax 645-5110, 645-5033, fax 645-5041; Apdo. 549, 2050 San Pedro) has carpeted rooms and includes breakfast in its rates. The address is . It borders a private reserve, and offers personal service, horseback riding, and a den with a fireplace. Rooms are around US$40 d; t and quads are also available.

One of the best values outside of Santa Elena proper, low-budget **Pensión Manakin** (☎ 645-5080) charges around US$20 d (for private rooms) or US$5 pp (for rooms with shared baths); meals are inexpensive; it's off the road to the R. Low-budget **Pensión El Pino** (☎ 645-5130) is a homestay next door.

With kitchen facilities in some rooms, moderate **Cabinas Los Piños** (645-5005/5252) range in price from around US$35-75. They stand in front of expensive **Hotel de Montaña Monteverde** (☎ 645-5046, fax 645-5320; Apdo. 70, San José), whose cabins adjoin a farm and woods. It has Jacuzzi, sauna, private reserve, conference room, TV den, gardens, and a restaurant. Rates run from around US$70 d to US$125 for a "honeymoon suite" with a private Jacuzzi. or call in the US.
www.ticonet.co.cr/montverde.html
monteverde@ticonet.co.cr

The imaginative, expensive **Belmar** (☎ 645-5201, fax 645-5135; Apdo. 17-5655, Monteverde) resembles an Austrian chalet; it's atop a hill. The Belmar has 34 comfortable rooms with fine wood finishing and private baths with showers. Rates are around US$70 d with tax. Triple rooms with student accommodation are available from May-Nov. for around US$50 pp including meals and taxes. Its international restaurant serves healthy food, and there's a pool.
belmar@sol.racsa.co.cr

Along a turn-off from the main road, **Soda Manantial** rents out spartan low-budget rooms. Inexpensive **Hotel y Restaurante El Bosque** (☎/fax 645-5129, ☎ 645-5158; Apdo. 27-5655, Monteverde) gives good value; it's priced at around US$40 d and guests receive a 10% discount at the restaurant. It may also be possible to camp here.
elbosque@sol.racsa.co.cr

Near the cheese factory, the inexpensive-moderate **Pensión Flor-Mar** (☎ 645-5009, fax 645-5580) is another alternative. It charges from around US$35-40 pp including meals. Camping is also available as is a cabin for rent. It's run by two of the original Quaker settlers. This is a good choice if you're not choosy about luxury and wish to be near the reserve.

Low-budget **Pensión el Tucán** (☎ 661-1007) is nearby. It has both rooms and more expensive *cabinas* of recent construction.

Attractive, moderate **Hotel Fonda Vela** (☎ 257-1413, fax 257-1416) is second or third nearest to the reserve. Rooms range from around US$70 d and up. It offers horseback riding, trails, and an attractive international restaurant with good food. **fondavel@sol.racsa.co.cr**

Inexpensive **Cabinas Mariposa** (☎ 645-5053) is just across the road; it has three cabins (around US$25 d with Costa Rican breakfast).

With space for 25 guests, inexpensive-moderate **Hotel Villa Verde** (☎ 645-5025, fax 645-5115) is 1,500 ft. (500 m) above the Fonda Vela. Charges here are from around US$90 d with three meals included and around US$35 less without meals; it has very good food at reasonable prices and, vegetarians are catered to upon request. More expensive villas (around US$75) house five. A conference room is on the premises. Students and researchers can also stay right in the reserve field station's dorms on a space-available basis. The cost is around US$20-30 pp including three meals. Call 661-2655 six weeks or more in advance for reservations.
estefany@sol.racsa.co.cr

OUTLYING: Home of the Canopy Tours (☎ 645-5243), the **Cloud Forest Lodge** (☎ 645-5243) is situated on a former cattle farm which has cloud forest tracts with trails. It has nine cabins, a small restaurant, and a TV lounge. Rates are around US$55 d, US$75 Eco Lodge San Luis is described below, following the Santa Elena section.

MONTEVERDE FOOD: The vast majority of the hotels have restaurants. If you have wheels and are cooking, it's much better to buy provisions in Santa Elena.

El Sapo Dorado has vegetarian as well as other health-conscious entrées. In addition, the moderately-priced **El Bosque** is open from 12-9 daily except Wed.

Hotel Fonda Vela also has a fine restaurant as does the **Villa Verde**.

The **Restaurante de Lucia** (☎ 645-5337) serves an assortment of fish and other dishes. It is near the Butterfly Farm. Expect to spend around US$20 pp for dinner.

Pricey (by Costa Rican standards) ultra-popular **Stella's Bakery** (☎ 645-5052) has coffee, brownies, German chocolate cake, and pies as well as lunches (pizza, salads, lasagna, and the like). Birdwatch from the back patio as you imbibe caffeine.

You can visit the **Lechería** or "Cheese Factory" (☎ 645-5029; open Mon. through Sat. from 7:30-12, 1-3:30; Sun. 7:30-12:30) where you watch the manufacturing process and get to sample the nation's tastiest cheese.

ENTERTAINMENT: There's not much to do here during the evenings. The liveliest place (especially on Sat. nights) is the **Bar Restaurante La Cascada** near the gas station. (Other entertainment is listed in the Santa Elena section).

MONTEVERDE SERVICES AND SHOPPING: There are no public phones in Monteverde except at the taxi and telephone service up the hill. Check at your hotel to see if the rate is reasonable and, if not, go up the hill or down to Santa Elena.

Horseback rides can be found at **Meg's Riding Stable** (☎ 645-5052) as well as other places including **La Estrella** (☎ 645-2751), and **El Establo** (☎ 645-5110); watch for signs or ask your hotel desk. **Establos Santa Elena** rents horses out for US$8 hr. (US$6 for children). They also offer a number of tours including one to El Gran Mirador (US$30; 6 hrs.) where you can see Arenal and another, an overnight trail through the forest to Lake Arenal. Dubbed "The Road Less Traveled," their overnight trip stops at Castillo (spartan digs) for the night; it's six hours on horse each way and costs US$70-85 pp depending upon the group's size. The cheapest horse rental is to be found at the **El Túcan** which charges around US$5/hr.

Canopy platform access (US$40) is offered by **Canopy Tours** (☎ 255-2693, 645-5243, fax 255-0061). You head up a large fig tree, zip across to another platform, and then descend. A natural history tour is also included.

Mount Cycle Adventures (☎ 645-6042/5061) offers mountain bike tours.

> Reader R. M. relates that "Gordo took us on a horseback ride fro his little business, The Stable, on the L-hand side of the road before Nueva Arenal, was very amusing and provided us with a memorable trip which included a dip in a warm, lovely natural lake that is off the beaten path."

SHOPPING: Open from 8-5 daily exept on Sun. (10-4) the **CASEM** (Comité de Artesanías Santa Elena-Monteverde) gift shop (☎ 645-5006) has local crafts and embroidered goods. While the goods may not enchant you that much, depending upon your taste, your purchase does support struggling local craftswomen.

Sarah Dowell's studio is a short climb above the cheese factory. Her watercolors depict local flora and fauna, and her paintings are reasonably priced.

Galeria Extasis, home of work by innovative Costa Rican wood sculptor Marco Tulio Brenes, is also worth visiting. It is S of the Disco La Cascada.

Open Mon. to Sat., 8-12, 1-5., and the **Hummingbird Gallery** (☎ 645-5030) a photographic gallery dedicated to the work of the famous Fogdens just before the reserve to the L.

STUDYING ART: The **Monteverde Studios of the Arts** (☎ 645-5434; APO 6-5655, Monteverde; 800-370-3331) are a set of five-day workshops held during the summer which offer room and board along with classes in ceramics, stained glass, textiles, photography, and other subjects.
www.mstudios.com
mstudios@sol.racsa.co.cr

STUDYING SPANISH: The only language school in the area is the **Centro Panamerico de Idiomas** (☎ 645-5036, 800-903-8950) which offers two-week programs with homestays.
www.cpi-edu.com
anajarro@sol.racsa.co.cr

Santa Elena

Situated on a ridge towering over the coastal plain, this small mountain village is the closest town to Monteverde. With its small church and rusting buses, it takes on a special ambience when the fog rolls in. In recent years it has been changing and is becoming more and more touristic. Nevertheless, the town remains a delightfully unpredictable place where you might see a lady, with a baby (sucking a pacifier and strapped to her back) driving an all-terrain vehicle go by one minute, only to be followed by a team or horses or a milk truck with metal canisters rattling.

SANTA ELENA ACCOMMODATION: Many of the places here have always been low-budget and spartan which makes it the ideal place for the traveler rich in spirit but poor in pocketbook. However, a few pricier places have been remodeled or are new.

Inexpensive and remodeled some years back, the **Hotel Arco Iris** (☎ 645-5067, fax 645-5022) has great views and an international restaurant with dishes flavored with garden-grown herbs; rates run from around US$30-40 d. They charge US$3 pp for camping. **arcoiris@sol.racsa.co.cr**

Popular with backpackers and very central, the **El Túcan** (☎ 645-5017, fax 645-5462) has rooms (US$7 pp) with shared bath as well as more expensive rooms with private bath and cabins (good value!) available.

Hospedaje El Banco, behind the Banco Nacional, has tiny rooms for around US$3.

The low-budget **Pensión Colibri** (☎ 645-5067) charges around US$4 for basic rooms; meals are available.

Pensión Santa Elena (☎ 645-5051) charges around US$8 for rooms with shared baths. **Pensión El Sueño** is near the church. Rates here include meals, and the more expensive rooms run around US$60 with private bath.

Tire hauling, San Luis

Set 10 m E of the Banco Nacional and run by a friendly Tico couple, the **Bed and Breakfast Marbella** (☎ 645-5153) offers rooms from US$20 d (no breakfast with shared bath) on up to US$54 (four in room with private bath and breakfast).

Cabins Don Taco (☎ 645-6023) have carpeted rooms.

Offering a tie-in with the "youth hostel" chain, the **Albergue Santa Elena** (☎ 645-5051, fax 645-5147) offers low-budget rooms and camping. It has a nice front porch.

On the way to the reserve, the **Miramontes Hotel** offers rooms and camping.

Further in after the turnoff is the **Sunset Hotel** (☎ 645-5048/5228) which has a restaurant.

The friendly **Pensión Flor de Monteverde** (☎/fax 645-5236) has doubles for around US$15 and triples (with shared baths) for around US$25. Three meals are an additional US$15 pp. Credit cards are not accepted. The hotel is 75 m up a dirt road which is out of town towards Monteverde and is between the Serpentarium and El Sapo Dorado. (*Accommodation further out of town towards Monteverde is listed above under the Monteverde section*).

If you wish to stay in this area for a longer period contact **Maximo Ramírez**

(☎ 645-2951) concerning homestays at a ranch 11 km away. You have to ride a horse or hike in; food and accommodation run around US$5 pd.

NEAR THE SANTA ELENA RESERVE: **Cabinas El Gran Hotel Mirador** (cell ☎ 381-7277, ☎/fax 645-5354) has 10 cabins with a total of 22 rooms. Spartan but functional, this is a good place to stay for non-yuppies who want to be a bit out of the tourist loop. They offer horseback trips to Arenal. (Varying opinions on these: avoid during the wet!) Rates (with breakfast) are around US$40 d, US$155 pp for students. Uncharacteristically (for the area), they do not accept credit cards.

Set one km before it, **Hotel Vista Verde** (cell ☎ 380-1527) offers rooms for around US$60 d with breakfast. Facilities include restaurant, waterfall with swimming hole on a private reserve, and views befitting the name. Pickup can be arranged by request.
www.vistaverde.com

FOOD: There are a number of places to eat. Budget travelers swear by the **El Tucán**; it is a good place to visit, get a cup of coffee, and sit outside and watch the world go by.

The **El Daiquiri Restaurant** (☎ 645-5133) is across from the church: they have inexpensive *casados*, they also own one of the local public telephone franchises. Service can be slow so be prepared for a wait.

Renowned for its pasta and wine, **Pizzeria de Johnny** is right before the Heliconia on the main road.

The town's most versatile place, hospitable **Chunches** (☎ 645-5147) serves expresso and snacks, has a washer and dryer, sells books (including this one), stationary, and other items.

FOOD SHOPPING: In addition to a number of small shops, there's the **Panaderia Jimenez** (which sells granola and bread, muffins, and cookies), the **Supermercado La Esperanza** (which also has a public phone), and (right next door) the Coopesanta Elena.

SERVICES AND TOURS: *See under "Monteverde"* The clinic has an English speaking physician. above.

ENTERTAINMENT: The evening mass at the church comes complete with singing and guitar accompaniment. Visit the lively bar at the **Taberna Valverde**. At the entrance here you might see a horse tethered up next to a sleek silver four-wheel-drive Suzuki jeep. Inside, cover versions of songs ranging from a Spanish version of "My Tutu" to Joe Cocker's remake of "With a Little Help From My Friends" blare over loudspeakers. If you don't dance yourself, have fun just watching the locals work out. The **Disco Orquideas** is out of town on the way to the Santa Elena Reserve. **El Sapo Dorado** is a bit further on up the steep hill and a bit upscale as well.

Another, quite unusual, alternative are the ATV and motorbike races held on Sun. on the way out of town near the Disco Orquideas. If you're staying in Santa Elena and want to visit the reserve, you can either walk uphill or take the bus from town early in the morning when it comes up to the top, relatively near to the reserve. If you wish to get to the Santa Elena Reserve from town, you'll either have to walk or charter a vehicle.

FROM MONTEVERDE: The road down is the same one you came up on. With great views of the Gulf of Nicoya and the

Nicoya Peninsula, it's a twisting and turning ride down; sit on the L for the best views. Buses to San José run daily at 6:30 AM and at 3 PM. When you want to leave, you can flag down the bus anywhere from the Lechería on down. If you want to be sure of getting a seat, buy a numbered seat ticket from the Hotel El Bosque (☎ 645-5221); it's better to do this as soon as you arrive. A bus runs to Puntarenas at 6 AM daily; change for San José at the Lagarto junction.

OTHER DESTINATIONS: A gravel road runs from Santa Elena to Tilarán. The same road branches for the Santa Elena Reserve and again for Los Juncos. The area is beautiful and birds abound, but it is also heavily deforested.

During the school year (Mar.- Nov.), a milk truck runs daily to Cabeceras (three hrs.), where you can connect to Tilarán. Ask at the Restaurant Daiquiri (☎ 645-5133) about current schedules. You can also do this with a four-wheel drive. It's a lovely drive past formerly forested pastureland and definitely the way to go as opposed to a repeat journey to the Interamerican.

A bus also runs from Santa Elena to Tilarán. It departs at 7 AM but does not leave from Santa Elena during the rainy season. From Tilarán, a *San Carlos* bus (which passes La Fortuna enroute) leaves at 12:30. From the main highway at the Lagarto junction, buses run to the NW; the junction for Nicoya (via a ferry crossing of the Río Tempisque) is at Km 168. Parque Nacional Barra Honda is en route.

BY CAR: See "getting here" above and take the opposite route back to your destination.

Vicinity of Monteverde

Ecolodge San Luis

Set at a gorgeous location at 3,300-4,000 ft. (1000-1,400 m) this beautifully designed lodge-research complex is set near primary cloud forest and other ecosystems. amidst 162 acres (65.6 ha) at the valley's head. Whereas there are any number of avowedly "ecological" lodges in Costa Rica, there is only *one*, Ecolodge San Luis, a place created with the avowed intention of bringing together researchers to mingle and share their work with visitors.

Designed to attract visitors who are intelligent, curious, and environmentally concerned, the lodge consists of three complimentary, interlocking components: housing and other facilities for students and researchers, a tropical garden along with stands of forest reserve, and a separate lodge.

Ongoing projects here include an organic garden, coffee haresting, and reforestation. There's also a fruit grove with 60 different fruit tree species. The driving force behind the lodge tropical biology's trailblazers Drs. Milton and Diana Lieberman. The Liebermans reside just up the hill in Monteverde and are well known researchers who stand at the forefront of their field.

GETTING HERE: Take the Panamerican to the Sardinal junction and follow the signs for Monteverde until you reach the San Luis turnoff and then follow the San Luis road past the Alto San Luis school and then turn R. The lodge may also be reached by horse (prior arrangement necessary), car, or sturdy vehicle from the San Luis turnoff near the Hotel Vela in the upper part of Monteverde. If you head down here at night on horseback, the fireflies put on a tremendous strobe light show.

BIRDING: There's tremendous birding in the area, and you may spot toucans right from your hammock. You might spot as many as 75 species of birds per day here. Bird species seen here include quetzals, laughing falcons, the black hawk-eagle, the great black hawk, sunbitterns, spectacled and mottled owls, the common potoo, keel billed toucans, emerald toucanets, and a number of hummingbirds. A stay at the lodge includes guided birding, so this is a tremendous opportunity for birders.

STUDY: A week-long course in tropical environments is offered. Morning hours are taken up with field trips, hikes, and lab work. Rates are around US$125 pp plus room and board. University credit is arranged for multi-week participants.

PRACTICALITIES: It was only necessary to cut one tree down while building the entire lodge complex, and it fits beautifully into its surroundings. Actually a converted cow barn, an attractive wooden building houses a dormitory which sleeps up to 30 in bunkbeds. A nearby bath house has powerful hot showers and flush toilets. Its kitchen and lounge serves meals family style. There's also a library. Electricity is provided by a generator. Each set of the slightly secluded cabins contains 12 rooms commanding great views of the hills off in the distance; there are 36 rooms altogether. Simple *campesino*-style meals are served. Vegetarians can be catered to, and the Tica chefs are getting better and better at it. (They found the very concept befuddling at first).

Rates are around US$60 pp, pn in dorm accommodation; this includes all meals, programs, and guiding. The cabins are US$190 d in the luxury range. Children 7-14 are US$40 pp. Special rates for students, researchers, and residents are offered.

In Costa Rica call or fax 645-5277 or write Apdo. 36, Santa Elena de Monteverde. In the US call 206-623-8850 or write Dept. SJO 2280, PO Box 025216, Miami, FL 33102-5216. In the US call Alta Travel Planners at 888-388-ALTA or 805-547-7065.
www.nashville.net~edutrop.home.html
edutrop@nashville.net

Catarata San Luis

To get to these gorgeous falls, follow the directions to Ecolodge San Luis as above. Then, you should head on down the road and follow the river up to the falls for around 40 min.; it's a somewhat rigorous trip so be sure to allow enough time.

Cañitas

Just a few min. N of Santa Elena on the Tilarán road, this settlement has hotels, restaurants, crafts, horse rentals, and guides. **Los Tornos** has a gold mine containing chalk and crystal deposits. Three hrs. on horseback from a fork situated before the town, the Quesada family's **El Mirador** (☎ 645-5087 for information) in **San Geraldo Abajo** is a set of spartan cabins and a dorm. Good rainforest hiking and some seven waterfalls are here. Views of both Lake Arenal and the volcano are stupendous. Cars (four-wheel-drive) can come here from Feb. to May; otherwise you'll need to horse it. Very inexpensive packages are available.

Albergue Ecoturistico Monte Los Olivos

One of the Albergues Ecoturisticos (☎ 283-8975, 252-7453, fax 283-9116, 283-9116), **Monte Los Olivos** is backed by the Arenal Conservation Area (a local environmental foundation), the World Wildlife Fund of Canada and the Canadian International Development

Agency It is also known as **Ecoverde**. The lodge (☎ 385-0092, 645-5059, fax 645-5131) is six km from Monteverde and on the road to Tilarán; it has nine cabins with hot water and a restaurant; some have private bath. It offers the opportunity to experience rural life on a dairy farm as well as go birding and hiking. Spartan-yet-functional digs have private or shared hot water bath. Transport to the cloud forest preserve are included in the inexpensive rates as are breakfast and transport from Santa Elena.
www.agroecoturismo.net
coprena@sol.racsa.co.cr

Parque Nacional Arenal and Environs

This is an area which is just beginning to be explored by overseas visitors, a great part of which has been proclaimed a national park on paper, but not in practice. Afternoon breezes blow across Lake Arenal — an artifical 32-sq-mile (82-sq-km) lake, created by damming a river and surrounded by rolling pastures and feeding dairy cows. While the river originally flowed E, it has been re channeled by the dam, and its waters now flow NW.

Enlarged for the construction of a hydroelectric plant, the town of **Nuevo Arenal** was built by the ICE to resettle the inhabitants. The same holds true for Nueva Tronadora, on the other side between San Luis and Río Chaquita. Composed of 50-70% pastureland, the San Carlos area to the SE was developed after the 1963 eruption of Irazú left much of the Meseta Central covered with ash and unsuitable for dairying. Today, many of the farms here have been snatched up by expatriates.

GETTING HERE: This is one of the easiest areas to access from either San José or Liberia. You may traverse part of the N central plain, either by driving or riding a bus from Tilarán around Lake Arenal via Fortuna to Ciudad Quesada and returning via Zarcero and Sarchí to San José. Specifics are provided below.

Tilarán

As you approach from a distance this small, virtually untouristed settlement, set high above Guanacaste plain, appears as a white square amidst rolling green pastureland. The town's name comes from a combination of the indigenous words *tilawa* (of many waters) and *tlan* (the spot or the place).

Tilarán is a government-planned settlement constructed between 1909-12. The town is cool, with a breeze that will really be a welcome relief if you're coming from the stifling Guanacaste plains. If you have the time to spare, it's a nice walk up to the cross on the hill overlooking the town. A rodeo and livestock show is held here during April.

GETTING HERE: Take a bus from C. 14, Av. 9/11 in San José at 7:30, 9:30, 12:45, 3:45, and 6:30; it takes 5-6 hrs. Another alternative is to approach via Ciudad Quesada, from Monteverde, or from Cañas.

SIGHTS: In addition to the lake and the hotsprings, there's at least one innovative project. Set five km from Nuevo Arenal and 11 km from the dam, **Arenal Botanical Garden** is the wondrous creation of Michael LeMay (☎ 694-4273); it's open 9-4 daily (except Sun.), and admission is around US$4. Self-guiding paths which pass by 3,000 or so plants.

PRACTICALITIES: Everything is located on or very near the main square. The nicest low-budget accommodation is **Cabinas Mary** (☎ 695-5749, around

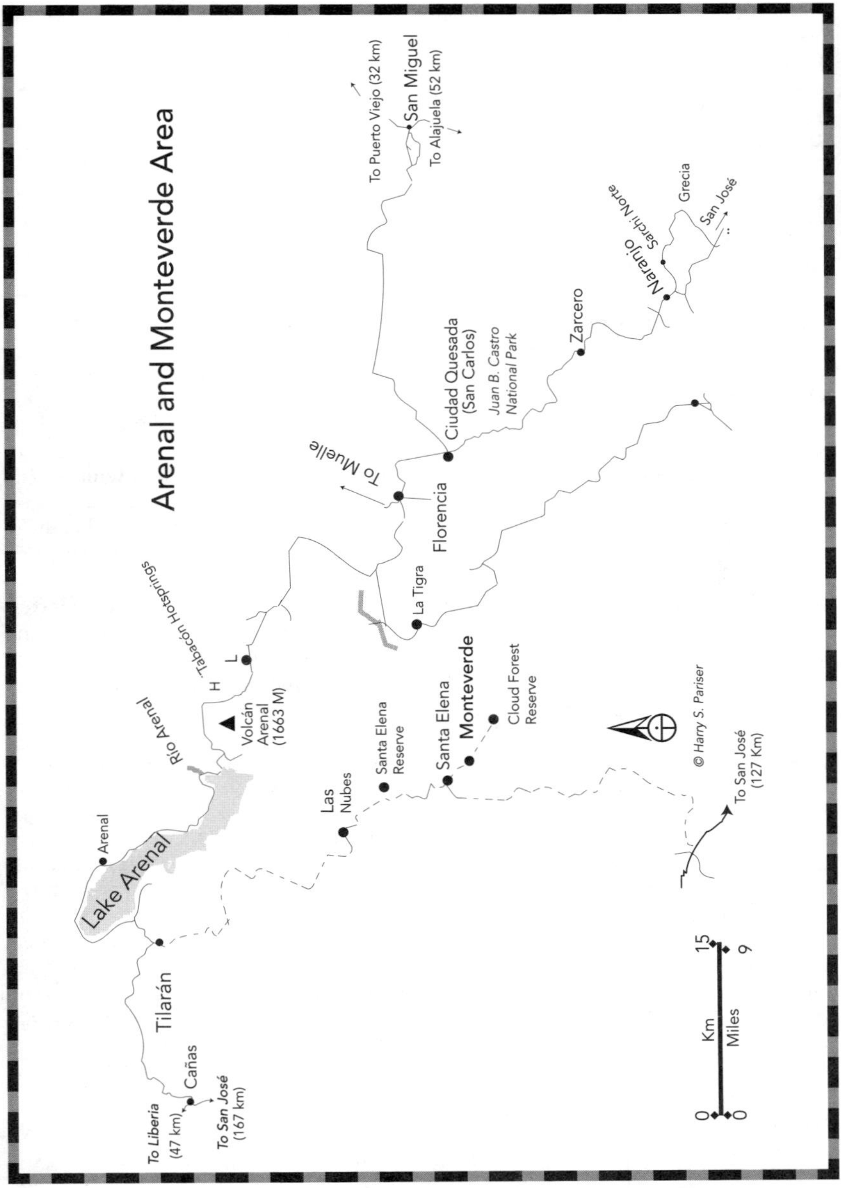
Arenal and Monteverde Area
To Puerto Viejo (32 km)
San Miguel
To Alajuela (52 km)
Grecia
Sarchi Norte
San José
Naranjo
Zarcero
Ciudad Quesada
(San Carlos)
Juan B. Castro
National Park
To Muelle
Florencia
La Tigra
Tabacón Hotsprings
H
L
Río Arenal
Volcán
Arenal
(1663 M)
Santa Elena
Reserve
Santa Elena
Monteverde
Cloud Forest
Reserve
© Harry S. Pariser
Las
Nubes
To San José
(127 Km)
Arenal
Lake Arenal
Tilarán
Cañas
To Liberia
(47 km)
To San José
(167 km)
Km
Miles
0
15
0
9

US$10 d); **Hotel Grecia** and **Hotel Central** are other alternatives.

Resembling a motel, **Cabinas Naralit** (☎ 695-5393) is inexpensive and charges around US$30. **Hotel Yasmine** (☎ 695-5043) has rooms for around US$18. **Cabinas Lago Lindo** (☎ 695-5555) has spartan rooms for around US$15.

A final alternative is inexpensive **Cabinas El Sueño** (☎ 695-5347) which has rooms for around US$25.

Right by the lake (and the first of many; see below), the **Hotel Bahía Azul** (☎/fax 695-5750) has rooms for around US$40 and up; rooms have TVs and refrigerators.

Of the many restaurants, the most deluxe is the **Catalá**. **El Parque** which has good service and reasonable prices. *Norteamericano*-run **La Carretera** (☎ 695-6654) have good pizza, pasta, and sandwiches. A good source of info on the area as well as a good stomach-filler. They are behind the cathedral.

Aventuras Tilarán (☎ 695-5008), which operates the outlying Albergue Arenal, arranges tours.

ENTERTAINMENT: For a drink, **Maleko's Bar** has the best atmosphere. **Films** are shown at the theater. Lots of hearthrobbin' tambourine beating and chanting takes place at **Iglesia Biblical Emanuel**. Basketball hoops are in the main square, but you'll have to bring your own nets.

FROM TILARÁN: On the way down to Cañas are immense ranches with names like "Los Angeles," containing green, almost totally deforested slopes filled with cattle munching their way to the slaughterhouse. From Cañas, you may change for Liberia. Express buses for San José and buses also run to Puntarenas and Guatuso at12:30, Arenal and San Carlos. If you're driving to Monteverde, you can take a dirt road that goes via Quebrada Grande.

OUTLYING ACCOMMODATIONS: Located at the first corner of the lake you come to after leaving town, **Mirador Los Lagos** (☎ 695-5169/5484, fax 695-5387; Apdo. 97-5710, Tilarán) has a restaurant and comfy *cabinas* around US$50 d) with hot water. As the name implies, it offers good views along with facials, massages, and yoga classes to boot. Vegetables are harvested from their organic garden, and personalized service is offered.

The 24-room **Hotel Tilawa Viento Surf & High Wind Center** (☎ 695-5050, fax 695-5766; Apdo. 92, Tilarán; 800-851-8929) is patterned after the Palace of Knossos in Crete. It offers windsurfing rentals and lessons, mountain bikes, canoeing, fishing, tennis, pool, handicap accesibility, and a restaurant (varying reports). Rooms are around US$75 d; more expensive ones have kitchenettes. It affords great views from the second floor. A number of packages are also offered including language study.
tilaw@sol.racsa.co.cr

Each of the six quite attractive rooms (around US$60 d) at the **Mystica Lake Lodge** (cell. ☎ 382-1499, fax 695-5387) have painted animals on their doors. Rooms have porches with lakeside views, and breakfast is included in the rates. The hotel's creators, an Italian couple who first arrived on an exchange program, gave it its name because they found the area to be magical and mysterious. Its Italian restaurant (pizza-oven equipped) commands great views.
mystica@quorum.nation.co.cr

Set next to the atmospheric Equus B.B.Q. Restaurant, **Xiloe Lodge** (☎ 259-9806/9192, fax 259-9882) offers a number of simple cabins from around US$40 which sleep from three to four. It has a pool, and you can also head down to the river. Horseback riding on the property is also available, and a "Full Moon Dance" is held monthly. Admission is free, and disco and salsa tunes punctuate the still of the moonlit evening. Informal horseraces also take place on the track nearby.

Near the village of Guadalajara and run by a helpful Tico couple, intimate ten-cabin **Río Piedras** (☎ 695-5247) charges around US$15 d. The restaurant is open from 7AM-10PM and serves Tico food including fresh guapote. They also offer horseback riding, fishing, and boating.

The Dutch-owned **Villas Alpino** (fax 695-5387) offers five inexpensive, attractively decorated *cabinas* (around US$40) which hold up to four; each cabina has its own stocked kitchenette as well as parking space and clothesline.

Rock River Lodge (☎ 222-4547/7338, fax 221-3011) has cabins from around US$35 d and rooms for around US$50 d. Its restaurant serves breakfasts and dinners.
rockriver@mastermind.net
rokriver@sol.racsa.co.cr

Offering small rooms in a garden setting, 12-room **Albergue and Club Altura de Arenal** (☎ 222-6455) charges around US$50 d including breakfast. After passing the Albergue, the rocky gravel road gives way to a paved road.

Eco-Lodge Lago Coter (☎ 257-5075, fax 2257-7065; Apdo. 85570, 1000 San José), a moderate-expensive "ecotourist"-oriented lodge stands at Lake Coter near the town of Nuevo Arenal. The comfortable facilities include a wooden plank-lined rainforest trail, with mountain biking, windsurfing, sport fishing, sailing, hiking, canoeing, and horseback riding all available. All equipment (right down to binoculars) is provided for its trips. Rooms (lodging only) are around US$60 s and US$75 d. A number of packages (including lodging, meals, and programmed activities) are available. Available tours include excursions to Caño Negro, Palo Verde, Corobicí river rafting, Ocotal (a beach tour), and a trip to Arenal and the Venado Caves.
www.eco-lodge.com
ecolodge@sol.racsa.co.cr

Guarded by Great Danes, **Chalet Nicholas** (fax 695-5387; Apdo. 72, 5710 Tilaran) is a bed and breakfast set near land being reforested by the owners. It offers three rooms for around US$40 s and US$50 d plus tax. Videos and books are plentiful, and horseback riding, hiking, shore and boat fishing, canoeing, and other activities are all available. Bountiful breakfasts include organic fruit and may be followed by a hike through old-growth rainforest directly behind the property. Owners Catherine and John emphasize that "It is for NON-SMOKERS ONLY!" It is two km. to the W of Nuevo Arenal.

A bed and breakfast commanding great views, **Puerto Las Lajas** (☎ 694-4169, fax 695-5387) rents large rooms for around US$30 d. There's horseback riding, windsurfing, fishing, hiking, and a floating dock set at the bottom of the hill.

La Ceiba Tree Lodge (☎/fax 694-4297, 385-1540) offers four large rooms, hammocks, and a giant ceiba tree. Rates are around US$ 30 s, US$45 d, plus tax.
fingerspm@sol.racsa.co.cr

Arenal volcano is a major attraction.

IN NUEVO ARENAL: The town of Nuevo Arenal sprang up after the area's original residents were relocated after the lake was created in 1973. This relatively affluent village, with its gravel streets, now has a number of places to stay — up from zero just a few years back!

Inexpensive (around US$15 d), the six-room **Lajas Restaurant and Hotel** (☎ 694-4169, fax 695-5387) is near the bus stop. **Cabinas Rodriguez** (☎ 664-4237) charges around US$6-10 d for its small room.

Seven-room and six-cabina **Hotel Aurora** (☎ 694-4245, fax 694-4262) charges around US$40 d including breakfast. Satellite TV is available in the lobby for your viewing pleasure.

Outside of town and on the way to Venado, **Toronto Cabins** (☎ 694-4131/4057, fax 694-4058) rents out for around US$12 d including breakfast.

Under the same management, luxurious, 28-rm. **Hotel Joya Sureña** (☎ 694-4067, fax 694-4059) has a restaurant, game room, meeting room, and pool.
www.allgoods.com/joyasurena
joysur@sol.racsa.co.cr

Set two km E of town, elegant five-room **Villa Decary** (ax 694-4330; Nuevo Arenal 5717 Tilarán, Guanacaste) is a converted coffee finca with attractively decorated rooms; each have separate entryways. There's good birding near the villa. Rates are around US$50 s and US$60-70 d and include generous breakfast; a separate bungalow is available for rent at around US$275 pw.

Back in town is the Italian **Ristorante Tramonti.** Another alternative is **Restaurante Sabor Italiano & Refugio Artesanal** (☎ 385-1474).

An intimate bed and breakfast in a 38-acre (16-ha) farm managed by artists, **La Ceiba** (fax 695-5387) charges around US$20 pp including breakfast. You can hike, bird, milk goats, garden, or sail here. Naturally enough, it has enormous ceiba tree on the premises.
fingrspm@sol.racsa.co.cr

Nine km from the dam, **Hotel La Marina de Arenal** (☎/fax 284-6573) is housed in a former dairy farm; it has attractively decorated cabins which charge around US$100 d. Eighteen more are on the way, along with a pool and cable TV. Horseback riding, canoeing, and windsurfing are included in the rates, and a trail leads down to the marina which has catamarans and windsurfers.

Set eight km from the dam on a denuded hilltop, Swiss Chalet-style, three-storey **Los Héroes** (☎ 443-9505, fax 284-6315) is like something right out of the alps. You expect to see Heidi come running across the lawn with blond pigtails and a plaid skirt and a surly St. Bernard to arrive with a wooden cask secured under its neck. It charges around US$50 d including breakfast for attractive, carpeted rooms. Needless to say, there are some Swiss dishes on its restaurant's menu, and there's a pool. They now offer package tours aboard a double-decker bus which departs at 8 AM on Tues., Thurs., and Sat. Rates are around US$90 pp which includes three meals and one night.

Catering to fishermen (guapote heaven!) and naturalists alike, luxury priced **Arenal Lodge** (☎ 289-6588, fax 289-6798) is almost at the end of the lake, about four km up a gravel road and some 17 km to the W of La Fortuna. Facilities include Jacuzzi, restaurant, billiard table, and library. Rates run from around US$75 d. Fishing runs US$175/four hrs.

INFORMATION AND SERVICES: Located in the small German restaurant of the same name, **Stefanie's Centro de Información Turistica** (☎ 694-4132, fax 694-4025) offers tours, kayak rentals, and Spanish instruction. The **Banco Nacional** changes traveler's checks, and the post office is next to the police station.

In La Union de Arenal, **Toad Hall** sells books, maps, and handicraft items.

SPORTS: Fishing and windsurfing are what's popular here. During the dry season, winds blow across the lake in 20 to 70 knot gusts. **Tico Wind** (fax 695-5387, 800-678-2252) rents boards for around US$45 pd or US$250 pw which includes your choice of equipment; lessons are also available. Others to contact include **Villas Alpino** (fax 695-5387), **Tilawa** (☎/fax 695-5050), Rock River Lodge (☎/fax 222-5457), and **Adventuras Tilarán** (☎/fax 695-5008). Horseback riding is offered at **The Stable** (☎ 253-3048) ; it's a good way to explore the area. Owner "Gordo" Murillo offers tours of his 200-ha farm and the area surrounding lakes Arenal and Coter. The farm is at km 47 outside of Nuevo Arenal.

Vicinity of Arenal

Volcán Arenal (Arenal Volcano)

With its sheer, classically-shaped cone, this majestic 5,358-ft. (1,633-m) active volcano occasionally rumbles, throwing up ash and rock. It is dangerous and definitely not recommended to climb this mountain. One tourist died and another was severly burned in 1988 climbing its slopes. Arenal is best viewed from a distance at night, when the fiery bursts and shooting molten rocks are visible. Its last serious eruption, in 1968, eradicated the town of Pueblo Nuevo, killing 78. During this eruption it shot out huge incandescent blocks. Most of these disintegrated when they landed, but many left impact craters — ranging in size from two m to 30 m — as far as 10 km from the volcano.

The volcano erupted again in May 1998, and lava flow halted just a km from the Tabacón Resort. note: Arenal has been declared a national park, but there is no advantage in paying the full fee except that you can get a bit closer to it. Despite the increase in fees, the road continues to be in terrible shape, and there are no facilities. The apparent reason for declaring it a park was so that the government could find a way to make a buck out of it!

ACCOMODATION NEAR THE VOLCANO: The closest place to stay near the volcano is at the **Arenal Observatory Lodge** (☎ 257-9489, fax 257-4220; Apdo. 1195, 1250 Escazú). Separated from the volcano by the chasm cut by the Río Agua Caliente, it was established as an official research station of the Smithsonian Institution and the University of Costa Rica in 1987. It offers a restaurant/bar and 24 rooms with private bath and hot water. Good excursions from here include a hike up adjacent Cerro Chato, with its green crater lake, and across the hardened lava flows. Rates range from US$50-100 d.
arenalob@sol.racsa.co.cr

The second closest place to stay near the volcano is **Arenal Vista Lodge** (☎ 220-2121/1712, fax 232-3321) which is near the village of El Cairo, 14 km W of La Fortuna and across the Río Agua Caliente. Attractive Swedish-style cabins are around US$65 d. Deluxe junior suites are also available (around US$100 d). It has an attractive glass-enclosed restaurant, and activities include mountain biking, birding, hiking, horseback riding, boat tours, and fishing.
explore@sol.racosa.co.cr

Linda Vista del Norte (☎ 380-0847) has a restaurant, great views and charges around US$65 d (with breakfast) for simple rooms. It has a 240-ha reserve.
www.vanweb.com
lindav@vanweb.com

A set of two-room cabins (around US$50 d, US$60 t) with picture windows facing the volcano, **Cabañas de Montaña de Fuego** (☎ 382-0759, fax 479-9106) is set one km before the hot springs. Camping (US$2) is also available as are camping equipment rentals. There are hiking trails on the property, and horseback riding is available. Cabañas **Arenal Paraiso** (☎ 479-9006) is next door, is similar, and is run by a brother.

note: *Other places to stay are listed under "La Fortuna" below.*

Tabacón Springs Resort & Spa

Named after a large-leaved plant (a cousin of tobacco), this open-air spa has been so expanded and remodeled in recent years that returning visitors will not recognize it. Tabacón (☎ 222-1072, 322-0780, fax 221-3075) is about 2.5 mi.(four km) beyond Lake Arenal.

Lovely gardens are spectacularly landscaped with heliconia, bamboo, and other ornamentals. It has a gourmet restaurant, five pools (two for children and three for adults), tiled waterfalls, massage rooms, changing rooms, lockers, gardens, and a curving water slide.

Arenal looms majestically above it all and glows red at night. Curiously, the large swimmming pool in front of the restaurant remains the most popular spot. The most popular photo op spot is under the wide artificial waterfall where you will see groups of swimsuit-clad Midwest-white teenage girls posing for posterity.

Mudpacks (US$9) and massages (US$26) are also offered. It's open daily from 10 AM-10 PM. Admission is steep: US$14 for adults and US$7 for for children. (If you can't afford this, lower-cost bathing opportunities are available nearby).

GETTING HERE: If you take a morning bus (2.5 hrs, US$1. 20) from Arenal, you can return in late afternoon. The road is bad, and there are likely to be encounters with cows and brahmin bulls blocking the road. Try to avoid this area on weekends.

ACCOMMODATION: The resort's 42 luxury guest rooms have a/c, TV, phones, and terrace. They are for people who like their creature comforts, but the overall atmosphere is reminiscent of a

If you find Tabacón to be a bit pricey for a dip, here are two alternatives. A second set of **hot springs** are across the road. Less glamorous, they also charge foreign visitors only US$5. There is also a free spot in the forest. Keep heading away from La Fortuna until you come to a forested area; follow the path. Watch for the small sign.
Another venue is **Baldi Hot Springs** (☎ 479-9651, 479-9652) which charges around US$70; a 70-rm. lodge is planned.

hotel chain. Shuttle service to the spa and restaurant down the hill is provided; it's around a ten min. walk. Rates are around US$85 s, US$100 d, and US$115 t plus tax.
tabacon@sol.racsa.co.cr

La Fortuna

Having the distinction of being the town closest to Volcán Arenal, this somnolent settlement has become a magnet for visitors in recent years.

GETTING HERE: Take a *San Carlos bus* at 6:30, 9:30, and 11:15 AM daily from Coca Cola (C. 16, Av. 1/3; four hrs.) in San José or board the bus at San Carlos (6:30, 9:30, 11:40, 1, 3, 3:30, 4:45, 6; 1.5 hrs.). There are also *buses* which continue on to Tabacón (13 km farther).

FROM MONTEVERDE: Take a 7 AM bus in front of the Cheese Factory.

> A bridge, located some 24 km W of La Fortuna, is extremely dangerous. It has no railings and claimed tourist lives in 1998. It follows a sharp curve in the road. Go slowly on this stretch.

BY CAR: From San José, drive via Naranjo, Zarcero, San Carlos (Ciudad Quesada), Florencia, and Muelle (three hrs. plus) or head to San Ramón and then proceed to La Tigra and on (slightly shorter but less scenic).

SIGHTS: To get to **Catarata La Fortuna**, follow the well-marked dirt road leading S from the L hand side of the church. Go 5.5 km to the small parking lot overlooking the falls. From here a trail leads down to the falls' base. This trail becomes unusable during the rainy season when it is also likely to be necessary — if you drive in — to have a four-wheel drive. If you would like to get here by horse, contact El Paraiso and Prof. Adrian Lobo in town or Finca de Cito which is on the road to Lake Arenal. A bridge is under construction which will render car access possible.

Another attraction is the **Laguna Cerro Chato** — an undeveloped, forested lake which is eight km from town; the last three km must be traversed on foot.

Set 45 min. from town, the **Venado Caves (Cavernas de Venado)** (☎ 296-2626/9005) may only be entered with a guide. These large caves (admission around US$6) are hardly your typical tourist spot. Visiting them is a muddy, slippery, clammy, oozy, bat ridden, and *quite* adventurous experience. To explore, it is necessary to wade through a river and get down and crawl on your hands and knees at times. Expect to see sights as diverse as a papaya shaped stalagmite, fossilized seashells, and cave dwelling fish. Bats number in the thousands, and you may see frogs and insects. Inside, the caves are a white and cream color with numerous stalactites and stalagmites (including one which looks like a papaya). Although each of the 12 chambers is tall enough to stand in, passageways between them are not.

Discovered after the finca's owner fell in a hole, the caves have been open only since 1991. The caves were first visited in 1945, explored by a Frenchman in 1962, visited by representatives of the US Atomic Energy Commission in 1969, and additional chambers ware discovered in 1990. Flashlights, helmet and face mask are recommeded, as are good shoes. Guides and flashlights are offered by the Finca Don Julio for a two-hour

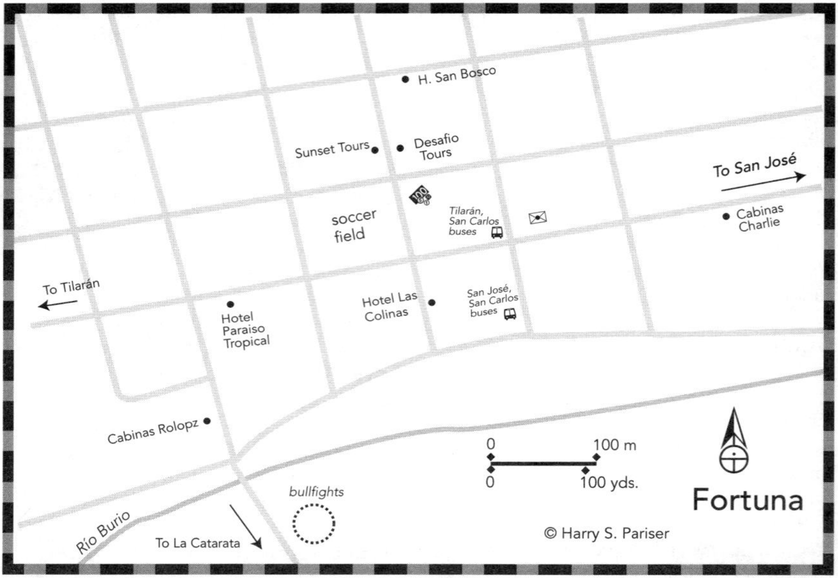

excursion. Be sure to bring extra clothes if you visit. No liability is assumed by the landowners so you visit at your own risk.

You may stay at low-budget **Cabinas Las Brisas** in the town of Venado four km away. A *bus* runs from San Carlos to Venado at 2, a 2.5-hr. trip.

Parque Nacional Tenorio is a 10,000-ha national park created in 1994. Only 30% of the land is in government hands. There are no facilities as of yet.

ACCOMMODATIONS: Fortuna has a range of accommodations which will fit any budget.

Run by a Brit-Tico couple, **Arenal Country Inn** (☎ 479-9670/9669, fax 479-9669) is set 800 m Sof the Catholic Church. It offers a/c 20 bungalows, two pools, restaurant, and conference area. Rates are around US$65 s, US$75 d, US$90 t, and US$205 d quad.

www.costaricainn.com
arenal@costaricainn.com

***TRIMED* HOTELS:** *With offices in La Fortuna, the Corp Hotel Tri-Med (☎ 479-9327, fax 479-9311) coordinate reservations for the following hotels and as well as for the* **Jungla y Sendero Los Lagos**. *They also havfe offices in Miami (☎* 305-273-6001) and San José (☎ 256-4256).
trimed@soflo.net

Set across the street from the elementary school, the **Hotel Guacamaya** has 26 rms. with refrigerator and a/c. Each has one double bed and one single bed. JIt has a restaurant and charges It charges around US$40 s, US$55 d, US$66 t.

Hotel Arenal Jirih stands a block W of the Catholic Church. It has 13 rms. with a/c. TV, and a restaurant. Rates are around US$38 s, US$50 d or t.

Female travelers should avoid the man who will greet you at the bus stop and will try to get you to go to his pensión. He takes care of the place for his family, lives there alone, and has a reputation for molesting female guests.

The **Hotel Paraiso Tropical** is on the S side of the church and offers seven rms. with a/c and refrigerator. Rates are around US$30 s, US$33 d. and US$40 t. It has a restaurant.

Set two mi. W of La Fortuna, the **Hotel La Pradera** has ten rms. with a/c, porches; deluxe rms. have Jacuzzis. It has a restaurant. Rates are around US$60-90 s, US$70-100 d, and US$80-105 t.

Five mi. W of town, the 16-rm. **Americas' Paradise Resort** is set on a cattle farm. Deluxe rooms have refrigerators. It has a pool, trails, and mountain biking. Rates are around US$65-80 s, US$80-95 d, and US$91-107 t.

Set on a dairy farm and forest reserve, the **Hotel Arenal Paraiso** is seven mi. to the W of town. It has 18 bungalows with porches, fans, and two d beds or one d bed and two s beds. Facilities include Jacuzzi, restaurant, gardens, mountain biking. Rates are around US$64 d, US$76 t. Sandard rooms are les expensive.

Hotel Montaña de Fuego is set eight mi.W and offers 42 bungalows. Each has two d beds or one d bed and two s beds. Rates arun around US$80-102 s, US$86-110 d, US$107-132 t, and US$ 130-153 q.

LOW BUDGET: Inexpensive **Cabinas San Bosco** (☎ 479-9050) is 200 m N of the gas station; it has rooms from around US$30-40 d depending on the digs; it has a pool and observation area. It is a block from the main drag.

Inexpensive three-storeyed **Hotel Las Colinas** (☎ 479-9107) has attractive rooms (around US$30 d) with private baths and hot water.

Down a quiet sidestreet, **Cabinas Ribera** (☎ 479-9048) charges around US$10 pp for rooms with fans and baths.

Hotel La Fortuna (☎/fax 479-9197) burned down in 1997 but is once again in operation. Basic rooms with private baths are around US$ 16 d, US$22 t. It is set one block S of the gas station. It has a restaurant, and tours are offered by the friendly owners.

Facing the park, low-budget **Hotel y Restaurante La Central** (☎ 474-9004, fax 474-9045) is headed towards a half-century of operation; rooms are around US$4.

Its neighbors include **Cabinas Emi** (☎ 479-9076) and low-budget/inexpensive **Cabinas La Amistad** (☎ 479-9035) which charges around US$5 as does **Cabinas Grijalba** (☎ 479-9129), Cabinas Sissy (☎ 479-9525), and **Cabinas Katherine** (☎ 479-9542).

Cabinas Charlie is another good low-budget choice which is four blocks E from the park.

Cabinas La Tejas (☎ 479-9077) offers attractive rooms with shared bath for around US$4. The people are friendly and will help for tour planning; ask them to connect you with William who can take you to the mini-volcano Chato.

Cabinas Carmela (☎ 479-9010) charges around US$10 pp.

Cabinas Rolopz (☎ 479-9058) has bright rooms for around US$25 d including breakfast.

OUTLYING: Set one km E of La Fortuna, **Las Cabañitas** (☎ 479-9400, 293-0780, fax 479-9408) has 30 highly attractive hardwood cabinas for around US$80 d. Facilities include a restaurant, two pools, and a poolside *palenque*. Some

The Catholic Church in downtown Ciudad Quesada (San Carlos)

rooms are wheelchair accessible.
gasguis@sol.racsa.co.cr

Located just outside town, **La Jungla y Sendero Los Lagos** (☎/fax 479-9126) is a large finca offering lakes, horseback riding, paddle boats and water bikes, cabinas, and camping. Its two small lakes (US$4 admission) offer swimming and paddleboating. The first lake is three km from the entrance, and the second is a two km walk further through the forest. A restaurant and campground are on the main road in the direction of Tabacón. Cabins (with fan and refrigerator) go for around US$60.

The 15-unit **Cabinas Rossi** (☎/fax 479-9023) has coffee shop, picnic tables and and is around two km from town, just past the La Catarata turnoff. Basic rooms have hot water and fans from US$20 d; a more expensive room has a kitchen.
cabrossi@sol.racsa.co.cr

Seven km (4.5 mi.) from town is **Rancho el Corcovado** (☎/fax 479-9090/9178) which is set on a 150-acre (62-ha) farm. Guests may pick their own fruit, fish in the lake, ride horses, or milk cows. Facilities include a restaurant, pool, and tennis, volleyball, and basketball courts. Rooms are around US$50 d.

Set off the road between La Tigra and Chachagua, **Hotel Bosques de Chachagua** (☎/fax 228-6619) has 240 acres (100 ha) of primary forest on its 370-acre (154-ha) grounds. It has 15 cabins (around US$85 d), restaurant, horseback riding, tours, and hiking. Packages are available.
chachagua@novanet.co.cr

Hotel y Restaurante La Pradera (☎ 479-9597, fax 479-9167) offers attractive rooms with hot water, fan or a/c, and private bath. Rates are around US$50-80.

Albergue Ecoturistico La Catarata (fax c/o Cortel in La Fortuna: 479-9178) has six cabins (around US$35 d) here and offers great views of the volcano. It has a butterfly farm, paca breeding, medicinal plant garden, and orchid nursery, Excursions are available as is camping (US$2). It is around 2.5 km from the falls.
www.agroecoturismo.net
coprena@sol.racsa.co.cr

FOOD: In addition to the hotels which have restaurants, you may dine at at **El Jardín**, which has a playground and is across the road from the gas station. Open-air **Choza de Laurel** serves Tico-style food on long picnic tables. Thatched-roof **Restaurante Rancho La Cascada** is next to the park. **Restaurant Pizzeria Italian** offers a variety of that nation's dishes. Another good restaurant is **El Lirio y Luna**. Also try **El Jinete**, **El Río**, and **Terruño**. **La Vaca Muca** (a pricey tour-bus stop) can be found three km W and on the way to the volcano. **El Coquito** is well out of town on the way to San Carlos.

Set nine km from town on the way to Muelle, **El Catalán** offers Spanish dishes including lobster *maresme*, *tortilla español*, and other dishes; wash it all down with sangria.

TOURS AND ACTIVITIES: Be wary of touts on the street who may claim to be tour guides. **Aventuras Arenal** (☎ 479-9133) has a sunset cruise on Lake Arenal and many other activities.

Sunset Tours (☎ 479-9415, fax 479-9585,) offers trips to Arenal, Caño Negro, and to other areas.
www.goldnet.co.cr/sunset/home.html
sunset@ns.goldnet.co.cr

Aguas Bravas (☎ 292-2072, 479-9025) offers whitewater rafting, kayaking, and other activities in the Fortuna and Sarapiquí areas.
www.hway.com/arenas/abravas
xijansa@sol.racsa.co.cr

Contact **Natanael Murrillo** (☎ 479-9087) about fishing trips on Arenal. **Repuestos y Acesorios** rents mountain bikes.

Hot Spots is an occasional newsletter published by **Desafio Tours** which offers horseback trips to Monteverde, rafting, e-mail service, and a book exchange.
desafio@sol.racsa.co.cr

Williams Personalized Tours (☎ 479-9364) has its headquarters at Cabinas La Amistad.

Ocarina Expeditions (☎ 253-4579) offerscombination hiking and horseback riding tours to the Río Celeste, hotsprings, waterfall, and other delights for around US$200 pp from San José.

BIRDWATCHING: Biologist Aaron Sekerak, author of *A Travel and Site Guide to Birds of Costa Rica*, runs **Ave Rica** (☎ 479-9076, 479-9447) excellent tours in the area; they are limited to four.
averica@yellowweb.co.cr

FROM LA FORTUNA: The bus stop is in front of the gas station and the Restaurant El Jardín. Buses run to San Ramón, to Ciudad Quesada, to Tilarán (connections to Monteverde), to Ciudad Quesada, and to San José. Get an early start. (*Note that buses to San José leave every hour from Ciudad Quesada*).

Ciudad Quesada (San Carlos)

Situated 48 km N of Naranjo and 95 km from San José, Ciudad Quesada (pop. 27,000) is popularly known as "San Carlos" because it's located near the San Carlos Plains, a major agricultural area. To get here, take a *directo* (preferably) near-hourly bus (5AM-6PM) from Coca Cola at C. 16, Av. 1/3). Another approach is to take the Tilarán-San Carlos bus.

SIGHTS: There is not a whole lot to do here. However, it is an interesting town to visit in that it can give you a feel for small town life.

Parque Nacional Juan Castro Blanco (Juan Castro Blanco National Park) was declared a national park in 1993. This area lies just to the S of San Carlos. It covers some 60,000 acres (24,000 ha) and protects the sources of several rivers as well as birds such as the quetzal. Juan Castro Blanco is named after a local individual who was instrumental in promoting national preservation in the area. European mining interests were denied permits to stripmine sulfur deposits here in 1990.

Ciudad Cutris is a set of pre-Columbian city ruins five km N of Venecia, an hour's bus ride from San Carlos. There is a basic *pensión* where you can stay in Venecia. There are no facilities at the site itself, and it is on privately-owned land, so ask permission first.

Zoológico La Marina is a private zoo near El Tucano which cares for and/or treats rehabilitating or illegally captured creatures.

ACCOMMODATION: The inexpensive 50-room **Hotel La Central** (☎ 469-0766, ☎/fax 469-0301; Apdo. 345, 4400 Ciudad Quesada) charges around US$25-30 for its rooms which have showers; there's also a casino and guarded parking.

Down the street, the recently constructed **Hotel Don Goyo** (☎ 460-1780) has sunny rooms with bath and a restaurant. It's similarly priced.

Also just off the park, low-budget **Hotel El Retiro** (☎ 460-0275) is one of the cheaper places; others include the **Diana**, **Lily**, **París**, **Los Frenandos**, **Uglade**, and **La Terminal**. Set to the N of town amidst landscaped gardens, the **El Nido Bed and Breakfast** (☎ 460-1322, fax 460-1145) charges around US$50 d; some rooms have shared bath.

Featuring a pool, two children's pools, restaurant, a small lake for fishing and boating, and a roller skating rink, **Balneario San Carlos** (☎ 460-0747; Apdo. 345, 4400 Ciudad Quesada) has *cabinas* for around US$10 with refrigerator and hot water. Dances are held on Sundays. To get here, follow the signs five blocks NW of the park.

OUTLYING ACCOMMODATION: A good place to experience the real Costa Rica, Cooprena(☎/fax 259-3605, 259-9430) operates the **Coopesanjuan Community Ecolodge** offers excursions and local flavor. Rates are around US$35 s, US$50 d, US$45 t.

www.agroecoturismo.net
cooprena@sol.racsa.co.cr

Termales del Bosque (☎ 460-1356, 460-4740) is a hot springs/natural sauna and botanical garden retreat near Ciudad Quesada which offers horseback riding, canopy exploration, locker service, coffee shop/ restaurant, and a lodge. Rates are around US$4 entrance (US$2 for children, and US$45 for cabins (breakfast included). It is much more downscale than El Tucano. Day visits (including canopy tours) are encouraged. It is open daily from 9-9.

canopy@sol.racsa.co.cr

Tilajari (☎ 469-9091, fax 469-9095; Apdo. 81, 4100 San Carlos) is in Muelle de San Carlos, 22 km N of San Carlos. One of the area's plushest hotels, it is run by James M. Hamilton, a former Peace Corps vol-

unteer who has lived in the area for more than two decades. His establishment offers luxury-priced a/c rooms and suites with private terraces. Facilities here include sauna, two pools, racquetball courts, and three lighted tennis courts — all amidst 40 acres bordering the Río San Carlos. You can take part in excursions including horseback riding through the 600-acre cattle ranch or a guided hike through the 1,000-acre tropical rainforest preserve. Rates are around US$85 d for standard rooms and US$110 for suites.
www.tilajari.com
tilajari@sol.racsa.co.cr
tilajari@tilajari.com

Some nine km N and near Boca de Arenal, **Río San Carlos Lodge** (☎ 469-9179/9194, fax 460-0391) is an old home five rooms, gardens, pools, and a restaurant; prices are around US$60 d with breakfast.

Set above the Río Platanar, the **La Quinta Inn Bed and Breakfast** (☎/fax 475-5260) is run by Costa Ricans returned after two decades in the US. Facilities include volleyball and basketball courts, pool, hammocks, and a sauna. Bunk beds are US$10 pp and rooms in their home are US$35 s, d, or t. Group rates with meals are available.

A 600-acre (248-ha) cattle farm with a 723-acre (300-ha) private reserve near Muelle on the way to La Fortuna, **La Garza** (☎ 475-5222, fax 475-5015; Apdo. 100-2250, Tres Rios) offers attractively furnished *cabinas* (around US$80 d) right by the river, a pool, restaurant in a converted farmhouse, and a three km hiking/jogging trail. Horseback riding, guided tours of the reserve, tubing and swimming in the river, fishing, and tours are offered
lagarza@sol.racsa.co.cr

Melía El Tucáno Resort and Spa (☎ 460-6000, 460-3152, fax 460-1692) is set 8 km (five mi.) to the NE of Cuidad Quesada and Aguas Zarcas at Agua Caliente de San Carlos, the large white gates of this luxurious inn open onto immaculate grounds; the premises include a first-class spa, saunas, thermal baths, three swimming pools, whirlpools, a small zoo, and a nearby miniature golf course. Packages are available, and the day use fee is charged. Rates run from around US$90 d to US$200 for the "presidential suites."

To get to the country club from San Carlos, take a San Miguel, Pital, Aguas Zarcas, Venecia, or Río Frio bus. From here you can drive E 20 mi.(32 km) to Hwy. 9. Turning E on Hwy. 9, you can head towards Puerto Viejo de la Sarapiquí, or turn right and a lovely stretch of road leads to San José via Heredia. Shuttle service (US$35 pp) is also available
meliatuc@sol.racsa.co.cr

While here, be sure to visit **El Marina Zoologica** (☎ 460-0946), a nearby non-profit facility which rehabilitates and then releases injured, confiscated, and abandoned birds, reptiles and mammals, as well as exotic pets.

FOOD: Restaurante Tonjibe, on the square, offers pizza, pasta, seafood and rice dishes; live music accompanies dinner.

Set inside the Centro Commercial on the plaza, the **Casa Loca** offers seafood, sandwiches, and a wide selection for carnivores. Gourmet diners will appreciated **Los Parados Restaurant and Pizzeria** (☎ 460-5302) which offers dishes such as jumbo shrimp cocktail, sandwiches, and grilled fish.

INFORMATION: The **Chamber of Tourism** (☎ 460-1672) offers maps and advice; it's generally open from 8:30-11 and 12:30-5 except Wed. PM and weekends.

Serendipity (☎ 556-2593) offers hot-air ballooning as well as other activities. **Canopy Tours** operates at the El Tucano.

SHOPPING: An *artesanía* cooperative in the park's NW corner sells local arts and crafts.

FROM SAN CARLOS: Beyond San Carlos, a road runs to La Fortuna, in the vicinity of Volcán Arenal, then over the Tilarán range to Arenal Lake and down to the Interamerican Highway at Cañas. From San Carlos buses depart for Río Frio, Fortuna, Tilarán (via Fortuna and Tabacón), and San José: catch a *directo*.

Laguna del Lagarto

Laguna del Lagarto (☎ 289-8163, ☎/fax 289-5295, 231-3816; Apdo. 995, 1007 Centro Colón) is one of the nation's most remote nature lodges. German Vinzenz Schmack purchased 265 acres (110 ha) of virgin rainforest in 1981, attempted to farm, and then switched to tourism. Poison dart frogs are common; the giants of the forest are labeled; vegetation is lush and spectacular. You may not see any mammals, but the overall ambiance is amazing.

FLORA AND FAUNA: You needn't step out of your hammock to see many of the 232 bird species. You might see chestnut mandibled toucans, belted kingfisher, golden-hooded tanagers, or other birds in the clearing and in the nearest old growth trees. Hummingbirds flock around the feeder.

The great green macaw is found in the area but is rare. They are best seen on the magnificent almond trees which provide them with food. You will definitely see parrots, parrots, and more parrots! Vinsenz acquired a resident green macaw after he persuaded its owner, a woman in the village, to allow it to relocate. Too fat to fly away, you will see it sitting on one of a select number of trees.

GETTING HERE: The lodge is past Boca Tapada after Pital. A paved road leads to Pital, then it's 18 mi.along a gravel surfaced road to Boca Tapada; the lodge is four km farther along a firm gravel road. Transport may be available. Otherwise, take a bus from the Terminal Atlántico in San José to Pital and then one to Boca Tapada.

There are a number of lagoons (actually flooded swampy areas). Their trees and dead tree trunks attract birds, particularly species such as great herons and ahingas. Paddling in a canoe around in these peaceful lagoons is a superb way to spend an hour or so each day.

Trails are well maintained, and walking sticks reside in a barrel right by the entrance. The main trail takes a little over an hour to traverse and ends at the path to a lagoon; it is intersected by four trails which permit you your choice of loops. If you head into the woods at 6, you may take one of them and return in time for breakfast.

Meals are hearty and well prepared. Special diets will be catered to. Added touches include special dishes such as roasted breadfruit, and carambola (starfruit) as well as other juices made from fruits grown on the property.

PRACTICALITIES: Laguna del Lagarto has a homey feel about it. There are two porch areas with chairs, tables, and hammocks as well as a comfortable dining area with bar. Tranquility is the rule

"This community protects green parrots." Sign near Boca Tapada.

here. No electric lights from neighboring lodges or towns intrude, no generator noise (electricity is line-fed), no television, and few-to-no vehicles pass: the main road dead-ends at a heart of palm plantation. The sole nightly entertainment comes when Vinzenz takes great delight in feeding beef to Charlie and the other caimans resident in the lagoon.

It has 14 rooms with private baths, six with shared bath, and a restaurant; more cabins are planned. Rates are around US$40 s, US$60 d including taxes; rooms with private baths are US$52 s, US$70 d including taxes. Meals (tax and service included) are US$ 6 breakfast, US$8 lunch, and US$11 dinner. Horseback riding and trips up and San Juan rivers are available. Activities include hiking, canoeing in the lake, and a boat trip up the Río San Juan (usually on Tues.) and the San Carlos.

lagarto@sol.racsa.co.cr

Caño Negro Wildlife Refuge

(Refugio Nacional de Fauna Silvestre Caño Negro)

Declared a reserve in 1984, Caño Negro is located 124 km (77 miles) N of Ciudad Quesada and 36 km E of Upala.This 9,969-ha (24,633-acre) swampy tract is one of the most inaccessible of the nation's wildlife refuges and, thus, one of the least touristed. A lake covers some 800 ha (1,977 acres) of the refuge; you need a boat to explore.

Endangered species residing here include *caímans*, crocodiles, ocelots, pumas, cougars, river otters, and tapirs. Among the ample birdlife are the nation's largest colony of neotropic olivaceous cormorants, roseate spoonbills, and the Nicaraguan grackle (found only here).

Tour agencies pay per-passenger entrance via the honor system because the understaffed park has no office at the Los Chiles area, and many tour companies enter there rather than at Guatuso because of poor road conditions at the latter. Cattle grazing, cayman poachers, and abuse by tourists is having a detrimental effect on the park.

Contact the reserve via the San José radio number (☎ 233-4070) or call 460-1301, the area's public phone. Camping is permitted, and there is also limited, low-cost lodging (see below); boat and horse rentals are available.

GETTING HERE: To get there take a direct Los Chiles bus (Auto transportes ☎ 460-5032, 255-4318) from Av. 9, C. 12 at 5:30 AM and 3:30 PM.

TOURS: The best time to visit is during the rainy season when there's the maximum amount of water. If hiring your own, expect to pay US$40-90 depending upon the type of boat and number of passengers. Ask at the **Restaurant El Parque** (by the *muelle*; ☎ 471-1032/1090: ask for Julia Pizarro) where you can also dine.

LOS CHILES ACCOMMODATIONS: Stay at the low budget Tico-style hotels or the **Caño Negro Lagoon Lodge** (☎ 225-1073, fax 234-1676), 15 km to the S, which provides simple rooms for around US$50 d, a restaurant, and tours (on foot, by boat, or on horse). The **Guájibal Lodge** (☎ 383-1206) and the **Cabinas jabirú** (☎ 471-1055, fax 471-1211) offer other, less-pricey alternatives.

UPALA ACCOMMODATIONS: In Upala you can stay in the inexpensive **Hotel Rigo**, **Pensión Isabela**, or the **Pensión Buena Vista**. Martin Bernard (☎ 228-4812, 289-8139) of **"No Frills"** offers low budget accommodation as well as trips on the Río Frio and to Nicaragua. Near Upala, **Los Ceibos Lodge** (☎ 221-7641, 222-4059, fax 233-9393) offers horseback riding and

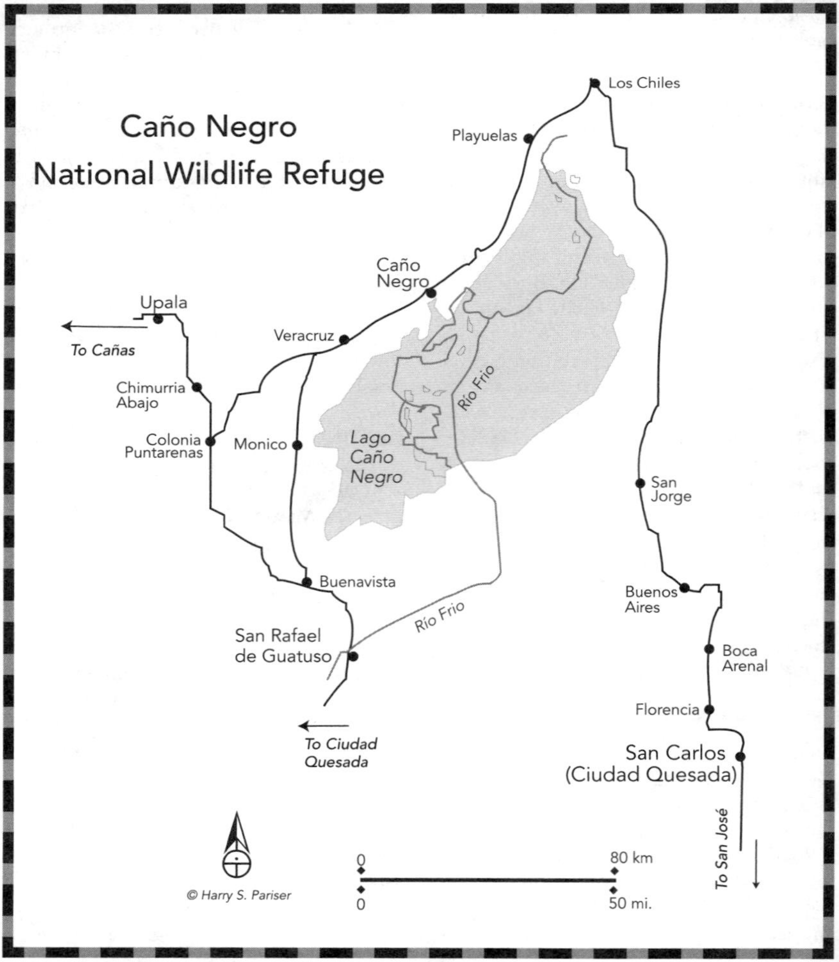

> If you really want to get away from it all, travel from Los Chiles by boat into Nicaragua. The town of San Carlos is on Lake Nicaragua. Spartan sportsfishing Hotel Mancarrón is on the Isla Sonentiname on the lake. The lake came to fame when the late Catholic priest and Sandinista Culture Minister Ernesto Cardenal established a commune which propogated a mix of the arts, revolutionary fervor, and liberation theology. The border is closed on weekends. Flights and a river ferry (12 hrs.) connect the area with Managua. This route is strictly for true adventurers.

guided walks. Buses run from San José to Upala (☎ 257-0061; C. 16, Av. 3/5).

Commanding majestic views, the **Albergue Ecoturistico Bijagua Heliconias** (☎/fax 470-0115, message: 224-2400) is set on the slopes of the Volcán Tenorio. It has six cabins (US$12 s,US$16 d, US$20 t) with private bath and hot water and a bar/restaurant and offers tremendous views, hiking to boiling mud pools, waterfalls, and a small crater lake. To get here travel to the village of Bijagua de Upala (36 km from Cañas enroute to Upala in Alajuela Province) and drive two km off of N6. Transport is available from the bus stop by request.
www.agroecoturismo.net
coprena@sol.racsa.co.cr

CAÑO NEGRO ACCOMMODATIONS: Stay at low-budget **Cabinas El Querque** (☎ 661-8464) which offers boat rides, hiking, and horseback riding.

GETTING HERE: You can also charter a boat from Los Chiles (stay at low-budget **Río Frio**, ☎ 471-1127) for US$60 and up to ply five hours down the Río Frio and back. Numerous lodges and tour companies also run tours up here. In the dry season, they can't go all of the way.

South From San Carlos

Zarcero

Zarcero is famous for the dozens of boxwood hedges which stand in front of its cottage-style church. These are in the shape of animals (bull, rabbit, and an elephant), dancers, oxcarts, even an airplane and a helicopter. A series of Daliesque arbor arches augment the path to the colorful church. They are the creation of gardener Evangelista Blanco who has been grooming them since 1964.

GETTING HERE: The bus (about 2.5 hrs.) leaves from the corner of C. 16 and Av. 3 near Coca Cola daily at 9:15 or you can take any of the hourly San Carlos buses from Coca Cola. Check in the Soda Los Amigos, to the S of the park, for the bus schedules. From Zarcero you can go on to the Arenal area. If you're driving (1.5 hrs.), get off at the Naranjo-Cuidad Quesada exit.

PRACTICALITIES: The **Hotel Don Beto** (☎/fax 463-3137) has two rooms with private bath and two rooms with shared. Breakfast is available, and Tica owner Flora Salazar is knowledgeable about the area. Rates are from around US$20 d for a room with shared bath. If you're in the mood for Italian food, try Restaurant La Montaña just before the town. Roadside stores in this vicinity, sell good jams and excellent cheeses.

Bosque de Paz Rain/Cloud Forest

The **Bosque de Paz Rain/Cloud Forest** (☎ 234-6676, fax 225-0203; Apdo. 130, 1000 San José) covers 400 ha (1,000 ares) of rainforest and cloud forest terrain. It is maintained by an idealistic and extreme-

ly hospitable Costa Rican family whose motto is "We believe in taking care of nature as a praise to our Creator." It is set in Alajuela province around 25 min. from Zarcero. Facilities include restaurant, two rooms, and daytours.
bosque@sol.racsa.co.cr

San Ramón de Alajuela

This farming town, set on the main hwy. to Puntarenas SW of Zarcero, boasts an enormous *feria del agricultor* (farmer's market) each Sat.; small **museum** (Museo San Ramón) is open weekday afternoons.

Bosque Nuboso de Los Angeles

This 2,000-acre (810-ha) private reserve and farm, owned by ex-President Rodrigo Carazo, has a two-km walking trail through virgin cloud forest, waterfalls, rivers, canopy tour, and horseback riding. Admission is US$14; a guide is US$7 add'l.

Set near the entrance, expensive **Hotel Villablanca** (☎ 228-4603, fax 228-4004; Apdo. 247-1250, San José) offers 20 small cabins with fireplaces for around US$100 d and rooms in the main house for around US$80. Food is US$25/day add'l., and you must also pay the trail fee daily! Lower-priced dorm rooms with cooking facilities are also available. Meals are served buffet style.

To get here take the road from San Ramón to La Tigra — found 200 m W of the hospital to the N of town — and follow the signs to Villablanca and the cloud forest. A paved road gives way to a gravel one. There's no bus transport from San Ramón (20 km away). A taxi costs around US$10 OW.
villablan@sol.racsa.co.cr

Valle Escondido Lodge

This lodge (☎ 231-0906, fax 232-9591; Apdo. 452, 1150 La Uruca) is set in a valley to the N of San Ramón and Los Angeles in San Lorenzo (a town which is also linked by road with Santa Cruz and Ciudad Quesada) in the midst of 400 acres of pastures as well as primary forest. It has 25 attractively furnished rooms (around US$70 d), international restaurant, and live music on Sat. Horseback riding, mountain biking, river swimming, tours, and hiking are available.
www.cmnet.co.cr
valle@ns.goldnet.co.cr

San Rafael de Guatuso

This small town, surrounded by cattle ranches, retains a laid back cowboy atmosphere. Maleku Indians, who live in three *palenques* in the surrounding area, practice subsistence farming and sell carved gourds to visitors.

Stay at the 10-room **Albergue Tío Henry** (☎ 460-2058) above the veterinary supply store. Roooms with shared bath are around US$10 and those with private bath and a/c are around US$20. Tío Henry offers tours, including a horseback trek which passes El Arbol de la Paz (an old tree made into a peace symbol by Oscar Arias) and continues on to a village where you dismount; dine on coffee, *tortillas*, and fruit; and then continue on foot to the La Paz waterfall before returning.

Ujuminica

This 1,500-acre (600 ha) crocodile and *caimán* farm is set on the banks of the Río Frio downriver from San Rafael de Guatuso and near Caño Negro reserve. Its name means "crocodile fell in the trap" in the of the Maleku language. Meals are served in a thatched-roof restaurant here.

The Northwest (Guanacaste)

Costa Rica's relatively arid NW is largely contained in the province of Guanacaste, an area quite distinct from the rest of the nation; its culture is largely *Mestizo* with some surviving Chorotega customs, such as use of the digging stick in agriculture and traditional forms of pottery. Another survivor is the *punto guanacasteco* which has become the national dance. In 1824, its inhabitants seceded from Nicaragua and elected to join Costa Rica. This late 20th-C Central American version of the Wild West, this is indisputably cattle country. And *boyeros*, tenders of oxen, as well as the *sauderos*, the local cowboys with their ornately decorated saddles, are mythologized folklore figures. Commonly seen in Santa Cruz, Liberia, and Nicoya, bullfights are a confrontation in which the bull is not injured.

Ferries

Car ferries run from Puntarenas to Naranjo, Paquera, and Tambor and return. (Times may vary with the season). This can speed your trip to the Nicoya Peninsula. A ferry also crosses the Tempisque River between Puerto Nispero (Cañas) and Puerto Moreno.

The **Playa Naranjo Car Ferry** (☎ 661-1069, 661-3834) runs at 3:15 AM, 7 AM, 10:50 AM, 2:50 PM, and 7 PM. It returns at 5:10 AM, 8:50 AM, 12:50 PM, 5 PM, and 9 PM.

The **Paquera Car Ferry** (☎ 661-3674) departs at 8:45 AM, 2 PM, and 8:15 PM and returns at 6 AM, 11:45 AM, and 6 PM.

The **Playa Tambor Ferry** (☎ 681-2084) also goes to Paquera. It departs at 5 AM, 12:30 PM, and 5 PM and returns at 8 AM, 2:30 PM, and 8:30 PM. It is owned by the infamous Spanish hoteliers the Barcelos.

The **Tempisque River Ferry** (☎ 685-5295) leaves from Puerto Nispero (Cañas) hourly from 5:30 AM-8:30 PM.

Note: Schedules can change so check in advance.

PENINSULA DE NICOYA: The most popular piece of the region is the Nicoya Peninsula which offers literally dozens of dazzling beaches. Isolated until recent years, many of the beaches have been developed, and tourist infrastructure is booming. If you still find things a bit rough-going, keep in mind that gradually roads are getting paved. And there is now good airline service available.

But the peninsula is not *just* beaches! There are also sugarcane, teak and *pochote* (rosewood) plantations; Nicoya is really village country. You can tell when you're in a really small town because there are no Chinese restaurants! There are a larger number of thatched-roof dwellings than you might see elsewhere, a reflection both of limited transportation and low income levels.

CLIMATE: Flat and dry, ranches occupy large expanses of former rainforest. This province turns green almost overnight after the rainy season commences. If you treasure solitude, May and June are really the months to visit. Though the rainy season, it is also green and, as the hotels are practically empty, you can stay wherever you choose.

?!: Guanacaste's name comes from the *guanacaste* (earpod) tree that offers shade on the pastures.

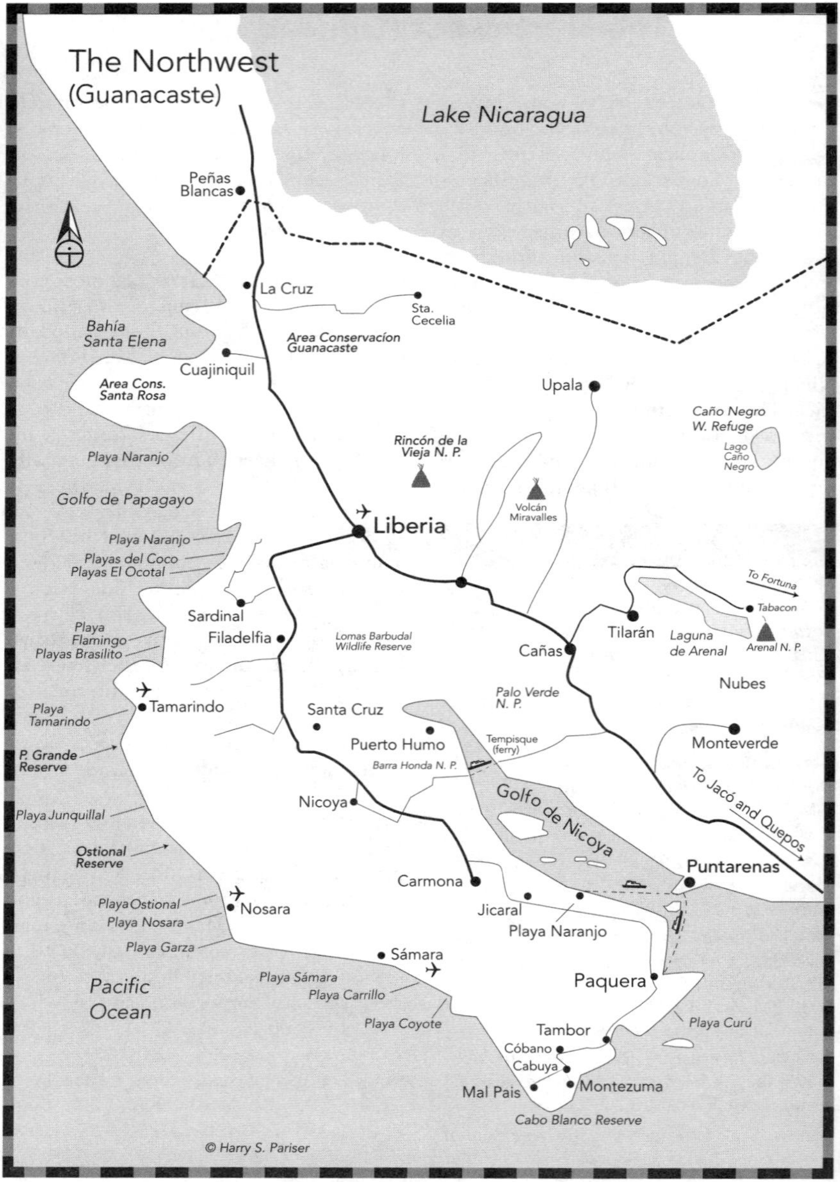
The Northwest
(Guanacaste)
Lake Nicaragua
Peñas
Blancas
La Cruz
Sta.
Cecelia
Bahía
Santa Elena
Area Conservacíon
Guanacaste
Cuajiniquil
Area Cons.
Santa Rosa
Upala
Caño Negro
W. Refuge
Lago
Caño
Negro
Rincón de la
Vieja N. P.
Playa Naranjo
Golfo de Papagayo
Volcán
Miravalles
Liberia
Playa Naranjo
Playas del Coco
Playas El Ocotal
To Fortuna
Tabacon
Sardinal
Tilarán
Laguna
de Arenal
Arenal N. P.
Playa
Flamingo
Filadelfia
Lomas Barbudal
Wildlife Reserve
Playas Brasilito
Cañas
Nubes
Palo Verde
N. P.
Playa
Tamarindo
Tamarindo
Santa Cruz
Puerto Humo
Tempisque
(ferry)
Monteverde
P. Grande
Reserve
Barra Honda N. P.
To Jacó and Quepos
Golfo de Nicoya
Nicoya
Playa Junquillal
Ostional
Reserve
Puntarenas
Carmona
Playa Ostional
Nosara
Playa Nosara
Jicaral
Playa Naranjo
Playa Garza
Sámara
Pacific
Ocean
Playa Sámara
Playa Carrillo
Paquera
Playa Coyote
Tambor
Playa Curú
Cóbano
Cabuya
Mal Pais
Montezuma
Cabo Blanco Reserve
© Harry S. Pariser

EXPLORING: A two-lane road, mostly paved, leads from the Puntarenas ferry terminal through Liberia, and on to Santa Cruz, Nicoya, and Jicaral, and there is plenty of bus transport along this route. This is one area where renting a car would definitely be an asset. You might want to rent one, tour around a few days staying in different places and then settle down in one spot for awhile. One approach is to do a circle, going up via Liberia and then on to Santa Rosa or Guanacaste park, next heading over and back through Nicoya.

If you pick Tamarindo, Nosara, or Sámara, you may have the added advantage of flying back, thus avoiding a somewhat grueling bus ride. Should you choose to drive, please don't let the seemingly light traffic lure you into speeding. At any time, you may come around a bend and encounter a *campesino*, steers, bicyclists, or a halted vehicle.

Another alternative would be to take the ferries from Playa Naranjo or (if you can get there) from Paquera. A final option is to use Travelair's flights from San José and Liberia to the coastal beaches or to fly to Liberia and take a bus from there. Despite the dust and the heat, Nicoya is a cyclist's paradise, as there are so few cars, and the surroundings are beautiful. Other regional activities include rafting down the slow-moving Corobicí, swimming, diving, sailing, horseback riding, and hiking.

Cañas

At Km 188, this hot and somnolent farming center (pop. 21,000) marks the turn-off to Tilarán and Lake Arenal. To get here, take one of five buses daily from C. 16, Av. 1/3, San José or take a Tralapa bus from C. 20, Av. 3. Base yourself here for the Palo Verde National Park or other reserves; otherwise stay in Liberia or up in cooler Tilarán.

PRACTICALITIES: Best bet in town is the trim Lowest-price place here is the **Nuevo Hotel Cañas** (☎ 669-1294, fax 669-1319) which offers rooms with a/c and fans, cable TV, and other amenities for around US$40 d.

Around 2.5 km N of town, the **Capazurí** (☎/fax 669-0580) is a family-run joint whose rooms have cold-water showers; breakfast is included in the rates (around US$30 d). They also allow camping.

There are a number of low-budget plaes **Cabinas Corobicí** (☎ 669-0241, around US$10) is six blocks E from the highway. The **Gran Hotel** is at the NW side of the plaza; and **El Corral** (☎ 669-0622, around US$30 d) and **Guillén** are at the SE side of the plaza.

In addition to local cuisine, there are a number of Chinese restaurants, including the **Lei Tu**, just off the plaza.

Inside the El Corral, **Transporte Palo Verde** (☎ 669-1091) runs trips (US$35-50) to Palo Verde in a motor launch via the Río Bebedero. To go directly to Liberia or Tilarán, use the new terminal at C. 1 and Av. 11; for San José or Liberia/La Cruz, stand by the highway and wait.

Centro Ecológico La Pacifica

This moderate 3,300-acre (1,332-ha) establishment (☎ 669-0050, fax 669-0555; Apdo 8, 5700 Cañas, Guanacaste), is located off the E side of the highway six km (four miles) N of Cañas. Named for the lady who designed the Costa Rican flag, this private reserve has labeled trees, over 225 species of birds, and a pool. All of the hardwood *cabinas* are equpped with fans and private baths;

some also have hot water and kitchens. Many of the photos in Dan Jantzen's classic *Costa Rican Natural History* were taken of captive animals here. Besides the forest reserve, which comprises one third of the area, visitors may tour the farm and the reforestation project. Added features include the nature trail *Sendero del Chocaco*, and a small museum in a restored Spanish *hacienda* which details life as it was in Guanacaste 100 years ago. The estate has 500 ha of land devoted to cattle, with the remaining 2,000 ha protected.

Rates are around US$80 d with private bath; rooms with shared bath and bunk beds are less expensive.

A restaurant, the Swiss-operated **Rincón Corobicí** is right on the river of the same name, just after the entrance. It operates a small campsite.

River rafting tours (around US$35 on up) down the gentle Corobicí are run by **Safaris Corobicí** (☎/fax 669-1091/0544; Apdo. 99, Cañas) and depart from here. They also rent bikes and operate mountain bike tours.
www.nicoya.com
safaris@sol.racsa.co.cr

warning: *There have been drownings on this river, so take care!*

Las Pumas

This extraordinary collection of felines constitutes one of the world's most unusual zoos. Here, you'll find jaguars, margays, pumas, and ocelots. All of the animals were rescued from the traps of poachers; most are delivered courtesy of MINEM, the Ministry of Natural Resources, Energy and Mines which is responsible for snaring illegal hunters. The "zoo" was created and managed by Swiss expat Lilly Hagenauer, former owner of La Pacifica. Lilly's collection began in 1967 after a friend gave her a margay, and the collection has kept on expanding ever since. Cages are nothing fancy but are functional, and each cat has its own story which Lilly will relate.

It would be pointless to re-release most of the animals into the forest as, having been trapped and kept captive, it would be difficult for them to reacclimate. In addition, the shrinking wilderness is making their very survival increasingly perilous. Lily finances the animals' upkeep through the sale of budgeriars (pastel-colored birds) and through visitor donations. Admission is free, but contributions are welcome. Las Pumas is set near the Rincón Corobicí restaurant (see above). It's open from 8-5 daily.

Las Juntas de Abangares

A former gold mining center for the region, these mines once attracted an international community of goldseekers and its ethnic diversity reflects this. The mine "El Silencio" here was closed at the behest of environmentalists in 1996. **SIGHTS:** The **Eco Museo** is an old mine structure. It is four km from the **Caballo Blanco Cantina** which also exhibits antiques from the gold mining era. The nearby community of **Los Angeles** is only accessible via four-wheel drive or horseback. Boston still has a community of gold panners.

PRACTICALITIES: Las Juntas can be reached by bus from San José (C. 12, Av. 7/9;10:45 AM, 5:15 PM; ☎ 256-8598), Puntarenas, and from Cañas (30 min.). Stay at low-budget **Cabinas Las Juntas** (☎ 662-0069). Eat here or at **Las Gamelas** or **La Familiar**. **Mina Tours** (☎ 662-0753, fax 662-0010), operates tours and can accommodate groups or individuals in their homestay.

La Ensenada Lodge

This small Italian-run lodge (☎ 228-6653/2655, cell ☎ 284-3921, fax 228-5281) offers the opportunity to participate in the daily activities of a farm which raises cattle and produces papaya, salt, and watermelon. There are great opportunities for birdwatching, photography, and horseback riding. You can also water ski, wind surf, and play tennis. Tours of Plao Verde and other locales are offered. The lodge is on the coast, 40 km to the S of Cañas. Rates are around US$100 d with meals.

Reserva Biolóaica Lomas Barbudal
(Lomas Barbudal Biological Reserve)

The meaning of Lomas Barbudal's name ("bearded hills") is obscure. This area was put under protection in 1986, partially because of its value as a watershed. As one might expect there are a number of natural springs. It also serves as a refuge for migrating birds, including egrets, herons, and grebes, and 201 species of birds have been identified thus far. There are also over 250 species of solitary bees which live alone rather than in hives. It has a number of the extremely rare cannonball trees (*balas de cañón*) whose dangling pungent fruits are hard spherical capsules the size of bowling balls and can number up to 300 per tree. The largest of the 175 tree species present, the sandbox tree lures scarlet macaws from nearby Palo Verde National Park who feast on its fruit. Camping is permitted, and there's a refreshment stand and a swimming hole.

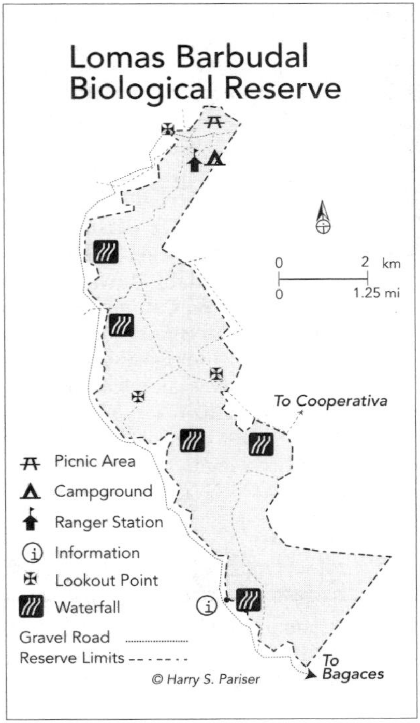

GETTING HERE: About three hrs. by car from San José, this biological reserve has its station 15 km (9 mi.) SE of the town of Bagaces, six km (four miles) from the Km 221 marker on the Interamerican Highway; it's just half an hour from Liberia. Four-wheel-drive vehicles are recommended during the rainy season. If you arrive in Bagaces, you can get to the reserve by chartering a taxi (about US$20-25 RT including waiting time). Otherwise, it's about six km each way from Pijijue, which is on the Interamerican Highway about halfway between Bagaces and Liberia.

PRACTICALITIES: Admission to the reserve is by voluntary donation. The

Centro Patrimonial de Lomas Barbudal (☎ 671-1062/1029), a visitor and community center, offers information as well as lodging for volunteers. An interpretive trail guide brochure is available. The best trail runs along the Río Catuyo NE from the Centro Patrimonial 1.5 km to a small waterfall. A loop trail is planned.

Bagaces is an attractive place to base yourself while visiting the reserve. Very basic cabins are available for rent. The best of the lot may be **Cabinas Eduardo Vargas** which has no sign but is near the plaza. Also try **Hotel Miravelles. Albergue Las Sillas** is set halfway between Bagaces and the turnoff for the reserve. **note:** The reserve was hit by a fire in March 1994 which raged for eight days, destroying 2,000 of its 2,400 acres. The forest is still under recovery.

Liberia

Liberia (pop.) 23,000 is both the of Guanacaste's provincial capital and its major town. Nicknamed *Ciudad Blanca* (White City) because its quartz-based subsoil was once used along with lime to construct the roads, Liberia was founded in 1769 and is the nation's only city with its own flag. The town is clean and attractive, with flamboyant-shaded streets and more bicycles than cars. There are no street signs so you pretty much have to ask directions in order to get around. The separation from Nicaragua, which was announced in 1814 and finally confirmed by an 1820 plebescite, is celebrated each July 25. Although most areas can be reached by bus, you'll want to have a car if you plan on doing day trips.

GETTING HERE: Buses leave hourly daily from C. 14, A. 1/3 in San José from 6 AM-8 PM with direct buses aat 3 and 5 PM. Also buses run from Av. 3, C. 18/20.

BY AIR: An important new development, the Aeropuerto Tomás Guardia "opened" in 1992 and has since been "inaugarated" and renamed twice: it's now known as Aeropuerto Daniel Oduber Quirós. It is largely intended to service charter flights, but still receives only a few. Some LACSA/TACA flights finish here after stopping at San José. *Travelair* (☎ reservations: 220-3054, sales: 296-1102, fax 296-2316; SJO 788, PO Box 025216, Miami, FL 33102-5216; information@travelair-costarica.com) flies to and from San José and Tamarindo out of here.

SIGHTS: There's not a lot to do in Liberia except walk around. Many of the houses have a colonial flavor. The corner homes often have a door (*puerta del sol*) on each side of the corner. The town square has an avant-garde Swiss-chalet-like church with a large broadcasting antenna. Grackles flock in the trees here at dusk, and a band plays occasionally in the evenings.

Located in a verdant and quiet neighborhood, **La Agonía**, a white church with a small park in front, dates from the era when the region was still part of Nicaragua. It's the perfect destination for a late afternoon stroll.

The **Casa de la Cultura** (open Tues. to Sat., 9-noon, 1-6; Sun. 9-noon), three blocks to the S of the main plaza, has an exhibit about the *sabaneros*, the region's cowboys, as well as an information service.

ACCOMMODATION: Liberia is a popular place during peak season so you'd be well advised to make reservations prior to arrival.

Moderate (around US$45 d with tax) 60-room **Hotel Nuevo Boyeros** (☎ 666-0995 fax 666-0203; Apdo. 85, Liberia, Guanacaste) has friendly management, comfortable a/c rooms with double beds and cold water shower, two pools surrounded by palm trees, and an outdoor lounge, as well as a large dining room.

Moderate and slightly cheaper 23-room **Hotel El Bramadero** (☎ 666-0371, fax 666-0371; Apdo. 70, Liberia), which has a/c or fans, pool, and restaurant, is located right at the crossroads across from the Nuevo Boyeros.

Luxury-priced but well-maintained and comfortable, the 44-room **Hotel Las Espuelas** (☎ 666-0144, fax 225-3987; Apdo. 58-1000, San José) has a/c, pool, restaurant, and gift shop. It's about two km down the road towards Santa Cruz. Rates are around US$ 70d.
herradu@sol.racsa.co.cr

Nearby 23-room **La Ronda** (☎ 666-0417) is inexpensive and has a pool.

Located 2.5 blocks to the R from Farmacía Lux in the town's center, inexpensive 24-room **Hotel La Siesta** (☎ 666-0678, fax 666-2532) has a pool and is quiet.

Also in the town center is **Posada El Tope** (☎ 666-0363, fax 666-2136) which has eight so-so rooms in an impressive old house; secure parking, kitchen use, and breakfast are all included. Rate are around US$ 15 d.

Moderate 52-room **Hotel El Sitio** (☎ 666-1211, fax 66-2059; Apdo. 134-5000, Liberia) is on the road towards Nicoya (175 m E of the Gasolinera Emesa); rooms have both fan and a/c, and phone and TV. Facilities include restaurant, car rental, three conference rooms, and two pools. Rates are around US$80 with breakfast.

Set next to the stadium, inexpensive **Hotel Daisyita** (☎ 666-0197/0897, fax 666-0927) has comfy rooms with fans as well as disco, two pools, and restaurant (groups only). Rates are around US$25 d.

Once the best low-budget place to stay during its incarnation as the Hotel Oriental, the 27-room **Hotel Guanacaste Travel Lodge** (☎ 666-0085, fax 666-2287) has now become a "youth hostel" and moved into the inexpensive range. It's just around the corner from the El Bramadero. They charge around US$22 d with tax; camping is US$44pp, and singles, quads, and five-person rooms are available. Tours and meal are offered.
www.asstcard.co.cr/guia/homp/htlguana.htm
htlguana@sol.racsa.co.cr

Other low-budget places include **Hotel Rivas** on the main square, **Hotel Liberia** (☎ 666-0161; 75 m S from the church), divey **Hotel Cortijo**, **Las Casonas**, and **Pensión Margarita** (☎ 666-0468), which is practically next door to the Cortijo and 250 m E of the park. Yet other alternatives include **Pensión Golfito** (☎ 666-0963) and **Pensión Central** near the park.

FOOD: Many restaurants are around or near the central plaza and the church. **Panaderia Alfa** (5 AM-9 PM) is good for breakfast. **Pandaderia y Repositería Montevidio** is just down from the church. Also in the vicinity, inexpensive 24-hr. **Restaurante Do Las Tinajas** has pizza, fried chicken and fish. An attractive place to dine is the **Jardín de Azúcar**, which has a wide selection and counter service. Near the church and the information center, **Pizza Pronto** serves pizza and cocktails in an attractive setting.

Some of the numerous Chinese restaurants near the market are **Hit Wa** and the **Chop Suey**. Others are grouped together in back of the church. **Soda La Rueda** and **Rancho Guayami** are pleasant places to eat down the street from the restaurant at the **Nuevo Boyeros**, which has 24 hr. service; the expensive but popular **Gran China** is across from the Boyeros, as is **Relax-Comidas Rapidas**. Intimate **Restaurante Pókópí** (meaning "very much" in Chorotega), along the road to Santa Cruz near the fire station, has a wide variety of continental dishes including pizza, fishburgers and shrimp.

SERVICES: There's no branch of the ICT here as yet. The best information source is your hotel or The Casa de la Cultura (see above).

At Centro Commercial Bambu, **Galería Fulvia** (☎/fax 666-1679) sells the work of local artisans as well as imported newspapers. Run by a native of Ecuador, it is one of the few cultural spots in Guanacaste. Owner Fulvia Cárdenas Forero also produces a literary magazine.

With offices in El Bramadero, **Adventura Rent A Car** (☎ 666-2349) offers car rentals. With offices in the same hotel, **Guanacaste Tours** (☎ 666-0306, fax 666-0307; Apdo. 55-5000, Liberia), one of the nation's best tour companies, operates tours to the Playa Grande, Santa Rosa, Palo Verde, rodeos and bullfights, and to three Nicoya beaches.

Sol Rent-a-Car (☎ 666-2222, fax 666-2898) is on the Ineramerican to the W and offers deliveries and pickups to hotels.
www.asst-card.co.cr/GUIA/HOMP/SOL.htm
sol@asst-card.co.cr

Toyota (☎ 666-0016) and National (☎ 666-1211) also have branches here.

Turistas Amigo (☎ 654-4238, fax 654-4039) offers tours ranging from turtle watching to Tamarindo's mangroves. **GuanAventura** (☎/fax 666-2825) is a mountain bike rental and repair shop. **Libreria Arco** has great postcards. **Instituto Británico** (☎ 666-0966; fax 253-1894; Apdo. 8184-1000, San José) offers Spanish courses.

ENTERTAINMENT: There's a movie theater and **Salon Riabeli** has live music on occasion. The trendiest place in town is undoubtedly the **Disco Kurú** (the Chorotega name for the *guanacaste* tree) next to the Restaurante Pókópi along the road to Santa Cruz. One other alternative for entertainment is to check out some of the local characters. For example you might find Jesus Christ wandering the streets with his staff. Bearded and barefooted and wearing a white tunic, Jesus has now married and has his wife and band of girls (all of whom also wear white) in tow.

EVENTS: The **Fiestas Civicas de Canton** are held in the first or second week in Feb. except during an election year when they are in mid-March. Three events — the Annexation of Guanacaste, Día de San Santiago, and the Feria Ganadera — are celebrated simultaneously on July 25. The Anniversary of the Annexation of Guanacaste Province commemorates the province's secession from Nicaragua, and the fiesta has folk dancing, marimba bands, horse parades, bullfights, rodeos, cattle shows, and local culinary specialties. The **Semana Cultural** takes place during the first week of Sept. On Dec. 24, the **Pasada del Niño** (children's parade) takes place.

FROM LIBERIA: Buses leave for San José, Playas del Coco, Playa Hermosa and Playa Panamá, La Cruz and Peñas Blancas (Santa Rosa and the Nicaraguan border), Filadelfia, Santa Cruz, Nicoya,Cuajinquil, Bagaces (Lomas Barbudal), Cañas (connections for Tilarán), and Monteverde. Check with your hotel or at the bus station for exact times.

Rincón de la Vieja National Park (Parque Nacional Rincón de la Vieja)

NE of Liberia, Volcán Rincón de la Vieja, rises to an impressive 6,216 ft. (1,895 m). One of five active volcanoes in the Guanacaste range, it is the mother of 32 small rivers and streams and 16 water-collecting gorges. The surrounding national park preserves 34,799 acres (14,083 ha) of terrain including tropical dry forests, bubbling mud pots, steaming vents in the earth, hot springs, and a whole host of wildlife.

warning: *The volcano is still active: the last eruption was in Aug.. 1999.*

> ?!¿ The name"Rincón de la Vieja" probably derives from an old lady who once lived here.

FLORA AND FAUNA: Found in groves, twisted and aromatic copel clusias delineate the border between the tropical intermediate forest and the volcano's summit. The national flower, the guaría morada orchid is found within the park's borders. Owing to the presence of four life zones within the park, wildlife is very diverse. There are peccaries, coatis, tapirs, sloths, jaguars, and white-faced, spider, and howler monkeys, as well as over 300 species of birds including the Montezuma oropendola and the three-wattled bellbird. One of the most eclectic inhabitants is a type of cicada that croaks just like a frog.

HISTORY: The region was first explored by German Karl von Seebach in 1864-65. The main crater's last active period was in 1966 when it erupted violently, inundating grazing land on the S slope. Eruptions continued into the next year. It erupted again in 1966-67 and in July 1970. The most recent eruption came in May 1991 when the volcano spewed a torrent of ash, rocks, mud, and water which destroyed two bridges and left around 500 nearby residents stranded.

GETTING HERE: There is no public transportation to the park. You must either hitch, hire a taxi, or drive in your own (preferably four-wheel-drive) vehicle. One route to the park (25 km N of town) leaves through Liberia's Barrio Victoria and heads to the Santa María sector. Another route extends off of Guadaloupe, five mi.(eight km) N of Liberia on the Interamerican Highway. It passes through Currubandé and the Guachipelín Hacienda where you can stay at the Albergue.

SIGHTS: Volcanic ground activity here is paralleled only by places in the Minhasa area of Sulawesi in Indonesia, Central Java's Bleduk Kuwu, Northern California's Lassen National Park, and in some of Japan's national parks.

Situated 7.5 mi.(12 km) from the park headquarters, **Las Pailas** (the large pans) covers a 123-acre (50-ha) area. In separate sections, semi-enclosed by brush, are boiling mud pots, vent holes leaking sulfurous steam, and mud leaping wildly from pits surrounded by vegetation coated with dried spots of white mud.

Sala de Belleza (Beauty Salon) is a set of seven bubbling grey mud holes where you may dip in a finger, let the mud cool off a bit, and apply it to your face as a mud pack.

Surrounded by wild cherry, **Las Hornillas** (the kitchen stoves), a group of sulfurous fumaroles, are found on the devastated SW slope.

Thermal springs of 108°F (42°C) two mi.(three km) from headquarters, the outdoor hot springs of **Loz Azufrales** are surrounded by groves of *encino* trees. Composed of four falls, three of which are more than 230 ft. (70 m) high, the hidden waterfalls are located on the SW slope of the volcano and have a bathing hole at their base.

Set SE of the active crater, the whale-shaped, 15-acre (six-ha) **Laguna Jilgueros** (Linnet Bird Lagoon) has a small island inside; quetzals, tapirs, and linnet songbirds inhabit the area.

CLIMBING THE VOLCANO: It's about 22 mi. (35 km) to the top and back, and it can be done in one day on horseback. **Las Espuelas**, the park post beyond the mud pots, is the best place to base yourself for a climb. As the routes are not clearly marked and it's easy to become disoriented when fog descends, you may wish to hire a guide.

There are two routes, high and low. The high route goes directly to the summit, while the low one passes by it. From the hot springs a meandering cattle path leads to the summit; when in doubt, steer R. This path leads through private property (ask permission) to Las Pailas. From here you climb to Las Espuelas where you should fill your canteens. Camping places are at the tree line; you might wish to stop for the night if it's overcast.

It takes a good two hours to the crater's edge and back; be sure to watch the weather because you can easily get lost in the mist. If it's clear, you'll find the trip to have been well worthwhile: the summit commands a view that can stretch as far as Lake Nicaragua, taking in the Nicaraguan peaks of Concepcíon and Madera and the Peninsula de Nicoya to the W.

other trails: The *Sendero Bosque Encantado* — with a small waterfall, mosses, ferns, and orchids — lives up to its name of "enchanted forest."

ACCOMMODATIONS: The park's adobe headquarters building has only camping sites (around US$2.50 pp) and food (US$5 per meal) available. Call the park's radio contact number (☎ 695-5598) in advance. Another alternative within the park is to camp; this is the best way to see wildlife. You can camp by the hot springs or, if you wish to see tapirs and possibly quetzals, camp by the lagoon; the best months for this are Mar. and April. You may also be able to stay in the old adminstration building: contact the NPS concerning the current situation.

Low-budget **Albergue Rincón de la Turista** is in the village of San Jorge near the main park entrance. Its owners, originally from San José, rent out horses and guides. Also in San Jorge are low-budget **Miravieja** (☎ 666-1045/2004) and **Rinconcito** (☎ 666-0636/2764, cell ☎ 380-8193; beeper: 224-2400) which charges around US$50 d for a stay on a dairy farm.

Another alternative is **Albergue Rincón de la Vieja** (☎ 256-8206, fax 256-7290; Apdo. 114, Liberia) a small but comfortable lodge and cabin run by born-again environmentalist Alvaro Wiessel Baldioceda on his Hacienda Guachipelín. In the middle of the estate, you'll meet Alvaro's four cats, three dogs, and toucan. A water-powered turbine provides power. From the lodge, all parts of the park are accessible by horse or on foot. In addition to the prices listed here (with YH member prices in parentheses), Alvaro has a number of packages available. Canopy tours are offered. Horses (1-10

hrs. with guide) cost around US$36/day (US$15/day); guide alone is US$10/ pp, pd (US$5/pp, pd); beds are around US$15 (US$8) each; meals are US$10 (US$6); and RT transport from Liberia is available for around US$8 pp. Ask about camping on the premises; rates are negotiable off season.
rincon@sol.racsa.co.cr

Yet another place is the seven-room **Hacienda Lodge Guachipelín** (☎ 442-2818, fax 442-1910; beeper 257-3232). It charges around US$30-40 d with breakfast. Camping is permitted, and a mud pool is nearby.
www.guachipelin.com
hacienda@intnet.co.cr

The inexpensive **Santa María Volcano Lodge** (☎ 235-0642, cell ☎ 381-5290, fax 272-6236) is in Colonia Blanca which is 18 km from San Jorge; it may be reached via Bagaces or Liberia (take an Aguas Blancas bus). It has a remodeled farmhouse and Swiss chalet-style cabins. It offers tours and horseback riding.

German-run **La Posada del Encuentro** (cell ☎/fax 382-0815) offers attractive rooms and has a restaurant, pool, tours, and camping in their rainforest reserve. Rates are around US$100 d with breakfast.
encuentro@complatinos.com

You can also stay at **Buena Vista Lodge** detailed directly below.

Buena Vista Lodge (Albergue Buena Vista)

The relative remoteness of Buena Vista Lodge (☎/fax 695-5147; Apdo. 373, Liberia) is one of its assets. Getting here is an experience in itself. You must travel 12 km N of Liberia along the Interamerican Highway, turn R at the crossroads for Cañas Dulces, and proceed three km farther to Cañas Dulces, then drive another 10 km, passing through a six-km-long portion of the vast 3,840-acre (1,600-ha) Hacienda Buena Vista, owned by Hermanos Ocampo Fernandez. The lodge is at the end of the finca's rough road and next to a large expanse of secondary forest. Views here are spectacular and sunsets even more so. Climb up to the plateau to the R to experience them.

ACCOMMODATION AND FOOD: The lodge has 11 rooms which face a screened central courtyard with a garden containing flowering plants. Set atop a pastureland, some of which is being reforested, the lodge deserves its name. There're plenty of chairs both inside and out to lounge around in. The food is basic fare (beans, rice, fried plantains, and accompanying fish, fowl, or meat), but it is cooked on a wood fire and is universally popular. The special large, thick tortillas are an added attraction. If you're lucky you can also sample the *coyol* (palm wine). A palm is cut down, and a square hole chiseled through it. The palm wine (a sweet, clear fluid) flows into the opening and is scooped out. Rooms are around US$18 for a bunk bed, US$21 for a twin-bed, and US$50 for a room with a bath. Meals are about US$7 for breakfast and US$9 each for lunch and dinner. Special prices are offered for Ticos and residents.

HIKING AND TOURS: A combination of secondary forest and brush (96 acres, 40 ha) stands right behind the lodge. The trails are beautiful, and one leads to a small waterfall. You can either ride 25 min. or go on foot to the hotsprings and steambath (a small house built atop a steaming mudpool), which are surrounded by pools of boiling mud. The path to these is through pasture. On the way you pass by *guanacaste* trees. A guide is suggested if you do go here. One of the most popular rides is to the **Hidden Waterfalls** in Rincón de la Vieja National Park. As you climb on horseback you face Volcán Orosi and Volcán Rincón de la Vieja off on the horizon. Below, the plains of Guanacaste unfold, and Santa Roque, Liberia, and Playas del Coco are spread out before you. The first waterfall you come to is Calingueros, which you can only view from a distance. The next is called Boriñquen. Owing to its smell, the third is known as La Mina de Azufra, and the fourth is called Tobagan and is good for swimming. Bamboo groves connect the last two. Other horseback trips (including one to the crater) are available.

Sector Santa Rosa (Guanacaste Conservation Area)

Originally the Parque Nacional Santa Rosa, Sector Santa Rosa was decreed a park in 1972 (in tandem with a 1996 decree proclaiming it a National Monument) in order to conserve it as a wildland area as well as a site of historical importance (the Casona Santa Rosa). Costa Rica's two international battles took place here. It offers 10,800 ha of regenerating tropical dry forest, a plethora of wildlife, and coastal beaches.

GETTING HERE: It may be accessed at one entrance, off of the Interamerican Highway some 23 mi. (37 km) N of Liberia. Although there is no door-to-door service, buses will drop you eight km from the entrance. Take a bus to Peñas Blancas from San José (☎ 255-1932) or a La Cruz (not Santa Cruz) bus from Liberia and request to be dropped at the "*entrada a Santa Rosa*."

As you approach after passing by Liberia, the landscape suddenly opens up to a vast and desolate deforested range on either side — a miniature version of the American West transported to Central America. You almost expect the Marlboro Man to come charging in on one side of the highway and the Lone Ranger and Tonto to appear in the distance on the other. The sense of desolation — so prevalent during the waterless dry season — increases as you realize that this was once all tropical dry forest.

A sign marking the Guanacaste Regional Conservation Area pops up to your R and — presto!— tropical dry secondary forest appears and along with it the sign for the entrance to Santa Rosa on your L. It is around five km further north to the entrance where you can either walk or hitch a ride (easy during the dry season) for the remaining 4.5 mi. (7.2 km). As it can be deathly hot during the dry season, it's preferable to make this stretch as early in the day as possible.

TOURS: Tours may be arranged through agencies in San José, Liberia, and lodges in the area.

PRACTICALITIES: The official camping facilities are excellent, and the fee is around US$2.50 pp (which is applied on top of the $6 pp, pd *gringo* entrance fee). Toilets, showers, and potable deep-well water are provided. As there are fig trees for shade and no mosquitoes, you could sleep outside during the dry season. The uncommonly seen but nevertheless present tapirs often both bathe and defecate in the same streams, so it's advisable to carry your own water while out and about. The ACG *comedor* in the administration area near the camping area, will provide meals if you order in advance. You can also camp at Argelia and at Estero Real in the bottomlands, 11 km to the W behind the beach at Playa Naranjo.

Accommodation (around US$25 w/meals; US$10 pp for room only) is also provided in the **Estación Biologica Santa Rosa** (☎ 666-5051, fax 666-5020) which opened in 1993. For groups, reservations are recommended eight days prior to arrival.
gmendez@ns.minae.go.cr

The nearest lodge outside the park to the S is the inexpensive **Santa Clara Lodge** (☎ 666-4054, 391-8766, fax 666-4047; Apdo. 17, 5000 Liberia) which is four km from the small town of Quebrada Grande and lies on the S boundary of the Sector Pailas of the ACG. Pickup in Liberia is available for no extra charge. There are seven rooms, some of which have shared baths. Actually a dairy farm, Santa Clara has a bar, restaurant, small mineral pool, and horses for rent. The lodge also offers an all-day horseback trip up to the top of Volcán Cacao. Six waterfalls and forest are also on the property. Rates are around US$30 s and US$40 d with breakfast; youth hostel card holders are offered a discount.
stclodge@sol.racsa.co.cr

In **Quebrada Grande**, you may stay at the low-budget **Central Social la Mata de Caña** which serves hearty lunchtime fare.

VOLUNTEERING: Earth Island Institute's **Sea Turtle Restoration Project** sends volunteers into the field here at Playa Nancite (to the N of Playa Naranjo) to work with turtles. For more information see "volunteering" in the introduction. Another contact is Roger Blanco, Coordinator of Research, Santa Rosa.
rblanco@acguanacaste.ac.cr

FLORA AND FAUNA: Vegetation varies from regenerating dry forest on ancient pastures to cactus on the coast, and from calabash tree forest to mangrove swamps by the coast. Fauna ranges from green iguanas and ctenosaurs, to sloths, tapirs, and opossums; howlers , whiteface; and spider monkeys; white-tailed deer and coyotes; 15 species of bats, and 253 species of birds (including great currasows).

Some 3,410 types of butterflies and moths are among the 10,000 or so insect species. Extraordinarily large populations of crabs reside near the coast. The best time and place to see animals is at dawn or dusk during the dry season at the watering holes at a few select sites in Santa Rosa's dry forests. Even during the wet season, although the animals lack motivation to congregate at waterholes, wildlife abounds here. Despite the year's heaviest rainfall, a Sept. visit is a good time to see leatherbacks laying eggs.

SIGHTS, BEACHES, AND HIKING: In order to maximize your chances of spying critters, try to plan your walks before 8 or after 4. You should note that the roads to the beaches are closed to vehicles in *invierno*, the rainy season.

Historic *hacienda* house **Casa Casona** (open daily, 8-4) contains a reconstruction of the Battle of Rivas. Its contents include period furniture, farm tools, rifles and swords, as well as a natural history exhibit. There are also stone corrals which date back more than 300 years. *Sendero Indio Desnudo* runs in back of the Casona; animals abound along the trail. In the dry season, wait for their arrival by the water hole near the three rocks with petroglyphs.

A number of fossils can be found five km upriver from where the road crosses the Río Nisperal. An indigenous rubbish *i* Call the Guanacaste Regional Conservation Area (☎ 666-5051, fax 555-5020) in Santa Rosa; it's best to show up there in person first to make arrangements.**www.acguanacaste.ac.cr**

heap with potsherds galore is near the Casa Argelia. There's a well here along with toilet facilities, and you can camp. The Argelia estuary's birds range from roseate spoonbills to white, green, and great blue herons to the Mexican tiger bittern.

THE BEACHES: A comprehensive tour here would ideally be done over two or three days. You walk (or drive) along a four-wheel-drive track from the camping area to Playa Naranjo . Enroute, you ford a stream, and come to a sign marked "La Cuesta," whereupon you descend 2.5 km to the sea, passing a viewpoint called the "Cañon del Tigre." At about 66 ft. (20 m) in elevation, there is a crossroads: the R hand path, *El Estero*, leads to a picnic area about four km away at the N end of Playa Naranjo, where there is camping. You must bring your own water.

The L-hand one, a **La Playa**, reaches the center of **Playa Naranjo** at Argelia, via a small rainy-season-only river, a salt marsh abounding with waterfowl, and Casa Argelia, home of the sector's caretaker. Despite a population of sandflies and mosquitoes, this four-mile (six-km) beach, where leatherbacks nest in Sept., is a splendid place to be. **Laguna el Limbo**, at its S end, is another area for birdwatching. **Isla Peña Bruja**, a gigantic rocky refuge for seabirds, lies just offshore. This "witch rock" is legendary in surfing universe as the spot with "the perfect wave." Continuing to the S, the beach changes to rocky bluffs. To the N, there's an estuary. Crossing it and continuing towards the N end of the beach, you follow the trail back inland to the Estero Real picnic area.

During the dry season, the road to Playa Naranjo is quite passable with four-wheel drive. Note that limits are placed on visitors during Semana Santa and other prime times.

About four km and two or three hours to the N, a steep, winding path leads to isolated, two-km **Playa Nancite**, a Pacific ridley turtle nesting beach. October is generally the busiest month. A small stream provides water for camping, but a permit is required. To enter, obtain one from the Administration Area. To get to Nancite from Argelia, ask for a map at the same main Administration Area.

HISTORY: Expropriated as a national monument in 1966, the Casona is the site of an encounter between Costa Rica troops and exploratory scouts sent out by American invader William Walker. Originally a second and non-contiguous portion of the park, the Murciélago Addition, established in 1979, added 24,700 acres (10,000 ha) expropriated from ousted Nicaraguan dictator Antonio Somoza, the remainder of the "state within a state" he had built in Guanacaste. The government expropriated Murciélago in 1979 and it was incorporated into the ACG in 1986. The area lying between Sector Santa Rosa and Sector Murcielago is a major portion of the bulk of the Santa Elena Peninsula and known as the Santa Elena property, and currently being expropriated by the government for addition to the ACG. It is the site of Oliver North's infamous airstrip for supplying Contras during the conflict to the north.

> "Ecotourism is Costa Rica's largest crop. The ecotourist — whether a school child, a visitor from Peoria, or a researcher — is a better kind of cow, and the Conservation Areas are the pastures."
> — Dr. Daniel Janzen, the driving force behind the creation of the Guanacaste Conservation Area.

SECTOR MURCIÉLAGO: This portion of the ACG, comprising some 24,710 acres (10,000 ha), is spectacularly scenic.

GETTING HERE: One bus daily runs from Liberia to Cuajiniquil at 3:30 PM returning at 7 AM; a 12:30 PM bus runs from La Cruz and returns at 6 AM. You would have to walk from Cuajinquil to the Murciélago entrance. By car, you must first pass the Santa Rosa ACG entrance road junction, continue N for around 10 km, and then turn L (W) towards Cuajiniquil; from there you can proceed four km N to Playa Junquillal (Sector Junquillal of the ACG) or 12 km SW to Bahía Santa Elena and then another eight to Playa Blanca. All of the roads are dirt, and passage is best attempted during the dry season with a four-wheel drive.

SIGHTS AND PRACTICALITIES: To the N of Cuajinquil, reached via a dirt road, is isolated **Playa Junquillal** where you may camp but need to bring water. The Sector Murciélago Headquarters has swimming holes and a camping area.

The alternative is to stay at low-budget **Cabinas Santa Elena** (☎ 679-9112, leave message) near Cuajinquil and some four km from Playa Junquillal. The fishermen here can take you out on trips; negotiate per boatload. Swim at Playa Blanca on the peninsula's tip. A car can make it out here during the dry season. Many of the coves formed by the irregular coastline are excellent for camping.

Sector Guanacaste (Guanacaste Conservation Area)

Guanacaste National Park was established in 1989 to protect animals and their migratory paths. Comprising 210,000 acres (84,986 ha), the park's terrain ranges from mangrove swamps at the edge of Santa Elena to cloud forests on the slopes of Volcán Cacao. Its 150,000-acre (60,704-ha) central area is where biologist Daniel Janzen hopes to restore the dwindling tropical dry forest.

Guanacaste National Park is incorporated within **the Guanacaste Conservation Area (ACG)** which attempts to bring a large area of land (423 sq. mi.) under a single plan and to have it benefit the entire community. The concept is sound because animals do not live within a single environment but travel according to season and food and water supply. Likewise, locals have to make a living and must accept the park. The area incorporates rainforest, cloud forest, dry forest, rivers, beaches, coral reefs, and some 325,000 plant and animal species — a figure which accountes for some 3-6% of the world total. Sadly, much of the forest has been damaged, so much so that the conservation area retains only two areas which still retain their pre-Columbian foliage.

PRACTICALITIES: The ACG has three biological stations located in its wetter E end. Located amidst cloud forests, **Estacion Biologica Cacao** has spartan dormitories reserved for researchers. It may be used provided you make prior reservations. (☎ 695-5577; gmendez@ns.minae.co.cr) Following prior arrangement with the acg, you get there by driving seven kmeast on the paved road at Potrerillos (where the rio tempisque crosses the interamerican highway to the south of the ACG) to the town of Quebrada Grande. About 1 km east of Quebrada Grande you turn north (left) on a dirt road that eventually becomes an incredibly rocky track that it is best to walk on, and it is about 10 km to the station.

Paths from the station lead to the summit of **Volcán Cacao** and downhill to **Estacion Biologica Maritza** (three hrs. on foot). Maritza (reservations ☎ 695-5577; gmendez@ns.minae.co.cr; around US$20 pp, pd for room and board) is also accessible by a four-wheel-drive vehicle road. It sits at the base of **Volcán Orosí**.

Featuring around 80 petroglyphs amidst pasture, **Llano de los Indios** is less than two hours away on foot.

Located on the Atlantic watershed, splendidly scenic **Estacion Biologica Pitilla** has spartan dormitories. Used primarily by researchers, they may be accessed with prior permission

It is a 8 km walk or you must have a four-wheel drive. Following confirming reservations with the ACG, you turn R (E) on the paved road to Santa Cecilia, a turn approximately 5 min. N of the turn W to Cuajiniquil. There is a government police checkpoint building at the intersection. When you get to Santa Cecilia, turn S (R) instead of entering town, and drive about 1.5 km S. The first dirt road on your R is the entrance to the road to Pitilla. **gmendez@ns.minae.co.cr**

Geothermal Power

Set at Volcán Miravalles, a **geothermal plant** (☎ 220-7338 for tour reservations) produces 5% of the nation's electricity; capacity will expand to 10% when a second plant opens in 1997 or 1998. Geothermal plant is powered by underground vapor; the humidity is separated from the vapor, and the dry vapor powers the turbines.

Miratur (☎ 673-0260) offers tours here which include a tour of the plant and a dip in the hot springs.

Nearest place to stay is **Parador Las Nubes del Miravalles** (☎ 671-1011, ext. 280) which has a restaurant as well as camping; they will take you to nearby waterfalls and to **Las Hornillas**, a set of steaming mud pots similar to those found near Rincón de la Vieja.

Los Inocentes

Another nature preserve molded from a cattle farm, the *hacienda* of Los Inocentes (☎ 265-5484, 679-9190, fax 265-4385; Apdo. 228, 3000 Heredia) is named after Nicaraguan Inocentes Barrios who owned the place. Los Inocentes is a popular stopover for tour groups. In addition to horseback riding and nature watching on the estate, day trips can be arranged to Santa Rosa and other locales. Room and board in the remodeled *hacienda* house (built in 1890) runs about US$60 pp, pd plus tax. An added attraction is a swimming pool. Many researchers have stayed here, and extensive background information on the area is available. Day trips are also available.

GETTING HERE: Turn R at a security post five min. N of the Cuajunquil turnoff where the sign reads "Upala" and "Santa Ana"; follow the road for 14.5 km until you see the "Los Inocentes" sign. By bus, disembark at La Cruz and take a taxi; ask if a pickup is possible here when making reservations.

La Cruz

The small border town of La Cruz is the northernmost point you're likely to reach in Guanacaste unless headed on for the border at Peñas Blancas. Nearby **Playa Jobo** is the nearest beach. Playa Pochote and Playa Nubes are also in the vicinity.

PRACTICALITIES: Buses from *San José* (around five hrs.) run from C. 16, Av. 3 (☎ 255-1058) at 5, 7:45, and 4:15. The return run is at 5:45, 8, 11, and 4. Buses also run from Liberia; check "getting there" below for times. Buses run to Playa Jobo at 5, 10:30, and 1:30. (If headed on to Nicaragua, see the section at the end of this book).
www.arweb.com/orosi
orosina@sol.racsa.co.cr

ACCOMMODATION: Three Corners Bolaños Bay (☎/fax 260-0527; Apdo. 773019, Heredia) offers 72 units for around US$ 90-115 d. It is a full-service windsurfing resort, and this will be your main reason for coming here. Rooms are simple but comfortable.
suschr@sol.racsa.co.cr
3cornco@sol.racsa.co.cr

Cabinas y Restaurant 2001 offers rooms (around US$20 d) with fan and private bath. The bus stops right in front.

Low-budget **Cabinas Santa Rita** (☎ 669-9062, ☎/fax 679-0962) has rooms with a/c or fans; they will guard your rental car if you are popping over the border to Nicaragua. the low-budget **Cabinas Maryfel** (☎ 669-9096), and the more basic **Pensión La Tica**. The **Hotel Iguana** (☎ 679-9015) offers simple rooms for around US$18-36.

Amalia's Inn (☎/fax 679-9181) offers attractive rooms (around US$50 d) with a pool and views. It exhibits the paintings of the late expat Americano artist Lester Bounds. It has a pool and satellite TV; teenagers and adults only please.

Low-budget **Hotel El Faro** is between the gas station and La Cruz on the highway.

Colinas del Norte (☎ 679-9132, fax 679-9064) is a moderate lodge (around US$55 d) set on a cattle farm just off the highway; it serves unusual local dishes and offers horseback riding.

Inexpensive **Cabinas Las Salinas** (☎ 233-6912, 228-2447/0690; Apdo. 449, 1007 San José) at Bahía Salinas one km to the S, where you can also camp or park your trailer. A restaurant, horseback riding, and boat rental are available. Much more expensive is Los Inocentes (see above).

Set opposite the bird sanctuary of Isla Bonaños, **Bonaños Bay Resort** (☎ 280-5275) is a growing enterprise which offers all-inclusive packages for windsurfers.

FOOD: Windblown **Restaurant Ehecatl** (Chorotega for "Wind God") overlooks the Bahía Salinas. Another alternative is the **Soda y Comedor Santa Marta**.

Isla de Boñanos Wildlife Refuge (Refugio Nacional de Fauna Silvestre Isla de Boñanos)

Sitting three mi. (five km) offshore from Puerto Soley, SW of La Cruz, this 37-acre (15-ha) reserve protects nesting seabirds: brown pelicans, American oysterbirds, and magnificent frigate birds. There are no facilities here, and visits are prohibited, but you can watch the avian action from offshore. You may be able to hire a boat in Puerto Soley.

Northern Nicoya Peninsula Beaches

Peninsula Nicoya's sandy coast is a major part of Guanacaste's claim to fame. Because of the higher comparable airfares and poor infrastructure, the coast's beaches are not exactly Acapulco — although the government and the developers are pushing them in that direction. In fact, there are still relatively few facilities, most are difficult to reach, and accommodation prices are high (some would say overpriced) for what you get.

> Richard Bolaños, owner of La Cafeteria (☎ 679-9276) in central La Cruz, conducts tours of Nicaragua and the nearby national parks of Costa Rica by arrangement.

Playas del Coco

Although the term "Playas del Coco" is also used to refer to all of the beaches in the area, it's commonly used for this beach in particular which is the major Tico tourist center on the northern Pacific coast. Although the place is pleasant enough, there's not really all that much here. Despite its name, there are not many palm trees. Off-season and on weekdays, it's a very peaceful place. But on weekends and holidays, it is noisy and overrun.

Coco beach is dramatically set on an extensive horseshoe-shaped bay dotted with gigantic boulders. Some fishing boats and North American yachts occupy much of the offshore harbor. The only advantage to coming here is the range of accommodation available for low-budget travelers. If you have the money, it's definitely better to go somewhere else.

GETTING HERE: Buses leaves Liberia around five times daily for the half-hour trip. On the way you pass by Sardinal where the major industry is beef, not sardines.

Pulmitan (☎ 222-1650, 666-0458) bus per day runs from C.14, Av. 1/3, San José at 8 AM and 2 PM for the five-hr. trip to El Coco.

Children at play in Playa Coco

ACCOMMODATIONS: Much of the accommodation is fairly basic and inexpensive, in keeping with the mostly Tico clientele. Shop around because— owing to price gouging— some places are overpriced. A few choices are listed.

Inexpensive 16-room **Cabinas Chale** (☎ 670-0036, fax 670-0303) have refrigerators, basketball courts, and a swimming pool. Rates are around US$20 and up.

The **Hotel Luna Tica** (☎ 670-0127, fax 672-0392) has inexpensive rooms near the beach. Rates include breakfast. Similarly priced, the **Hotel Anexo Luna Tica** (☎ 670-0279) is nearby.

Five-room **La Villa del Sol** (☎/fax 670-0085) is an intimate French Canadian run bed and breakfast with a garden and pool. Rates are around US$50 d.

Given its name because of its gardens, Italian-run **Villa Flores** (☎/fax 670-0269) is a two-storey wooden house which is set 100 m from the beach; it has a porch and hammocks. Rooms have fans and baths. Rates are around US$40 with breakfast.

One km from the village, moderate-luxury **Flor de Itabo** (☎ 670-0292, fax 670-0003; Apdo. 32, Playas del Coco) is one of the classiest joints in the area with a/c and pool. Rates run around US$40-80 d.

Rancho Armadillo (☎ 670-0108, 223-3535, fax 267-0441, 670-0441) has a number of model armadillos and is guarded by two stone armadillos at its front gates. It has a pool and is presumably popular with armadillos. Rates are around US$45-65 s or d.All rooms are a/c and have oceam views It's located just S of the main road into the village; turn R where the road divides and watch for a rock reading "Rancho Armadillo." Diving, fishing, tours, and surfing are arranged.
www.ranchoarmadillo.com
armadil@sol.racsa.co.cr
monkeybusiness@costarica.net

About 2.5 km to the E of Playa de Coco is luxurious **Hotel El Ocotal** (☎ 670-0321, fax 670-0083) which is set overlooking a great beach with tide pools. Rates are from around US$80 s, US$90 d not including tax; children under 12 are free. Rooms have a/c, fan, refrigerator, satellite TV, and phone. Facilities include restaurant, Jacuzzi, pools, tennis court, as well as other activities.
elocotal@sol.racsa.co.cr

On the way to Playa Ocotal, moderate **Hotel Villa Casa Blanca** (☎/fax 670-0448; Apdo. 176, 5019 Playa Ocotal) is a Canadian-managed Spanish-style 10-room and two-condo bed and breakfast (around US$60 d on up). Each room is individual. It has a good reputation. There's a tennis court and pool. Horseback riding, fishing, diving, and bike rental can be arranged.
vcblanca@sol.racsa.co.cr

FOOD: Bob's Famous Cajun Restaurant is a good place to try.

SURFING: You can hire a boat from Tamarindo, Ocotal or here to take you out to **Potrero Grande** where a R point break with swift and hollow waves is found. It's also known as "Ollie's Point" after Oliver North.

TOURS AND SERVICES: The town now has a bank. **Guanacaste Adventures** (☎ 257-8588 # 1499; 800-799-0055) has a resident ornithologist and offers tours to places as far afield as Nicaragua.
billbeards@netrunner.net

FROM PLAYAS DEL COCO: Buses return to Liberia around six times daily. The San José bus leaves at 9:15 AM. Playas del Coco can be used as a base to explore the surrounding area, but public transportation is scarce.

Selected Dive Operators in Guanacaste

Name	☎/*fax*	*Location*
Bill Beard's Diving Safaris	☎672-001, fax 672-0231	Playa Hermosa
Mario Vargas Expedition6s	☎/fax 670-0351	Playa del Coco
Virgin Diving	☎ 670-0472, fax 670-0403	Hotel La Costa Playa Hermosa
Costa Rican Diving	☎ 654-4021, ☎/fax 654-4148	Santa Cruz
Flamingo Dive Shop	☎ 654-4403	Playa Flamingo
Edge Adventure Company	☎ 654-4578	Playa Flamingo
Holiday Scuba	☎ 654-4010, fax 654-4402	Hotel Aurola Playa Flamingo
Pacific Aquatic Adventures	☎/fax 238-0378	Nosara
Rich Coast Diving	☎670-0176, fax 670-0165	Playas del Coco
Diving Safaris	☎/fax 670-0012	Playas del Coco
Mario Vargas Expeditions	☎/fax 670-0351	Playa del Coco
Virgin Diving	☎ 670-0472, fax 670-0403	Hotel La Costa Playa Hermosa
Costa Rican Diving	☎ 654-4021, ☎/fax 654-4148	Santa Cruz
Flamingo Dive Shop	☎ 654-4403	Playa Flamingo
Edge Adventure Company	☎ 654-4578	Playa Flamingo
Holiday Scuba	☎ 654-4010, fax 654-4402	Hotel Aurola Playa Flamingo
Pacific Aquatic Adventures	☎/fax 238-0378	Nosara
Rich Coast Diving	☎ 670-0176, fax 670-0165	Playas del Coco

Playa Hermosa

Several kms long, much quieter, and just N of Playas del Coco, this curved, comely beach lives up to its name. Good swimming and water sports are available here. Unfortunately, it has become more and more developed over the years.

GETTING HERE: A direct bus (☎ 666-1249) leaves San José (C. 12, Av. 5/7) at 3:20 for here and Playa Panamá. A bus — which continues on to Playa Panamá — runs from Liberia at 7:30 AM, 11:30 AM, 3:30 PM, 5:30 PM, and 7 PM. It's around five hrs. from San José by car.

ACCOMMODATION: Surrounded by gardens, pleasant **Hotel Playa Hermosa** (☎/fax 670-0136; Apdo. 112, Liberia) is right on the beach. It has rooms for around US$40 d and a restaurant.

Restaurant/Cabinas Vallejos (☎ 670-0417) offers simple rooms with private baths for around US$10 pp; it has a restaurant.

Villa Boni Mar (☎ 670-0397) offers a set of duplexes with kitchens for around US$40 on up.

Villa de Sueño (☎ 670-0027) is an intimate eight room hotel run by French Canadian expats. It is set 200 m from the beach, and facilities include a gourmet restaurant and pool. Rates are around

US$60 d.
delsueno@sol.racsa.co.cr

Sula Sula (☎ 672-0116, fax 672-0117) offers six units right on the beach. It has a pool and restaurant. Rates run around US$ 80d on up.

The 14-room French Canadian-run 14-room **Hotel de Playa "El Velero"** (☎ 670-0036, fax 670-0016; Apdo. 49-5019, Playa Hermosa) charges around US$75 d on up Facilities include tours, sailing (US$55 pp for a five-hour sail), pool, equipment rentals, and a gourmet French restaurant.

The **Playa Hermosa Inn** (☎/fax 670-0163) is a large house with a pool which rents expensive rooms and an apartment.

Bed and Breakfast El Oasis (☎ 670-0222) charges around US$45. It has a pool and horseback riding. **Villa Boni Mar** (☎ 670-0397, 487-7640) has a pool and offers apartments for around US$50 Parque Nacional which hold six.

Forrest's Beach House (☎/fax 803-763-0557) offers low-budget digs in a four-bedroom house and camping as well as real estate sales and rentals.

The **Sol Playa Hermosa** (☎ 670-0405, 290-0560, 800-33-MELIA; fax 670-0349, 290-0566) has 54 a/c units with Color TV as well as 47 villas, 24 of which have a private pool. Facilities include restaurants, fishing, discos, poolsand volleyballs.
www.solmelia.es
hremosol@sol.racsa.co.cr

Hotel la Costa is an expensive and exclusive villa-style resort.

Set to the S, **Hotel Finastera** (☎/fax 670-0293) offers rooms (around US$40 d with tax) with hot water and fans and has a restaurant.
finastera@hotmail.com

FOOD: There are several inexpensive seafood restaurants on the beach. **Cabinas Playa Hermosa** has an Italian restaurant. **Aquasport** specializes in *paella*.

SERVICES: Located at about the middle of the beach, **Aquasport** (☎ 672-0050) rents out a range of equipment: surfboards, windsurfing boards, sailboats, kayaks, and snorkeling gear. They also sell groceries, cash travelers checks, rent their phone, and act as a post office; they also have a casual but good restaurant which has a number of seafood dishes.

Bill Beard's Diving Safaris (☎ 672-0012 fax 672-0231) are legendary and were formerly associated with the Hotel Ocotal.
www.diving-safaris.com
billbeards@netrunner.net
diving @sol.racsa.co.cr

Playa Panamá

This long sweeping, panoramic beach is named after the tree that is found here in abundance. It looks out onto the Gulf of Papagayo. Bars and *pulperías* are at the S end; the best option here is camping to the N. The **Costa Smeralda** and the **Blue Bay Village Papagayo** are two all-inclusive large resort hotels here.

The Papagayo Project

This project is the only one of its kind in Costa Rica. Papagayo, a highly controversial government-owned project on the Bahía Culebra to the N end of Playas de Coco, had its origins under the Oduber administration (1974-78) but has come of age only in the 1990s. The government has purchased land near the 17 beaches; the infrastructure (wells for potable water, electricity, telephones, and roads) has been put in place.

No environmental impact study was done because — according to former Tourism Minister Chacón (who served during the Calderón administration) — none was required by law. He criticized environmental groups for "not wanting any tourism" and, in 1994, he called officials with the Ombudsman's Office "liars."

Theoretically, the resorts are to be attractive and not environmentally destructive but much of the land used for hotels was covered with tropical dry secondary forest. Other controversies regarding the hotels here still ensue.

Heading South to Flamingo

The next set of beaches are still the peninsula's resort central, and the road network makes this almost a separate region. Buses run as far S as Potrero. To get here by car from Playas del Coco, continue S on 21 to an intersection on the other side of Filadelfia and take the road that heads SW. Or take any bus and get off at Comunidad (also known as Bar Tamarindo) at the intersection of the Liberia-Nicoya road.

You can also take any bus and get off at Belén, where buses pass at approximately 10:30 and 2:30 for Playas Brasilito and Potrero. Just after the town plaza, a road leads to Huacas where you go R, then R again after about 200 m to reach Brasilito, Flamingo, Potrero, and Pan de Azúcar.

Tralapa (☎ 221-7202) runs a *directo* here from C. 20, Av. 1/3, daily at 8 and 10.

SANSA (☎ 221-9414, 233-0397, 233-3258, fax 255-2176) flies as does *Travelair* (☎ reservations: 220-3054, sales: 296-1102, fax 296-2316; SJO 788, PO Box 025216, Miami, FL 33102-5216; information@travelair-costarica.com).

note: Information on getting to Playas Grande, Tamarindo, and Junquillal is in the "Parque Nacional Las Baulas" section below.

> **Ecotrans** offers **shuttle service** (US$5 pp) between Flamingo and Potrero beaches well as airport and golf course (US$10 pp) transfers. Many restaurant and hotels also offer shuttle service.

Matapalo

Not to be confused with the beach town to the S of Quepos, this village is reached by heading straight on from Huacas rather than taking the Brasilito turnoff. Playa Grande (see description below) is straight on from the town. Overlooking Playa Conchal, the luxury-priced **Condor Club** (☎ 654-4050, fax 654-4044) is five km from Playa Brasilito. Facilities include pool, disco, restaurant, tennis, basketball, volleyball, tours, TV, and a/c. The **Hotelito y Pizzeria La Paz** (☎/fax 654-4259) is an attractive pizza place with picnic tables outdoors. Rooms run from about US$30-60. Down the road to Playa Puerto Viejo, **El Encanto** serves Costa Rican dishes.

Brasilito

Set across from the lagoon and river mouth, this settlement has a mediocre grey sand beach, fishermen, small stores, basic *cabinas*, and good camping (at **Camping Brasilito**, ☎ 654-4001). Two buses per day run here from Santa Cruz.

Cabinas Brasilito (☎ 654-4013) is near the soccer field. Dark rooms with fans run around US$25.

Hotel Brasilito (☎/fax 654-4237) has 15 rooms (around US$30), restaurant, and horseback riding and boat tours. **compes@sol.racsa.co.cr**

El Caracol Cabinas y Restaurant (☎ 654-4320) offers attractive rooms with fans (around US$30) as well as a thatched-roof restaurant. Camping is also possible.

Moderate (around US$30 pp) **Cabinas**

Diving off the **Catalina Islands** offer sightings of sea turtles, manta rays, and spotted and bottlenose dolphins as well as mgnificent patches of coral and iridescent fish. They lie offshore from Potrero and Flamingo.

Conchal (☎ 654-4257) have fans and offer boat and bicycle rentals as well as horseback riding.

Luxurious condominium hotel **Hacienda Las Palmas** (☎ 231-4343; Apdo. 10, 5150 Santa Cruz, Guanacaste) is up on the hill just outside of town. It offers a/c, pool, restaurant, and cable TV.

Inexpensive **Mi Posada** (☎ 680-0953) has basic rooms with private baths.

Go along the beach half an hour to reach **Conchal**, once a sheltered white sand beach known for its huge shell mound. The presence of the 310-rm. Melía Playa has transformed the area, and lowlife developers have trucked away shells to use for touristic endeavors.

The 310-unit **Melía Playa Conchal Beach and Golf Resort** (☎ 654-4123, 293-4915, fax 654-4181, 293-4916) is a spiffy luxurious new resort which has an 18-hole golf course designed by Robert Trent Jones. Facilities include restaurant, health club, pool, casino, disco, and watersports.
www.solmedia.es
mconchal @sol.racsa.co.cr

Costa Rica Riding (☎ 654-4106) offers a special tour which covers 42 beaches in five days and six nights. Riders stay in luxury digs and pass through remote areas. **crriding@sol.racsa.co.cr**

Sail the area and travel as far afield as Coco Island (10 days RT) with the ***Papagayo*** **(☎ 654-4911, fax 654-4064)**, a 45-ft. ketch.
papagayopete@hotmail.com

Playa Flamingo

Just five min. N of Brasilito, this development's real name is Punta Plata. There's no town here and very little shade. There are a number of luxury hotels here.

Flamingo Marina Resorts (☎ 290-1858, fax 231-1850; Apdo. 321-1002, San José) is a combination of the Flamingo All-Suites, the Flamingo Marina Hotel, and the Club Playa Flamingo.
www.flamingomarina.com
hotflam@sol.racsa.co.cr

FOOD: Amberes Restaurant offers European cuisine as well as a disco and casino. Aside from the gourmet hotspots, you can eat at **Marie's Restaurant** (☎ 654-4136), run by British-born Marie Yates, which has its own swimming pool and a variety of local specialties (marked on a blackboard) at reasonable prices. Specialities include French toast, a Mexican platter, and seafood.

Or try **Tio's Bar and Restaurant** (just outside town) or the **Marina Trading Post**.

SERVICES: Marina Trading sells clothing, souvenirs, and snacks. Set outside the town, **Flamingo Beach Sports Center** has tennis courts, softball, and a golf driving range. The **Flamingo Marina** (☎ 654-4203, 222-8303) provides services

?!? Canadian George Howarth renamed Flamingo Beach in the 1950s because he mistook the resident roseate spoonbills for flamingos. (The original name was Playa Blanca). He once defended his property at gunpoint and likened residents of Basilito and Potrero to "natives of darkest Africa." As part of the Cold War enclave mentality of its inhabitants, many of the first homes here had bomb shelters.

for yachties. They provide electricity, and owners can park boats here while they travel around the country.

Car rental is available in the area. Ask your hotel.

Playa Potrero

Potrero Beach is around the bay from Flamingo and six km from Brasilito. From here, you can walk to deserted, secluded beaches such as Danta, Dantita, and Precita. There is a wealth of accommodation here.

The 35-room **Bahía Potrero Beach and Fishing Resort** (☎/fax 654-4183; Apdo. 45-5051, Santa Cruz) has restaurant, pool, scuba, fishing, windsurfing, water skiing, kayaking, and horseback riding. Lushly landscaped, it has a relaxed, low-key atmosphere. You might feel that you are at someone's home; there are hammocks about and plenty of beach to explore. Rates are luxury to ultra-luxury.
bahiaresort@villtrop.com

There are a number of smaller places. Located three km before the village, **Cabinas Cristina** (☎/fax 654-4006) offers three inexpensive units (around US$35 pn) with cooking facilities and refrigerator. There is also a small pool and a house (US$65) for rent.

Cabinas Bahía Esmeralda (☎ 654-4480, fax 654-4479) has attractive and sunny rooms for around US$40; they also have a two-bedroom home rental and pizzeria.

Endless Beach Condos (☎/fax 654-4135) offers attractive condos (around US$200) which sleep six.
endbeach@sol.racsa.co.cr

Casa Los Ocho Hijos (☎/fax 654-4014) has rooms with fans for around US$12.

Maiyra's (☎/fax 654-4213) offers cabins for around US$30 and camping for around US$3 pp.

Cabinas Costa Azul (☎ 654-4183) is similarly priced and has a restaurant. **Bar/Restaurant/Cabinas Rancho Azul** (☎ 654-4153) offers spartan cabins (around US$30 for three).

Cabinas Isolina Beach are quiet and similarly priced; some units have kitchens.

Casa Sunset Cabinas B&B (☎/fax 654-4265) have a pool and rent for around US$55 d with breakfast.

Casa Salty Pelican B&B has a room for around US$50.

FOOD: Places to dine include the **La Perla Restaurant, Harden's Garden Bakery and Café, Los Palitos Restaurant** (Chinese dishes), **Restaurante El Grillo** (French food), and the **Soda y Restaurant Playa Potero** (which also has a mini mart).

The **Surfside Way Liquor/Super** provides alcohol and culinary goods. **Surfside Bakery** sells you-know-what.

SERVICES: Guanacaste Connections (☎/fax 654-4227) makes travel arrangements. **Jalisco Horseback Riding** (☎ 654-4106) provides tours as well as private lessons. **Bongo's Laundromat** will take care of your laundry. You can study Spanish while in Playa Potrero by contacting **Academia Pacifica** (☎ 255-1001).

The new Spanish Colonial-style **Palo Arco Mall** is the place to go to shop.

Toucan Jungle Sports Bar will keep TV junkies from going cold turkey.

Playa Pan de Azucar

Located 15 km (nine miles) past the turnoff at Huacas, this beach, claimed by the hoteliers to be the most beautiful in Costa Rica, provides the scenic backdrop for luxurious 26-room **Hotel Sugar Beach** (☎ 654-4242, fax 654-4239; Apdo. 90, Santa Cruz, Guanacaste).

It has good snorkeling spots and some wildlife including iguanas and howler mon-

keys. Facilities include a restaurant, pool, and charter boat rental. Rooms are a/c and have ocean views. New units are duplexes which are centered around the lawn. All rooms have attractively designed doors. Expect to pay from US$100 d on up with tax. Activities include boogie boarding, snorkeling, kayaking, volleyball, fishing, and horseback riding. Call 800-458-4735 in the US and Canada.
www.sugar-beach.com
sugarb@sol.racsa.co.cr

About 10 km offshore to the W, **Isla Santa Catalina**, a rocky islet, is one of the nation's few spots where the bridled tern nests (from late March to Sept.). Rent a boat from one of the resorts. The bus runs only as far as Potrero.

Parque Nacional Las Baulas de Guanacaste (Las Baulas National Park)

Formerly known as Tamarindo National Wildlife Refuge, Playa Grande, a 230-ft.-wide beach is a nesting site for leatherback turtles from Nov. to Jan., when as many as 200 of these bulky *baulas* may nest; it's also a popular surfing spot.

To get here, proceed straight ahead on the road from Huacas rather than turning R for Brasilito. There are no direct buses, but buses to Flamingo from San José (10 AM) and Santa Cruz (10 and 2) stop in Matapolo (see above) where you can get a taxi on to Playa Grande.

Its first 125 m (412 ft.) — which stretches from the high tide mark, starting at the point to the N of Playa Grande and then S to include Tamarindo and Playa Langosta — was formally declared a national park in July 1995. Turtle watching is now permitted only from platforms along the edge of the beach, and the operation is supervised by local guides.

Unfortunately, numbers of nesting sea turtles is declining: 700 came ashore in 1992 but only 450 in 1996 and 215 in 1997-98. Poaching is still a problem, and it is thought that lights from the hotels may be luring hatchlings to the shore. Disturbingly, Los Colinas, a large resort, is planning a beach club directly on the beach. Guides allegedly operate without proper supervision.

The park has a new **visitor's center** (1997) as well as the **El Mundo de la Tortuga** museum (US$5 admission) which offers environmental education. To see sea turtles nest contact **Coopetamarindo** near the entrance to town.

The offshore groves of protected mangroves, which include all five species and occupy the majority of what once was the 400-ha (1,236-acre) Tamarindo reserve, can best be seen by boat. Rent one in Tamarindo.

ACCOMMODATION: Set about a half-km before Playa Grande and around two km from the beach itself, inexpensive Centro Vacacional Playa Grande (☎ 237-2552) offers large rooms with kitchens for around US$30. It has a pool and restaurant.

Expensive (around US$80 d) 11-room **Hotel Las Tortugas** (☎/fax 653-0458; Apdo. 164, Santa Cruz de Guanacaste) is ecologically oriented and has a restaurant, Jacuzzi, turtle-shaped pool, horseback tours, canoes, fishing, scuba, surf and boogie boarding; it also provides good information. It is attractively designed to mimimize impact on nesting turtles. Co-owner Louis relates that "our entire staff is from the local village from families that at one time eked out a subsistence living from gathering turtle eggs. We are not fancy but strictly ecotouristic." Environmentalist and turtle researcher Anny Chaves maintains that

the without owners Louis and Marianela "the Playa Grande refuge would not exist."Some rooms have a/c Rates with tax are around US$60-85 d (US$40-50d during the low season). More expensive suites hold four.
www.cool.co.cr/usr/turtles
www.tamarindo.com
nela@cool.co.cr

Rancho Las Colinas (☎/fax 293-4644) has a restaurant, horseback riding, and water sports. Rates run from around US$60 on up to ultra-luxury.

Casa Mirage (no ☎), near the beach, rents out rooms for around US$40 on up.

Billed as a "conservation project," German-run **Villa Baulas** (☎ 228-2263, 289-7666, 680-0869; Apdo. 111-6151, Santa Ana 2000) borders mangrove swamps along the village's estuary Facilities include pool, restaurant, and tours. Rates are around US$70 d including breakfast.

Hotel Villa Baula (☎ 653-0493, fax 653-0459) has rooms as well as bungalows. Rates run around US$60-90d. Its restaurant serves both German and Indonesian food.
hotelvb@sol.racsa.co.cr

Moderate **Playa Grande Retreat** (☎/fax 653-0475; 800-916-7999) offers a *casita* and a cabina without a kitchen.
www.tamarindo.com/kai

More basic digs are to be found at **Cabinas Las Baulas**, two km from the beach.

STUDY: Drexal University, the Park Service, and Earthwatch have set up a volunteer program (☎ 233-4989).
www.coas.drexel.edu/environ/costa-rica

> ***URL*** **www.tamarindo.com** has information about the area.

> Be aware that Playa Grande is a reserve. Don't hasten the extinction of the sea turtle. If contributing to this park, be sure that you send money directly to Fundación de Parques Nacionales or other involved organizations. Money placed in collection boxes you see may not go for this purpose!

Playa Tamarindo

Once a small, quiet, and peaceful fishing village, Playa Tamarindo has developed a resort atmosphere and is becoming more and more garish as the beer and cigarette advertising signs move in, and surfers cruise down the beach in their cars. The area is famous for deep-sea fishing, especially for sailfish and marlin. Playa Grande, across the bay, has been transformed into a wildlife refuge (see above).

The prosperity exuded by the resorts here contrasts sharply with the impoverishment of the surrounding countryside. Development has come at a price. The most recent controversy surrounds the US$10 million Proyecto Turístio Bahía Langosta which has invoked the ire of local environmentalists upset about the mangrove destruction. As with many of the S Tamarindo beachfront properties, the condo development lies within the 50-m strip above the high-tide line which has been declared "inalienable" under Costa Rican law. However, the area concerned was staked out for development prior to the law's 1977 passage.

While here be sure to check out Playa Langosta which is a short drive away. To get to the surrounding beaches, take buses from Villa Real, three km away.

GETTING HERE: This resort is located 13 km (eight miles) S of Huacas and is easily reached by public bus (six hours, 320 km)

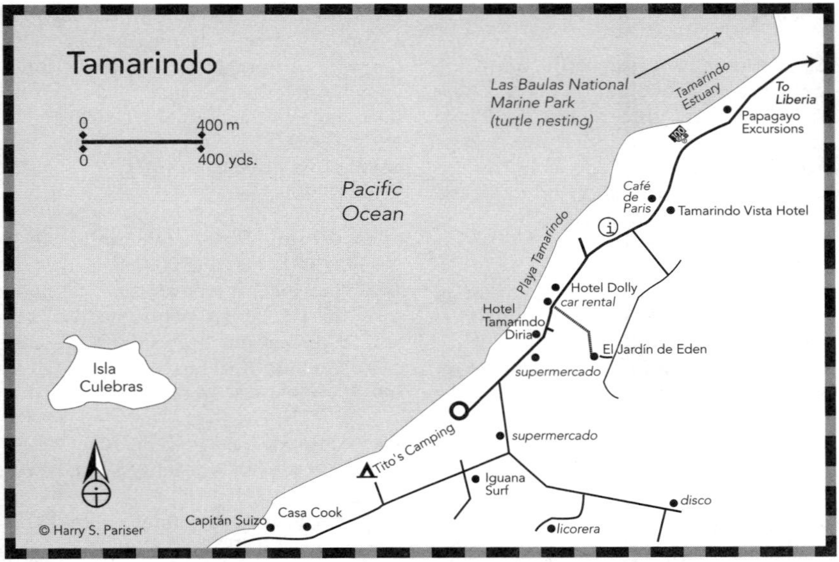

year round from San José; it's about an hour from Liberia by car. An *Empress Alfaro* bus (☎ 222-2666) leaves at 3:30 PM from C. 14, Av. 3/5 and a *Tralapa* bus (☎ 221-7202) leaves at 4 PM from Av. 3, C. 20.

Buses depart Santa Cruz for Tamarindo daily around three times in the morning and afternoon. By car (one hr. from Liberia), the Tamarindo turnoff is 13 km S of Huacas; *SANSA* (☎ 221-9414, 233-0397, 233-3258, fax 255-2176) flies and continues on to Playa Sámara. *Travelair* (☎ 220-3054, 232-7883 fax 220-0413; information@travelair-costarica.com) flies daily, and its Nosara and Carrillo flights also stop here. Most hotels have airport pickup.

> Exercise caution while swimming at either Playa Grande or Playa Tamarindo. Visitors have drowned in these waters, and rescues are commonplace.

ACCOMMODATION: The attractively designed **Residence Luna Llena** (☎ 653-0082, fax 653-0120) is near the Iguana Surf in Tamarindo and offers two-storey bungalows with kitchens. Rates are in the expensive range; units hold up to four.

The 20-room **Cala Luna** (☎ 653-0214, fax 653-0213), a self-described "oasis of exotic luxury," offers thatched-roof villas from US$240. Each have TV, a/c, phone, CD player, washer, and kitchen. It offers a restaurant, horseback riding, mountain biking, a pool, tennis, and other activities.
www.cataluna.com
reservations@cataluna.com

Hilltop **Finca Monte Fresa** (☎ 653-0241, fax 653-0243) has five apartments with baths and balconies, restaurant, and pool. They offer sunset and other cruises aboard their boat the *Salmonique III*.
www.tamarindo.com/sam

samonique@sol.racsa.co.cr

Set on Punta Langosta, on the south end of the beach, **Sueño del Mar** (☎/fax 653-0284) has only three rooms and one suite. It has some of the area's most attractively decorated rooms. Rates are in the luxury/ultra-luxury range and include a generous breakfast.
www.tamarindo.com/solmar
suenodem@sol.racsa.co.cr

Catering to surfers, the **Rodamar** offers camping (around US$2 pn) and offers spartan *cabinas* (around US$20 pn).

Inexpensive 28-unit **Cabinas Pozo Azúl** (☎ 680-0147, 654-4280) have fans, hot plates and refrigerators. Rates are around US$20 (up to 3) and US$35 (with a/c).

Oleaje Hotel (fax 654-4223) offers five Spanish hacienda-style a/c *cabinas*. for around US$50.

Expensive 22-room a/c **Hotel Pueblo Dorado** (☎/fax 222-5741) offers a restaurant and pool. Write Apdo. 1711, 1002 San José.

The 34-room luxury **Hotel El Milagro** (☎ 653-0042, fax 653-0050; Apdo. 145, 5150 Santa Cruz) offers a disco, pool, scuba, horseback riding, a casino, and other activities. Rooms are A-shaped bungalows with wood ceilings; youchoose to use a/c or fan. Rates are around US$70 d.
www.elmilagro.com
flokiro@sol.racsa.co.cr

Hotel Tropicana (☎/fax 653-0261) offers rooms (around US$50) with a/c or fan. It has a Jacuzzi and a pool.
tropican@sol.racsa.co.cr

On a hill 150 m from the beach, the ultra-luxury, attractively designed French-run **Hotel El Jardín del Eden** (☎ 653-0137, fax 653-0111) offers 18 Mediterranean-style rooms and 12 apartments, *three* pools, and a Jacuzzi. Most rooms have balonies or terraces. It's around 150 m from the beach. It is run by Marcello Marongiu along with his wife Aurora and his son Giulio. French and Italian gourmet food is served. Rates range from around US$80-165 d with breakfast.
www.jardin-eden.com/hotel
hotel@jardin-eden.com

The 70-rm. **Hotel Tamarindo Diría** (☎ 653-0031, fax 653-0031; Apdo. 476, 1007 San José) offers a/c, tennis, pool, satellite TV, conference room, Jacuzzi, and a restaurant. Rates (around US$ 120 d) include breakfast.
tnodiria@sol.racsa.co.cr

Fan-equipped **Cabinas Zully Mar** (☎ 226-4732) are clean, inexpensive, and centrally located.

Cabinas Alberto has large rooms with fans for around US$20.

Set in the hills near town, the **Bella Vista Village Resort** (☎/fax 654-4036; Apdo. 143-5150, Santa Cruz) offers six luxurious conical thatched-roof *cabinas*; all have fully equipped kitchens. There's a pool, restaurants are nearby, and the hotel provides services ranging from car and sports equipment rental to tour bookings. Rates run around US$90 during the winter season and go down to US$50 during the "green." Taxes are additonal. Sunsets are on the house.
www.tamarindo.com
belvista@sol.racsa.co.cr

More isolated luxury-priced 57-room **Tamarindo Resort** (☎ 223-4289, fax 255-3785) is set 150 m S and 200 m E of the Diría. It's an American-owned set of *cabinas* withfan or a/c; there's a pool and restaurant.

The **Pasa Tiempo Hotel and Restaurant** (fax 654-4223) has its thatched-roof units centered around a pool. It charges around US$65 d.

Casa Blanca (☎ 653-7003, fax 653-0074) offers attractive luxury units (around US$85) with kitchenettes, fans, and pool. **csimmons@sol.racsa.co.cr**

Across the street are the a/c **Nahua Garden Suites** (680-0776), a set of attractively designed ultra-modern condos (around US$80) which also offer weekly and monthly rates. There's a pool, garden, and kitchens.

Rainbow colored in keeping with the name, **Cabinas y Restaurante Arco Iris** have cabins with imaginative decor (around US$30) as well as vegetarian dishes in their restaurant.

Albergue Mamire is next to the **Bar Patchanka**. It has has six rooms from around US$40 up to the luxury range.

Elegantly and innovatively designed, **Hotel Capitán Suizo** (tel 653-0075, fax 653-0292) offers 22 split-level suites. It has an open-air restaurant and a large pool. Rates are luxury to ultra-luxury.
www.tamarindo.com
capitansuizo@ticonet.co.cr

A popular spot which offers friendly Canadian hospitality, **Casa Cook** (☎/fax 653-0125) has two one-bedroom cabinas and a luxury villa which has two bedrooms separated by a large kitchen and dining/living area. All units have fully-equipped kitchens with fans. In the US call Dan Smith at 500-675-0421 or 510-653-0125.
www.tamarindo.com
casacook@sol.racsa.co.cr

Set 300 m S from Capitán Suizo, **Villa Alegre** (☎ 653-0270, fax 653-0287) is a bed and breakfast run by a California couple. Accommodation ranges from single rooms to two-bedroom suites. Rooms and *casitas* are given names such as "Enjoy Japan," "Enjoy Caribbean," and "Enjoy Guatemala" and are decorated thematically with travel souvenirs. A/c is optional, and breakfast is served. Rates are around US$115 d.
www.tamarindo.com/alegre
vialegre@sol.racsa.co.cr

Also near the Capitán Suizo, **Casa Sueca** (☎/fax 653-0021) charges around US$100 d for suites with kitchens; monthly rates are available.
vikings@sol.racsa.co.cr

Hotel Pasatiempo (☎ 653-0096, fax 653-0275) has rooms set in thatched-roof duplexes which accommodate up to five; each has its own patios with hammock or chairs, is named after a beach, and sports a wall mural. There is a pool, bar, and Tex-Mex restaurant. Rates are around US$ 50 d.
www.tamarindo.com
passtime @sol.racsa.co.cr

CAMPING/BUDGET: **Tito's Camping** offers spots for US$3 pp; it has a restaurant. The next step up is **Cabinas Rodamar** which charges US$4 pp for simple rooms and is 500 m down the road.

Pensión Doly (☎ 680-0174) offers spartan but clean accommodations for around US$8 pp.

Inexpensive **Cabinas Marielos** (☎/fax 653-0141) feature a garden environment, a communal kitchen, and bike and boogie board rentals. Rooms are around US$25 d, US$35 t, US$45 quad or quint.

FOOD: Hotel restaurants are listed under "accommodations" directly above.

Portofino's Pizzeria is an Italian-run open-air bistro which serves pizza and other delights.

The **Sunrise Café/Nogui's** is at the end of the main drag and offers Tico dishes (as well as lobster) at reasonable prices.

Fiesta del Mar specializes in seafood.

Tercer Mundo also has fresh fish. **Bahía Flamingo** has fish specials.

Coconuts is pricey but good and creative, as is **Restaurant El Milagro**.

La Meridiana is an authentic gourmet Italian restaurant open daily 11-11; entreés average around US$10. It is 100 m from the main road and to the L from the Zully Mar.

Cantina Las Olas is set on the side road heading towards Playa Langosta. It serves inexpensive Tex-Mex dishes including fish burritos and veggie fare.

Others include **Arco Iris Veggie Restaurant**, **Stella's Italian**, and the **Cordon Bleu**. Another place to try is **Café de Paris** (formerly**Johan's Belgian Bakery**), open 6-5:30. It is now run by French who have opened a restaurant and art gallery next door.

The **Supermercado El Pelícano** is well stocked. You can rent rooms, houses, boogie boards, umbrellas, beach chairs, and other things next door.

ENTERTAINMENT: During the tourist season, the **Resort Club Tamarindo**, a surfer's watering hole, offers weekly live concerts. Music ranges from *merengue* to *reggae* to *salsa*. Ask around about other discos. Other alternatives are the **No Hay** and the **Crocodile Lounge.**

INFORMATION AND TOURS: Set at the end of the road, the **Tamarindo Information and Welcome Center** offers advice. Check out the locally-produced *Tamarindo Newsletter*.

Located at the town's entrance, **Papagayo Excursions** (☎ 653-0254, 653-0257, fax 680-0859, 225-3648; Apdo. 162, 5051 Santa Cruz) offers a range of excursions from scuba to fishing to horseback riding.

papagayo@sol.racsa.co.cr

Tamarindo Sportsfishing (☎/fax 653-0090) has two boats. Others to contact include **Warren Sellers Sportfishing** (☎ 653-0186) and **Capullo Sportfishing** (☎ 653-0048).

If you've always wanted to ride around in a **horse and buggy**, Charles Boeger operates one as a taxi and tour bus. He's generally found in front of the Hotel El Jardín del Edén during the evening.

The **Palm Shop** (☎/fax 654-4223) offers services ranging from information to air tickets to film developing.

The **Iguana Surf Shop** rents snorkeling gear, bikes, jet skis (regrettably), short and long boards, and offers kayak tours. The **Robert August Surf Shop** also has surfing gear.

Horseback riding on the beach is also a popular activity.

GOLF: The **Rancho Las Colinas** (☎/fax 654-4089) and the **Melia Playa Conchal Resort** (☎ 654-4123) also have courses.

LANGUAGE STUDY: Instituto de Wayra Espanol (☎/fax 653-0359) teaches Spanish as well as Latin dance.

www.spanish-wayra.co.cr

spanishw@sol.racsa.co.cr

FROM TAMARINDO: Buses depart for San José at 5:45 AM and also at 1 PM on Sun. (*Empress Alfaro*) and 8:30 AM (*Tralapa*). *Sansa* and *Travelair* also fly. Advance tix should be bought on weekends and holidays.

Playa Junquillal

Another wide, nearly deserted beach and surfing hotspot. Sea turtles also nest here.

GETTING HERE: *Tralapa* (☎ 221-7202) runs a direct bus daily (six hrs.) at 2 PM from Av. 3, C. 20, San José. Other buses run from Santa Cruz. You can also take the Tamarindo flight (see above).

By car from Tamarindo, you should head 18 km S to the "27 de Abril" intersection. Then turn R and head 12 km to Paraiso where you turn L. If coming directly from Liberia, turn to the R before Santa Cruz and proceed to the "27 de Abril" intersection.

PRACTICALITIES: The seven-room German-run **El Castillo Divertido** (☎ 653-0428) is an attractive hotel which has rooms from around US$45 d; breakfast and dinner are served. As its name suggests, it resembles a play castle.

At around US$50 d with tax, the Swiss-run **Guacamaya Lodge** (☎ 223-2300, 210-1000) has rooms with terraces facing the pool and a thatched-roof restaurant.
alibern@sol.racsa.co.cr

German-run **Hotel Hibiscus** (☎/fax 653-0437) is on the outskirts of town; it has rooms for around US$40 and a European-style restaurant.

An exclusive, nature-oriented resort, luxurious 10-rm. German-owned **Hotel Serena** (☎ 653-0430; Apdo. 17, Santa Cruz) has fans, pool, sauna, tennis, horseback riding, and an extensive videocassette collection. It is one of the nearest hotels to the beach.

Luxurious and isolated **Hotel Antumalal** (☎/fax 653-0425; Apdo. 49, Santa Cruz, Guanacaste) is the oldest hotel and also the priciest. It has a/c, a gourmet international restaurant, disco, tennis courts, two pools, diving, hiking, volleyball, beachside campfires, fishing with locals, and horses. Named after the Chilean god of the sun, it has 23 cabins (around US$85) and 11 bungalows (similarly priced); both have fans.
antumal@sol.racsa.co.cr

Least expensive is **Hotel Playa Junquillal** (☎ 653-0432; Apdo. 22, Santa Cruz; 408-356-7005, fax 408-257-2006; 888-666-2322); they charge campers US$4/night for the use of their facilities.
www.playa-junquillal.com
hotel@playa-junquillal.com

Junquillal Bar/Restaurant/Cabinas has basic rooms for around US$30.

Set about a km N of the beach, expensive-luxury, Canadian-owned 24-room **Iguanazul** (☎/fax 653-0123; Apdo. 130, 1550 Santa Cruz) has pool, gourmet restaurant, game room, snorkeling, volleyball, surfing, video (extra US$10/night), mountain bike rentals, and horseback riding, as well as tours. It has its own bus service (US$40 RT) twice per week. An additional two to three hotels are planned along with some 40 homes, 60 condos, and an organic farm. Rooms run around US$60 d, US$80 quad and up. To get here turn L at the soccer field and follow the signs.
www.ticonet.co.cr/iguanazul
iguanazul@ticonet.co.cr

Camp at **Camping Los Malinches** (☎/fax 653-0429) near the Iguanazul or at **El Malinche** (☎ 655-0433) in town which also has rooms for low-budget travelers. They have a store and sell bus tickets.

La Puesta del Sol is a gourmet Italian restaurant run by Italians who traveled the world for two decades in search of the perfect place.

FROM JUNQUILLAL: The direct bus to San José generally departs at 5 AM. It's possible to continue down the coast all the way to Playa Carrillo, but a four-wheel drive is recommended.

> R. M. writes "spectacular cooking at **Catarana**. **Tiki's** is good for *panqueques*. I strongly advise passing on the pasta at **Las Baulas**."

Playa Avellanas

This popular surfing beach, which has the reef break "Guanacasteco," is five km S of Tamarindo and 4.5 km N of Paraiso. Surfers stay at **Freddy's Surf Camp**, but you should be wary of thieves.

Also here and catering to surfers, **Gregorio's** (☎ 226-7914) charges around US$20 for its cabins; it has a restaurant.

Moderate (around US$45) and attractive **Lagartillo Beach Hotel** (☎ 257-1420, fax 221-5717) has a pool. It's a short walk to Playa Lagartillo

At nearby Playa Negra is the inexpensive **Mono Congo** (cell. ☎/fax 382-6926; Apdo. 177-5150, Santa Cruz) which is owned by a Florida architect; it's popular with surfers such as Robert August (from the "Endless Summer" movies). Rates are around US$40. Horseback riding is offered.

Also here is thatched-roof **Hotel Playa Negra** (☎ 382-1301, fax 293-0332; Apdo. 31, Santa Cruz) offers well-designed circular bungalows, a pool, and restaurants. Rates are around US$60 for up to four.

At Playa Punta Pargos, **The Reef** is a set of three cabins, restaurant, and campground. It also caters to surfers and is a short walk from Playa Negra.

Playa Nosara

The name of this village derives from the river which, in turn, is named after an Indian. The daughter of a chief, Nosara married a young warrior named Curime from another tribe. Despite his outsider status, he was appointed guardian of some gold statues. After another tribe attacked, Nosara slashed her wrists to prevent their capture, and the blood springing from her wrists generated the river.

Many retired foreigners live in this area, and it is the peninsula's center of expatriate life. Surfers flock to the mouth of the Río Nosara and to Playa Guiones, a three-km stretch of sand, and snorkelers will explore the reefs off of Playa Guiones.

Wildlife abounds — owing both to the nature reserve and a moratorium on hunting that stretches back nearly two decades. Controversy centers around the paving of the last 25 km of the road into Nosara; at present, the area has largely four-wheel-drive access, no taxi service, and only two buses arrive per day. This is a quiet destination, not suited for the disco crowd.

> ☛ The town of Nosara is five km from the beach. Things are spread out so a car is definitely an asset.

GETTING HERE: In San José, take an Empresa Alfaro (☎ 222-2666) bus from Coca Cola at 6AM daily for around US$6. It takes six hrs. for the 300 km trip. There's generally one bus (three hrs.) per day from Nicoya at 1 PM. It returns at 6. (The road may be impassable during the wet season).

BY CAR: If driving, a four-wheel drive is mandatory during the wet season and desirable at other times.

BY AIR: *SANSA* (☎ 221-9414, 233-0397, 233-3258, fax 255-2176) flies to Carrillo and has package tours. *Travelair* (☎ 220-3054, 232-7883 fax 220-0413; information@travelair-costarica.com) also flies daily to Carrillo. Ask your hotel if they will pick you up. Otherwise it is a US$25 taxi ride.

ACCOMMODATIONS: Campers should stay near **Olga's Bar**, a restaurant on Playa Pelada which will supply water. (Be sure to check over your bill carefully).

Next to the gas station in the village of Nosara (five km inland from the beach), low-budget eight-room **Cabinas Chorotega** (☎ 682-0836) supplies fans; baths are shared. **Cabinas Agnnel** is another, similarly-priced alternative.

Luxury-priced 16-room **Hotel Playas de Nosara** (☎/fax 682-0495; Apdo. 4, 5233 Nosara) offers a pool, restaurant, and spectacular views of both beaches. They will meet you at the plane.

A moderate bed and breakfast which also has a good restaurant, **Almost Paradise** (☎/fax 682-0763) has a hillside garden with a fruit orchard.

Serving not inexpensive soups and sandwiches, the **Gilded Iguana** (☎/fax 682-0749) rents moderately-priced, furnished efficiency apartments (around US$50). Bridge is played here on Sat.

The **Condominio de las Flores** (☎ 682-0696) has two-bedroom, two-bath apartments for around US$500 pw, US$1,500 pm.

The inexpensive-moderate **Rancho Suizo Lodge** (☎ 682-0057, fax 682-0055; Apdo. 14, Bocas de Nosara, 5233 Guanacaste) is near the beach and offers a restaurant, tours, and evening video screenings. Use of boogie boards, snorkeling gear, and bicycles is included as is breakfast. Ratea are around US$50-80.

Around 3.5 km from the beach, **Casa de las Huacas** (fax 682-0856) is a bed and breakfast (around US$50 d) set on a hill.

Set four km out and also Swiss-owned, the moderate 8-unit hospitable **Hotel Estancia** (☎/fax 682-0178; Apdo. 37, Nosara) has a restaurant with a waterfall, pool, forest reserve, and tennis court. Rooms are a/c or fan ahd have refrigerator and dining area; complimentary breakfast is included. Rates are around US$60 (including tax) on up. Horseback riding, fishing, tennis, fishing, biking, and snorkeling are offered.
estancia@nosara.com

Santa Fe-style ecologically-minded **Lagarta Lodge** (☎/fax change 682-0035, fax 682-0135) has eight rooms for around US$55-70 with breakfast. All rooms are in separate units and command impressive views. It offers mangrove and horseback tours around its private reserve, **Reserva Biologica Nosara**. More than 200 bird species may be sighted here.
www.nosara.com/lagarta
lagarta@sol.racsa.co.cr

Cabinas and Restaurant Almost Paradise (☎/fax 685-5004; Apdo. 15, Bocas de Nosara) had its start as an art gallery, metamorphosed into a restaurant, and now has rooms for around US$50 with breakfast. Coffee is included; dinner reservations for non-guests are available.

Giardino Tropicale Restaurant, Pizzeria, and Cabinas (message ☎ 682-0378) offers Italian meals and rooms from around US$15 on up. For information on weekly or monthy **home rentals** which include maid service and utilities, call 680-0747.

Low-budget travelers should stay in the village. Otherwise, **Casa Río Nosara** (☎ 682-0117, fax 682-0182) offers simple accommodation for around US$15 pp; it has an inexpensive restaurant as well.
casarionosara@nosara.com

ON PLAYA GUIONES: **Playa Guiones Lodge** (☎ 232-3637/2100, fax 231-6346) is a set of thatched roof cottages at the beach's S end. Facilities include horseback riding and scuba.

Hotel Estrella del Pacifico (☎/fax 682-0856) is set to the N and is attractively landscaped; facilities include pool, restaurant, and tennis court. It has rooms from around US$40 on up.

Hotel Casa Tucán (☎ 682-0113, US fax 805-962-1855; Bocas de Nosara, Codi 5233-91 Gte.) stand across the road.

They offer four "theme" studios with kitchenettes which sleep up to four. A/c is available. It has a full-service gourmet restaurant with Sunday Brunch. Rooms are around US$ 40 s, US$ 60 d, and special weekly and monthly rates area available.
casatucan@nosara.com

A two-story small white home, Swiss-run **Hotel Casa Romántica** (☎/fax 682-0019; Apdo. 45, 5233 Nosara). Set amidst landscaped gardens, six condo units are linked to the house via a covered walkway. The spacious rooms are in the house. Candlelight dining on the patio attracts many locals. Rates are around US$60 d.

The **Monkey Trail** (☎/fax 227-0088) is a nice home with amenities such as a washing machine; it offers weekly and monthly rentals as well as one night stands.

FOOD: Some restaurants are listed under "accommodations" above. The only Tico-priced restaurant in town is **Restaurant Nosara** right by the soccer field. **Monkey Business** sells sandwiches and whole wheat bread; they also rent boogie boards.

Café de Paris (☎ 682-0087, fax 682-0089) is a hotel with bakery and poolside restaurant. Rooms and bungalows range around US$40-85; some have a/c.
www.nosara.com/cafedeparis
cafedeparis@nosara.com

One of the most popular eating spots for resident expats is **La Lechuza**, about two km from the beaches towards the village. Set between Nosara and Garza on Playa Guiones, **La Dolce Vita** offers gourmet food; it specializes in Italian dishes and fresh seafood served up with home grown veggies and herbs. **Pascholi Jungle Bar and Restaurant** is on Playa Guiones and serves Continental-style lunches and dinners.

Supermercado La Paloma and **Supermercado Nosara** provide your food supply needs.

TOURS: Casa Río Tours (☎ 682-0117, fax 682-0182) offers canoeing, kayaking, fishing, or turtle watching.
casarionosara@nosara.com

Tuanis offers souvenirs, tourist info, and a book exchange. It is in a blue house to the L of the Bocas de Nosara soccer field.

LANGUAGE STUDY: The German-owned **La Escuela de Rey de Nosara** offers Spanish language intensive courses.

YOGA: The luxury **Nosara Retreat** (☎ 682-0071, fax 682-0072; 888-803-0580) offers a yoga "Wellness Adventure Program."
yogaretreat@nosara.com
www.nosara.com/yogaretreat

FROM NOSARA: A bus returns to San José at 12;45 PM and to Nicoya at 6 AM. *Sansa* and *Travelair* also fly.

Refugio Nacional de Vida Silvestre Ostional
(Ostional National Wildlife Reserve)

Ostional National Wildlife Reserve (9,692-acre; 3,923-ha) was established in order to protect this vital nesting site for ridley, leatherback, and green turtles, Its forested stretches inhabited by coatis, monkeys, kinkajous, and other wildlife.

As many as 120,000 ridleys arrive during four to eight-day stretches between July and Dec.; these are separated by two- to four-week intervals. In exchange for patrolling the nests, locals here have been granted limited rights to harvest the eggs of the first arrivals.

Sadly, the late 1990s were years of conflict for the reserve, as locals fought with environmentalist activists Anny Chavez and her husband Leslie du Toit.

Other attractions here include **India Point**. The beach here has innumerable ghost crabs and other crabs, as well as lizards. There are also many tide pools containing everything from sea anemones to starfish. When you visit, report to the turtle cooperative at the beach's upper end.

GETTING HERE: A bus (four hrs.) runs here daily from Santa Cruz at noon during the dry season; it can be approached by road either from Santa Cruz through Marbella (dry season through July or later) or you can drive through a river (dry season only) N from Nosara.

VOLUNTEERING: Earth Island Institute's Sea Turtle Restoration Project (☎ 415-488-0370, fax 415-488-0372, PO Box 400, Forest Knolls, CA 94933) sends volunteers into the field here.
www.igc.apc.org/ei/strp/strpindx.html
seaturtles@earthisland.org

PRACTICALITIES: Call 680-0467 for *cabina* reservations as well as information on turtle activity. Locals will sell you meals and low-budget *cabinas* are available for rent.

Bahía Garza

With thatched huts and cool sea breezes, exclusive and luxurious **Villaggio la Guaria Morada** (☎ 682-0784, 233-2476, fax 222-4073; Apdo. 860, 1007 C. Colón, San José) here offers diving, sportfishing, horseback riding, a restaurant, and a disco. Be careful when signing for bills here; there has been a report of mistakes.

Hotel Villas Taype (☎ 682-0188, fax 682-0187) has a pool, open-air restaurant, boutique, and tennis courts. They charge around US$70 with breakfast; its bungalows charge around US$100 for up to six.
taype@infoweb.co.cr

Casa Pacifico B & B (682-0856) has rooms for around US$20 pp with breakfast. They also have a restaurant.

Vida Ville Super Mercado here has a wide selection of natural foods and also sells fish and lobster.

Playa Sámara

With a long grey beach which widens at low tide, this fishing and farming settlement is popular with windsurfers and swimmers; it has more facilities than the average village. To get to adjacent Playa Cangreja, you may walk through the river or ride around the airstrip.

GETTING HERE: Roads leading here are in bad shape. *Empress Alfaro* (☎ 222-2750, 223-8227, 223-8361) runs direct, six-hr. buses daily at noon from Av. 5, C. 13/14 in San José. The bus schedule to and from Nicoya varies according to the season but generally leaves around 3 and 5, with one rainy season departure at noon.They return at 6 AM and 2:30 PM Call *Empress Rojas* (☎ 685-5353) in Nicoya to confirm.

BY CAR: If you're driving from Nosara, you'll have to ford two small, shallow rivers. It's about a 1.5-hr. drive direct from Nicoya.

BY AIR: The airport is at Playa Carrillo, five min. by car from Samará. *SANSA* (☎ 221-9414, 233-0397/3258, fax 255-2176) flies on Mon., Wed., and Fri. *Travelair* (☎ 220-3054, 232-7883, fax 220-0413; information@travelair-costarica.com) flies daily.

ACCOMMODATION AND FOOD: Featuring a restaurant and disco, more costly **Cabinas Los Almendros** still qualifies as inexpensive.

Hotel Discotheque Playa Sámara offers basic lodging for around US$20; it has a restaurant.

Run by Germans, moderate **Hotel Marbella** (☎/fax 233-9980) has both rooms and apartments. It offers a restaurant as well as bike, car, motorbike, and surfboard rentals. The **Belvedere**, also German-run and across the street, is a bed and breakfast which houses its guests in A-Frame cabinas.

The thatched-roof **Hotel Giada** (☎/fax 656-0132, fax 656-0131) has attractive European-style rooms for around US$50 d.

Set at the beach's N end around 3.5 km from town and a km from Playa Carrillo, luxury to ultra-luxury **Villas Playa Sámara** (☎ 656-0110, 256-8228, fax 656-0109, 221-7222) promotes itself as an "art and nature" resort. Facilities include pool, windsurfing, fishing, scuba, horseback riding, tennis, casino, and restaurant. All-inclusive packages are available. The hotel has an annual contest at which Costa Rican artists-in-residence compete on a theme.
www.costarica.tourism.co.cr/hotels/samara/samara.htm
htlvilla@sol.racsa.co.cr

Expensive-luxury 20-room **Hotel Las Brisas del Pacifico** (☎ 680-0876, 233-9840, fax 233-5503, 661-4040, fax 661-1487; Apdo. 490, 3000 Heredia), set apart from the village and to the S of the beach, has outstanding German cuisine, fans, pool, Jacuzzi, horseback riding, and watersports equipment. German is also spoken.

Luxury **Hotel Sámara Beach** (☎ 233-9398, fax 233-9432) offers attractive rooms with a/c or fans.

Moderate Quebecquois-run **Casa del Mar** (☎ 232-2241, fax 685-5004) is a refurbished home turned into a bed and breakfast. Rates run from around US$40 for a room with shared bath.
casamar@sol.racsa.co.cr

Cabinas Comedor Arena (message ☎ 685-0445) offers 12 cabinas for around US$30.

Cabinas Belvedere are set on a hill and offer breakfast.

Italian-run **Isla Chora** (☎ 257-3032 or 232-3087, 296-1864, 223-1647, fax 256-9376 in San José; 656-0174, 656-0175 in Samará) is the town's largest development and offers well designed *cabinas* and apartments which caters to weathy Ticos as well as foreigners. Rates are around US$75 pn for one of the ten *cabinas* (each hold five) and US$110 for one of the four apartments (hold six). It has an Italian ice cream parlor, boutique, and restaurant.
hechombo@sol.racsa.co.cr

On a hilltop overlooking the ocean, **Apartotel Mirador de Sámara** (fax 685-5004) is an elegant and intimate hotel with six apartments and a *mirador* with tremendous views. Each apartment has a long dining table, kitchen, and other facilities. It opened in 1995.

LOW BUDGET: Campers may stay at **El Acuario**, 100 m S of the soccer field; a campsite (shower and toilets) is US$2 pp. Another alternative is **Camping Cocos** which is 250 m from the main road; take the last L before the beach; they also have inexpensive cabins. There are a number of *hospedajes* and *cabinas* here of which the most attractive is **Hospedaje Yuri**. Others include **Cabinas Milena**, **Caginas Magaly**, and **Cabinas Punta Sámara**.

FOOD: In addition to the fare offered by hotel restaurants, **Colochos** serves inexpensive seafood dishes.

Playa Carrillo

Some five min. by car from Sámara, this white sand beach has waters becalmed by the offshore reef. There are spartan, inexpensive *cabinas* here as well as a local restaurant, the **Bar Restaurant El Mirador**.

Specializing in fishing, the luxury-class **Guanamar Beach & Sportfishing Resort**

(☎ 656-0054, fax 656-0001) offers fans, restaurant, pool, private airstrip, horseback riding. and water excursions including diving. Its sister resort is Isla de Pesca on the Caribbean coast, and "two-ocean fishing" can be arranged. Write Apdo. 7-1880, 1000 San José. In the US call (800) 245-8420, 305-539-1630, fax 305-539-1123 or write Costa Sol International, 1717 N Bayshore Dr., Ste. 3333, Miami, FL 33132. From Carrillo, the road to Hojancha is bad, but it's paved from there to Mansión.

If you're traveling S towards Playas Coyote and Caletas, you must ford the Río Ora at low tide.

Monte Alto Forest Reserve

The **Monte Alto Forest Reserve** (☎ 659-9089) includes a one-ha orchid garden as well as a cultural museum with a live demonstration of a sugar mill. A lodge offers dorm rooms for around US$10 pp. Meals are also available.

Organized as a response to the problem of water shortages attributed to deforestation, the Monte Alto Forest Reserve Foundation began as an effort by three concerned local residents and has grown to encompass 242 ha of primary, secondary, and regenerating forest. The reserve was awarded the 1996 Guayacan National Environmental Prize which recognizes community efforts to preserve the environment.To get here, turn R at Mansion onto an unpaved road leading to Hojancha, 10 km farther. The reserve is 5 km to the S and along a steep four-wheel-drive road.

Playa Coyote

This is a beautiful and untouristed beach. The easiest way to get here by road is via Jicaral. A car would be perfect for exploring this area. Direct buses leave for Coyote at 3:30 from C. 12, Av. 7/9. In the area are also Playa Islita and Playa Jabilla (good surfing).

The former has the 30-room **Hotel Hacienda Punta Islita** (☎ 231-6122, 296-3817, fax 231-0715; Apdo. 6054-1000, San José) which has a private airstrip, Jacuzzi, gym, tennis courts, pool, restaurant, conference room, fishing, horseback riding, and other faciliities. *Travelair* (☎ 220-3054, 232-7883 fax 220-0413; information@travelair-costarica.com) flies here daily from San José.

www.nacion.co.cr/netinc/puntaislita
ptaisl@sol.racsa.co.cr

Set halfway between Cabo Blanco and Playa Sámara on the SW coast, **San Francisco de Coyote** offers accommodation and is four km from the beach. Stay and eat at low-budget **Rancho Loma Clara** (☎ 670-1236).

Playa San Miguel

This small beach town is a 20-min. drive from Coyote. It has a great beach; kayaks and surfboards may be rented. Buses (six hrs.) run here from San José (C. 12, Av. 9) at 6 AM and 3 PM.

The artist-run **Blue Pelican Inn and Restaurant** (reservations ☎ 233-6421) has a pool and garden; it offers accommdation in cabins and even a tree house. Rates are around US$26 per room. The bunk-bedded group room will hold five. Its restaurant features Portuguese dishes such as *Caldeirada*, a fish stew.

A ranch converted to garden estate, **Hotel Arca de Noe** has thatched-roof bungalows (around US$ 45 d; low-budget rooms also available; breakfast included) whose spacious rooms with individual designs. Facilities include shared kitchen, pool, meals by special request, horseback riding, and kayaking. You may also dine at the **Blue Pelican** (see

above) or at the **El Ranchito**.
arcanoe @sol.racsa.co.cr

Santa Cruz

Surrounded by hills, this small, very attractive, somnolent town (pop. 15,000) has the ruins of a bell tower from an old church and more greenery than you'll find in all of San José. Settled around 1760, its original name (*Las Delicias*) was changed in honor of a wooden cross which had been placed on the house of one of the first settlers. The town is a possible base for visiting the Brasilito and Flamingo beaches.

POTTERY: The brown-colored, traditional Chorotega-style pottery commonly seen here comes from **Guaitil**, a craft center near Santa Bárbara, 10 km to the E. A bus runs there about every two hrs. between 7 and 5. Here, you may watch artisans knead clay, sand, and water, and form it into coils with which they hand build pottery. Shop at the Cooperative for items.

GETTING HERE: *Tralapa* buses (☎ 221-7202) leave for Santa Cruz from Av. 3, C. 18/20, at 10:30, noon, 4, and 6. Also try the *Alfaro Co.* on C. 16, Av. 3/5. Most buses to Nicoya (☎ 222-2750; C. 14, Av. 5) also run through Santa Cruz. The town can also be approached from Liberia, Nicoya, and the beaches.

PRACTICALITIES: Stay at either the moderate **Hotel Diría** (☎ 680-0080/0402, fax 680-0442; Apdo. 58, Santa Cruz, Guanacaste) or the less expensive 40-room **Sharatoga** (☎ 680-0011, Apdo. 345, Santa Cruz, Guanacaste), both of which offer a/c and swimming pools. While the Sharatoga is next to the Tralapa terminal, the Diría is on the N outskirts.

Hotel La Pampa (☎ 680-0348) has rooms fron around US$25 (with fans) and up (for a/c). It has the **Restaurant Las Casuelas**. **La Estancia** (☎ 680-0476, fax 680-0348) is slightly cheaper Other low-budget places include **Pensión Santa Cruz** next to the Tralapa bus station and **Pensión Isabel** (☎ 680-0173), a block away and more peaceful. Low-budget-inexpensive **Hospedaje Avellanas** (☎ 680-0808)is near the Banco Anglo.

Featuring videos every evening, **La Taberna** serves pizza and Chinese grub. For **nightlife** check out thatched-roof **Salon Palenque Diría** or the Diría or Sharatoga hotels on weekends. The **Malambo Boutique** is the place to go for clothes shopping.

☛ **Coopetortillas**, a former airport hangar converted to a cooperatively-run restaurant, stands three blocks S of the church on the main square.

FESTIVALS AND EVENTS: The celebration for the **Black Christ of Esquipulas** held each Jan. 15 includes folk dancing, bullfights, and marimba music. Days begin with Catholic mass. Booths sell handicrafts.

Held every July 25, the **Anniversary of the Annexation of Guanacaste Province** commemorates the province's secession from Nicaragua. Featured are folk dancing, marimba bands, horse parades, bullfights, rodeos, cattle shows, and local culinary specialties.

FROM SANTA CRUZ: Buses leave for San José regularly. Call *Tralapa* (☎ 221-7202) for schedules. The bus for Tamarindo leaves from the bus stop two blocks W and one block N of the church. Buses also run to Paraíso (four km from Playa Junquillal) Another alternative is to hire a taxi to take you out to the beaches. Bargain!

DIRIA NATIONAL FOREST AND WILDLIFE REFUGE: This lovely reserve was established by presidential decree in 1991. It consists of steep tropical humid premontane forest. A government-run lodge provides dorm accommodation plus food for around US$25 pp, pd. It can hold up to 30 and has slide projectors and a TV/VCR. The park needs donations in order to grow. For more information call the regional office of the **Tempisque Conservation Area** in Santa Cruz (☎ 680-1820) or the main office in Hojancha (☎ 659-9039).

Nicoya

Located 48 mi.(78 km) from Liberia, Nicoya (pop. 10,000) is the last stop in a slow-moving but beautiful bus ride. Named after an indigenous chieftain, this pleasant place is the peninsula's major town — one which makes a good base for exploring the area. Its chief attraction is the recently restored white colonial **Iglesia San Blas** which also functions as a religious art museum.

GETTING HERE: *Empresa Alfaro* (☎ 222-2750) buses leave San José from C. 14, Av. 3/5 at 6, 8, 10, noon, 1, 2:30, 3, and 5; advance tickets are mandatory. The 296-km trip takes around six hrs. While some buses cross by the Tempisque Ferry, others arrive via Liberia.

BY CAR: Allow four hrs. for the trip. Watch for the ferry signs after you pass the Las Juntas turnoff. Another approach is via Liberia and down past Santa Cruz.

ACCOMMODATION: There are a few cheap digs. Down the street and across from Cortel, **Hotel Ali** is low-budget, as is **Hotel Elegante** (☎ 685-5159). **Hotel Anexo Playa Sámara** (☎ 685-5544) is near the town's entrance; it's also low-budget (around US$6 pp), and rooms have private baths and fans. **Hotel Chorotega** (☎ 685-5245) is one of the more attractive options. Airy **Pensión Venecia** (☎ 685-5325) next door is slightly more expensive.

Slightly upscale, a/c **Hotel Jenny** (☎ 685-5050) is still inexpensive as is **Los Tinajas** (☎ 685-5081) in the town center.Set at the edge of town, **Hotel Curimé** (☎ 685-5238, fax 685-5530; Apdo. 51, Nicoya) has 20 noisily a/c cabins with refrigerators, TVs, and separate living areas. Rates are a.round US$50 d.

FOOD: A large number of Chinese restaurants, including **Restaurant Jade**, border the square where fruit drinks are served from stands. Near the park, **Café Daniela** offers Tico food, pizza, and bakery items.

FIESTA DE LA YEGUITA: In this event, held on Dec. 12, solemn-faced villagers carry the image of the Virgin of Guadalupe through the streets. To a flute-and-drum accompaniment, two dancers, one of whom carries a doll, pass through La Yeguita, "the little mare," a hoop with a horse's face. Other festivities include bullfights, fireworks, and band concerts; traditional foods made from corn are dispensed.

FROM NICOYA: The bus station is located at the edge of town. Buses depart for San José at 4:30, 6:30, 8:30, 11:30. For Liberia buses depart half-hourly or hourly Buses also run to Playa Naranjo, Mansíon, Nosara, Sámara, Quebrada Honda, Cupal, Belén, La Virginia, Quirmán, Juan Diaz, Playa Parmona, Hojancha, Pozo de Agua, Puerto Humo (Palo Verde), Rosario, Moracia and Corralillo. Check at the station for current times.

Parque Nacional Barra Honda
(Barra Honda National Park)

The 5,671-acre (2,295-ha) Barra Honda park is nine mi. (14 km) from Nicoya. The series of caverns found here — delving from 50 to 600 ft. (15-200 m) into the bowels of the earth — are Barra Honda's star attraction. The water and the hiking trails are the only other attractions. You may enter the caverns only in the company of a ranger guide. The abundant animal life in the caves includes bats, rats, birds, sightless salamanders, and fish.

GETTING HERE: Take the Nicoya-Santa Ana bus (under two hrs.) or the Quebrada Honda bus, which passes within one km of the entrance. It's a two-km walk to the park from Santa Ana. From Nicoya buses also depart for Barra Honda village (six km away).

BY CAR: If driving from San José, take the Tempisque Ferry (or the bridge once complete) and then go through Quebrada Honda and Tres Esquinas to get to the park. From Liberia, take Carr. 21 S and turn N just before Mansión.

TOURS: San José's **Ríos Tropicales** (☎ 233-6455, fax 255-4354; www.riostro.com; info@riostro.com) offers tours; they are well equipped for cave exploration, and **Turinsa** (☎ 221-9185) also runs tours. **Olman Cubillo** is an independent tour operator (☎ 685-5580, Spanish-only), and **Luis Alberto Diaz** (☎ 685-5406) in Barra Honda also offers tours.

EXPLORING THE PARK: The nearly flat, white mesa here can be climbed from the NW side. Atop the 1,186-ft. (575-m) summit, there are a large number of holes in the rock and reverberating echos as you walk. Bordered by whimsically-shaped rock formations, the view from the S edge is extraordinary. To get here follow the *la Ojoche*, *la Trampa*, and *la Terciopelo* trails. The six-km *Sendero al Ceibo* leads to a waterfall graced with formations of calcium carbonate.

HISTORY: Forays began here in 1967 when a group of speleologists began explorations with the intent of determining whether the Barra Honda peak was a volcano or a single system of caves. Because visitors had taken the smell of bat excrement emanating from Pozo Hediondo for sulfur and the whirring of bat wings for volcanic activity, Barra Honda had been mistakenly assumed to be a volcano. At the behest of the NPS, the Cave Research Foundation of the US surveyed the caves in Dec. 1973. Results show that these caves date from the Paleocene epoch, some 70 million years ago. Spectacular formations are the result of dissolution of limestone by calcium carbonate in rainfall over millions of years.

The park was hit by a forest fire in March 1997 which destroyed 5% of its forest.

THE CAVES: One of the most explored caves with the most numerous and striking formations, **La Terciopelo** (Fer-de-Lance) is 180 ft. (55 m) deep. One formation in this cave, known as the organ, produces different musical tones when struck.

With a total depth of 590 ft. (108 m), **La Trampa** (The Trap) has the steepest

> In March 1993 a German newlywed couple wandered off the trails at Barra Honda and died from dehydration. Inform the rangers where you are going and be sure to carry plenty of water.

dropoff at 171 ft. (52 m). Containing the largest caverns, it has one whose interior is composed of eye-dazzling pure white calcite.

El Perico (The Parakeet) is 69 ft. (21 m) deep. Home to millions of buzzing bats, **Pozo Hediondo** (Fetid Pit) sinks to 361 ft. (110 m), and the **Sima Ramón Canela** (Ramón Canela Pothole) is 115 ft. (35 m) deep. **Los Seis** (The Six) descends for 656 ft. (200 m).

Human remains have been found in **Nicoa** cave. **Santa Ana** has small grottos containing minutely intricate and delicate formations. There also are amazing collections of stalactites and stalagmites. Other unusually shaped formations found in the caves include grapes, curtains, fried eggs, pure white chalk flowers and needles.

If you wish to go down in the caves, make arrangements a week in advance; no visits are allowed during the rainy season or during Holy Week.

ACCOMMODATION: While there's no water on the mesa, there is a designated camping site near Terciopelo which has water and picnic tables. Another good spot, which has streams, can be found in the forest, but it's 1.5 hrs. away, and is difficult to locate.

Run by locals, **Las Delicias Ecotourism Project** has three inexpensive *cabinas* (US$12 pp), a campsite (US$2.50 pp), gift shop, and restaurant. Guides are also available through them. This is a unique project and worthy of your support. A stay here allows you to explore not only Barra Honda but also surrounding national parks such as Palo Verde and Santa Rosa, both of which are 1.5 hrs. by car. To reserve, leave a message in Spanish at 685-5580.

About 20 minutes drive away in the direction of Quebrada Honda, **Observatorio Natural Montaña Vista de Halcón** (☎ 685-5411/5881, 237-6240; Apdo. 985, Heredia) offers a traditional ranch house, camping, and tours to a nearby waterfall and lookout point.

Coopeortega

This ecotourism project is run by Cooprena (☎/fax 259-3605, 259-3401, an umbrella organization.

This community-run lodge in Bolsón de Santa Cruz on the Río Tempisque, offers horseback riding, birdwatching, and boat tours; meals are with local families.

www.agroecoturismo.net
cooprena@sol.racsa.co.cr

Parque Nacional Palo Verde (PaloVerde National Park)

Palo Verde National Park is set amidst limestone hills at the head of the Gulf of Nicoya in the "V" formed by the merger of the Río Tempisque with the Bebedero. Most of the park either floods or turns to swamp during the rainy season, with the exception of the limestone outcrops to the N. There's a nature trail along a dike, but the birds assemble on the riverbanks during the dry season; a boat would be ideal.

Named after the famous biologist, **Refugio de Vida Silvestere Dr. Rafael Lucas Rodríguez** makes up the adjoining jigsaw puzzle piece of this reserve. While this park-and-reserve combination may seem an integral whole to the visitor, slightly different rules and regulations apply to the wildlife refuge and to the park (see below).

FLORA AND FAUNA: Hundreds of different species of waterfowl either migrate here or reside permanently; among these are the rare jabiru stork and all manner of ducks, spoonbills, and herons. At park headquarters you can see the scarlet macaw in a tree pining away for his lost mate: one of the reasons that macaws are endangered is that they mate for life. At the waterholes one can observe armadillos, deer, peccaries, howler monkeys, and coatis.

Another, decidedly less elegant denizen, is the cow. Cattle grazing has been allowed in order to cut down on the number of cattails which are drying up the park.

HISTORY: The park was originally the S end of an enormous ranch, extending from the Río Tempisque to the slopes of Volcán Miravalles, established by David Russell Stewart in 1923. It was commonly known as Finca Wilson after Stewart's pseudonym. At that time the Organization of Tropical Studies (OTS) chose Palo Verde as the dry forest site for a comparative ecosystem study, a relationship which has continued to this day. The government expropriated the property for an ITCO agricultural project in 1975, and the Palo Verde National Wildlife Refuge was created in 1977.

GETTING THERE AND PRACTICALITIES: For information contact the Tempisque Conservation Area Headquarters (☎ 670-1062 or 670-1290) in Bagaces. From San José take the 7:30 AM bus (C. 14, Av. 1/3) to Cañas where you transfer to the Bebedero bus from the market. From Bebedero you can either hike three hours to the park, passing by nine mi. (15km) of rice plantations on rough roads, take a taxi or, if you've called ahead by radio (☎ 233-5473), rangers might be able to pick you up. Although the ranger's bunkroom is available by reservation, you'll need to bring your own mosquito net; you can also camp at park headquarters.

Across the river from the park, **Rancho Humo** (☎ 255-2463, 255-3573; Apdo. 322, 1007 San José) offers inexpensive-moderate accommodation with good food. It contains two properties: the Zapandi Lodge (around US$40, rooms sleep four; done in mock indigenous village style) and the more deluxe 24-room Rancho Humo Hotel (around US$85 d) which has a/c rooms and balconies. It's near the village of Puerto Humo. Horseback riding and trips to Palo Verde are offered.
www.arweb.com/birds
ecologic@sol.racsa.co.cr

Italian-run **La Ensenada** (☎ 228-6653/6655, fax 289-5281) is set to the S of Palo Verde; it's expensive but rates include horseback and boat tours. Another alternative instead of staying in the park is to stay in Cañas and drive out daily.

TOURS: Based in Liberia, **Guanacaste Tours** (☎ 222-9407; Apdo. 55-5000, Liberia) operates a fine tour here. After hotel pickup early in the morning, you are sped to the dock in an a/c bus where you board a boat for the park. Along the river, startled birds fly up as you approach, monkeys roam the trees, and crocodiles scurry into the water— leaving a muddy groove in their wake. Pizotes and sloths may also be sighted. After a picnic lunch ashore, you walk to the administration building. Along the way you might see families of iguanas, and birds. A corral at the center of the administrative area occasionally holds steers. After hiking around the area, you return to the boat and you are treated to a spin past the Isla de Pájaros ("Island of Birds") which is populated by cormorants, cattle egrets, ibis, and herons.

A number of other operators also offer fine tours which are likely to be similar.

Refugio de Vida Silvestre Palo Verde

Also known as the **Rafael Lucas Rodríguez Caballero Wildlife Reserve**, this refuge occupies the N portion of the reserve, and contains a variety of habitats, ranging from marsh and lagoons to dry forest, evergreen groves and pasture. Inhabitants include deer, peccaries, white-faced monkeys, waterfowl, and crocodiles. In addition to wildlife, from its trails you can see the adjacent Río Tempisque, the Isla de Pájaros at its center, and the Tempisque flood plains.

PRACTICALITIES: At Puerto Humo, across the river from the refuge, there's a makeshift dock with a marooned boat and a pig wandering in the mud foraging for food. Nearby are ducks, chickens, longhorn steers, and cud-chewing cattle. Ask around about renting a boat. A bus runs here from Nicoya. Keep in mind that this route is better attempted during the dry season. The other entrance to the refuge is 32 km to the L from the gas station in Bagaces, to the N of Cañas. You may be able to stay at the OTS facility in the reserve if it's not chock-a-block with researchers. They charge around US$55 pd for room and board for adults. Contact them (☎ 240-6696, fax 240-6783; Apdo. 676, 2050 San Pedro) before your arrival.
www.ots.ac.cr
laselval@ns.ots.ac.cr

Guanacaste Tours (☎ 666-0306, fax 666-0307; Apdo. 55-5000, Liberia) runs tours here for around US$85 pp. For more information regarding this reserve, contact the Departamento de Vida Silvestre, Ministry of Agriculture (☎ 233-8112; C. 19, Av. Central/2).

Tempisque Ferry

The **Tempisque River Ferry** (☎ 685-5295) leaves from Puerto Nispero (Cañas) hourly from 5:30 AM-8:30 PM.

In recent years, there have been problems with this service. The old ferry, badly in need of replacement, stopped operating in 1990. The new US$500,000 ferry had too much draft for the shallow route, and its design was incompatible with either of the ferry piers. Happily, this conflict has been solved.

If crossing with your car, expect to spend about a half-hour total. Late afternoon (after 2 PM) and Sundays (after noon) are the worst times to cross. Expect delays of an hour or more. If crossing from E to W, birdwatchers should check out the small estuary about 300 yards (300 m) from the ferry entrance, which teems with life during the winter season.

Plans are underway to build a bridge near the site of this ferry, and it may be done someday before either Dan Quayle is elected president or Manuel Noriega finishes his prison term.

The Southern Nicoya Peninsula

This area is so difficult to reach from the N that it's really almost a separate region; administratively, it's considered part of Puntarenas, rather than Guanacaste. Infrequent buses run from Nicoya to Naranjo but, from there to Paquera, you need your own vehicle. Two ferries, to Naranjo and to Paquera, ply the waters from Puntarenas. Another dead-end route is to take a bus from Jicaral to Playa Coyote, a once-deserted beach which now has a growing number of new facilities.

True horse and cattle country, this area has a large number of thatched roof homes. Watch the monkeys scamper through the trees lining the roadside, and walk mile after mile without seeing a passing vehicle — just as well considering the dust on the roads! Unfortunately, a portion of this area near Playa Tambor has been degraded through development.

GETTING HERE BY BOAT: The **Paquera Car Ferry** (☎ 661-3674) departs at 8:45 AM, 2 PM, and 8:15 PM and returns aat 6 AM, 11:45 AM, and 6 PM.

The **Playa Tambor Ferry** (☎ 681-2084) also goes to Paquera. It departs at 5 AM, 12:30 PM, and 5 PM and returns at 8 AM, 2:30 PM, and 8:30 PM. It is owned by the infamous Spanish hoteliers.An a/c section upstairs (US$4) offers If driving, get there as early as two hours beforehand or you may not get on the next boat.

The **Playa Naranjo Car Ferry** (☎ 661-1069, 661-3834) runs at 3:15 AM, 7 AM, 10:50 AM, 2:50 PM, and 7 PM. It returns at 5:10 AM, 8:50 AM, 12:50 PM, 5 PM, and 9 PM.

Playa Naranjo

There's no beach and only a small settlement here. But there are a few places to stay in the area. On the edge of town towards Nicoya, the inexpensive-moderate **Hotel de Paso** (☎ 661-2610) has rooms with a/c or fans, pool, and a restaurant.

With a shuttle bus that meets the ferry, moderately-priced 36-room **Hotel Oasis del Pacifico** (☎/fax 661-1555; Apdo. 200, 5400 Puntarenas) has fans, restaurants, pool, and some rooms with hot water. It also offers tennis, horseback riding, gym, and fishing. For around US$3, you can use their pool, beach, and shower facilities for the day.

Seated on the bluff overlooking Bahía Gigante, on the way to Paquera, inexpensive-moderate **Rancho Bahía Gigante** (☎/fax 661-2442; Apdo. 1866, San José), has pool, nature trails, pier, fans, restaurant, horseback riding, and fishing. The more expensive condo units have a kitchen.

Paquera

Staying in this town might be an alternative to staying overnight in Puntarenas and catching the 6 AM ferry. However, the ferry terminal is five km from town, and you'll have to squeeze yourself on beforehand because it's always packed by the time it passes by. With only two short streets which intersect at 90 degree angles, there's not much to do, except perhaps shop for a machete or a saddle in the general store or shoot pool. There are a few cheap places to stay and eat here.

Refugio Vida Silvestre Curú (Curú National Wildlife Refuge)

Curú has three sand beaches (all of them private) and a wide variety of flora and fauna. This family-run reserve covers 3,000 acres (1,214 ha), an area which includes a farm, (312 ha) of wildlife refuge (84 ha), and an area of *Regimen Forestal*, forest land (1100 ha) under protection. The main ranch house complex is where you first arrive. A monkey and a number of iguanas reside here. Mangos are also grown, and it's memorable to watch the family and workers bring in the harvest.

HISTORY: Federico Schutt de La Croix established a plantation here in 1933 and made clear to his wife that he wished the surrounding nature to be preserved. In 1974, squatters invaded the area, and much of it was declared by the government to be a *Regimen Forestal*. The wildlife preserve designation came in 1982.

FLORA AND FAUNA: Seven habitats are found here: beach, littoral woodland, mangrove swamp, deciduous forest, semi-deciduous forest, and hill forest. Reforestation is underway with ten different native species being planted. White-tailed deer, white-faced capuchin monkeys, and over 222 species of birds can be seen; leatherback, Pacific ridley, and hawksbill turtles also nest here.

GETTING HERE: Curú is off the main highway between Paquera and Cóbano, and you can also visit by boat as many guests staying at Playa Tambor do almost daily. It's not necessary to have a reservation; you will need to pay at the gate. The reserve is open daily from 7-4.

PRACTICALITIES: Spartan cabins may be available if they are not occupied by researchers. Food is simple but well prepared. Vegetarians will be catered to. Mangos are served in season. Contact Doña Julieta by phone or fax at 661-2392 or at 223-1739 in San José. (Note that there is no direct phone to the premises). You may also write to Apdo. 206-5400, Puntarenas.

TOURS: **Personalized Tours** (☎ 257-0507: 24 hrs.) will bring you here on a package from San José and will do an outstanding job of guiding you around. If you're in a small group, and would like to visit here with the services of a guide who is also your friend, than this is the way to go!

HIKING: There are number of wonderful hikes here. Most of the land you pass through has been disturbed, but there are birds and monkeys aplenty. One of the easier hikes is the *Finca de Los Monos*. Another trail, the *Colorada*, leads in the opposite direction and passes by a lookout point. If it's been raining, you should take the bottom fire road. Follow the sign at the open pasture to **Punta Quesada**, a small but gorgeous beach with uniquely attractive layered rock formations. Both here and elsewhere along the shore you can see Isla Tortuga offshore. Be sure to keep to the trail, pack out your rubbish, and remember that no alcohol may be brought into the reserve.

Bahía Ballena/Tambor

On the S coast of Nicoya Peninsula, Tambor in Bahía Ballena is a calm black sand beach. Many *norteamericano* retirees have settled in this area. Playa Tambor is the site of a Spanish chain's hotel whose environmental policies have been widely criticized in the media, including *La Nacíon*, *The Tico Times*, and *Conde Nast Traveler*. Well-documented media reports documented draining of a swamp, removal of a hillside, and other violations. In 1998, they were again fined for violations at a nearby location where they are expanding operations. For information regarding the current situation contact the Asociación Abientalista y Naturalista Cuaremarpro de Montezuma, Apdo. 1126, Pavas.

GETTING HERE: The Cóbano-bound bus goes here from the Paquera ferry terminal.

PRACTICALITIES: A set of ten cabinas made with handcrafted hardwood, the **Tambor Tropical** (☎ 683-0011, fax 683-0013) is an adult-only facility which has a restaurant and Jacuzzi. Rates range from US$125 d (including continental breakfast but not tax) on up. In the US, call 503-363-7084.

members.aol.com/tambort/tambor.htm
tamborcr@sol.racsa.co.cr
tambort@aol.com

Low-budget/inexpensive **Hotel Dos Logartos** (☎ 661-1122, ext. 236), next door, is named after the two points in the distance that appear to resemble crocodiles. Other alternatives are inexpensive **Cabinas El Bosque** (☎ 661-1122, ext. 246) and **Cabinas Tambor Beach**. Eat at **Scruffy's** (by the school on the main road entrance to Tambor), **Dos Logartos, Soda Carlos**, or at **Cristina's** which is across from the school. **Cristina's** also has low-budget cabinas. **Pulpería Los Gitanos** is down the beach from Dos Logartos.

At the village of Pochote to the N, **Zorba's Cabinas** offers attractive cabins for around US$25. The **Restaurante El Río** serves local dishes; it's on the Río Panica two km from Tambor.

Set on the S end of the bay, the **Bahía Ballena Yacht Club** has a **restaurant** which features a different culinary theme every night. Everything from scuba to sea taxis can also be arranged here.

Past Tambor, the ultra-luxury **Tango Mar Resort and Club** (☎ 289-9328, 683-0001, fax 683-0003; 800-648-1136; Apdo. 3877, 1000 San José) has a pool, restaurant, satellite TV, fishing and diving gear, car rentals, and the nation's only seaside golf course (a 10 hole, par 3 and 4 executive course) as well as illuminated tennis courts. Its 18 rooms each have a patio which faces the beach. The one- or two-bedroom thatched *cabinas* rest on columns and have kitchenettes, Jacuzzis, and stained glass domes. The two- and three-bedroom tropical suite villas are at the top of the hill. It attempts to follow ecological codas and to protect the nesting sea turtles. Rates are around US$160 d on up.
www.tangomar.com
info@tangomar.com

Playa Montezuma

Montezuma is the most popular spot on the Nicoya Peninsula's southern tip, and the area surrounding the compact village offers some of the nation's finest beaches. Once dubbed a backpacker's heaven, prices have skyrocketed and social ills have arrived.

GETTING HERE: Relatively hard-to-reach. A **ferry** (1.25 hrs., US$2) leaves from Puntarenas to Paquera at 6, 11, and 3. Overnight in Puntarenas to make the

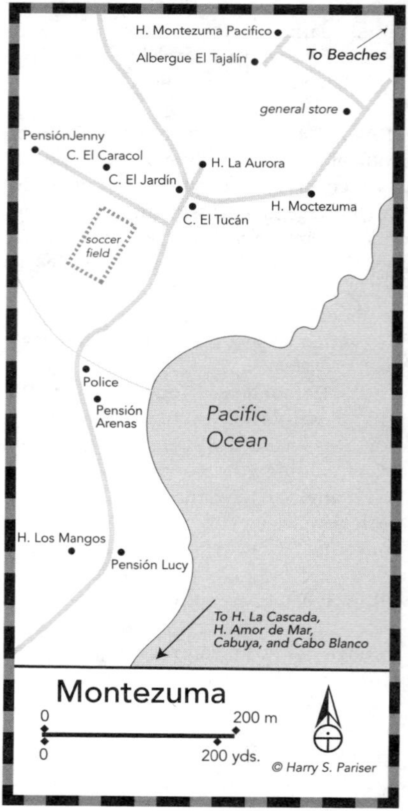

first boat. The return run is at 8 and 5 (additional runs on Mon., Thurs., and Sat. at 1), and buses from Montezuma depart at 5:30 and 2 to meet these boats.

A bus leaves from the ferry landing to Cóbano and Montezuma. At times the two-hour journey may seem so sluggishly interminable that you'll think you're on a slow boat to China. All that's missing are the sails, seas, and salty breeze. (An express bus also runs). If it's the rainy season, buses terminate in Cóbano, seven km from Montezuma. There you can take a communal taxi, from US$1-5 depending upon the number of passengers. Or you can take a taxi (around US$25 for up to six) directly from the ferry to Montezuma).

BY CAR: There's no real advantage to driving here, but, if you do, you should be aware that the road is basically impassible by anything but four-wheel-drive vehicles during the rainy season.

ACCOMMODATION: During the dry season, it's better to call ahead to reserve. To write the hotels listed, address the envelope to Montezuma de Cóbano.

LOW-BUDGET ACCOMMODATION: Prices have risen sharply. The two lowest-budget places in town (at around US$8 pp, pn) are **Pensión Arenas, Pensión** and **Hotel Lucy** (☎ 642-0273). Near Lucy's, **Casa de Huéspedes Alfaro** (☎ 642-0259) provides inexpensive accommodation with private baths. **Hotel Moctezuma** (☎ 642-0058) is set in the center. **Cabinas La Cascada** (☎ 642-0273) is an inexpensive, recently-renovated set of cabinas which rent for around US$35 pn. Low-budget **El Caracol** offers thatched-roof accommodation. Low-budget/inexpensive **Cabinas El Capitan** (☎ 222-3790) is also an option.

Cacti

Any visitor to the Nicoya Peninsula will notice the proliferation of cacti and other scrub vegetation. Cacti were classified into a single genera comprising 24 species by Linnaeus in 1737. The name is Greek for "the bristly plant." The oldest fossilized cacti remains are found in Colorado and Utah and date from the Eocene Era some 50 million years ago. Cacti have evolved to suit a hot, dry climate. Their need to reduce surface area — in order to deter evaporation and for protection from the sun's rays — have resulted in flattened, columnular, grooved, bumpy, globe, and barrel-shaped plants.

Evolution has transformed their leaves into spines and their branches into *areoles* — localized regions which carry spines and/or bristles. The stems are responsible for photosynthesis. Shade and light diffusion is provided by bumps, warts, ribs, spines, and hairlike structures. These structures also serve to hinder evaporation and hold dew. The thick, leathery flesh stores water effectively and is resistant to withering and may endure up to a 60% water loss without damage.

Stomata (apertures) close during the day but reopen at night in order to stave off water loss. Blossoms generally last for only one day, and nearly all depend upon animals for pollination.

MORE EXPENSIVE: In the moderate range, **Cabinas El Jardín** (☎ 642-0284), at the entrance to town, offers rooms (around US$50) with private bath and fan. It has an Italian restaurant. Right across the road is inexpensive and homey

Comfy nine-room **Hotel La Aurora** (☎ 642-0051) is just to the L as you enter the village; it has balcony with hammocks as well as shared refrigerator and kitchen. Breakfast is served. It charges around US$40-50 d.

Cute **Cabinas El Tucán** (☎ 642-0284) has rooms for around US$15.

Hotel Amor de Mar (☎ 642-0262) provides inexpensive-to-moderate accomodation for around US$50-60. They have a good restaurant and a homey atmosphere. **shoebox@sol.racsa.co.cr**

Hotel Montezuma Pacifico (☎ 642-0200; Apdo. 470-2120, San José), next to the church past Parque Infantil, charges in the moderate-to-expensive range depending upon whether rooms have fan or a/c and/or kitchen included. It has a restaurant and offers transport from San José.

Set 50 m N of the church and in front of the park, **Albergue El Tajalín** (☎/fax 642-0061) offers 18 rooms (around US$35) with private bath and fan.

Cabinas Mar y Cielo (☎ 661-2472) has inexpensive rooms (US$35-40) which include fan and private bath.

OUTLYING ACCOMMODATION: Camping Momaya is five min. down the beach to the E. It has showers, a good location, and is safe and right on the beach.

For a respite from the hectic (in season) village, try the eight-room, Spanish ranch-style **Finca Los Caballos** (☎/fax 642-0124). This "Ranch of the Horses" is set above a river and next to tropical forests. It commands great views and has a pool. Hammock are abundant, rooms have patios, and there's a small food. Activities include birding, renting bikes, hiking, and day and day (and overnight) horseback rides. Its restaurant serves "gourmet quality healthy international food." Rates are around US$50 s, 60 d plus tax. **www.centralamerica.com/cr/hotel.caballos.html naturelc@sol.racsa.co.cr**

Hotel Los Mangos (☎ 642-0259, fax 661-2320) has ten Balinese-style bungalows, ten rooms, restaurant, pool, mountain bikes, and horseback riding. Rates are around US$55/ bungalow, and US$40/ room.

On the beach about a 15 min. walk from town, entrepreneurial *norteamericano* and Dutch expats Lenny and Patricia have a beautifully designed set of luxury-priced hand-crafted cabins overlooking the beach; each has a refrigerator, stove, sink, toilet, miniature fan, and an exterior cold water shower. A similar two-bedroom cabin is nearby as are a number of concrete domes which have similar facilities. Contact them at **El Saño Banana** (☎/fax 642-0272) in town.

note: *Other outlying accommodation is listed under "Cabo Blanco."*

RESERVA KAREN MOGENSON FISCHER: Sadly, Karen Mogensen died in 1994. Her property — once one of the most delightful places for low-budget visitors to stay — has been donated to the park service. Karen was one of the nation's leading environmentalists, and her husband Olaf was responsible for the establishment of Cabo Blanco as well as (to a large extent) through his brutal murder there— to Corcovado National Park. It is closed to the public, but tours (☎ 650-0201, fax 650-0355) will be given to prospective donors. (The intention is to expand the land within the reserve).

FOOD: Practically every hotel here has its own restaurant. Most popular is **Chico's Bar**. Food in Montezuma is comparatively expensive (around US$6 per feed and up), partially because almost everything is brought in, and partially because the locals have found that tourists will pay that much. During the peak season and early in July, a number of small restaurants service Ticos and charge moderate prices. But the rest of the year the least expensive restaurant is the small porch top place to the R way up the hill after the waterfall on the way to Cabo Blanco.

Playa de los Artistes serves Italian food in an open-air atmosphere. Fish is a specialty.

El Saño Banana serves vegetarian food; dinners are around US$4 a feed which includes admission to the laserdisc cinema, showing flicks nightly. (Even if you don't see them, you can definitely hear them!)

Las Bermellas is next to the *pulpería* and has excellent, affordable Tico dishes.

The **Swiss Bakery and Café** serves good breakfasts and pastries.

Marisqueria y Soda La Cascada is just to the R of the entrance to the waterfall. **Soda Momaya** is on the beach. **Pizzeria del Sol** sells slices. A **vegetable truck** arrives every other day. The ***pulpería*** is legendary for overcharging foreigners.

SERVICES: Centro Internacional de Comunicación (☎/fax 661-2320) is a phone, fax, and e-mail center. It's generally open from 8:30-1 and 3-8.

Libreria Topsy serves as both bookstore and book exchange.

Operating out of the Cobano computer center, **Finca Pura Vida** (marine band 23) rents out motorbikes.

COBANO PRACTICALITIES: If, for some reason, you should need or want to stay here, the **Hotel Caoba** (☎ 642-0219) has rooms for around US$8 with shared bath, more with private. It has a restaurant. The **Cabinas Gremlar** (☎ 642-0225) is cheaper and also has a good restaurant. The town has a bank and is a good place to load up on supplies.

SIGHTS: The premier attraction of the area is its beaches. From the village, the main ones are all the way on the L as you face the sea — one after another. Exceptional among the exceptional, **Playa Grande** appears to stretch on forever. There are two waterfalls. The first is reached by a seemingly interminable walk (around 1.5 hrs.) past beach after beach. It falls into a cove inaccessible at high tide.

The second is to the R after the bridge on the way to Cabo Blanco. After a short path, you reach the river, which you follow along as best you can until the falls comes into view. At its base is a swimming hole. Don't climb this waterfall: an American visitor fell to his death in Jan. 1990!

> Touts will try to steer you to hotels. Ignore them. There have been at least one case of "date rape" drugs being used in Montezuma; single women should be careful with locals buying them drinks.

FROM MONTEZUMA: It's possible to walk or to ride horses even as far as the Cabo Blanco Biological Reserve which is undoubtedly the best side excursion. A taxi (around US$10 pp, RT) marked "Cabo Blanco" also makes the trip; the driver will wait for you to return. (There is no run on Mon. or Tues. when the park is closed. It leaves at around 9 AM from the town center).

Buses leave for the ferry daily at 5:40, 10, and 2; they meet the ferry. There are around another three buses daily during the high season.

From the dock in Puntarenas, it's a 10-min. walk to the bus stop.

BOAT CHARTER: Located across from the Hotel Moctezuma, the boatmen's cooperative will arrange charters around the Montezuma area as well as to points as far afield as Nosara, Puntarenas, Jacó, Manuel Antonio, and Dominical.

Reserva Natural Absoluta de Cabo Blanco (Cabo Blanco Absolute Nature Preserve)

This 2,896-acre (1,172-ha) peninsular reserve is chock-a-block with innumerable tree and wildlife species . Open 8-4, you need either a rental car or a taxi to get here. No camping is allowed. Bring water.

FLORA AND FAUNA: In addition to the large variety of trees, there are innumerable animals ranging from monkeys to anteaters as well as a great variety of birds. Frogs and toads congregate around a pond in the center of the reserve. A number of small caves also house bats. Tide pools abound at Balsita and Pais beaches: here you can find crabs, starfish, mollusks, and sea cucumbers. Leaving their caves to lay eggs, crabs appear on the beaches *en masse* from March to June.

HISTORY: This "white cape" has been known since the days of the *conquistadores.* Although the reserve was established in 1963, it is the only stretch of wilderness in the nation that had already been preserved intact before the creation of the NPS in 1970. This protection was due to the farsighted vision of Olof Wessberg, a Swedish expatriate, who raised the money to save the area; a plaque near the museum memorializes him.

SIGHTS: The great mass of rocks at the reserve's tip give the reserve its name and date from 20 million years ago. Check out the magnificent views of the sea and diving birds from the paths which run along the tip.

On the W side, **Playa Balsita** is one of the nation's few totally undeveloped beaches. Unfortunately, the sand fleas here make life miserable.

Playa Cabo Blanco is on the other side and is linked by a trail. Both are about three hrs. RT from the ranger station.

Covered with thousands of seabirds, **Isla Cabo Blanco** is about two km from the reserve's S tip. A rocky mound with almost sheer walls, it measures 1,604 by 259 ft. (500 by 140 m). If you have a boat, it's possible to land on the island and climb to the top by the abandoned lighthouse.

ACCOMMODATION AND FOOD: Cabinas Las Rocas (☎ 642-0393) is an inexpensive homestay near Cabuya. Rooms run around US$20. Discounts are given for long term, and Spanish classes are available.

Estudio Los Almendros nearby has camping and offers movement classes.

Hotel Celaje (fax 661-2320) is also in the area and has moderate cottages grouped around a pool and near the beach.

Fernando Morales (☎ 661-3234: message) has a variety of inexpensive rooms for rent in his house which is now known as **Cabinas Cabo Blanco**. He's just S of the Río Lajas, some five km from Montezuma. He also offers camping for less than US$2 pp, and Spanish lessons are also available.

Delicious **Restaurante El Ancla de Oro,** nearby and about 1.5 km from Cabo Blanco, offers inexpensive thatched-roof *cabinas* plus camping. **Pensión Cabo Blanco** is also here as is the low-budget **Cabinas Lila**.

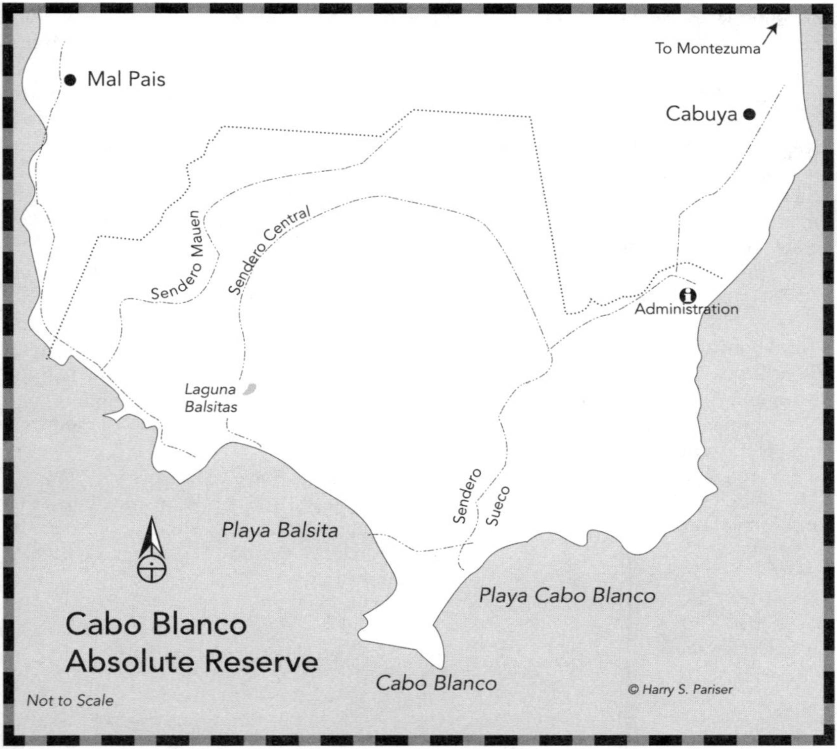

The **Paniagua Guevera** family have a campground as well as operate a low-budget homestay;they're about a half-km before the reserve. You can also camp near the river, where you can see heron and pink ibis.

Playa Mal Pais

A mecca for surfers, this relatively remote area is set to the N on the reverse side of Cabo Blanco. (Entrance from this side is *closed*). The main access is through Cabuya: a summer-only road runs here. Two to three buses per day (depending upon the season) run from Cóbano to Malpaís and Santa Teresa. You can also charter a taxi or else hike from Cobano.

The **Surf Camp** (☎ 642-0047) offers basic low-budget digs and camping.

Bosque Mar (☎ 226-0475; 619-447-0475 in the US) has inexpensive *cabinas*. Its restaurant serves meals for about US$6 a feed.

Run by Italians, **Tropico Latino Lodge** (☎ 642-0062) has six spacious cabinas, restaurant, lots of hammocks, and proximity to Playa Theresa. Rates are around US$60 d.

www.centralamerica.com/cr/hotel/tropico.htm
tropico@centralamerica.com

El Sanctuario de la Luz (☎ 642-0238) was established in 1995 by a group of new ageists (one of whom saw a vision of the same beach while staying at the New Age town of Sedona, Arizona).

Star Mountain Eco Resort (☎ 296-5656, fax 642-0047) is a few km away from the beach and near Cabo Blanco. It has rooms for around US$25 pp with shared bath and US$65 d; rates include breakfast.
www.starmountaineco.com
info@starmountaineco.com

Hotel Sunset Reef/Marine Lodge (☎/fax 506-642-0012; Apdo. 100-5364, Cobanó, Puntarenas) is at Cobanó (near Montezuma). the 14-rm. a/c hotel has a pool, restaurant, and offers excursions. So far 108 species of birds have been sighted around the lodge's vicinity.
sunreef@sol.racsa.co.cr

SAN MIGUEL BIOLOGICAL STATION: Set 2km S of Mal Pais, the San Miguel Biological Station (☎/fax 645-5277 in Monteverde) is the latest project of tropical biologists Diana and Milton Lieberman who also spearheaded Ecolodge San Luis near Monteverde. The station is staffed with national park personnel and resident naturalists. Courses, workshops, conferen ces, seminars, and educational programs of all kinds are available. These include hiking, tidepool walks, snorkeling, birdwatching. The station holds up to 30 in bunk beds; meals are served family style; the reserve may only be reached on foot.
www.nashville.net~edutrop.home.html

Playa Manzanillo

Set about 14 km NW of Mal Pais, this beach is long and shaded. Eat at the **Atardecer Dorado** ("Golden Twilight") Restaurant.

Pacific Coast: Puntarenas to Panama

One of the nation's last frontiers, this area was until recent years one of the least explored by visitors. Most headed S from Puntarenas to Manuel Antonio and skipped the rest. These days, it is becoming increasingly developed, with both the Golfito area and the Osa Peninsula enjoying a population boom. There are the botanical gardens of San Vito; the national parks of Chirripó, Corcovado, and La Amistad; a number of privately owned and operated lodges and reserves; and the surfing hot spot of Pavones.

EXPLORING: If you use *SANSA* (☎ 221-9414, 233-0397, 233-3258, fax 255-2176), you can fly to Quepos, Palmar Norte, Coto 47, and Golfito. *Travelair* (☎ 220-3054, 232-7883 fax 220-0413; information@travelair-costarica.com) also flies to Quepos, Golfito, and Palmar Sur.

Planes also fly into the Osa Peninsula, but the only non-charter (also with Travelair) is from Golfito to Puerto Jiménez.

Buses run to San Vito and as far S as the Panamanian border. Remote points serviced range from Carate, at the edge of Corcovado National Park, to the up-and-coming but ultra-remote resort beach of Zancudo. The Interamerican is the best road.

The 61-km *costanera sur* runs from Barranca to Palmar Sur. The US$10 million project includes 13 bridges. A second major road under construction, a 38-km four-lane highway, will run from Ciudad Colón near San José to Orotina (near Jacó) on the coast.

Puntarenas

The Pacific coast equivalent of Limón, Puntarenas (pop. 150,000) is a major port town. It is situated near the major port of Caldera, which nowadays handles the shipping business; the town remains the business center of the western region.

Placed on the extended sandspit which gives it its name, Puntarenas has universally been described in disparaging terms. one which has little to offer the visitor in terms of sights but which does serve as a transit point to the Gulf of Nicoya and the Nicoya Peninsula While Limón has a funky kind of charm, Puntarenas has perhaps more funk than charm.

But it's not nearly as bad as its detractors make it out to be. Among the pluses are an attractive yacht club and port headquarters as well as a very friendly populace. And, as it is only four blocks wide for most of its length, you're never far from the sea. It may also on its way to being a "beach resort" again. Restaurants now line the waterfront, water quality levels have improved dramatically, and spiffy new beach cleaning equipment now operates daily.

Renovations (funded through a US$15-million grant from the Taiwan government) allowed the town to rebuild the docks and erect an artisan's plaza. Ships began docking at the cruise ship port right in town in 1998, and this should help the recovery still further.

GETTING HERE: *Empresarios Unidos de Puntarenas* (☎ 221-5749, 223-2610) has buses leaving from C. 16, Av. 10/12 in San José every half-hour from 6 AM to 9 PM for the two-hour, 110-km trip. Buses also run from Liberia and from Quepos, as well as from other locations. Train service has been discontinued.

HISTORY: Founded during the 18th C., Puntarenas was opened to foreign ships in 1814, but few arrived until 1846 when the completion of the cart road opened the coffee export trade. Unattractive because it lacked a natural harbor, proper wharves and customs sheds were constructed only in the 1870s. After its linkage to San José by rail in 1910, Puntarenas became the paramount Pacific lowlands port and commercial center. But since construction of the outlying commercial port of Caldera in the 1980s, Puntarenas retains only its fishing industry. The town suffered considerable damage during the March 1990 quake.

SIGHTS: Except for the church, there's not much to see, only the seaside atmosphere to savor. Take a walk along the **Paseo de los Turistas**, a tree-lined walkway adjoining the beaches. Cruise ships dock at Caldera to the S.

SWIMMING: Although outlying areas remain polluted, it's now entirely safe to swim right in town. To reach the best nearby beach, **Playa Doña Ana**, take the Mata Limón bus. The **Marine Historical Museum** is next to the INS building downtown; *gringos* are charged US$1, locals: US$.50.

RESERVA FORESTAL PEÑAS BLANCAS: Located NE of the city off the Interamerican Highway, this forest reserve is the most proximate plot of nature. Established to protect valuable watersheds, this 5,930-acre (2,400-ha) reserve has no facilities, but there are a few trails along the Río Jabonal which cuts through its center. Rising from 1,970 to 4,600 ft. (600-1,400 m), it supports tropical dry and moist zone deciduous forest as well as wildlife, including monkeys, racoons, pacas, kinkajous, opossums, and 70 species of birds.

ACCOMMODATIONS: In the event that you need to overnight here, a wide selection of places to stay is available. However, it can be difficult to find a room on weekends.

Near the tip of the peninsula and the ferry dock is **Hotel Las Brisas** (☎ 661-4040, fax 661-2120), a moderate hotel with seaward-facing rooms. It was built by owner Peter who speaks Engish, Spanish, Italian and his native language of Greek; his restaurant also serves Greek specialties (see "food" below). The a/c rooms are comfortable and priced around US$50 d with discounts for longer stays available.

The 28-room **Gran Hotel Imperial** (☎ 661-0579), a wooden structure near the bus stations at the corner of Paseo de los Turistas and C. Central, faces the water. One of the best inexpensive hotels, it has a classic Caribbean character.

One block N of the microwave tower, inexpensive **Hotel Cayuga** (☎ 661-0344; Apdo. 306, 5400 Puntarenas) is not wildly atmospheric but is clean and modern with a/c. Rooms run from around US$20-35. It is near the downtown bus stop.

On the Paseo de los Turistas (Av. 4, C. 5/7), inexpensive (around US$25 d) **El Oasis del Pacifico** (☎ 661-0209, fax 661-0745; Av. 4, C. 3/5) has rooms from around US$35, a small pool, and a blaring disco.

Cabinas Central (☎ 661-1484) is comfy and charges around US$15 d.

The low-budget **Chorotega** (☎ 661-0998; C. 1/Av. 3) has rooms with private bath are in the inexpensive range (around US$25 d).

Even cheaper and relatively clean, the fan or a/c 44-room **Ayi Con** (☎ 661-0164) is near the market at C. 2, Av. 1/3. It is a good place to stay for the night in terms of backpacker-style value. Rates start at around US$6 pp.

Inexpensive to moderately-priced 46-room **Hotel Tioga** (☎ 661-0271, fax 661-0127; Apdo. 96, Puntarenas) is located near downtown facing the beach. The hotel was a crowd pleaser in its heyday and is still a comfortable place to stay. It has a/c, pool, restaurant, and beach umbrellas. Rates run from around US$40 d and up plus tax.
tiogacr@sol.racsa.co.cr

Hotel Colonial (☎ 255-3234, 661-1833, fax 255-3122) offers large a/c rooms with baclonies for around US$55 d with breakfast. It has a pool, private dock, tennis court, and disco.

On C. 25 just in from the sea, **Cabinas El Jorón** (☎ 661-0467) charges around US$20 d for rooms and US$55 for cabins with a/c and refrigerators.

The **Pensíon Cabezas** (☎ 671-1046; Av. 1, C. 2/4) has simple rooms for around US$6 pp; doubles with bath are around US$15.

On C. Central/Av. 3 next to the Paquera boat dock, the **Hotel Río** is in the low-budget range.

Slightly more expensive is the and the **Pensión Chinchilla** (C. 1, Av. C /2).

A bit cheaper if you get the rooms with shared bath(around US$25), the **Gran Hotel Chorotega** (☎ 661-0998), is at Av. 3 at C. 1.

In the same area, inexpensive **Hotel la Punta** (☎/fax 661-0696) has a pool and restaurant. It charges around US$30 d; a/c rooms are higher.

Charging around US$ 80-100 d, the 42-room **Hotel Yadran** (☎ 661-2662, fax 661-1944) has two pools and two restaurants. Its rooms have a/c, cable TVs, and

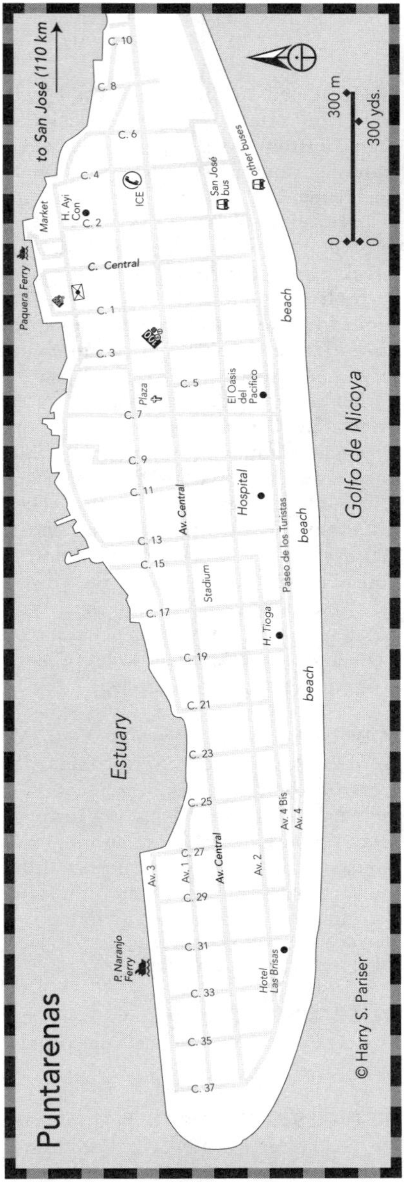

phone. It also has two conference centers: one holds 30 and the other 100.

FOOD: Open-air diners line the beach, and a row of attractive new sodas line the waterfront. Although the area yields a lot of shrimp, most are exported, making it expensive locally.

The **Hotel Las Brisas**, near the terminal for Nicoya, offers the only authentic Greek food in the nation. Try their salad with olives and feta cheese or their fish cooked in Greek-style (when available); prices are reasonable and the food and service are good.

Other good eateries include the waterfront's **La Caravelle** and **Restaurante Miramar**. Sample the **Mandarin** or the **Restaurant Victoria** for Chinese food. The **Hotel Cayuga** is another good restaurant downtown. Others are in the vicinity of C. Central and Av. Central. You may also eat at any of the town's many inexpensive *sodas* or in the central market. Featuring music and dancing on weekends, the **Restaurant Kahite Blanco** is on the N side at Av. 1/C. 19.

TOURS: The yacht ***Calypso*** (☎ 256-6767, fax 233-0401; 800-566-6716) offers day tours on their catamaran stopping at a secluded beach (see "Islas de Tortuga" below) in the Gulf of Nicoya. It brings passengers from San José and departs from the yacht harbor. Combination tours are also offered as are several other tours.
www.calypsotours.com
calypso@calypsotours.com

ENTERTAINMENT: Puntarenas has many bars. The **Hotel Yadran** has a disco and a casino.

FESTIVALS AND EVENTS: Beginning on the Sat. nearest July 16, **Puntarenas Carnival**, the Fiesta of the Virgin of the Sea, commences with a regatta featuring beautifully decorated fishing boats and yachts. The carnival which follows has parades, concerts, dances, sports events, fireworks, and the crowning of the queen. During the dry season, the Casa de la Cultura presents a number of plays and concerts.

MARINAS: The **Hotel Portobello**, **Colonial**, and the **Yacht Club** offer complimentary mooring and use of their facilities for visiting sailboats.

FROM PUNTARENAS: This is the aquatic jumping off point for Nicoya.

The **Playa Naranjo Car Ferry** (☎ 661-1069, 661-3834) runs at 3:15 AM, 7 AM, 10:50 AM, 2:50 PM, and 7 PM. It returns at 5:10 AM, 8:50 AM, 12:50 PM, 5 PM, and 9 PM.

The **Paquera Car Ferry** (☎ 661-3674) departs at 8:45 AM, 2 PM, and 8:15 PM and returns aat 6 AM, 11:45 AM, and 6 PM.

The **Playa Tambor Ferry** (☎ 681-2084) also goes to Paquera. It departs at 5 AM, 12:30 PM, and 5 PM and returns at 8 AM, 2:30 PM, and 8:30 PM. It is owned by the infamous Spanish hoteliers the Barcelos.

BY BUS: When returning to San José, even a day or two after a holiday, buses can be crowded, and you may be forced into a lengthy wait in the sun. Buses leave from Av. 4 (C. 2/4) one block E (towards the mainland) of the main square. Other buses leave from the seaside shelter opposite the bus station for San José. These include the *Santa Elena bus* (the village before Monteverde) and the *Quepos bus*; the *Barranca bus* leaves from the market.

Vicinity of Puntarenas

One of the nation's newest roads, the *Costanera* runs to the S, passing Playa Doña Ana, Mata Limón, Caldera, Playa Táracoles, Playa Herradura, Carara Biological Reserve, Playa Jacó, Esterillos, Quepos, and down to Playa Dominical, before cutting inland to San Isidro de El General. Between Puntarenas and down the coast to Jacó and beyond, there are a number of good surfing beaches.

The **Dona Aña Recreation Area** is a sheltered beach about two km S of town which, along with neighboring Boca Barranca, is popular with surfers. **Mata Limón** is is one of the nation's original beach resorts and is set on an estuary across from the port of Caldera.

The Offshore Islands

Islas de Tortuga

One of these islands in the Gulf of Nicoya is privately owned and rented out for day use by charter companies. With its own beach and coconut glade, this place is the subject of a widely published photograph showing a couple entering a beautiful palm grove with a totally deserted beach behind them. It is a popular destination for excursions and three or four boats may arrive here almost simultaneously, which tends at times to make this private paradise a bit cramped these days.

Calypso Island Tours (☎ 256-6767, fax 233-0401; 800-566-6716) is the longest and best established. Aboard their catamaran the *Manta Raya*, you cruise past beautifully landscaped islands through the Gulf of Nicoya and on to the Pacific. Food and fruit are served on the way. You are bussed in from San José or you can board in Puntarenas. A gourmet buffet lunch (loads of vegetables, beans, *corvina*, and *tortillas*) is served at tables covered with white table cloths in a shady grove on the beach. Package tours (including Monteverde and destinations in Guanacaste) are also available.

www.calypsotours.com
calypso@calypsotours.com

The other lines differ mainly in details. **Bay Island Cruises** (☎ 296-5551, fax 296-5095) has an air conditioned boat with tinted windows, while the **Fantasy Yacht Tours** (☎ 222-4752, 255-0791, 661-0697) are geared towards those with smaller pocketbooks. Other competitors are **Costa Sol** (☎ 239-0033) and **Sea Ventures** (☎ 255-3022).

Isla San Lucas

Once a penal colony, San Lucas has now been closed. The government is planning to do something with it sooner or later.

The Biological Preserves

One of the nation's most beautiful scenic regions, the Gulf of Nicoya is sprinkled with an array of glistening, gem-like islands. Rescued from development, the islands of Guayabo and the two Negritos were protected in 1973 and Los Pájaros followed in 1976. Taken together, they comprise 363 acres (147 ha), all covered with thorny huiscoyol palms and huge populations of birds.

Really just an enormous, almost inaccessible 17-acre (6.8-ha) rock, **Guayabo** has over 200 nesting brown pelicans, the largest such colony found in Costa Rica; frigatebirds and brown boobies abound as well.

Some 11 mi. (16.5 km) S from Puntarenas, the twin **Negritos** (198 acres or 80 ha in total area) are separated by the Montagné channel. Both are difficult to get to.

Set 13 km (eight miles) NW of Puntarenas, nine-acre (3. 8-ha) **Pájaros** shelters a variety of nesting seabird species including the easily-terrorized pelican.

Isla Gitana

Lying off of Puntarenas near Bahía Gigante, this island — run by US expats Linda Ruegg and Dany Haizman — boasts a full service marina, four *cabinas*, (around US$50 including meals) pool, laundry service, kayaks and windsurfing equipment for rent, a jungle bar, and a restaurant. Potlucks are held each Sat. PM at 4:30. They will meet arrivals at the Paquera pier (US$15 pp) or at Bahía Gigante (US$3 pp) by prior arrangement or can pick you up in Puntarenas or Paquera at other times. Call 661-2994 for more information.

Reserva Biólogica Carara (Carara Biological Reserve)

Beautiful Carara Biological Reserve preserves what remains of the central Pacific coast's once-abundant forests. It is set near the mouth of the Río Grande de Táracoles right by the Río Turrubales; both of these partially form the park's N boundary. A number of access roads, make for easy hiking, and a trail near the ranger station leads to riverside hot springs. Camping is prohibited.

NOTE: Admission is charged at the prevailing *gringo* rate of US$6. Two of the most popular trails are now limited to 60 at a time. Many day tours come here. If this is your chance to see scarlet macaws, go for it. Otherwise, there are better places to go for nature (ones without hiking trails running parallel to a highway for example).

GETTING HERE: Buses between Jacó and San José pass by the entrance. Be sure to ask the driver to let you off. The best times to visit are early morning and late afternoon. As Carara is 68 mi.(110 km) from San José, you may want to base yourself at more proximate (but even nastier) Jacó. If you're driving, be sure not to leave anything of value in your car as thefts in the area are common.

Gulls on Nicoya Gulf

One really good way for the novice to go is with trained bilingual biologist **Serge Volio** (☎ 226-9273).

Another popular tour in the area is to Río Grande de Tárcoles where the **Jungle Crocodile Safari** (☎ 643-3231 in Jacó) offers a tour led by a croc-wrestling Tico. The tour also feeds the beasts with large chunks of horseflesh. Also in the area, **Manglares de Carara** (☎ 257-9682/5691) runs tours of the area's mangroves which offers ideal conditions for birdwatching.

> If you drive to Carara, be sure to park your car in a safe place in order to avoid a break in!

FLORA AND FAUNA: Most of the area's original forest cover and the surrounding ecosytems remain intact. Carara is set in a transition zone between the dry N Pacific and the more humid S and has 61 plant species, six species of palms, and a number of huge trees including the *ceiba*. Its small lake is almost entirely covered by water hyacinths and other aquatic plants.

Meaning "river of crocodiles" in the Huetar language (presumably after the denizens in the Tárcoles), Carara has a wealth of animals, many of whom fled from the surrounding terrain after their abode had been transformed into oil palm plantations and thus laden with toxic waste. Hummingbirds, toucans, and scarlet macaws number among the avian all stars.

HISTORY: The reserve's land was originally part of La Coyolar, a 44,478-acre (18,000-ha) estate founded by Fernando Castro Cervantes. After his death in 1970, the *hacienda* was controlled by a foreign corporation until it was expropriated by the government in 1977 for the purpose of settling landless farmers. The next year 11,600 acres (4,700 ha) were peeled off to form the reserve. An organization working to support the reserve is **Fundación Gran Carara** (Apdo. 469, 1011 San José; ☎ 234-1867, fax 253-6338).

ACCOMMODATION: Lodges are beginning to spring up around the circumference of the reserve as its fame grows. The least expensive places are in Tárcoles (see Tárcoles below).

Luxurious **Hacienda Doña Marta** (☎ 253-6514, 253-5629, 428-8126; fax 234-0958) in Cascajal de Orotina offers six *cabinas* surrounding a swimming pool and lounge area. The farm raises mangoes for export, cattle for milk and meat, and grows *pochote* trees for commercial use. **toraja@sol.racsa.co.cr**

Another lodge near the reserve's entrance is luxurious **Villa Lapas** (☎/fax 220-2414, fax 663-1516). It has 49 rooms with either a/c or fans and is set in a canyon near the river. It has a restaurant, conference and game rooms, pool, horseback riding, and hiking trails. Rates run around US$70 pp and include food and drinks. It is now an Allegro Resort.

Yet another alternative is **Tárcoles Lodge** (☎/fax 267-7138) which is run by the same folks who bring you Rancho Naturalista, a nature lodge near Turrialba. The lodge is surrounded on three sides by saltflats, on which thousands of birds flit about at low tide. Expect to spend about US$400-500/week, including transportation; there is a three-day minimum (including transport) at US$70-US$80 pd. Various packages/tours (including one of the estuary by boat) are also available. Write Apdo. 364, 1002 San José or

Dept. 1425, Box 025216, Miami, FL 33102-5216 for more information.

Near San Mateo and set amidst four acres of tropical gardens, **El Rancho Oropéndola** (☎/fax 428-8600) has a pool and trails. Rates are around US$50 for a cabin, and a full "American" breakfast is included.

The Iguana Park

The Iguana Park (☎ 240-6712, fax 235-2007) opened in 1994 and is the pet project of German-expatriate biologist Dagmar Werner and her Fundacíon Pro Iguana Verde.

In some ways resembling a chicken farm, the farm contains and information center, trails, a restaurant ("iguana burger" and the like), and a giftshop/handicraft center. Enter the enclosure, and you and your reptilian brain may spend as much time as you wish with these green beasts. Most of the iguanas you see will be released at the age of seven months; others will be kept for breeding purposes. Entry fees range from US$2.50 for locals and students to US$10 for foreigners; trail guides are US$10 extra. Profits are earmarked for community development and reforestation.

Canopy Tours (☎ 226-1315, fax 235-2007) also operates here and will take you up for around US$30. To get to the park head past Athenas and Orotina entrances and pass over railway tracks. In lieu of heading down the road to Jaco, head under the bridge and continue along until you reach a sign reading "Puriscál, San Pablo, and Coopebarro." Take this road R towards Coppebarro and stay on it for a couple of min. until you see the sign for the park.

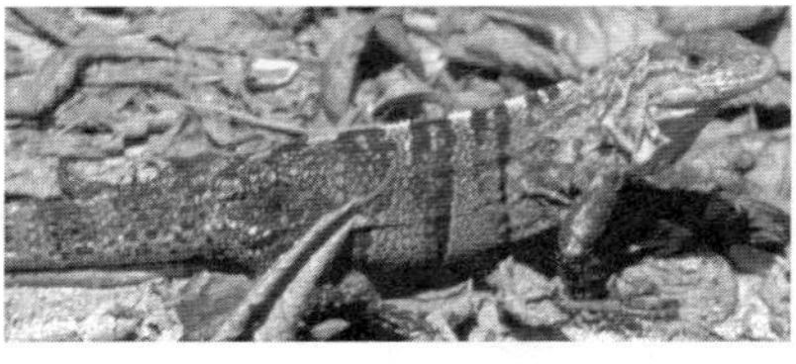

La Catarata (Agua Viva)

This 200-m high waterfall (☎ 236-4140) is set off by itself near the town of Bijagual. Open daily 8-3 during the dry season, the property is owned by French Canadian Daniel Bedard who, working with seven other men six days a week and ten hours per day, took seven months to clear a path. which charges around US$8 for entry. It's a strenuous 45-min. hike to the falls, and you should bring sufficient water. Camping is permitted for around US$7. To get here by bus, take the 8 AM *Orotina* bus from San José and then take the 11:30 AM *Bijuagual* bus from there.

Also near the falls, **Complejo Ecologico La Catarata** (☎ 661-1787) offers horseback tours, camping, and a restaurant.

Pacific Coast Beach Towns

Punta Leona

This area is named after its large rocky point which is said to resemble a crouching lion. Formerly a private club, expensive/luxury **Hotel Punta Leona** (☎ 231-3131, fax 232-0791) offers a/c, restaurants, disco, soccer, and basketball. Beaches are nearby, and rooms with kitchens are available. Its exclusivity has excited controversy.

> "Taking out that hill is actually beneficial for the environment..."
> – Los Sueños Marriott Beach and Golf Resort saleswoman as quoted in the *Tico Times* (1999).

Also here is **Leona Mar** (☎ 231-2868), a 24-room set of condos which are for sale and for rent (around US$160 pn and up during the high season). Facilities include a/c, cable TV, and full kitchens with microwaves and dishwashers. Surrounded by trails, it overlooks the beach and has a pool. Guests are permitted access to all of Hotel Punta Leona's facilities.

Be sure to ask about the radio-tracking devices being installed on hatched here. In Oct. 1994, the then President José María Figueres himself strapped himself into a harness and was raised into the treetops to secure the first of 20 nest boxes. The purpose of the six-foot-long boxes — constructed using plastic tubing and designed to resemble the holes in trees customarily used as nests— is to provide additional nesting sights as well as protection from poachers.

Attractive and luxurious **Villa Caletas** (☎ 257-3653, fax 222-2059; Apdo. 12358, 1000 San José; SJO 852, PO Box 025216, Miami, FL 33102-5216) set atop a steep hill and accessed by a cement road. Set near Punta Leona and between Jacó and Tárcoles, it is designed for honeymooners and couples seeking a romantic getaway. It has two gourmet restaurants, a unique pool, attractively landscaped grounds, a Greek-style theater (with summer classical music concerts), pool, and a miniature waterfall. The beach may be reached either by hiking or via four-wheel-drive. Eight-rooms, 13 villas, and two jr. suites all offer mini-bar, spacious baths, and a/c or fans. There is also a master suite and three suites with private pool. Room rates range from around US$125 d plus tax.
www.distinctivehotels.com
caletas@ticonet.co.cr
caletas@sol.racsa.co.cr

SPORTS: **J. D.'s Watersports** (☎ 356-1028, fax 352-6324) offers diving, fishing, river cruises, and other activities.
www.centralamerica.com/cr/tours/jd.htm
phoyman@aol.com

Playa Herradura

The dock here was constructed for the filming of the movie *Columbus*. Inexpensive **Cabinas Herradura** (☎ 643-3181) can hold up to ten. **Cabañas del Río** (☎ 643-3029) has small, inexpensive two-bedroom houses.

A newcomer on the scene, the controversial 212-rm. **Los Sueños Marriott Beach and Golf Resort** has been alleged to be yet another environmentally destructive hotel However, unlike others (such as the one at Playa Tambor), it is so far in environmental compliance. However, an entire hill is to be razed, a huge 250-slip marina built, and some 20 luxury homes are to be developed. Locals are mixed about the project: it has brought jobs but they are fearful of losing their tranquilty and privacy.

The **Faro Escondido** is a condo and home planned-development project at Playa Escondida Finally, **campers** can stay at the campsite.

Tárcoles

This undeveloped fishing village is one km from the highway. To get here, disembark at "Invu de Tárcoles" and walk for 20 min. Lying 600 yds. from the center of town, **Hotel El Parque** is in the inexpensive range.

The low budget **Cabinas La Guaria** (☎ 661-0455) and the more expensive **Cabinas Carara** are also here. For scuba, **Centro de Buceo Joaquín** offers 17 different courses as well as international certification.

PACIFIC COAST

Playa Jacó

Largely popularized by the efforts of the Hotel Irazú which opened its Jacó Beach Hotel here (now a Best Western), this small settlement has been transformed into a resort village catering to charter tourists. It has one of the nation's famous surfing beaches — one with dangerous rip currents; only capable swimmers should enter its waters. (If you are caught, don't try to fight a rip current: just swim parallel until you are freed from its grip, then return to shore.)

If you're not a surfer, you won't find the rock-laden beach to be particularly attractive and you may prefer to hang out by your hotel's pool. Jacó is a place for those who appreciate satellite TV, a pool, and creature comforts. Adventurous travelers who want to explore Costa Rica will not be very happy here.

The ICT has built **Núcleo Bri Bri**, a complex near the beach with parking, showers, and lockers. The town is basically one main street with hotels on either side. For information on the area, contact the Jacó Chamber of Commerce (☎ 643-3003).

> ***URL*** **www.jacobeach.com**

GETTING HERE: Buses (Transportes Jacó, ☎ 223-1109, 232-1829, 643-3135) leave Coca Cola (C. 16, Av. 1/3) at 7:30, 10:30, and 3:30 for the 3.5-hr., 102-km trip; they're packed on weekends (which has express departures at 7:15 AM and 7:30 PM. All buses to and from Quepos also pass by. Buses from Puntarenas depart at 5 AM or 1:30 PM from near the former train station.

DRIVING: It's about a two-hour drive from San José: take the Atenas turnoff (don't miss it!) on the Puntarenas road. From Puntarenas, it's about an hour on a good road.

> ☛ The surf along the main part of the beach is for experienced surfers only. Mellower waves are to be found at the end of the beach which is more sheltered. Surfing is actually at its best here during the the rainy season.

ACCOMMODATION: Stay here if you must! Here some suggestions:

Popular and friendly 18-room a/c **Hotel Club de Mar** (☎/fax 643-3194; Apdo. 107-4023, Jacó) has fully equipped apartments with balconies. It has a library, pool, and gourmet restaurant. Horseback riding is available on trails behind the hotel. Surrounded by nature, it's out by itself on the S end. Rates are from around US$80 d including tax. This is probably your best choice if you can afford it.

Hotel Amampola (☎ 643-3337, fax 643-3668; Apdo. 133, Playa de Jacó) has rooms from around US$90 d. It's four blocks from the beach and is one of the newer hotels. Facilities include bicycle rentals, pool, Italian restaurant, casino, and disco.

On the beach, luxury a/c 45-rm. **Hotel Cocal** (☎ 643-3067, fax 643-3082, 800-732-9266; Apdo. 54, Playa de Jacó) has pools, gardens, casino, and a restaurant. Rates are around US$90 d and include breakfast buffet.

cocalcr@sol.racsa.co.cr

The German-run, moderate 24-rm. **Hotel Pochote Grande** (☎ 643-3236, fax 220-4979; Apdo. 42, Jacó) has a pool. Its attractive rooms can sleep up to four and

have kitchenettes. It is popular with charter groups.
www.centralamerica.com
pochote@sol.racsa.co.cr

The pleasant 23-room **Cabinas Las Palmas** (☎ 643-3005) has gardens, parking, and more expensive rooms with kitchens. Rates are around US$60 d.

Outside of town, ultra-luxury **Hotel Hacienda Lillipoza** (☎ 643-3062, fax 643-3158) has tennis courts, restaurant, a/c, cable TV, poo. Surfers should ask about discounts from May to Dec. here.

The **Villas Estrellamar** (☎ 643-3102, fax 643-3453) has 20 bungalows and apartments with kitchettes. It has a pool and some units have a/c. It caters to a European crowd. Rates are around US$50-60 d.
brunot@sol.racsa.co.cr

Inexpensive **Centro Vacacional Bancosta** (☎/fax 643-3016, ☎ 223-3326) is the first place you come to on the N end; kitchens are included.

Inexpensive **Cabinas Gaby** (☎ 442-0354, 643-3080, fax 441-5922) has rooms with kitchenettes (around US$35 d) as well as a pool.

Next to the main bus stop, low-budget **Cabinas Antonio** (☎ 643-3043) is clean, has fans, and stands next to its **Restaurant Fragatas**.

Cabinas Los Ranchos (☎ 643-3156) offers inexpensive rooms with stove, refrigerator, and private bath.

On the beach 100 m (300 ft.) from the bus terminal, inexpensive Belgian-run **Hotel El Jardín** (☎ 643-3050) has a fine if expensive restaurant and includes breakfast in its rates. Nearby, low-budget **Cabinas y Restaurante Clarita** (☎ 643-3013) is good value.

Cousin of the Best Western Irazú, luxury **Best Western Hotel Jacó Beach** (☎ 220-1441/1725, 643-3064, fax 232-3159, 800-272-6654 in the US, 800-463-6654 in Canada) has a restaurant, swimming pool, and rents surfboards. It offers a discount for surfers who bring their boards with them. It's often packed with Canadian charter tourists.
jacohote@sol.racsa.co.cr

Around the corner and down the street, the 30-room expensive-luxury **Copacabana** (☎/fax 643-3131) has wonderful colorful murals on its walls. Facilities include restaurant, live entertainment, kayak and boogie board rentals, and a satellite dish for sports reception.

Clean if a bit sterile, **Cabinas Garcia** (☎ 643-3191) is inexpensive.

The inexpensive **Hotel Lido** (☎ 643-3171) is nothing special; it does have a pool.

Catering to surfers, low-budget/inexpensive friendly **Cabinas Emily** (☎ 643-3328/3513) will do everything from fixing your surfboard to helping you bring it from San José.

Groups of of six to eight will find, inexpensive **Cabinas Las Sirenas** (☎ 643-3193) a good value.

Renting three-bedrooms by the week, luxurious **Chalets Tangerí** (☎ 442-0977/3001; Apdo. 622, 4050 Alajuela) has kitchens and adult and children's pools.

Expensive **Hotel Tangerí** (☎ 643-3001, 442-0977; fax 643-3636, 433-2819) has a/c or fan and refrigerator.

Cabinas Pacific Sur (☎ 643-3340) is clean and inexpensive.

Run by Texans, inexpensive **Los Ranchos Bungalows** (☎/fax 643-3070) caters to the surfing crowd. It has accommodation for from one to eight and run from US$30 d.

The 10-rm. French-run **Villa Creole Apartotel** (☎ 643-3298) offers a pool, gourmet French restaurant, choice of a/c or fans, and a pool. Each bungalow has a kitchen and patio. Rates are around US$50 d and US$80 for six! Weekly and monthly rates are also available. This is a good place to stay if you are in Jacó to relax. It is off of C. Lapa Verde near the La Salida Leboun bus stop.

Apartotel Flamboyant (☎/fax 643-31460 has cabins for around US$50 and a pool.

Simple **Cabinas Cindy** (☎ 643-3485) are low-budget.

Inexpensive and good for groups, **Hotel Bohio** (☎ 643-3017) offers seven apartments as well as eight older *cabinas*.

La Cometa (☎ 643-3615) is French-Canadian run inexpensive hotel.

Moderately-priced and placid, Austrian-run **Villas Miramar** (☎ 643-3003) offers pools, gardens, and kitchens. It's next door to the Bohio.

Moderate **Paraiso del Sol** (☎ 643-3250, fax 643-3147) is on the beach.

Attractive, moderately-priced **Apartotel Las Gaviotas** (☎/fax 643-3092) has a pool and blue-and-white-themed rooms (around US$650 with kitchenettes and patios.

Popular with surfers, moderate **Cabinas Nirvana** (☎ 643-3502) has a small pool and units with kitchens.

Expensive **Paraíso del Sol** (☎ 643-3250, fax 643-3137) are a set of modern-style apartments with pool, a/c and fans, and kitchens.

Moderate eight-room **Cabinas Zabamar** (☎ 643-3174) has one adult and two children's pools, as well as refrigerators in its rooms.

Camping El Hicaco (☎ 643-3004) provides beachside sites; it has a restaurant.

Set next to the Banco Nacional, inexpensive, basic **Cabinas Recreo** (☎ 643-3012) has a pool.

Inexpensive motel-style **Cabinas Doña Alice** (☎/fax 643-3061, 237-1412) is near the beach and the Red Cross. Their newer *cabinas* are in the moderate range and are nicely done up. There's a restaurant and small pool; weekly rates are available. The place is popular with Ticos.

Inexpensive **Cabinas Calypso** has some rooms with kitchens.

Cabinas Marea Alta (☎ 643-3317) are inexpensive units with cement floors and a utensil-less kitchen; it's to the back of a *soda*.

Featuring a pool and kitchenettes, **Apartamentos El Mar** (☎ 643-3165, 730-1098) are safe and secure.

With kitchens as well as a small pool in front of each unit, moderately-priced *cabinas* **Casas de Playa Mar Sol** (☎ 643-3016, 223-3326) are ideal for families.

Apartamentos y Tienda Nicole (☎/fax 643-3384/3501) offers rooms for around US$40 as well as kitchens.

Sole D'Oro (☎/fax 643-3172/3247) has rooms with kitchenettes (around US$60) and Jacuzzi and pool.

Condotel Jacó Tropical (☎ 643-3511) has a set of two-storey cabins (around US$40 d) with kitchens.

With kitchenettes, a/c, pool, and TV, luxury **Hotel Jacofiesta** (☎ 643-3147, fax 643-3148) has a restaurant, pools, a/c, cable TV, and is one of the best hotels in the area.

Inexpensive **Chalets Santa Ana** (☎ 643-3233) is across the street and good value for groups. Kitchens are in the higher-priced units (around US$35).

One- and two-bedroom moderate **Restaurante y Cabinas Naranjal** (☎ 643-3006) is next to the Catholic Church.

Moderate **Hotel Club Marparaíso** (☎ 643-3277, 221-6601) has fans, Jacuzzi, pools, and more expensive units with kitchens. Check out their newest rooms. **Cabinas John Paul** (☎ 643-3106) are next door to it.

Also offering camping (around US$2 pn), low-budget **Cabinas Madrigal** (☎ 643-3230) is somewhat deteriorated.

Los Canciones del Mar (☎/fax 643-3277)

is an oceanfront condominium hotel with expensive units and a pool.

The **Malparaiso Hotel and Club** (☎ 221-6544, 643-3277, fax 221-6601) has both adult and children's pools along with a restaurant. It charges around US$45.

Beachside Apartotel Catalina (☎ 643-3217, fx 643-3544) offers suites from US$30 d; it has a pool.

Hotel Hacienda Lilipoza (☎ 643-3062, fax 643-3158) has ultra-luxury a/c suites with TVs and phones, two restaurants, pool, tennis courts, and horseback riding.

The **Zabamar Resort** (☎/fax 643-3174) has nice rooms for around US$20-40 d. It has trees, a pool, hammocks, and a restaurant.

Dutch-owned **Mar de Luz** (☎ 643-3259) has attractive a/c rooms with private terraces (around US$60); it has a pool.

The expensive-luxury **Los Villas Paradise** (☎ 296-2022, fax 296-2023) offers large rooms from around US$55 d; it has a restaurant, pool, and Jacuzzi.

Hotel Pochote Grande Jacó (☎ 643-3236, ☎/fax 220-4979) has a pool, gardens, and rooms (around US$60 d) with refrigerators and balconies.

Jacó Sailor Camping is a surfer dude place.

FOOD: Good places to eat include **Cabinas Doña Alice**, **El Jardín**, **Killer Munchies,** and **Pollo Asado Borinquen**.

Villa Creole is a Belgian-run gourmet restaurant. It is 400 m E and 200 m N and 100 m W of the Apartotel Los Gaviotas.

In the midst of mango trees near the gas station on the S end of town, **El Bosque** is good for breakfast as well as for seafood.

Java Beanies Coffee House serves affordable breakfasts.

Capitán Coco serves fish and chips.

Pizzeria Bri Bri, next to the ICT facility of the same name, has passable pizza.

One of the best places to try is **Restaurant Marisquería Los Manudos**, on the street leading to the airport, which has *ceviche* and a wide variety of seafood ranging from octopus to sauteed whole fish.

El Ceviche del Rey offers Peruvian dishes, and **Jaco Bell** serves Mexican food.

The Candian-owned **La Piraña** serves sandwiches, salads, and other items for lunch; surfers have their own menu. There're also a number of vegetarian items, and an international menu is offered at dinner. It's in the Yellow Corner Arcade. Others to try include **Restaurante El Gran Palenque Barcelona** (Spanish cuisine accompanied by live guitar music) and **Restaurant Fragatas**. Expresso is served at a restaurant across from the Bohio. Shop for food at the **Rayo Azul**.

SERVICES: Both a **public phone** and a **coin laundry** are near the Aparthotel Flamboyant. Change money at **Banco Nacional**. The local pharmacy, **Botiquin Garabito**, is near the bank. The PO and a health center are at the **Centro Municipal** at the town's S end.

Car rental is available at the Hotel Jacó Beach's *Fantasy Rent-a-Car* (☎ 220-1441), from *Elegante* (☎ 643-3224), and from others.

Boats for cruising or fishing can be rented next to the bus stop; call 643-3002. Rent bicycles from hotels, the store next to the Hotel El Jardín, or at the **Ferretería Macho e Hijos**. **Fun Rentals** (☎ 643-3242) has everything from snorkeling gear to bikes and scooters.

Maravillas Naturales (☎ 643-1113) rent bicycles and offers Internet connections. **bicycle@sol.racsa.co.cr**

Taxi companies include **Taxi 30-30** (☎ 643-3030) and **Taxi Jacó** (☎ 643-30009).

El Bujo is a unique gift shop which shares space with The Garden Café along the main street.

The Yellow Corner arcade, at the strip's S end, contains the **Heliconia Art Gallery** as well as the **Loro de Plata** jewelers.

Salva la Selva (☎ 643-3622), at the end of the beach near the Hotel Club de Mar, is the nation's only surf shop which sells custom designed boards. Boogie board and surf board rentals are also available.

Mother of Fear Surf Shop (☎ 643-3799) rents boards and offers instruction.

Chosita del Surf (☎ 643-1308, 643-3328) offers supplies and rentals. **chuck@sol.racsa.co.cr**

Rafting Safaris (☎ 643-3151, 221-5371) offers runs down the Río Tulín with a BBQ lunch.

Kayak Jacó/Aguamar Tours (☎ 643-1233, 385-1385) also offers runs down the Río Tulin as well as sea kayaking. **neilka@sol.racsa.co.cr**

The Serenity Spa (☎ 643-1624) offers a variety of treatments.

The **Lagar-Tico** (☎ 643-3745) is set by the town entrance and offers informative educational tours.

ENTERTAINMENT: One of the pluses is that Jacó has a lively nightlife. Try **Disco La Central** (right on the beach opposite Tienda La Flor), **Foxy's Disco** (on the road to the airport), or the disco at the **Hotel Jacó Beach**. **Papagayo Disco** is next door to Los Ranchos. **Centro Vacacional Bancosta** (☎ 643-3116) has live calypso on Thurs. and Sunday.

FROM JACÓ: Buses run to San José at 5 and 3. Inquire about buses to San José arriving from Quepos and those running to Quepos or Puntarenas.

VICINITY OF JACO: Stretching some 10 km, **Playa Hermosa** is situated about five km S of Jacó; surfing contests are held every Aug.

On the outskirts of the beach, 43-room two-storey luxury **Hotel Terraza del Pacifico** (☎ 643-3222, fax 643-3424) is the nicest place to stay. It has an Italian restaurant which also serves up *típico* fare, a small gambling room, and motorbike rentals. Rooms have cable TV, a/c, and phone. Opened in 1998, Fuego del Sol (☎ 643-3737, fax 643-3736) offers hot tub, pool, gym, and restaurant. Rates are around US$50 s, US$60 d, US$70 t. **terraza@sol.racsa.co.cr**.

Moderate **Las Olas** (☎ 643-3687) caters to surfers; it has a pool and fans and kitchens in the rooms. Rates run around US$40 d; triples, quads, and quints are also available. **lasolas@sol.racsa.co.cr**

Less expensive **Cabinas Vista Hermosa** (☎ 643-3422, fax 224-3687) are next door. Also here are **Villas Ballena** (☎ 643-3373/4) which offers cabins with kitchenettes. You may dine at reasonable **Ola Bonita**.

Esterillos Oeste is 22 km S. It has heavy surf but is relatively undeveloped. You may stay here at low-budget **Cabinas Las Caletas** (☎ 771-2143), the inexpensive **Famoso** (☎ 779-9184), and the inexpensive **Cabinas Don José** (☎ 238-1876).

Playa Esterillos Este is 30 km to the S; stay here at luxury-priced and secluded **Hotel El Delfín** (☎ 771-1640; Apdo. 2260, 1000 San José), which has a pool, library, table tennis, shuffleboard, horse-shoe pitch, and bicycles.

The 10-room French-speaking **Auberge du Pélican** (fax 777-9108, 643-3207; Apdo. 47, Parrita 6300) which charges US$30d (shared bath) and US$40d (private bath); taxes are additional. It has a restaurant, pool, and bar. Two rooms are handicapped accessible.

The moderate **Fleur de Lis** (☎ 779-9117, fax 779-9108) is a set of cabins. Less frequently visited, **Playa Bejuco** and **Playa Palma** are farther along and inland.

On the Río Parrita and 44 km S from Jacó, **Parrita** has basic accommodation.

Quepos and Manuel Antonio

Sometimes you'll hear it called Quepos, at other times Manuel Antonio. While Quepos refers to the town (30,000 pop.) at the base of the hill leading to the resort area, the name Manuel Antonio refers to **Parque Nacional Manuel Antonio**, the national park, as well as the surrounding resort area.

There are three major **beaches** which, taken together, extend for three km. Two of these, Espadilla del Sur and Playa Manuel Antonio, are sheltered and offer safe swimming. (Playa Espadilla Norte now has lifeguards). Although the area is strikingly beautiful, it is becoming increasingly expensive — some maintain ridiculously overpriced — and no longer the haven for low-budget travelers that it once was years ago.

If you are serious about your love of nature and want solitude, you may want to give this park a miss. The park itself is in high demand. A 600-person-pd limit has been placed on visitors. (It is relatively empty on low-season weekdays).

On the other hand, this is no Maui or Disneyland. While more experienced travelers may find it overdeveloped, it is a pretty good place if you want a lot of options for things to do; there are more and more things all of the time!

HISTORY: This area was first "explored" by Juan Vásquez de Coronado who found the Quepoa, a subtribe of the Borucas, in residence when he arrived in 1563. These Indians were largely wiped out in succeeding years from disease, intertribal warfare, and theft of their lands by the Spaniards. Built by United Fruit in1939-41, Quepos, like Golfito, was originally laid out as a company town, established in order to service nearby plantations. When production of African palm oil supplanted bananas as the local crop during the 1950s, after Panama disease had destroyed the banana crop, Quepos became the only town to actually suffer a population decline during the second half of the 20th C.

The name "Manuel Antonio," applied to the area at the S, came from a now-vanished memorial plaque to a Spaniard who died during a skirmish with a group of Quepoa. Like Cahuita and (in part) Tortuguero, Manuel Antonio, the smallest national park, was established to preserve the offshore marine life, which would otherwise have been finished off by the development of tourism facilities. Around a half-century ago, it was public land, before the government gave it away.

An American purchased the area in 1968 and erected iron gates to prevent access by outsiders. The townspeople responded by demolishing them. The municipal government ruled that, as the road was public, barriers could not be erected. Tiring of the problem, the owner sold the property to a Frenchman in 1972. He, in turn, erected concrete barriers to prevent cars from passing.

After journalist Miguel Salguero suggested that the park be nationalized, the local community enthusiastically rallied around the cause. The fact that the new owner was working on plans for a resort clinched the matter. The land was expropriated from around a dozen property owners, and the 1,685-acre (682-ha) park was established in Nov. 1972. It was increased by more than 988 acres (400 ha) in 1980. (Today, with some 200,000 visitors each year, it is the most popular park after Poás and Irazú). The park was hard hit by a tropical storm in 1993.

In Feb. 1992, Park director José Antonio Salazar announced in the Tico Times that "we have a park which is dying." The park has become an "island" because squatter settlements, agriculture, and touristic development have barred animals from access to areas outside of the park. This is a particular problem for the endangered squirrel monkeys because the park's area is too small to sustain a healthy population. Many hotels do not have proper sewage systems, and the waste flows into an estuary which runs through the local streams and lagoons before ending up in the ocean. Salazar charged the owners with a "destructive mentality," maintaining that "they want to earn money

as quickly as possible, and they don't care what happens to anything else."

In 1995, Salazar revealed that 1.75 ha of land declared to be park territory (but not yet paid for) had been clearcut illegally. "The government has owed them for the land for 22 years. I think the owners have tolerated a lot," Salazar commented. The clearcut land was on property owned by a consortium of US and Costa Rican lawyers.

According to Salazar, around 175 million *colones* (around US$1 millionat the time) are needed to purchase the land, and the park brought in an estimated 138 million *colones* in 1995. But 25% goes to the local municipality and the remainder goes to the National Parks Fund. Currently none of the money is reserved for purchasing park land but proposed legislation may change this.

Certainly, the changes of the past few years have been destructive. The privately owned path that ran down from the Mariposa to the beach has been widened so as to allow heavy equipment access to build a beach resort, and the squirrels and sloths have fled. Hundred-year-old royal palms were toppled in the process. In Feb. 1993, then Tourism Minister Luis Manuel Chacón called for the partial or total razing of 23 businesses near Manuel Antonio which are 50 m or less from the high tide mark or have improper permits to operate inside the 150 m municipal strip.

Although construction in front of this line is prohibited, enforcement is subject to exceptions on any official level, given a little palm grease. The minister also cited a number of businesses such as Restaurant Mar y Sombra and Cabinas Manuel Antonio who have failed for years to meet health regulations for proper garbage disposal and sewage systems. The beaches are now often covered with rubbish, the lagoon at the park's entrance has been polluted, and water is not rationed because of increased demand.

A new Italian-financed project, Olas del Pacifico is a nine three-story apartment buildings and a shopping center just 100 m from the beach and 250 m from the park entrance!

Legislation passed in 1998 allows half of the proceeds from ticket sales to go into a locally-managed trust which will purchase park lands still under private ownership. Some 47% of the lands in the park have still not been paid for. Still, no regulatory and zoning plan has been instituted to date. Without one, the long-term future of the park's fragile ecosystem appears bleak.

If you are up for an adventure and want to see a less frequented side of Costa Rica, try taking the **old road to Quepos**. Enroute you will pas through an oil palm plantation and past majestic vistas. It takes around five hours. Buses also come this way: they depart from Coca Cola at 5 AM and noon and return at 4:30 AM and noon.

To follow the route take the highway W to Ciudad Colón, then turn R just after the first intersection in the town where you should see a sign marked "Quepos 119 km" and then a second sign: "Quepos/Parrita." The road worsens and is unpaved (but in fair condition) past Salitrales (35 km from Quepos). From the intersection at the end turn L for Quepos (29 km) or head R for Jacó (25 km).

Enroute stop for lunch at the **Bar/Restaurant Rey Lio** , a white-and-blue painted structure.

GETTING HERE: Indirect buses leave for Quepos from the W end of Coca Cola at 7 AM, 10 AM, 2 PM, and 4 PM for the 145-km, 4.5-hr. trip; buses go on to Manuel Antonio from here. Direct buses for Manuel Antonio (four hrs.) leave from Coca Cola at 6 AM, noon, and 6 PM. For information call *Transportes Morales* at 223-5567, 777-0101. If you're having luggage placed in the baggage compartment, keep an eye out: things have been stolen.

OTHER BUS ROUTES: Buses from Puntarenas (231 km, 3.5 hrs.) leave at 5 and 2:30. Contact *Transportes Blanco*, ☎ 531-1384. Buses run from San Isidro to the S at 7 and 1:30.

BY AIR: *SANSA* (☎ 221-9414, 233-0397/3258, fax 255-2176) flies daily except Sun. for around US$40, and *Travelair* (☎ 220-3054, 232-7883 fax 220-0413;) also flies daily.
information@travelair-costarica.com

GETTING AROUND: A great area to walk around in! However, Manuel Antonio's roads make for some very steep promenading. Buses ply regularly back and forth on the 30-min., seven-km run between the terminal in Quepos and the park entrance. Many hotels have shuttle services. Rental cars are available from a number of hotels here, but it's preferable to make your reservations for them while still in San José.

Taxicabs running from Quepos charge a reasonable sum for the ride in a shared taxi.
Elegante Rent a Car (☎ 221-0066, fax (506) 221-5761; US and Canada: 800-283-1324) in Quepos, rents cars.
www.centralamerica.com/cr/tran/elegante.htm
elegante@centralamerica.com

SIGHTS: Next to town is an astonishingly wide beach. At low tide you might see a local practicing his karate moves or some expatriate American jock types hauling surfboards out of their four-wheel drives. You are advised to avoid swimming at this beach, which has been found to be contaminated.

Up the hill is the old banana plantation residence compound which now services the palm oil trade. A town within a town, this private estate is pretty amazing. It even has its own cliffside swimming pool complex perched above the sea, with surrounding thatched huts. The area's fishing operation is just across the bridge on the way out of town.

GAIA ANIMAL SHELTER: Set on the road between Quepos and Manuel Antonio, this shelter adopts animals captured from the wild and prepares them for reintroduction. Admission is around US$4 for foreigners and US$1 for Ticos; children under 12 are free. Call or fax 777-0535 for an appointment.

Rainmaker

This 1500-acre reserve is set in the 40,000 acre Fila Chonta range, an area that includes peaks of 1700 m (5,600 ft.) as well as some 2,500 plant species in four different life zones. The Fila Chonta area is the largest non-protected area in the Central Pacific Coast region. Very steep, it a crucial area to preserve, both from the the standpoint of biologcal diversity and the maintenance of watersheds.

The enchanting tours serve as excellent introductions to natural wonders. The guides are enthusiastic and wil show you those subtle features of the rainforest that you would definitely miss on your own.

There are two varieties: ground (on foot) and aerial (up and across on seven impressive canopy bridges). It costs around $39 for the Rainmaker tour and US$65 for the canopy hike. It is 20 km from Quepos and 12 km from Parrita. (The name comes from the area's high rainfall).
www.rainmaker-com
rainmkr@sol.racsa.co.cr

VISITING THE PARK: You must walk through an inlet (or wade during the rainy season, when the water may reach waist-level or higher) to get to the entrance (open 7-4), where you pay before proceeding. Admission is at the current *gringo* rate of US$6; **the park is closed on Mon.**, and numbers are restricted to 600 per day Tues. to Fri. and 800 on Sat. and Sun.

The first beach, **Espadilla del Sur**, has a spread of *manzanillo* trees; steer clear of them! This northernmost beach, curved and rather steep, has large, boulder-like islets just offshore.

The next path leads to **Cathedral Point**, a detour which offers great views of the surrounding seascape including views of the 12 offshore cays which are part of the park. An enormous rocky promontory which separates the two beaches, it was once an island: over the course of tens of thousands of years, sand deposits have now connected it to the mainland — a feature known as a *tombalo*. The ancient forest here includes *sura*, *panama*, *guapinol*, royal palm, and other species.

Right across the way, **Playa Manuel Antonio** is the best place to stop for a swim. The most beautiful beach, it is calm, with a gentle slope; at low tide, it has a shallow pool on its W side filled with hundreds of multicolored fish. From here, a steep path leads to a *mirador* with a great view.

If you proceed across another promontory, past the turnoff for the administrative building, you come to the park's third beach, **Puerto Escondido** ("Hidden Harbor") — one which practically disappears during low tide. From here a very deteriorated trail leads across Punta Serrucho to **Playita de Boca de Naranjo**. Watch your valuables closely while on these beaches.

PARK FLORA AND FAUNA: There are at least 138 species of trees here including the *vaco o lechoso* (milk tree) which, when tapped, produces a milky sap that was once an important dietary staple. The nation's only dangerous tree, the *manzanillo* lines the beaches. (See "forbidden fruit" under "Plant Life" in the Introduction). A small red mangrove swamp lies behind Espadilla Sur. The park also is home to the black *guapinol*, a dark-leaved tree that is found only here and in a few forests farther S.

All told, there are 99 mammals (including 59 bats) and some 353 species of birds. The park is one of the best places around to see agoutis, rodents which appear to be a cross between a rabbit and a guinea pig, with the mannerisms of a squirrel. During the early morning and late afternoon hours, watch out for capuchin, squirrel, or howler monkeys, and three-toed sloths.

As you proceed along the paths in the park you'll be sure to notice the most ubiquitous wildlife: scores of bright orange-and-black-shelled land crabs (*tahalín*) who smoothly duck into their homes on your approach. With their orange eyes and eggplant-purple claws, they look like the end product of a hyper-imaginative toddler turned loose with his first set of Crayolas. If cornered,

> Despite its reputation, Manuel Antonio doesn't have to be expensive. Off season, rooms are discounted up to 50%, and there are always a large number of inexpensive *cabinas* available. By eating in the local restaurants in Quepos, you can trim your expenses further. Keep in mind that Feb. and March are both the hottest and driest months. Bring everything you need with you, especially prescriptions, film, insect repellent, and other items.

these curmudgeonly crustaceans will raise an open claw in defense.

PARK CONDUCT: It is illegal to anchor a boat closer than 100 m to the shore. Under no circumstances should you feed any animals! Do not contribute to the garbage problem.

Quepos/Manuel Antonio Practicalities

QUEPOS ACCOMMODATION: Although you'll be closer to the beaches if you stay up the hill in Manuel Antonio, many visitors prefer Quepos in order to experience its small town flavor. It's generally less expensive for food, better value for lodging, and has a great disco, the Arco Iris. The major drawback is that thievery is becoming increasingly common — even when hotel guests are asleep in their rooms.

One of the better places to stay is inexpensive **Hotel Ceciliano** (☎ 777-0192) which has clean rooms with fans and private bath; other rooms have shared bath. Be sure to get a room away from the TV set, and bargain for the large dorm rooms if you come with a group.

Just nearby, low-budget **Hotel Quepos** (☎ 777-0274), above the SANSA office, is quite alright; it charges around US$20.

Nearby **Cabinas Helen** (☎ 777-0504) offers rooms for around US$8. Moderate, attractive **Villas Cruz** (☎ 777-0271, fax 777-0050) has kitchens and porches.

The a/c 28-room **Best Western Hotel Kamuk** (☎ 777-0379, fax 777-0258; Apdo. 18, 6350 Quepos) is one of the priciest places in town. Facilities include a/c, phones, bar/restaurant, casino, pool, coffee shop, and boutique. Rates are around US$60 s or d.
www.kamuk.co.cr
info@kamuk.co.cr

Hotel El Parque (☎ 777-0063) is low-budget and spartan.

Hotel Sirena (☎ 777-0528, fax 777-0171) is an expensive-luxury hotel with a/c and pool.

Inexpensive **Hotel El Pueblo** (☎ 777-1003) is right near the bus station and charges around US$25 on up.

Inexpensive **Hotel Mario** (☎ 777-0339) is another option, as is moderate-expensive a/c **Hotel Paraíso** (☎/fax 777-0082) which has kitchens. Low-budget to inexpensive accomodations include **Hotel Majestic**, **Hotel Mar y Luna** (☎ 777-0394), 12-room **Hotel El Malinche** (☎ 777-0093, mosquito coils mandatory, around US$15; more expensive a/c rooms US$30), **Hotel Ramus** (☎ 777-0245), and the **Viña del Mar.**

Apartotel El Coral is just around the corner from **Hotel Linda Vista**. Inexpensive **Cabinas Ana** (☎ 777-0443, 23-5567) holds up to five and is near the soccer field.

Low-budget, hospitable **Cabinas Doña Alicia** (☎ 777-0419) has three rooms in some of its units.

Near the church, inexpensive **Hotel Ipakarahi** (☎ 777-0392) is good value. Also here is inexpensive **El Cisne** (☎ 777-0590).

Expensive **Hotel Villa Romántica** (☎ 777-0037) is owned by Germans; it has a pool.

In front of the bus station, **El Mirador del Río** (☎ 777-0290; Apdo. 88, Quepos) offers *cabinas* and camping.

Set 120 m E of the bus station, **Hotel Villas Morsol Inn** (☎ 777-0307) offers a/c, refrigerator, laundry service, and hot water.

Low budget **Villas Verano** (☎ 777-1495) is a set of small cabins; homestyle meals served in a nearby home are offered. (Accomodation fuqrther up the road is listed under "Manuel Antonio accommodation" above).

The **El Paraiso Apartotel** (☎ 777-0082) offers expensive suites and apartments; it has a restaurant.

A final alternative is the 12-room **Hotel del Mar** (☎ 777-0543; Apdo. 77, Quepos).

OUT OF TOWN: **Dennis Arnold** (☎ 777-1379, fax 777-1558) has a farm on the Río Naranjo, 14 km inland from Quepos. He serves lunch to visiting birdwatchers and has a cabin for rent.

JUST BEFORE TOWN: **Cabinas Los Horcones** (☎ 777-0000) has low -budget *cabinas* for less than US$20.

Villas del Arenal (☎/fax 777-0171) has expensive. fully furnished apartments with kitchens, TVs, and a/c. It also has a pool, Jacuzzi, and restaurant.

MANUEL ANTONIO ACCOMMODATION: Since this is a major tourist area, things tend to be pretty pricey and are becoming increasingly so. There are more than 100 licensed facilities now operating in the area!

Proceeding up the hill from Quepos, **Club Caribe** (☎/fax 777-0134) has rooms from around US$20; Italian and Tico dishes are prepared upon request. **Cabinas Geylor** (☎ 777-0561) has rooms for around US$15 with private bath.

Apartotel Los Corales (☎ 777-0006) has rooms with fans and kitchens which are in the moderate range.

Cabinas Tauro (☎ 777-0229) has rooms for around US$15. d (☎/fax 777-0037) has expensive rooms which are surrounded by woods.

Mil Rios (☎/fax 777-0595) is in a private reserve; rates start around US$30 d and kitchenettes are available.

Condominios El Pájaro Azul (☎ 777-1046, fax 777-1241) is a set of luxury one- and two-bedroom houses; it's next door to **Restaurante Du Lu**.

Inexpensive (around US$25-40) five-unit **Cabinas Pedro Miguel** (☎/fax 777-0035; Apdo. 17), one km out, has a pool and a *típico* restaurant that operates in season.

Across the road, atmospheric **Hotel Plinio** (☎ 777-0055, fax 777-0558; Apdo. 71, Quepos, Puntarenas) offers three different types of rooms. Facilities include , trails (with observation tower), children's pool, adult pool, hammocks, and small library. Moderate rates (around US$60 and up) include breakfast in the popular-yet-inexpensive restaurant.
www.hotelplinio.com
plinio@sol.racsa.co.cr

The moderate/expensive 20-room **El Mirador del Pacifico** (☎/fax 777-0119) is owned by Germans. It's topped off by a bar/restaurant.

Featuring a/c, pool, Jacuzzi, kitchens, private terraces, and a/c or fans, Santa Fe-style **Mimo's Hotel** (☎/fax 777-0054) is in the expensive range; its rates include breakfast.

Homey **El Mono Azul Restaurante Natural** (☎ 777-1548; Apdo. 297, Quepos) serves salads, pizza, fish, and homemade pastries at prices very reasonable by area standards. Movies (with Spanish subtitles) are shown nighly at 7:30 Their nine cabinas range from US$35 on up.
www.maqbeach.com/monoazul.html
monoazul@sol.racsa.co.cr

Bahías Hotel (☎ 777-0350, fax 77-0279) is expensive, but moderate in the low season. It has a pool, and some units have Jacuzzis.

Sula Bya-ba (☎ 777-0597, fax 777-0279) is another expensive hotel. Expensive **Bungalows Las Palmas** (☎/fax 777-0051) are a set of thatched-roof condos with a pool.

The 22-room **Hotel California** (☎ 777-1234, fax 777-1062) has a pool, Jacuzzi, waterfall, and restaurant. It also has a 30-m-high observation platform (shared with Hotel Plinio). Rooms (around US$60

fan d, US$80 a/c d) have kitchenettes and balconies. Each has a different wall mural. Simple bamboo cabins run around US$30 d.
www.hotel-california.com
hotelcal@sol.racsa.co.cr

Operating under the auspices of very friendly Polish owners Andy and Chris, the **Hotel Las Tres Banderas** (☎ 777-1871, 777-1284, 777-1528, fax 777-1478) offers moderate a/c rooms with Cable TV/VCRs; suites have refrigerators, and microwaves. It has a pool and Jacuzzi. Rates are around US$60 d plus tax.
www.hotel-tres-banderas.com
info@hotel-tres-banderas.com

Hotel Villa Teca (☎ 777-1117, fax 777-0279; Apdo. 180-6350, Quepos) offers a group of 40 ultra-luxury duplexes with a/c, pool, Jacuzzi, and restaurant. Rates are around US$90 d with breakfast.
hvteca@sol.racsa.co.cr

Inexpensive **Cabinas Tropicales** (☎ 777-0455) are a set of reasonably priced rooms.

Up a hill from the main road, **La Colina** (☎ 777-0231, fax 777-1553) offers attractive rooms (around US$60 d plus tax) which are set around the owners' home. There are similarly-priced two apartments for longer stays. Facilities include restaurant (breakfast is included), optional a/c in rooms, and pool.
www.lacolina.com
lacolina@sol.racsa.co.cr

Surrounded by a private nature reserve, luxury **Cabinas el Salto** (☎ 777-0130, fax 241-2938; Apdo. 119, Quepos) offers pool, horseback riding, and a bar and restaurant. Breakfast, dinner, and a nature tour are included in rates.

Attractive **Hotel El Lirio** (☎/fax 777-0403, fax 777-1182; Apdo. 123, Quepos) has fans and hot water; breakfast served. It charges around US$30 d and up.

Apartments Flor Blanca (☎/fax 777-0032) has a/c rooms with refrigerators for around US$30.

Villa Escondida Apartments (☎ 777-1138) has luxury units. Luxury **Hotel las Charruas** (☎/fax 777-0409) is across the road.

Moderate/expensive **Hidden Village Cabinas** (☎ 777-1138) offers rooms from around US$55 d; more expensive units have kitchenettes.

The attractively designed, ultra-luxury **Tulemar Bungalows** (☎ 777-0580/1325, fax 777-1579; Mail Stop SJO042, PO Box 023569, Miami, FL 33102) opened in 1995. A very special oasis of tranquility, the resort's spacious octagonal bungalows are raised on pillars on the slopes of a largely forested hill. (The owners are structural engineers.) A steep and winding road winds past them and down to a gem of a beach with a beach bar. It has a pool, snack bar, trails, and mini mart. Its octagonal cabins hold up to four. Units have two rooms with shared bath. One has kitchen and two sofabeds, the other, two beds, TV/VCR (rental tapes are available) and desk. The bath has one of those accordian pull-down mirrors that permit you to psychoanalyze every zit, and a nice and wide two-person tub-shower unit with sliding doors. Some fun could be had here. have TV/VCR, phones, kitchenettes, hair driers, and a/c. There are a number of short hiking trails, restaurant, and on-property tours .

Rates are steep: from US$139 d plus tax up to US$330 plus tax four up to four during the height of the high season. A hearty complimentary breakfast (Tico or Americano) is served by the pool where you may be entertained by spider monkeys. Staff is friendly and headed by personable Alexandra Monje.

www.tulemar.com
tulemar@sol.racsa.co.cr

The **Ylang-Ylang Ocean View Apartments** (☎ 777-0184) has rooms from around US$65 with kitchenettes.

Farther up, luxury **Hotel Divisamar** (☎ 777-0371, fax 777-0525; Apdo. 82, Quepos) has 37 rooms. with hot water, a/c or fans, restaurant (high season only), casino, and pool.

Cabinas Buena Vista (☎/fax 777-0345/1002) has two attractive homes available for weekly rental (around US$400-600 pw).

Perched on a hillside with a classic postcard view of Punta Cathedral off in the distance, the ultra-luxury **Hotel La Mariposa** (☎ 777-0355/0456, fax 777-0050; Apdo. 4, Quepos) is renowned throughout the land for its view and atmosphere. The Spanish-colonial-style hotel centers around its terrace restaurant which has white archways and pink chairs. A lower level holds a swimming pool and bar. Below in a semicircle are five two-storey white houses containing two rooms with two beds each. Taking a bath in your room here is like bathing in a small garden. The hotel strikes a happy medium between elegant politeness and warm informality. It's named after the butterflies that continued to frequent the area even after the structure was completed. While you're on the premises be sure to check out the early Quepos weatherstone. Their van offers free shuttle service to and from SANSA or Travelair flights as well as to and from the park. Call (800) 223-6510, US; (800) 268-0424, Canada.
www.lamariposa.com
htlmariposa@msn.com

The ultra-luxury **Makanda-by-the-Sea** (☎ 777-0442, fax 777-1032; Apdo. 29, Quepos) a series of isolated villas, is nearby. It has hammocks, gardens, and views galore. It offers pool, Jacuzzi, and gourmet restaurant. Rates (around US$150 d, US$200 for villa) include breakfast.
www.makanda.com
makanda@makanda.com

Away from it all, **Nature's Beachfront Apartment Hotel** (☎ 777-1475) is set on the beach of course. Rooms (around US$30-60) offer shared or private baths. A suite (US$120) holds up to seven.
beachfront@maqbeach.com

Villas Nicolas (☎ 777-0481, fax 777-0451Apdo. 236, Quepos) are spacious, well-equipped, and highly attractive villa-units with hammock-equipped balconies. It has a small pool and a tropical forest ambiance. Rates are from US$60 d on up; some units have kitchenettes; discounts offered for longer stays.
www.hotels.co.cr/nicolas
nicolas@sol.racsa.co.cr

El Parador (☎ 777-1411, fax 777-1437) is an isolated ultra-luxury hotel with miniature golf course, tennis courts, Jacuzzis, pools, health club, disco, gourmet dishes, and a helicopter pad for those with a helicopter.
parador@sol.racsa.co.cr

Luxury and ultra-luxury **Hotel El Dorado Mojado** (☎ 777-0368) is next. A bed and breakfast, inexpensive **Altamira Inn** (☎ 777-0477) follows.

Villas El Parque (☎ 777-0096, fax 777-0538; Apdo. 111, Quepos; SJO 1140, Box 025216, Miami, FL 33102-5216) commands a tremendous view from its unit's Spanish-style hammock-equipped balconies. Facilities include 34 suite-style villas w/kitchenettes, restaurant, and a/c. Three pools are set amidst tropical forest. Rates are from around US$80 d. plus tax.

www.vparque.com
vparque@sol.racsa.co.cr

Opened in 1995, popular **Si Como No** (☎ 777-1250, fax 777-1093) is designed to harmonize with the environment. Only one tree was removed to build the property. Hotel grey water is used for irrigation, food waste is composted, and all wood used in construction came from tree farms. It has a pool, Jacuzzi, water slide, nature trails, gourmet restaurants, and conference room. Its collection of ascending and descending stairways and stained glass decor gives it something of an M. C. Escherian feel, one supplemented by a smidgen of Hollywood gaudiness. The best rooms have balconies, a full kitchen (including a refrigerator stuffed with pricey munchies), and your choice of fans or a/c in each room. The hotel promotes itself as "eco friendly." While it has more claim to the label than many, it is doing only what *all* of the hotels should be doing as a matter of course! (Most of its clientele still *drive* here from San José of course). The complex includes a deli, juice bar, Costa Rican artists gift shop/gallery, the offices of Rainmaker (ecological reserve), , and a THX laser cinema showing predictable sex-and violence Hollywood fare as well as some better quality stuff. Rates are around US$175 d on up to US$$221 d for the deluxe rooms (taxes and breakfast included). It is full most of the time so reserve well in advance. In the US call 800-237-8201 or write Mail Stop SJO 297, PO Box 025216, Miami, FL 33102-5216.
www.sicomono.com
information@sicomono.com

Ultra-luxury **Albergue Turístico El Byblos** (☎ 777-0411, fax 777-0009; Apdo. 15, Quepos) has a/c cabins for up to three and pool, French restaurant, and hot water. It has received mixed reports.

The 43-rm. **Hotel Costa Verde** (☎ 777-0187, fax 777-0560, 888-234-5565; SJO 1313, Box 025216, Miami, FL 33102-5216) is one of the nicer places to stay in the US$70-100 price range. It offers two pools and an open-air restaurant and trails on-property. They charge around US$65 for an efficiency (queen-size and full-size beds); studio and penthouse units are also available.
www.hotelcostaverde.com
costaver@sol.racsa.co.cr

Featuring a garden and rooms with fans, refrigerators, and hot plates, **El Colibrí** (☎/fax 777-0432; Apdo. 94, Quepos) accepts no children under the age of 10. It has 10 rooms and two apartments, a pool, and ponds with seven varieties of frogs. with Rates are around US$75 d.

Hotel Casitas Eclipse (☎ 777-0408, fax 777-1738) are a set of 125 luxurious Mediterranean-style dwellings; some units have kitchens. Charges are around US$120 d (US$200 for the entire two-bedroom *casita*). There are two pools and a restaurant.
www.crica.com
eclipse@sol.racsa.co.cr

Located off of a dirt road, expensive **La Quinta Cabinas** (☎/fax 777-0434; Apdo. 76, Quepos) has units with or without kitchenette Set on a hilltop, it has a pool and gardens.

Friendly and Costa Rican-run, the **Villa Nina Hotel** (☎ 777-1628/1554, fax 777-1497) has rooms from around US$50 and up including breakfast. It has nine rooms with kitchenettes and balconies, small pool, and snack bar.
villanina@sol.racsa.co.cr

Luxury **Arboleda Beach and Mountain Hotel** (☎ 777-1056, fax 777-0092; Apdo. 55, Quepos) has beachfront cabins with bath, fan, and terrace on its 19-acre (eight-ha) grounds; surfboard and catamaran rentals are available.

With a small pool and cabins, expensive-luxury **Best Western Karahé** (☎ 777-0170, fax 777-1075; Apdo. 100, 6350 Quepos) has a restaurant, fans, and refrigerators. Restaurant meals are included in luxury-unit rates. They also have some inexpensive *cabinas*. It is right along the beach.
karahe@ns.goldnet.co.cr

Down at the beach, moderate **Cabinas Piscis** (☎ 777-0046) has a small restaurant.

The moderate a/c **Hotel Delmar** (☎ 777-0543) is to the L; it has a restaurant and garden with views.

Near the Mar y Sombra and right on Playa Espadilla, inexpensive **Cabinas Ramirez** (☎ 777-0003) has dark and noisy fan-equipped *cabinas* which hold up to four. They also allow camping.

Hotel and Cabinas Espadilla (☎ 777-0416, 777-0903; Apdo. 30, Heredia) have kitchenette and fans; unpretentious and reasonably near the beach. Rates are around US$50-70 depending if you want a/c or not.
www.maqbeach.com
spadilla@sol.racsa.co.cr

Inexpensive **Cabinas Los Almendros** (☎ 777-0225) has fans and restaurant.

Billed as a "youth hostel," low-budget to moderate and spartan **Costa Linda** (☎ 777-0304) has cooking facilities.

Cabinas Aymara is also low-budget and nearby. **Vela Bar** (☎ 777-0413; Apdo. 13, Quepos) has inexpensive rooms as well as moderate *cabinas* to its rear; some have balconies, a/c, and kitchens.
www.maqbeach.com
velabar@maqbeach.com

The luxury **Hotel Villabosque** (☎ 777-0401, fax 777-0401) has fans or a/c.

The **Grano de Oro** (☎ 777-0578) also has low-budget rooms next to its restaurant. Low-budget **Cabinas Irarosa** are next. It offers clean rooms with fans and private bath for around US$5 pp.

Moderate **Cabinas Los Almendros** (☎ 777-0225) are on the L at the road's end. Also here are **Cabinas ANEP**, a set of very low-budget *cabinas* owned by the public employees' union and rented to members of John Q. Public during slack periods.

Back on the main road, inexpensive **Hotel Manuel Antonio** (☎ 777-0212/0255; Apdo. 88, Manuel Antonio), has fans and a restaurant. Rates are around US$8pp. Ask about camping for a fee.

Formerly La Casa del Sol, **Verde del Mar** (☎/fax 777-1805, fax 777-1311; Canada: 604-925-4772; Box 348, Quepos) is set just a five min. walk from Manuel Antonio National Park. It has a restaurant and pool; rooms (around US$60-80 d) have satellite TVs and kitchenettes.
verdemar@sol.racsa.co.cr
ahenders@istar.ca

Other places to stay in the area include luxury **Hotel Del Valle Pura Vida** (☎ 777-0040), moderate **Cabinas Harold and Carolyn** (☎ 777-0331), and luxury **Hotel Casa Blanca** (☎ 777-0368).

CAMPING: Because of sustained environmental damage, camping is no longer permitted inside the park, but you can camp on Playa Espadilla. However, don't leave your things unattended.

HOME RENTAL: If you're staying for a while, this is an option you might consider. Many houses are advertised by signs. Anita Myketuk (☎ 777-1002) of the Buena Nota has a house for rent.

MANUEL ANTONIO FOOD: Nearly every hotel has its own restaurant. Low-budget travelers will find pickings sparse; most restaurants are designed for those with oodles of moola, and Quepos is a better bet.

The **El Mono Azul Restaurante Natural** (☎ 777-1548) is a good bet. (See mention above under accommodation).

The most famed place to eat is the **Mariposa** Call for reservations. They also have a la carte food available daytime.

Hotel Plinio is renowned for its Italian food and homemade bread.

El Byblos rivals the Mariposa for French cuisine.

Bahías offers 46 different varieties of cocktails and seafood dishes.

Serving US-style food, the **Barba Roja** bar (opposite the Divisamar) is expensive but popular.

For Italian food you might try the **Restaurante Du Lu**.

Pizzeria Italian Club also has Italian dishes. **Pickles Deli** serves ice cream, salads, and sandwiches; it's in the Centro Si Como No.

Set next to the Hotel Villas del Parque, **Richard's**, reached by a steep set of stairs, serves international dishes.

The Arboleda Beach and Mountain Hotel has the **El Cangrejo** snack bar and the **Mallorca** restaurant.

Mar y Sombra, set where the road from Quepos meets the beach, is the most reasonably priced of the beachside restaurants; the **Del Mar Bar** is nearby. **Vela Bar** offers vegetarian and seafood specialties.

QUEPOS FOOD: The best dining values for low-budget travelers are in and around the bus terminal in Quepos. There are any number of moderately-priced places to eat.

Popular with visitors, **El Gran Escape** (The Great Escape) is near the bridge.

Dos Locos serves Mexican food and is reknowned for its margaritas.

Gastronomia L'Angulo is a great Italian deli.

Just across from the bridge heading out of town, **Mirador Bahía Azul** has moderately-priced seafood.

La Marquesa has reasonably priced Tico food.

Try the seafood at the **Quepoa** or eat at the **Pizza Gabriel**. Also try the **Nahomi** (by the post office), **Angelus**, and the **Arrecife**. Still others include **Soda Ana**, **Restaurante Isabel**, and **El Kiosko**.

ENTERTAINMENT: Maracas Disco is by the pier.

SHOPPING AND SERVICES: Anita Myketuk's **Buena Nota** (☎ 777-1002, fax 777-0345)) is an a/c gift shop located near the Manuel Antonio beach area and is sandwiched between the Karahe and Pisces hotels. Anna is friendly and helpful, and her shop offers a wide variety of goods including books.
buennota@sol.racsa.co.cr

Galeria Costa Rica, in town and run by two expats, offers a wide variety of goods.

Another place for info is at the **Quepos Activities Center** (☎ 777-1526) which is across the street from the bus station.

Near the bus station, the **Lynch Tourist Service** (☎ 777-1170/0161, fax 777-1571) offer a wide range of services including taxis to the airport.
lyntur@sol.racsa.co.cr

Internet access is offered by **Cyber Loco** (☎ 777-1489) which is above Dos Locos Restaurant in Quepos.
oasisame@sol.racsa.co.cr

La Botánica (☎ 777-1223) sells organically grown spices as well as natural health and beauty products. **Botíca Quepos**, on the corner of the main drag heading towards Manuel Antonio, is the local pharmacy. A

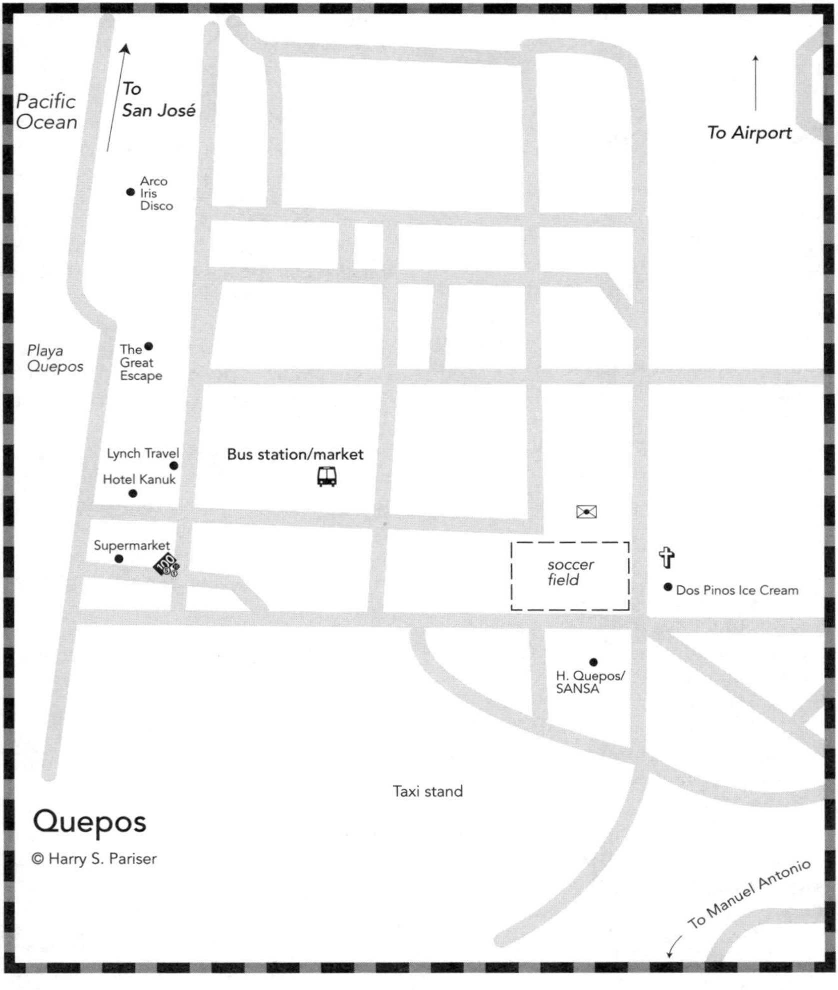

laundry is around the corner from the Restaurant Isabel. Dr. Cecilia Quesada, an English speaking **dentist**, has her office downstairs from the Hotel Quepos.

LANGUAGE STUDY: **La Escuela D'Amore** (☎/fax 777-1143; Apdo. 67, Quepos), a "Spanish Immersion Center," is next to the Hotel del Mar which is 200 m from Playa Manuel Antonio. Call or fax 414-781-3151 or 213-912-0600 in the US. **www.amerisol.com/costarica/edu/damore damore@sol.racsa.co.cr**

Its competitors are **Pura Vida Learning Adventures** (☎ 777-1661) which offer Spanish classes as well as surfing lessons. **puravida@www.eco-era.com**

TOURS: An enthusiastic environmentally-conscious expert on local flora and fauna, **Leodan Godinez** (☎ 777-1908) conducts walking tours through the park. He'll point out animals you might not otherwise see and show you medicinal herbs, trees, and plants. On the hike—which is tailored to suit your age, physical condition, and interests— you might see sloths, monkeys, and agoutis..

Besides Rainmaker (see box, p. 214), **Iguana Tours** (☎ 777-1262/0574) also offers sea kayaking on the Isla Damas estuary, whitewater rafting, and other excursions. They are next to the Si Como No complex.

Pura Vida (☎ 777-0909, fax 777-0779) offers three-hr. tours (US$35) daily at 3 PM which stop at Playa Biesanz and then head out to the sea to look for dolphins.

Sunset Sails Tours (☎ 777-1304) offers late-afternoon cruises daily.

Brisas del Nara (☎ 777-1889, ☎/fax 777-1889) offers horseback tours daily which visits waterfalls. They are 30 min. from Quepos. They have a good reputation.

Ríos Tropicales (☎ 777-0574, 233-6655, fax 255-4354; www.riostro.com; info@riostro.com) and **Unicorn Adventures** (☎ 777-0489) offer a variety of excursions; the former has kayaking.

Costa Rican Dreams (☎ 777-0593, 239-3387, fax 239-3383 in San José; Apdo. 79, 4005 San Antonio de Belén, Heredia) offers fishing charters.

The **Blue Inn** (tel/fax 777-1676) runs fishing trips out of here as well as Drake Bay and Flamingo.

Also try **Skip's Sportfishing** (☎ 777-0275).

Amigos del Río (☎ 777-0082) offer boat trips, rafting, horseback riding, and mountain biking as well as snorkeling.

Rios Locos (☎ 777-1170, fax 777-15710 also offers rafting and kayaking tours.

J. P.'s Sportfishing Tours (☎ 257-8503, 257-7829, fax 222-8134; Quepos ☎/fax 777-0757, 777-1613; 800-308-3394) works primarily out of Quepos from Dec. to May.

Adventuras Poseidon (☎/fax 77-0935; Apdo. 185, 6350 Quepos) is another Manuel Antonio-based operation.

Rancho Los Tucanes (☎ 777-0290) offers an all-ages horseback tour to a set of waterfalls. Breakfast and lunch are served in their private restaurant.

Luna Tours (☎ 777-0725), Hotel Malinche in Quepos, specializes in sportfishing.

The **Damas Caves Rainforest Tour** (☎ 777-0070) takes you on a full-day trip on horseback (four hours) into the caves and past waterfalls with swimming pools. The impressive caves have stalactites, stalagmites, and thousands of bats!

HORSEBACK RIDING: **Marlboro Stables** offers riding; lunch is included. It costs US$45 (US$55 with transport from Quepos).

EVENTS: The three-day **Fiesta del Mar**, Festival of the Sea, takes place around the end of Jan.

FROM QUEPOS: Buses run from Quepos to San José; take a direct buses which depart via Manuel Antonio. Buy advance tickets at the bus terminal office which generally closes for lunch between 11 and 1.

Both the San José and Puntarenas buses pass by Playa Jacó. If you take the San Isidro-bound bus (five hrs.), you pass through extensive palm oil plantations on the way to Dominical. The ride really gives you a feel for the immense size and range of the industry, the workers and their lifestyle, and the monotonous but fascinating plantation-style architecture which characterizes such developments. Bridges on the way bear the imprint of the US Corps of Engineers.

Heading South from Quepos

Silencio Community Ecolodge

Set in Silencio near Savegre 25 km NE of Dominical and 30 km from Quepos, **Silencio Community Ecolodge**, a farming cooperative (☎ 259-3401, 259-8442, fax 259-9430; Apdo. 6939, 1000 San José) offers accommodation along with activities which include hiking, rafting, and other tours. This is a great way to experience local life.

www.agroecoturismo.net
cooprena@sol.racsa.co.cr

Matapalo

Set 25 km from Quepos, this village has surf and a small number of hotels and restaurants. As usual, be wary of rip tides. To get here, take a San Isidro-bound bus from Quepos.

PRACTICALITIES: There are an increasing number of places to stay here.

The Jungle House (☎ 779-9255) is near the beach and has rooms (US$25) and cabins (US$35).

Cabinas Piedra Buena (☎/fax 779-9255) offers rooms in a house and cabins (around US$25-40); it has a restaurant/bar.

Inexpensive **La Terraza del Sol** (☎ 771-1092) has *cabinas* (around US$20) and a French restaurant. **Cabinas Matapalo** has two cabinas (US$20) and are across the road

El Coquito del Pacifico (☎ 222-4103, fax 222-8849) has rooms from around US$40; it also has a restaurant and rentals. There are also a few other places.

Moderate **Coicita** (☎ 777-0161, fax 777-1571) is a spice farm which offers river rafting and horseback riding; packages are available.

El Oasis Americano (☎/fax 777-1092) sends and receives faxes and e-mail messages. They also have cabins (US$20) and offer horseback tours.
oasisame@sol.racsa.co.cr

Express del Pacifico is an open-air garden restaurant on the main road which serves expresso, pizza, and other international dishes.

Hacienda Barú

Hacienda Barú, a private nature reserve has an 830-acre (330-ha) hacienda with rainforest, lowland forest, pasture, cacao plantations and fruit orchards, mangroves, a beach, and an estuary. There are over 200 acres of untouched old growth rainforest here as well as another 260 acres with secondary growth. Hunting has been prohibited here since 1976, and you might see anything from a puma to an anteater or a chestnut-mandibled toucan here.

GETTING HERE: The estate is located one km NW of the Río Barú along the road from Quepos to Dominical. Keep your eyes peeled for the "HDA. BARU" sign or ask at the El Ceibo gas station.

TOURS: A variety of tours are available, and accommodation is in the works. You can hike in the rainforest, kayak at night, watch birds in the lowland swamp area, trek all day and visit some petroglyphs, or camp in the jungle and possibly see nocturnal mammals. Horseback tours are also available — including a "horse and hike" special. The "Night in the Jungle" involves a combination of horseback riding and hiking. You stay in a screened enclosure in the forest for the night. The newest venture at Barú is a canopy platform. Prices run US$25-60. If you are a school group, ask about their special services.

PRACTICALITIES: Cabins are US$50 d, plus US$10 for each additional person. Continental breakfast is included. Other meals are available. Their booklet ***Trails & Tales*** will enhance your visit. Call 787-0003 or fax 787-0004. Write SJO-0114, 1641 NW 79th Av., Miami, FL 33126-1105.
www.cool.co.cr/usr/baru/baru.html
sstroud@sol.racsa.co.cr

Playa Dominical

The seaside village of Dominical is located in a spectacular natural area, 19 mi.(30 km) S of Quepos and 22 mi.(36 km) W of San Isidro. The beach here is beautiful, but rip tides can make it deadly. The area has only been settled since the early 1900s when Victor "Chucuyo" Sibaja settled here and planted — along with bananas, rice, and beans — *dominicos*, a variety of plantains. A *dominical* is a plantation that grows *dominicos*. Before the 1930s, there were no roads. The first public telephone was installed in 1977.

Since the beginning of the 1990s, Dominical has undergone a radical transformation from a somnolent village almost entirely lacking in tourist facilities to a glittering magnet for surfers, aspiring developers, and rainforest conservationists. In some areas, the Ticos have sold out and US expats control all of the property. This has resulted in a real boom in the area, and the completion of the road will further spur development. Although there have been and are bad apples present, the majority of the foreign owners are both anti-development and environmentally conscious. And they seem to be having some success against their more greedy compatriots.

These days the town is developing: the road to Quepos has been asphalted and the village now has direct phone lines. Tourism is booming, and locals have been getting involved with tourism as well. Iguana hunting has decreased, and the Friends of Nature are working to stave off turtle poachers by collecting eggs to be placed in a turtle nursery.

GETTING HERE: Buses run from Quepos (four hrs.) and (Uvita-bound) from San Isidro. If driving, note that the only paved (albeit potholed) stretch of road is between San Isidro and Dominical. Allow an hour.

ACCOMMODATION: Places are sprouting up all the time, and there is now a huge variety from which to choose.

At the town's entrance, inexpensive (around US$30-40) **Albergue Willdale** (☎ 787-0023, fax 771-0441), is also known as "Cabinas Willy." They rent river kayaks, inner tubes, and a sailboat; there's also a gift shop.

The same owner rents **Villa Cabeza de Mono** which overlooks Uvita and Playa Hermosa. The fully furnished, four-wheel-drive accessible villa rents for around US$900/wk. (US$125 pn) and has a kitchen (food supplied) and pool.

In town and near the beach are the inexpensive **Cabinas Nayarit** (☎/fax 787-0023), which also have a/c houses for rent (low-budget if there are six of you) or US$30 d. Also inexpensive are beachfront **Cabinas San Clemente** (☎ 787-0026) next door, and low-budget **Cabinas El Coco** (☎ 771-2555), which has a weekend disco. Inexpensive **Cabinas La Residencia**

(☎ 771-2175) is nearby.

The **Río Linda Hotel** (☎ 771-2009, fax 771-1725) offers rooms with a/c or fans from around US$40; it has a Jacuzzi, pool, and the **Maui Restaurant**. Slightly higher-priced but very high quality (hardwood cabins with private bath and fans), **Hotel-Cabinas Punta Dominical** (☎ 787-0016, fax 253-4750; Apdo. 196, 8000 San Isidro de El General) has good food and horse rentals. Trips to Isla del Caño can be arranged here.

Once a low-budget hotel, Cabinas Roca Verde is now **Hotel Roca Verde** (☎ 787-0036; fax 787-0013); it is is approximately a km S of the village. Rooms with private bath are priced at around US$85 d. It has a restaurant, pool, and bar.
www.doshermanos.com
doshnos@sol.racsa.co.cr

Set on a ridge overlooking the ocean, British-run **Pacific Edge** (fax 787-0031) charges around US$52 per cabin. Attractive cabins are lighted with solar power (12 V). It has a restaurant.

The **Happy Toucan Lodge** (☎/fax 771-1903) offers duplexes with breakfast (around US$40). The hammock on the porch and the pool may make a happy toucan out of you.

The attractive **Villas Río Mar** (☎ 257-1138, 787-0052, 787-0053, fax 787-0054; Apdo. 1350, 2050 San José) set on the banks of the Río Barú, have beautiful gardens. It offers 40 private thatched-roof bungalows, pool, Jacuzzi, and bar. Rooms have refrigerators, couches, bar, and porch. Mountain bikes, kayaks, horses, and a restaurant are also on the property. It charges around US$80 d.
catalog.com/calypso/concert/hotel/vriomar.htm
riomar @sol.racsa.co.cr

OUTLYING ACCOMMODATION: These can also be booked through the **Selva Mar Reservation Service** (☎/fax 771-1903) in San Isidro.
www.cool.co.cr/usr/baru/baru.html
sstroud@sol.racsa.co.cr

Hacienda Barú (see separate section preceding) has its own cabins. Overlooking the Río Baru, **Mike's Cabins** start at around US$25. You may also stay in Uvita (see later in this chapter).

Rates at moderate **Cabinas Escondidas** include breakfast. Other meals (around US$8 pp) are additional. A beach is nearby. There are three cabins, guided nature walks, horseback riding, mountain bikes, Tai Chi or Chi Kung classes, and snorkeling equipment. Vegetarian meals are popular with visitors.

Cabinas Río Lindo (☎/fax 787-0028), near the town's entrance, has rooms for about US$40.

Two km from the main road, **Restaurant El Manú** (☎ 235-6895) rents out cabins and villas which have pools. A horseback ride and walk away, the **Finca Los Duarte** offers two basic *cabinas* for around US$20. Contact Selva Mar (☎/fax 771-1903).

Set two km S of Dominical, **Costa Paraíso** (☎/fax 787-0025; Apdo. 578, 8000 San Isidro, Pérez Zeledón) offers attractive cabins and apartments. from around US$40-60 d; weekly and longer rates are available.

Las Casitas de Puertocito (☎ 787-0048) are a set of six split-level cabins halfway between Dominical and Uvita. Rivers and beaches are available, and horseback riding and a restaurant are offered. Rates are around US$50 d.

ESCALERAS AREA: This area runs along a mountainous dirt road off of the village of Dominicalito; it is becoming an increasingly popular place to stay.

Woody Dyer's **Finca Bella Vista** (☎/fax 771-1903) centers around a comfortable, traditional wooden red mahogany

> If you just show up at a hotel or lodge in the Dominical area you should be able to negotiate a better rate, provided that they have space available. It helps if it's off-season, if there are two or more of you, and if you plan on staying more than a night or two. Arriving without a reservation gives you the option of checking out some places and finding the right one for you. If you're going to be arriving late or coming during Christmas, for example, you may wish to use **Selva Mar** (☎/fax 771-1903) or contact those who have direct lines.

farmhouse commanding a tremendous view; this is best appreciated while lounging on the porch in one of the comfortable hammocks. Rooms are simple and share two showers. There's also a kitchen/dining area. Woody lives in the house nearby with his personable wife Yorlenny and their children. Food is simple, hearty fare such as scrambled eggs with peppers and homemade *nachos* with cheese, beans, vine ripened diced tomatoes, and *natilla*. This is a good place if you want to relax and take it easy. Woody has a great horseback tour (see "waterfalls") of the waterfall along with other excursions, and also has a small house for rent. Pickup in Dominical is available. Rates are around US$15 pp, pn.

Nearby **Finca Brian y Milena** (☎/fax 771-1903; Apdo. 2-8000, San Isidro de El General) offers visitors the chance to explore life on an experimental fruit farm which produces over 100 varieties of fruits, nuts, and spices. Brian will show you around the farm, and you may be lucky enough to sample durian or rambutan in season. (Brian will also show non-guests around for a charge of US$22 pp which includes lunch). Brian and Milena also have a wood-fired riverside hot tub, and their farm commands panoramic views of the area. Milena cooks with vegetables from their garden, and her style is unique: "Costa Rican cooking with a healthful twist." Herbal teas are also available.

Charges are around US$36 pp, pd (US$38 if you are here on your own) with a discount of US$2 pd applied as you stay longer (second day is US$34, third day is US$32, etc.). Rates include cabin, three hot meals (plus breakfast on the day you leave), hiking tours, and the riverside hot tub. The cabin is spartan and reached by heading up a small hill; you have complete privacy.

Hiking and horseback tours are available, and a four-day trek to Salto Diamante (a series of seven waterfalls; see "waterfalls" later in this chapter), stopping at the homes of locals along the way, is also offered. Altogether, there are five different packages available. If you wish, they will meet you at any one of five locations in Dominical with a horse for you at an additional charge ranging from US$10-20 pp. This is not the place to stay if you wish to be waited on and catered to hand and foot; Brian and Milena have their own lives to lead, so this is definitely a give-and-take situation. If you would like to get the most of your visit, it would be better (and a much more rewarding experience) to hang around for a few days and get to know them and the area. Otherwise, you'd be better off spending the night in town.

Up the hill, a divorce has closed, **Escelaras Inn** .Check to see if it has reopened under new owners by the time of your visit.

FOOD: Places range from simple and local to gourmet.

Soda Laura (pancakes, *casados*, or fish and shrimp), **Soda Atardecer**, and **Soda Nanoya** are recommended. **La Campana** offers Italian dishes .

Probably the only gourmet restaurant in the world which has broken surfboards hanging suspended from its ceiling, **San Clemente** serves everything from Tex-Mex to Cajun to pizzas. Entrees range from grilled mahi mahi to French toast stuffed with fruit. It's on the L side of the road and just past the soccer field as you enter town.

You can also eat at **Roca Verde**, **Mani Gordo**, **Mare Nostrum**, the **Maui Restaurant**, **Punta Dominical** (great views) or at palm-thatched **Salon el Coco**. A new addition is the **Dos Hermanos** market.

Gringo Mike's is a combo pizzeria, deli, and bakery.

Enroute to Uvita, the **Casitas del Puertocitas** serves Italian food.

Restaurant/Bar El Barú, in Plantanillo, offers local food and seafood at reasonable prices.

> Exercise caution while swimming at Dominical or Dominicalito beaches. Stay in shallow water because riptides can be deadly!

FISHING: Call **Roca Verde** at 771-2333. They also offer scuba diving and snorkeling. Another possibility is **Río Mar Boat Tours** at the same number.

WATERFALLS: One of the nation's most impressive waterfalls in the is right near Dominical. Formerly known as **Salto de Santo Cristo**, **Catarata Barú** is a popular spot. Entrance is on private land so you must pay a relatively steep 500 *colones* pp to enter. In return, you get the right to rent an innertube which can be used in the pool below the falls. There's a sort of improvised shower-curtain structure to one side near the base of the falls where you can change clothes. The two-tiered falls are well worth the effort. One path to the L leads off to a great view of the first tier. Another, to your R, leads down to the pools at the second tier.

Woody (at the Bella Vista) offers one of the best trips here (around US$40 pp), simply because his horses go by a longer and more scenic route. While others start from the coastal road and cut across, Woody's trip leads up the Esceleras road and through the forest. Enroute, you pass by majestic vistas, and your guide may point out a sloth or a toucan. When you pass through the deforested stretches, you'll know you're in the vicinity. You dismount inside the pochote plantation which surrounds the entrance. Santo Cristo is less scenic during the rainy season when its waters are often dirtied by soil runoff.

Don Lulo (☎ 771-3187; also offers tours here for US$35 pp including breakfast and lunch.
ciprotur@sol.racsa.co.cr

A closer alternative, **Catarata Posa Azul** is up the road from the Bella Vista on the Dominicalito Rd. It's a good place to cool off in after a beachside excursion.

Finca Brian and Milena sponsors two-night trips to Catarata Barú and on to **Salto Diamante**, a stellar set of seven falls. Longer stays (of up to five days) can be arranged. You may stay under a rock overhang (if you have a tent) and with a hospitable local *campesino* family. The trip has proved highly popular; stop by and talk to Brian about arrangements.

TOURS: Contact the **Selva Mar Reservation Service** (☎/fax 771-1903; Apdo. 215-8000, San Isidro de el General) for complete information regarding outlying accommodation, area tours, and other opportunities. These include tours to Rancho La Merced, their boat excursions in Uvita, and their visit to the farm of the Duarte family where you can see traditional sugar making. You can visit their offices in San Isidro. In the US, write c/o AAA Express mail, 1641 NW 79th Av., Miami, FL 33126.

The Roca Verde has "**La Primera Tienda**," a gift shop with tour booking.

Five min. by car to the E, **Tropical Waters** (☎/fax 787-0031) can arrange hotels and tours and offers advice. They can also hook you up with Camp Santo Cristo, a place for wilderness tours and backpacking. **jfair@santo.cristo.com**

Also inquire at the **post office/information center** next to San Clemente Restaurant.

STUDYING SPANISH: The **La Escuelita de Dominical** (☎/fax 787-0012, 771-2175, 787-0005, fax 787-0006) provides Spanish classes and arranges homestays. Youth hostel card holders will receive a discount. **domini@sol.racsa.co.cr**

FROM DOMINICAL: Possibilities are basically unlimited, but you have three choices in essence: head for Uvita, head back to Quepos, or travel up to San Isidro and proceed from there. One direct bus currently runs from Uvita at 5 and Dominical at 6 and then continues on to Quepos and San José. The return runs at 4 and arrives back in Dominical at 9. From Dominical you can travel to San Isidro at 7 and 3:30.

There is also a road from Dominical to Palmarl; this may have been paved by the time of your arrival, and there may now be bus service. Check before departing from the area. **note:** Be sure to check with residents regarding these times because they have changed from time to time in the past.

Parque Nacional Marina Ballena Uvita (Ballena Uvita National Maine Park)

Located to the S of Dominical, **Ballena Uvita National Maine Park** is the nation's newest (and only offshore) reserve. Offshore is the most extensive coral reef on the Pacific coast as well as the offlying Islas Ballena (nesting grounds for brown boobies, frigate birds, and ibises) where humpbacked whales tour in the company of their offspring from Dec. to April.

To get here, take the 9 AM or 4 PM bus from San Isidro which passes through Dominical.

ACCOMMODATION: Inexpensive **Cabinas Los Laureles** (reservations: ☎/fax 771-1903; around US$10 s, US$18 d) are set amidst laurel trees. Meals and horseback riding are available.

Rancho La Merced (☎/fax 771-1903) is a working cattle farm which includes a forest reserve and offers a day's rounds with the cowboys (US$60 pp) if you wish. Their **Cabina El Kurukuzungo** is secluded and rents for around US$35 d; meals are provided upon request or you can cook for yourself.

Set at the edge of the village, **Cabinas El Coco Tico** (reservations: ☎/fax 771-1903) offers six motel-like units (around US$20). You can eat in the family's *soda* nearby.

Soda La Cooperativa is the place to go for food.

IN BAHÍA: This settlement is near the beach and two km S of the bridge over the Río Uvita. The cheapest place to stay here is with **Victoria Marín** whose home is next to the *telefono publico*. Low-budget **Cabinas Villa Hegalba** rents clean and simple rooms for around US$15 d with tax; the friendly couple also provide a camping area. Similar places include **Cabinas Uvita** and **Cabinas María Jesus**.

Set in Bahia Ballena, **Villas Bejuco** (☎771-0965) charges from around US$45 d, US$55 t for cabins with hot water; pool and restaurant are on the grounds.

Cabinas Ballena (☎ 220-4263), six km S of Uvita, is set amidst 600 acres of primary forest and faces the beach. German-run, it has restaurant, four-rm. beach house, and excursions. Rates run around US$25-60.

Villas Hotel Gaia (☎/fax 256-9996; Box 809, 1940 NW 82nd Ave., Miami, FL 33126) is a Dutch-owned-and-operated "wilderness hotel" It offers 12 attractive wooden cabins with solar-heated water and fans, a gourmet restaurant, great birdwatching, horseback riding, cave kayaking, sportsfishing, and pool with bar. It is 15 km S of Uvita and near the settlement of Ojochal and Playa Tortuga. Rates are US$65 s, US$110 d.
hvgaia@sol.racsa.co.cr

Villas El Bosque (fax 786-6358) is set near the Río Ojochal and is one km from the beach. It has attractive bungalows (US$ 60) with kitchens and balconies.

L'Auberge El Perezoso (fax 786-6358) offers rooms (around US$45 with breakfast) which command ocean and mountain views; gourmet food is served, and a telescope is available.

Cabinas and Restaurant Flamingo (☎ 771-8078) offers bungalows (around US$25) with private bath and kitchenette.

Set up in the hills, **Villa Armonia** offers rooms and a bungalow (with kitchenette) for around US$30-35.
rammire@ibm.net

Las Ventanas de Osa Wildlife Reserve is a secluded private reserve with birdwatching. Stay must be arranged in advance. It is now owned by Roca Verde in Dominical and is undergoing renovation which should be finished in the early 2000s.

Camping is permitted at Playa Piñuela; get your water from the park service there. Low-budget travelers can stay at the **Cabinas Delgado** which are next to a lumberyard. **Cabinas and Restaurant Flamingo** (☎ 771-8078) allows camping for US$4 per tent. **El Anciano del Pacifico** (fax 788-8210) also offers camping in Ojochal.

In the vicinity, **El Ultimo Refugio** offers low-budget accommodation and an all-you-can-eat dinner specials on Fri. nights.

Cascada Hostel is a backpacker's facility (US$8-12 pp, pn; from US$48 pw) which has been recommended by a reader. It has a hot shower, organic garden, vegetarian restaurant, hot shower, laundry facilities, book exchange, Spanish classes, and workshops. It also offers camping, kayaing, mountain biking, snorkeling, and work exchange opportunities. Ask for Edwin at the pink colored soda in Uvita (US$3) or walk 20 min. Remember to bring a flashlight.

TOURS: The **Soda La Cooperativa** is on the main highway, the Costanera Sur, before you turn towards the coast. A *pulpería* belonging to the Diaz family is nearby. They'll show you how to get to the waterfalls and accompanying pools which are on the Río Cortezal. At low tide you can find any one of a number of snorkeling spots. Fishermen can take you out to watch birds, fish, snorkel, or scuba dive. Selva Mar Reservation Service (☎/fax 771-1903) can arrange tours through here and can provide for boat transport. You can also contact

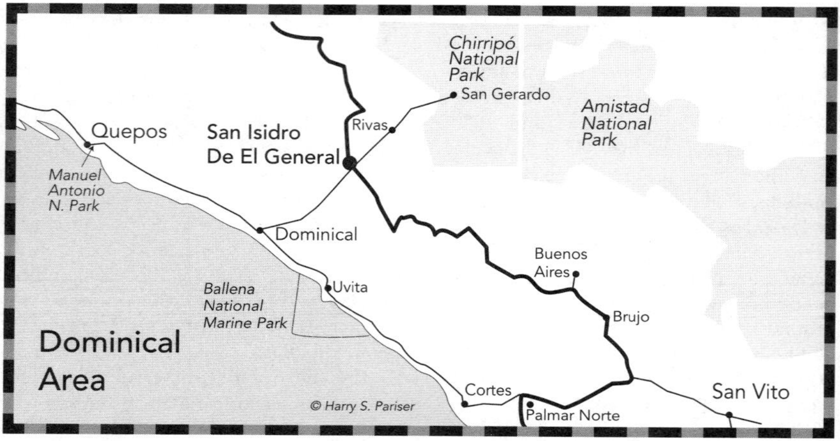

León Victor Gonzales by leaving a message for him at his *pulpería* in Uvita (☎ 771-2311).

Located just before Uvita and just after Playa Hermosa, **Rancho La Merced** (reservations — 24 hrs. advance: ☎/fax 771-1903) also offers horseback tours covering beach, river, mangrove, and rainforest. Lunch is included.

Freddie (fax 786-6358) out in Ojochal offers Dec.-April tours by boat of Isla Garza.

The **Villa Gaia** (☎/fax 256-9996) in Uvita will take you out on wildlife tours of the mangroves with members of a local cooperative who formerly cut the trees for charcoal.

DIVING: Contact **Ballena Divers**; they can take you out to Caño Island (US$80-110) or let you dive offshore (US$60).

KAYAKING: Kayak Joe (satellite ☎ 00874-761-353-193) takes people out for around US$50 pp for a day trip on kayaking trips which include seaside cave exploration.

San Isidro de El General

San Isidro (pop. 32,000) has grown up since the opening of the Interamerican Highway: the first cars arrived only in 1945! Founded in 1897, it lies 85 mi. (137 km) from San José.

San Isidro is a good place to use as a base; the beaches at Dominical are just 22 mi.(35 km) away. It also is a great place to stay if you want to experience the charms of the nation's small towns. This very pleasant place has the ambience of the frontier. You can see *campesino* cowboys strutting their stuff down the main street. The town is ridiculously compact. Note the prosperity of the town center: almost every home is nice and shelters a car.

GETTING HERE: If you're going to Golfito by bus either from San José or from Quepos, you'll probably want to break your journey here. It's also the perfect place to base yourself for a trip to Chirripó.

On the way you pass over **Cerro de la Muerte** (Hill of Death), the highest spot on the Interamerican Highway. Watch on the L for the ruins of a shelter; it's possible to see both coasts from here when it's clear. This is *páramo* terrain—highland shrub and tussock fields more common in the Andes than in Costa Rica. Although the name antedates the highway, it is a dangerous stretch of road to drive if there's fog. Starting here, during the next 28 mi.(45 km), the road drops down from 10,938 ft. (3,334 m) to 2,303 ft. (702 m).

From San José, *Musoc* (☎ 222-2422) and *Tuasur* (☎ 222-9763) buses leave hourly along C. 16, Av. 1/3. Get advance tickets on weekends and holidays.

Buses also depart from Uvita, Dominical, Golfito, and San Vito.

SIGHTS: San Isidro's main square has what surely must be one of the nation's least architecturally endearing churches — a pink and white concrete structure whose bells appear to be undergoing an epileptic fit each time they ring! The church's interior isn't much better. Up by the front to the R of the altar are slots for *caritas* (San Isidro, Jesus Crucificado, etc.), and the small room behind contains a mysterious white box covered by a white veil: it represents the body of the crucified Christ.

Inaugurated in 1990, the town's **cultural complex** has a 400-seat theater, museum, exhibit hall, and workshops for artisans and fine artists. It's next to Café el Teatro.

The new market in town is well worth a visit, and the old one has been transformed into the **Southern Regional Museum** which displays items from the area's indigenous peoples. A beautiful **waterfall** is a few km past Brujo on the R. It's also possible to tour the **Pindeco pineapple processing plant** in Buenos Aires to the S.

Born out of the need to protect the surrounding water supply, the volunteer-run **Centro Biológico Las Quebradas** (FUDEBIOL; tel 771-4131; Apdo. 95, San Isidro de Pérez Zeledón.) is set four km NE from San Isidro and offers butterfly garden, trails, and camping. Admission is US$6. It is closed Mon. and during Oct.

ACCOMMODATION: Inexpensive **Hotel Amaneli** (☎ 771-0352) is also right in town; be sure to get a room which is not facing the Interamerican Highway.

LOW BUDGET: The best deal around for low-budget travelers is the **Hotel Astoria**, under the "Derby" Restaurante Pepe Timba neon sign on the square. The rooms with private bath (US$4 pp) are the best value. Try to get one of the six rooms in the area to the rear of the reception desk.

Similarly priced is the *pensión* (☎ 771-0349) behind **El Jardín** restaurant and down from Cinco Menos.

Another low-budget **Hotel Chirripó** (☎ 771-0529), is right beside the park and across the way. It has singles US$8, doubles (US$20), triples (US$30), and quads (US$35). All have private baths. Rooms at the back are quieter.

i **Ciprotur** (☎ 771-6096, fax 771-2003) is a tourist information and promotion center. It is located next to the electricty company (ICE) in San Isidro.
ciprotour@sol.racsa.co.cr
www.ecotourism.co.cr

Brunca Tours (☎ 771-3100, fax 771-2003; ; e-mail:) is also located here. They offer tours, fishing, and rafting.
ciprotour@sol.racsa.co.cr

Selva Mar Reservation Service (☎/fax 771-1903) will make reservations for the Dominical area.
sstroud @sol.racsa.co.cr

OUTLYING: Inexpensive and clean a/c 50-unit **Hotel del Sur** (☎ 771-3033, fax 771-0527, San José: 234-6191; Apdo. 4, 8000 San Isidro de El General) is five km (three miles) S of town; it offers a restaurant, pool, gardens, tennis court and other sports facilities. A variety of rooms (including *cabinas*, which sleep up to five) are also available. They offer a number of tours and activities (mountain biking, kayaking, gold panning, etc.) through the **Gulfo Dulce Tour Guide Association** (☎/fax 775-1179/1991).
www.ecotourism.co.cr/HotelDelSur
hoteldelsur@ecotourism.co.cr

Rancho La Botija del Sur (cellular ☎ 382-3052; Apdo. 287-8000, San José) is a special place: a rental cabin set amidst pre-Columbian petroglyph-inscribed stones. These are from the Cabécar, a tribe who lived here almost 3,000 years ago. It has a pool, *soda*, and tours and is six km from San Isidro on the Rivas road. Admission is US$5, US$3 for children. The cabin is around US$55d, US$75 t with breakfast.
ciprotur@sol.racsa.co.cr

Paraiso Tropical (☎ 770-5080, page 224-2400) is a set of cabins commanding a spectacular mountain view; they are 20 min. from San Isidro and set on the right. Each rents for around US$70 d, US$90 t. Facilities include restaurant and pool.
Cabinas Tinamaste (☎ 382-8660) are set on the road to Dominical (around 20 min. before you reach the village) and offer beautiful cabins (US$25) as well as hiking.

FOOD: A good place to eat lunch or dinner is the **Marisqueria Marea Baja** which is near the main square. Also try the **Restaurante Los Reyes** and **El Tenedor**. The classiest cuisine is at **Hotel del Sur**. Cheap food is found at the **Soda Nevada**, at **El Ranchito** (across from the park), and in the **Mercado Central**.

OUTLYING: Mirador Vista Del Valle (☎ 284-4685) is 15 km from San Isidro. It offers Tico dishes including trout. **Mirador La Torre** (☎ 771-6462, 771-6096) is five min. N of town; it also has live music at night.

ENTERTAINMENT: There isn't much to do in the town itself — unless you catch one of the mobile discos coming through. If you're around on Sat. afternoons, you can visit the *subasta* (stockyard) where **auctions** take place; you might see them selling teams of oxen.

FESTIVALS AND EVENTS: The town's **fiestas civicas** are held from the end of Jan. to the beginning of Feb. Activities include a cattle show, agricultural and industrial fair, bullfights, and orchid exhibition. On May 15, the **Día del Boyero** ("Day of the Oxcart Driver") is celebrated with activities including parades featuring brighly colored oxcarts and the blessing of animals and crops by the local priest.

WHITE WATER RAFTING: Largely a Class IV river, the Río General poses a challenge for even the most experienced river runner. **Ríos Tropicales** (☎ 233-6455, fax 255-3454; www.riostro.com; info@riostro.com) and **Costa Rica Expeditions** (☎ 257-0776, 222-0333, fax 257-1665; costa-rica@expeditions.co.cr; www.expeditions.co.cr) are among the companies offering river and kayaking trips. Locally, **Brunca Tours** (☎/fax 771-3106) offers tours. Check with them for details.

SERVICES: The best place to change money is at **Bazar Xiomara** which is across from El Cinco Menos.

The Teribes

Térraba is the main settlement of the Teribe indigenous people of Central America. The Teribe were moved here in 1710 after a team effort on the part of Franciscan missionaries leagued with the Spanish militias. Atlhough those who remained in Panama have managed to retain much of their culture, those in the Costa Rican reserve have lost most of their heritage. Teribes own only some 10% of the reserve's land; the remainder has been sold to outsiders attracted by the expansion of the PINDECO/Del Monte plantation.

The Asociación Cultura Teribe is the main activist organization here. Over the course of the past few years, they have completed a number of projects including a *rancho cultural* (meeting place), tree nurseries, a health clinic, and have offered a number of workhops — ranging from Teribe spiritual teachings to workshops for locals; they have also opened a small museum.

A medical clinic will also preserve traditional remedies, and a garden with medicinal plants has been started. Visitors who are genuinely interested in the Teribe culture are welcomed. Contact the Asociación Cultural Indígena Teribe (ACIT) or the Comisión Cultura Teribe who will show you around and exchange ideas. Visitors are requested not to shoot pictures indiscriminately. Donations may be made in the form of checks and made out to the Asociación Cultural Indígena Teribe and mailed to them at Terrabá, Buenos Aires, Puntarenas.

For **information** about the area, contact Chamber of Commerce President **Luis Quesada** (☎ 771-2525) at the Hotel Chirripó.

LANGUAGE STUDY: SEPA (☎ 771-4582, fax 771-8841; c/o AAA Express Mail, 1641 NW 79th Av., FL 33126) offers Spanish language study programs along with volunteer opportunities.
www.online.co.cr/sepa
selvamar@sol.racsa.co.cr

FROM SAN ISIDRO: *Tuasur* and *Musoc* (☎ 222-2422, 710-0414) run direct buses hourly to San José (136-km trip, 3.5 hrs, US$3). *Tracopa* (☎ 771-0468) runs indirect buses.

Buses for Uvita and Dominical (1.5 hrs.) depart daily at 7:30, 1:30, and 3:30. Buses for Quepos run at 7 and 1:30 and pass through Dominical.

A bus (five hrs., ☎ 773-3010) runs to Puerto Jiménez (on the Osa Peninsula and a gateway to Corcovado) at 5:30 and noon.

There are also connections to San Vito (5:30 and 2:30), Palmar Norte, Ciudad Neilly, and Golfito.

Parque Nacional Chirripó (Chirripó National Park)

This 105,000-acre (42,500-ha) park is a hiker's paradise, one best explored during a two- or three-day hike combining stays in mountain shelters with ones in the comfortable new lodge. Established in 1975, it includes 12,530-ft. (3,819-m) Cerro Chirripó, the nation's highest point, as well as two other peaks over 12,500 ft. (3800 m). The area is famed for its *páramo* — a high, tundra-like zone which often frosts (but never snows) over.

GETTING THERE AND PRACTICALITIES: Take a bus from San Isidro de El General at 5 AM and 2 PM (be sure to take the bus to San Gerardo de Rivas) or charter a taxi (around US$15); it's a beautiful two-hour ride up to the San Gerardo entrance. Here you check in at the ranger station where it's possible to camp; there's a steep shortcut up to the park from here which can cut an hour from your time (see below).

If you're planning to make it up to the mountain hut in one day (a rough trip with an altitude gain of 6,900 ft., 2,100

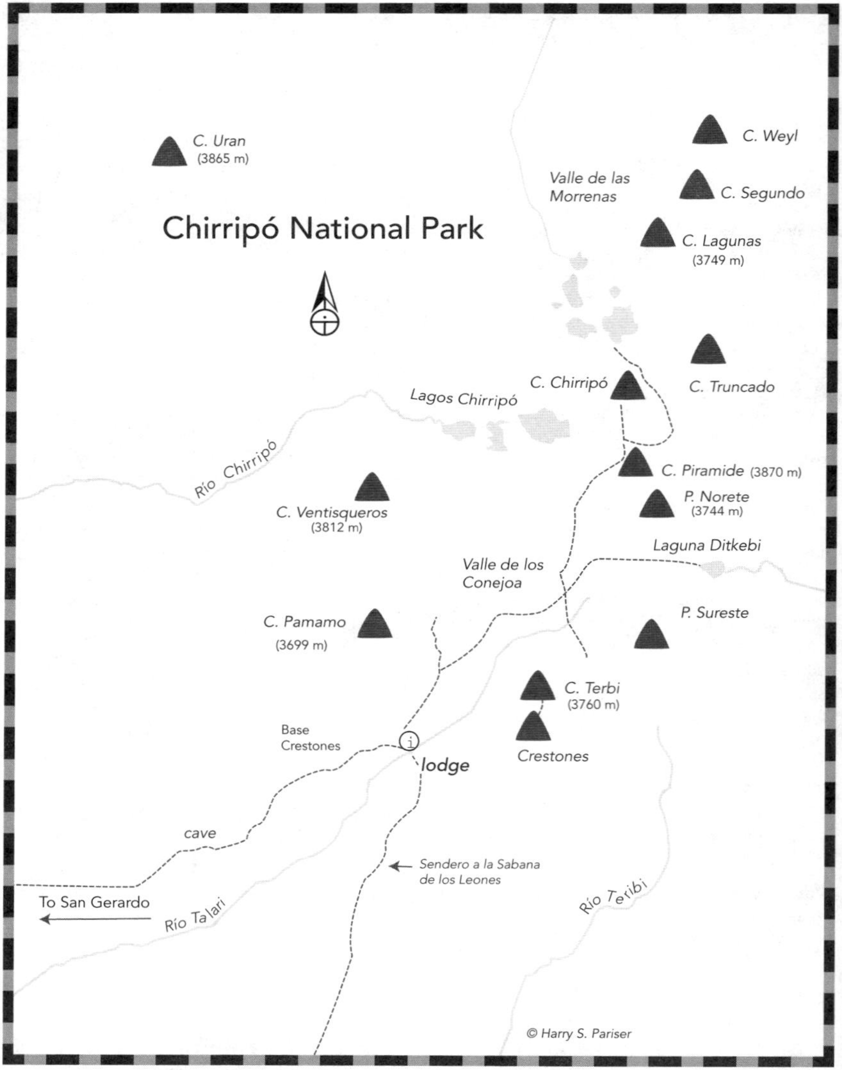

m), it's better to stay put for the day. In town you may rent out a room at the low-budget **Soda and Cabinas Chirripó** at the low-budget **Soda El Decanso**, at the low-budget **Cabinas Marín**, at the low-budget **Albergue Turístico Chirripó** (which sits atop a gigantic boulder overlooking the river), or at the low-budget **Roco Dara** which has baths with hot water and cheap meals. **Elimar** is more expensive because the rooms have private baths; it also has a bar/restaurant.

The 10-unit **Cabinas y Restaurante El Descanso** (☎ 771-1866) has rooms with board for around US$15/person. It is 200 m from the park office.
ciprotour@sol.racsa.co.cr

During the rainy season, it rains daily, generally in the afternoon, so you'll have to get an early start. There are three mountain huts where you can stay.

TOURS Ocarina Expeditions (tel. 253-4579; Apdo. 1265-2050, San José) offers trips to Chirripó and Corcovado.
www.ocarinaexpeditions.com
ocarina@sol.racsa.co.cr

Be aware that visitors are currently limited to the level of 40 persons pd so be sure and get in your **reservations** (☎ 771-3155, 771-5166) in advance. (Your arrival must be within the next 30 days). Also be cognizant of the fact that a fire started by careless hikers lodging in a hut near Monte Sin Fé in 1992 consumed some 5,000 acres. Be very careful with fire!

OUTLYING ACCOMMODATION: Albergue de Montaña Río Chirripó Pacifico (☎ 771-6096, 771-4582, fax 771-2003, 771-1903; Apdo. 517-8000 Costa Rica), is an eight-room mountain lodge near Rivas. It offers restaurant, hiking trails, and horseback riding. It charges around US$50 d with continental breakfast. It is 17 km from San Isidro (around 50 min. on a gravel road).
ciprotour@sol.racsa.co.cr

Chirripó Preparation and Pointers

Warm clothes and sleeping bag are necessities as temperatures often drop to freezing. Bring binoculars, rain gear, a compass, and at least one liter water container pp. Waterproof boots are a necessity in the rainy season. Fires are prohibited in the park so you must bring a stove if you intend to cook. Two basic maps are provided at the station; if you plan to go off the beaten track at all, you should have purchased a map in San José. Don't count on the rangers to be well informed about the park, but they may be able to give you an idea of the number of people hiking there and help you rent a pack horse and guide should you want them. The local hotels can also be of help.

PORTERS: Locals will carry your pack (around US$20 per load each way with a limit of 30 lbs; ☎ 771-1866); arrange in advance at the ranger station.

El Pelicano Mountain Lodge offers rooms with shared baths for around US$25. Owner Rafael Elisondo has a gallery here with his "root" art sculptures.
ciprotour@sol.racsa.co.cr

TOURS: Jungle Trails (☎ 255-3486) offers tours, and **Costa Rica Expeditions** (☎ 257-0776, 222-0333, fax 257-1665; costa-rica@expeditions.co.cr; www.expeditions.co.cr) can tailor a tour for you.

FLORA, FAUNA, AND TOPOGRAPHY: *Páramo* covers 65 sq. k). The edge of the *páramo* extends from around 10,826 ft. (3,300 m) and above. This often-thick, stunted vegetation rarely tops 12 ft. (four m). Surrounded by a cloud forest the "savanna" itself is treeless. Six different types of *páramo* vegetation, including a species of dwarf bamboo, cover it. The most common tree is the evergreen oak. The lakes at the peak — unique in

Central America — were formed by glaciation more than 25,000 years ago during the Pleistocene Era. Situated at 10,170 ft. (3,100 m), the Sabana de los Leones (Savanna of the Lion) is so named because "lions" (pumas) and cougars are frequently spotted here.

There are 73 species of birds; variety diminishes as the altitude increases. Quetzals are abundant. Another feature of the higher cloud forest, the *jilguero* (black faced solitaire) cries out from the treetops.

ENTERING THE PARK: The best way is via the "Thermometre," which was once a shortcut and is now the main route. From the ranger station turn L and walk through the village. Going R at the first fork, descend and cross a bridge, then continue on to another river and bridge; get water here. After a few houses, you'll see a sign marked "*Cerro Chirripo*"; walk through the pasture. Keeping about 300-600 ft. (1-200 m) away from the forest on your R, head up until you come to a wired enclosure with a gate to its R. Enter and head R, following a path which ends suddenly; then follow the ridge on your L up to a wire fence crossed by a set of stone steps. You are now on the main trail, *Fila Cemeterio de Maquina*, which follows the ridge.

The park boundary is about one or two hours farther, and the first camping spot (*Llano Bonita*: a flat, grassy area) is two or three hrs. after that. Signs are placed every two km (or so) along the way. To get water follow the trail another 20-30 min. to find a fork on the L marked "*Agua Potable 200 m.*" There's a rough shelter here (not a place you would choose to sleep in) and a steep path behind it takes you down to a small stream.

Continuing through a steep, once burned-out area *(La Cuesta del Angel)* for another three to four hours, you enter *Monte Sin Fé* and then reach a small stream with a large cave *(refugio natural)* to the L, about 1.5 hrs. from the huts below, where you can sleep if necessary.

Next you must climb *La Cuesta de los Arrependitos* ("Hill of the Repentants") where the trail circumnavigates the side of a mountain. The first proper shelter is another hour or so away; you'll pass a *"Valle de Leones"* sign about 20 min. before it, and the shelters lie in the valley below the accordion-folded sharp peaks of Los Crestones. The two dorm-style cabins at *Refugios Base Crestones* sleep up to 40. Both have kitchens with potable water and cooking utensils. Flies can be horrific.

Depending upon your physical condition, it will have taken you eight to 16 hrs. to reach the first hut and ranger station.

NEARBY HIKING: Surrounded by rocky peaks and mountain passes, sandy **Valle de Los Conejos** (Rabbit Valley), from which all the rabbits beat a hasty retreat after the 1976 fire, is covered with dwarf bamboo. Cerro Crestón borders it on the SE, and its pinnacles rise towards the N and W.

Lakes are found at the base of the **Valle de los Morrelas** and **Valle de Lagos** (Moraine and Lake Valleys). These crystal-clear cold lakes, which measure up to an acre and sometimes freeze over, are popular bathing spots with tapirs, and the entire animal community — from large cats to brocket deer to rabbits— arrives and drinks their fill on occasion. (Stay in Valle de los Morrelas at the hut; obtain keys from the San Gerardo ranger station). From here, you can climb **Cerro Urán** and head along the *Camino de los Indios*; you should hire a local to show you the way.

OTHER APPROACHES: You may also begin from **Canaán**, a village a few km further into the valley. This is a bit longer but avoids the steep beginning. Stay here in the low-budget **Cabinas Navarro** (☎ 771-0433, ext. 101) which are next to the *soda*. An entirely different, only recently opened route commences at **Herradura** and extends over Cerro Urán and Chirripó; it necessitates hiring a guide which may be arranged through Parques Nacionales. Stay at the low-budget *cabinas* in Herradura

MOUNTAIN CLIMBING: Chirripó is not as difficult to climb as it appears. On a clear day, it's possible to see the Valle de General, parts of the Atlantic and Pacific Coasts, the Turrialba and Irazú volanoes, and several other peaks. Continue on to the second hut and follow the sign; it's about an hour to the base of Chirripó Grande and then another half hour to the top; the **Lago San Juan** (chilly swimming) is on the way. Start before dawn from the second hut to get the best views.

There's also a trail from here to **Cerro Terbí** (12,352 ft., 3,765 m), a peak which, unlike Chirripó, can be seen from the first hut. From the top of this peak, you can see well down into Panama. **Los Crestones**, a series of steep, needlelike rock pinnacles are nearby; they can also be reached from the first hut in about an hour.

From the first hut, there's a rough trail down to **Sabana Chirripó**, a large, light-brown marsh. From the top of Cerro Terbi, it's possible to continue on to Pico Sureste (12,247 ft., 3,733 m), Pico Noreste (12,283 ft., 3,744 m), and Cerro Pirámide (12,490 ft., 3,807 m). Other peaks that may be climbed include Cerro Páramo (12,136 ft., 3,699 m), Cerro Ventisqueros (12,506 ft., 3,812m), Cerro Uran (10,935 ft., 3,333 m), Loma Larga (12,254 ft., 3,735 m), Cerro Truncado (12,680 ft., 3,865 m), and Cerro Laguna (12,300 ft., 3,749 m).

The **new lodge** houses up to 60 hikers at four to a room, baths with cold showers, communal kitchen (with meal preparation being planned), and socializing space. No aesthetic charmer but surely an improvement on what came before, the lodge necessitated some 4,000 two-way trips up and down the mountain on the part of hundreds of laborers. The US$800,000 donated for its construction came from the United Nations. It costs US$6 pn to stay here, and camping is prohibited unless you are on the three-night Chirripó loop for which a guide is required (☎ 771-1199 to reserve one).

VICINITY OF CHIRRIPÓ: There are a set of **hot springs** in the vicinity of Herradura. to get here continue up the road for a km or so until you see a brown house to your L; turn R and head up a steep trail for 15 min.; you may need to pay a small fee at the brown house.

The New Dam

A planned dam, a US$2.3 billion privately-financed project, would flood a 300-sq. km area from Buenos Aires to Coto Brus. This dam was first planned in the 1960s. It was nearly constructed in the 1970s in order to power a proposed ALCOA aluminum refinery which was cancelled after a student protest. The village of Curré will be flooded, and — understandably enough — the area's indigenous peoples oppose the idea of flooding their ancestral lands. In addition to the flooding, some 25 km of the Interamerican would be submerged (which would necessitate rerouting the road through the Cabagra Reserve which, in turn, would leave it open to invasion by squatters. Although no longer online (due to lack of funds), the ICE is still planning to build it.

"Reader R. M. writes "We spent a few nights at Finca Anael. It is definitely a place for the adventure traveler as getting to it is quite a project. You must have a four-wheel-drive. Heading south on the Pan-American, you take the Buenos Aires exit. The road dead ends in front of the technical school and then turn R and then L when the road goes L. Stay on the dirt road through the fields until you see a water tower on your L. Turn L here. When you reach a "Y" fork, take the road to the R which leads up a hill. Stay on this hill until you see a small, pretty sign by the road that leads to the gate. This is some 10 km from Buenos Aires but a 1.5-hr drive. Eugenio, the bird specialist, took us on incredible hikes daily. Spectacular food. very restful and idyllic. Is it a Buddhist community? It was never explicitly stated. But their activities are planting hundreds of trees and rare orchids, organic agriculture, hosting student interns, and educating the local community."

About three hours on foot from the village of Herradura, three km from San Gerardo de Rivas, is low-budget **Pensíon Quetzal Dorado** (☎ 771-0433, ext. 109). It's another good place from which to explore Chirripó and Cerro Urán.

At Rivas-Perez Zeledón, **Talari Mountain Resort** (☎ 771-3102, ☎/fax 777-0341) has eight cabins, pool, fruit tree orchard, restaurant, and horseback riding. It's from US$40 d plus tax on up including continental breakfast. A free shuttle service will be provided from San José if advance notice is given.
talaripz@sol.racsa.co.cr

FROM CHIRRIPO: Buses depart from San Gerardo for San Isidro at 7 AM and 4 PM. Francisco Elizondo of Posada El Descanso offers transport to San Isidro by arrangement.

From San Isidro to Golfito

Finca Anael/Dúrica Biological Reserve

This self-sufficient reserve is operated by a group of some 42 back-to-the-landers who farm organically, raise goats, meditate, and so forth. Expect to spend around US$40 pp for food and lodging; all profits go towards buying more land. To get here, you must drive on a bad road for an hour from Buenos Aires and then hike or horse it in. Arrangements (Apdo. 9, Buenos Aires; fax at the PO: 730-0003) must be made a week in advance. Call Annie McCornick (☎ 240-2320, fax 223-0341) or Amancio (☎ 730-0028: Spanish only).
www.gema.com/durika
durikas@gema.com
durika@sol.racsa.co.cr

Parque Nacional Piedras Blancas (Piedras Blancas National Park)

North of Golfito, Parque Nacional Piedras Blancas is one of the nation's newest national parks, and it is the only one in Costa Rica directly connected with a lodge. The flora and fauna of Las Esquinas have many of the citizens of the nation of Austria to thank for their preservation.

GETTING THERE: The lodge is accessible by regular cars all year round. From San José, drive 300 km S for 5-6 hrs. to Villa Briceño (Km 37) and follow signs four km farther to the lodge. From Golfito, take the dirt road six km to La Gamba and then follow signs to the lodge. Pickup can be arranged at Villa Briceño if you're coming from San José by bus. (Take a bus bound for San Isidro and change or take a Golfito or San Vito bus and get off at Villa Briceño.

HISTORY: One of the nation's newer national parks, Piedras Blancas has a long and complex history. Originally designated to be part of Corcovado National Park, the area was designated Sector Esquinas and later Piedras Blancas. A resident of Vienna, US-born Austrian classical violinist Michael Schnitzler is the guiding light behind both the creation of the park and this lodge. Michael and his wife first came to Costa Rica in 1989 and fell in love with the country, both the nature and its people. Returning six months later, they bought a home at Playa Cacao near Golfito.

Continued visits brought awareness of deforestation issues. Michael found himself feeling uncomfortable enjoying the nature while trees were tumbling all around. Flying over in a plane, he and his wife noticed that the Esquinas forest was being deforested. Inquiring, they were told that the area had been declared a national park by decree and the government was looking for people to buy the property because there were about 140 landowners, many of whom had logging permits. The area was destined to remain a park on paper only until the land had been bought.

Under Costa Rican law, even though the area had been designated a national park by the Ministry of Parks, the Ministry of Agriculture could issue logging permits for the same area as long as the land is in the possession of private owners. So Michael started a nonprofit, Rainforest of the Austrians, in Vienna in 1991 with the intention of collecting funds. Certificates are presented to donors, and each donation has been around US$40. More than 20,000 certificates have been sold. However, only around 20% of the land earmarked on paper for the park has been purchased so far. The Schnitzlers initially attemped to obtain Austrian government funds for purchasing land, but, for political reasons, the government was unable to purchase land in a foreign country.

However, the Austrian government was interested in working for sustainable development. At the 1992 Earth Summit in Rio, they had pledged to spend US$18 million on tropical Third World projects over the next three years. The criteria was that the projects be involved with helping the people and save the forest at the same time.

It took two years, but Michael finally persuaded the Austrian government to back the project. The area's residents were enthusiastic about the concept of ecotourism as an alternative. Prior to this, they had been hunting, logging (both legally and illegally) and saw a greater potential. It took nearly two years of lobbying.

Profits from the lodge will be invested in the community. Short term gain is provided by employment. While that is nothing unusual (all lodges employ locals), the difference is that all of the other lodges are in private hands (mostly owned by foreigners) and much of their profits stay or go abroad. Esquinas, however, belongs to a foundation; all profits are to be channeled towards community projects such as building a new school, bringing in a doctor and dentist, and agricultural projects.

Logging has ceased in the areas surrounding the lodge, and a little over half of the Esquinas forest has been saved from destruction and has become part of the park. A research station. located at the entrance to the property, is run by the foundation in conjunction with the University of Vienna and this lodge is open to students and biologists from all over the world who are pursuing rainforest research.

So far, students from Germany and Austria have been studying everything from climatology to frogs, to plants and butterflies. Three things tie these all together: conservation (supported by the Austrians), sustainable development (supported by the Austrian government), and research. It is the only project of its kind in the world.

The project is financed through Austria's Development Aid Program, and the lodge is owned by the Austro-Costa Rican non-profit "Asociación Progamba." Its employees are all members of this association of 70 farming families.

Land has been purchased by the Park Service via checks given directly to the landowners. The Park Service conducts negotiations with the landowners and decides what tracts to prioritize for purchase and what price to pay. Almost all of the land (except for one small valley with 20 families) is unpopulated. The owners live somewhere in the area outside the park so no expropriation has been necessary. Payment, on average, is about US$320 per hectare. Most of the land was acquired by the squatting so the sale is pure profit. The foundation has problems with landowners who come to Michael and want to sell him the land, mistaking him for Mr. Moneybags!

A new twist in the park's history came in July 1995 when COMBOS, a Costa Rican NGO, purchased 420 ha from five farmers in the area in using money donated by sources as diverse as the Lolapalooza rock festival and the US Fish and Wildlife Service; some of the backers hope to receive "emissions credit" for the carbon dioxide consumed by the trees. This idea is known as "joint implementation" and, ironically, would allow polluters to continue polluting *in situ* by acting to preserve tropical rainforests which, in turn, would give them credits.

HOW TO HELP: Donations to the park may be sent to Regenwald Der Osterreicher, Posteach 500, A-1181, Vienna, Austria. Each US$50 donated purchases 500 sq. m. You will receive a certificate in return.
verein@regenwald.at

HIKING: Anyone is free to visit and hike the trails free of charge. Expect to spend a minimum of several hours in order to make a visit worthwhile. Trails here are steep and sometimes treacherous. Be sure to carry one of the bamboo staffs you'll find by the lodge. *Terciopelos* are common so be sure and be careful to stay on the trails. On the trail you might see blooming heliconias and bromeliads, sight birds such as the *pavon*, hear howler monkeys, or have a *terciopelo* cross your path. Most of the trails extend through hilly secondary forest.A number of trails begin from behind the lodge. Many are steep (bring one of the walking sticks to be found at the lodge), and muddy. They interconnect in a chain and pass by some small waterfalls.

An old logging trail leads past some beautiful heliconias to some old growth trees. The area around the lodge is largely disturbed.

ACCOMMODATION: The **Esquinas Rainforest Lodge** (☎ 382-5798, fax 775-0631; Apdo 183, Golfito) houses its visitors in five very attractive two-unit cabins which overlook the pool and main lodge. The main building incorporates a living area, library, shop, bar, and dining area. A stream feeds the filtered pool. Set near the lodge, the research station accommodates five to eight student researchers. You'll probably see one or more of them during the course of your stay. High-season rates are around US$95 s, US$150 d, US$165 t and include three meals

and taxes. Special rates are offered to students, residents, groups, and for long-term stays. Packages are also available. Excursions include hiking, swimming, kayaking, horseback riding, excursion flights, and other activities.
esquinas@sol.racsa.co.cr

Special summer educational programs are also offered. Call 506-385-5418
whuberas1.botanik.ac.at

Golfito

Laid out as a company town, hot and humid Golfito was established in order to service nearby banana plantations. After disease and strikes led United Fruit to flee from the Limón area in 1938, the company set up shop in Golfito, literally constructing the town. Approximately 15,000 migrated, and the town bustled with vitality. Prolonged strikes, among other factors, led to the area's abandonment in 1985, resulting in a 15-year somnolent slump. Copper sulfides, left as residues of pesticides employed in banana cultivation, have rendered the soil unsuitable for anything other than African palms which do not require much labor.

While the establishment of the duty-free zone has brought about some improvements, it threatens to ruin the languid, seedy atmosphere which gives the town its appeal. With new hotels and restaurants springing up like mushroooms, the area may never be the same again. On weekends, the town now becomes populated with Ticos arriving to shop at the duty-free zone. Topping all of this off, the area is in the midst of a property boom. Still it has a truly majestic backdrop, and locals still calculate time not in terms of hours but according to low and high tides.

Downtown Golfito

GETTING HERE: It takes seven hours by bus over the Talamanca mountain range on the Interamerican Highway. Buses (☎ 221-4214) leave from San José (C. 2/4, Av. 18) for the eight-hr., 339-km trip. You can also take any Zona Sur bus to Río Claro where you can intercept one of the frequent buses from Villa Neily. From San Isidro, direct buses depart at 10; otherwise, you will have to change at Río Claro (where you can catch a bus or a *colectivo*).

SANSA (☎ 221-9414, 233-0397, 233-3258, fax 255-2176) also flies daily as does Travelair (☎ 220-3054, 232-7883 fax 220-0413; information@travelair-costarica.com).

GETTING AROUND: Inexpensive buses run from Las Gaviotas through to the duty-free port and airport. Shared taxis are around US$.75-$1 per ride. Water taxis run to outlying destinations. They are quite expensive, and you have to bargain.

SIGHTS: There really isn't much to do around the town of Golfito itself. One yachtie pundit tells the story of two decked-to-the-heels *gringas* who walked into Las Gaviotas at Playa Tortugas and asked where the beach was! The honest truth is the nearest beach is two hours away and named after a mosquito.

Getting sloshed is more popular than getting splashed: the main pastime in Golfito is sipping beer and shooting the bull. The town is full of characters, including a number of aging retired military expats, and it's a joy to have a drink here. For teetotallers there's not much else to do except take a walk through the Pueblo Civil and on down to the Zona Americana — which now has been retitled the Zona Libre since it became duty-free.

You might also want to hike up the hill to the facility-free, wet and very wild **Golfito National Wildlife Reserve**. This 3,235-acre (1,309-ha) reserve safeguards the area's water supply. The more than 125 species of shrubs and trees include four that are nearing extinction: manwood, plomo, butternut, and purple heart. In addition there are more than a dozen species of fern, 11 of heliconia, and 31 species of orchid. Four types of monkeys reside here as do margays, jaguarundis, agoutis, pacas, and anteaters. During the wet season, there are more than 70 species of birds in residence. Camping is permitted, but the unmarked trails are slippery. The easiest access is via a gravel road running from the beginning of the soccer field near Las Gaviotas; only the first of the eight km is passable by non four-wheel-drive vehicles.

ZONA LIBRE: Costa Rica's answer to the pyramids, this last project of the Arias Administration opened in April 1990 under a cloud of confusion. Created in order to spur business in economically moribund Golfito, the complex has excited enormous controversy — becoming the subject of innumerable banner headlines in the national press. San José's businesses (mainly the Av. Central crowd) felt the competitive crunch, and pushed unsuccessfully to have the "duty-free" zone's duties knocked upwards from the current 60%, a move which would have undoubtedly transformed the complex into another governmental white elephant or, given the size and scale of the project, a white mastadon.

The original plan was to have visitors spend 72 hours. Since the computerized enforcement mechanisms were not ready, and there were too few hotel rooms to make minimum stays enforceable, the limit was initially waived and will be applied in incremental stages as hotel capacity increases. Currently,

Ticos are permitted to purchase US$400 worth of merchandise every six months and must stay overnight.

ACCOMMODATIONS: Because there are a limited number of hotel rooms, it is impossible to get a room if you arrive on weekends when the consumers converge on town. Next to the airstrip, expensive **Hotel Sierra** (☎ 750-0666, fax 750-0087), at around US$75, offers disco, restaurant, and tours. Nearby it are the **Koktsur** (☎ 775-0327, fax 775-0703) which charges around US$12 and the **Jardín Cervecero Alamedas** (☎ 775-0126), a seafood restaurant which has cabinas for around US$25.

Next to Jardín Cervecerio Alamedas and near the airport, **Hotel Costa Sur** (☎ 750-0871, fax 750-0832) is inexpensive (about US$25).

The Family-run comfortable low-budget **Cabinas Casa Blanca** (☎ 750-0124, around US$10 d) are S of the Zona Libre and in front of the ICT office.

The **Hotel Golfo Azul** (☎ 775-0871) has rooms for around US$40 d. Low-budget **Hospedaje Familiar** (☎ 750-0217) is across the street; kitchen access is permitted to guests.

Right across from the entrance to the former United Fruit dock, the **Hotel Del Cerro** (☎ 750-0556, fax 750-0551) has a restaurant and inexpensive (about US$25 d), attractive rooms.

The **Centro Turístico Samoa del Sur** has moderate *cabinas*. Opposite it, the relatively new **Cabinas Miramar** has rooms for around US$10 which rent with private bath.

Near the municipal dock, low-budget **El Uno** has windowless rooms. Another low-budget place (around US$15 d) is **Hotel Golfito** (☎ 750-0047); get the two rooms which face the water. The **Delfinia** (☎ 750-0043) falls in the low-budget range with shared bath; more expensive rooms have a/c. **El Puente** (☎ 750-0034) is higher priced but has a/c.

The inexpensive **Costa Rica Surf** (☎ 750-0034; Apdo. 7, Golfito) is a popular hangout: about US$16 its rooms; ask for one of the few which have windows. The low-budget **Pensión Familiar** is well down the road towards the pier.

One of the best places to stay is moderate **Las Gaviotas** (☎ 750-0062, fax 750-0054; Apdo. 12, Golfito), which doubles as a yacht club/restaurant and has a pool. The very large, comfortable rooms (US$50 d) have a/c and hot water. (Stay in the ones termed "cabinas:" they have separate entrances, US$85). New and more expensive two-bedroom apartments are available. It's outside of the main part of town at the end of the bus line.

Nearby Hotel **El Gran Ceibo** (☎ 750-0403) offers eight low-budget (US$20) *cabinas* with fan and private hot-water bath. Three inexpensive a/c *cabinas* (US$30) are available.

Farther out on the road to Río Claro, **La Purruja Lodge** (fax 750-0373) offers low-budget *cabinas* with baths for around US$20.

To the NE of town, inexpensive **Cabinas Palmer** (☎ 750-0357, fax 750-0373) are near Restaurant Sieta Mars.

FOOD: La Dama del Delfin Restaurant (☎ 775-0235, fax 775-0042), across from the Hotel Costa Rica, is a friendly expat-run cafe which serves American-style food including big breakfasts.

There are a number of good places to dine within the compact Pueblo Civil. The **Coconut Cafe** is across from the gas station, has good coffee and other delights, and is a good source of information.

Bar and Restaurant La Cubana serves seafood dishes at reasonable prices. Look for it 150 m E of the gas station, on the upper road running through town.

Another good-value place is **El Jardín**, serving vegetarian plates, pizza, and other dishes at affordable prices. **Restaurant La Eurekita** is set in the middle of the Pueblo Civil overlooking the water. **El Balcón** is above the Hotel Costa Rica Surf. Others include **Femary Pizza Restaurant** near the former RR station and **Bar and Restaurant Cazuelita** which is near the airport and serves up Chinese dishes.

Outside town (around C 200 by taxi) is the **Río de Janerio Restaurant**, which offers spaghetti and other food popular with *norteamericanos*. They also rent horses and can take you for a ride if given advance notice, at around US$5 per hour. The open-air, thatch-roofed **Rancho Grande** is nearby. In a converted home, **Jardín Cervecerio Alamedas** serves seafood and cold beer; it is near the free zone complex. Other places to try include the **Costa Rica Surf** and Chinese **El Uno** near the dock. **Las Gaviotas** has a good seafood restaurant as does **Restaurant Siete Mares**, outside of town to the NE. For an unusual meal try dining on the **Fiesta**, a floating restaurant berthed in the Sandbar Marina on the peninsula.

ENTERTAINMENT: This town really gets lively only on weekends. The **Samoa** has a disco with live entertainment at times; another disco is the **Palanque**, and the **Club Latino** is down the road.

EVENTS: An annual five-day **Marine Festival** is held every Oct. Activities include surfing competitions, parades, and a song fest.

SERVICES: The **ICT** (☎ 775-0496) may be able to provide some information.

La **Dama del Delfin Restaurant** (☎ 775-0235, fax 775-0042), across from the Hotel Costa Rica, is one of the local watering holes (see restaurant mention above). They offer tours, left luggage, info, book exchange.

The **Centro Turístico Samoa del Sur** rents bicycles and boats.

The **Hotel Sierra** runs tours as do **Golfito Land-Sea Tours** (☎/fax 775-1614). **landsea@sol.racsa.co.cr**

Marinas include **Las Gaviotas** (☎ 750-0062, fax 750-0544), the **Eagle's Roost Marina** which is between town and the Sandbar Marina. The **Sandbar Marina** (☎/fax 750-0874/0735) operates a fishing barge tour aboard the ***Fiesta*** (a floating restaurant berthed in the marina) as well as offering jet boat rentals and fishing, snorkeling, and scuba diving trips. Their boat, the ***Phoenix***, runs luxurious sportfishing charters with gourmet meals. The **Banana Bay Marina** (☎/fax 775-0838) has water and power hookups, a guest-only restaurant, and other services.

The **Asociación de Boteros** (☎ 750-0712) offers expensive water taxi services. Rates are about US$60 to Puerto Jiménez, Playa Cativo, or Pavones, US$2.50 to Playa Cacao, and US$52 to Casa Oriquideas. The office is across from the ICE.

Change money at the *bomba* (the gas station to the L of the municipal dock).

FISHING: **Ian Mac Allister** (☎ 775-0268) runs **Golfito Sport Fishing** operates two boats. Write Apdo. 73, Golfito or call 288-5083, or fax 750-0373. **Hidden Treasures** (☎/fax 750-0373) offers trips on ths luxurious *Inzan Tiger*. In the US, write 1101 SW Washington, Ste. 120, Portland OR 97205. To charter the *Venecia* call 233-9355/9567. Outside of town, the foremost fishing camp is the **Sailfish Rancho** (See description in following section). Also try **Leomar** (☎ 750-0230, fax 750-0373), **Sandbar Marina** (☎ 750-0874), or **Zancudo Pacific Charters** in Zancudo (☎ 750-0268, fax 750-0105).

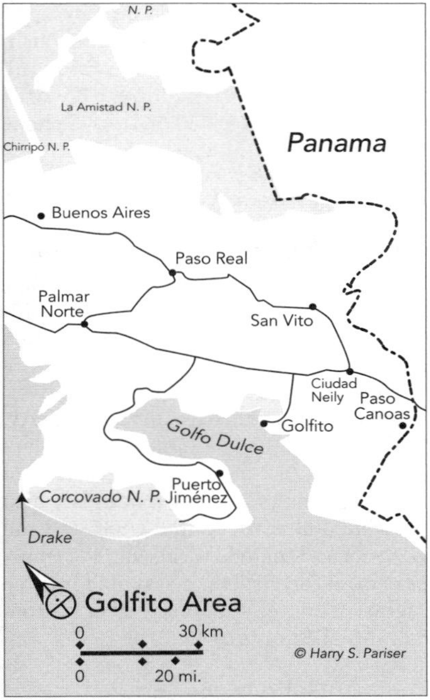

FROM GOLFITO: San José buses leave from near the ferry terminal.

SANSA (☎ 221-9414, 233-0397, 233-3258, 775-0303, fax 255-2176) flights depart from the airfield as do *Travelair's* (☎ 220-3054, 232-7883, fax 220-0413; information@travelair-costarica.com), which also stop at Palmar Sur en route. If they tell you the flight is full, it's worthwhile to show up; two seats are always held until the last minute for passengers coming from Puerto Jiménez, and chances are that you'll get on.

For Puerto Jiménez, the gateway to Corcovado, you can take the ferry, next to El Uno, or fly (with Travelair; information@travelair-costarica.com) for a reasonable sum; Sansa also flies.

Along the Golfo Dulce

Golfito's tourist "industry" has grownin by leaps and bounds. Much of the expansion has been along the **Golfo Dulce** ("Sweet Gulf") to the N of town. Unfortunately, this area is only accessible by boat, which can make visiting expensive unless you're staying on a package. All places here are owned and run by expatriates.

Playa Cacao

Playa Cacao is the nearest "beach" area which is swimmable. To get here, you must take a water taxi (about 20 min.), or in the dry season brave the "road" that was built in 1968. There are a few places to stay. **Villas Playa Cacao** (☎ 227-7924, fax 226-3957) are luxury cabins which rent for around US$300-600 pw. Also here are **Bungalows Las Palmas** (around US$35 d, US$50 t) which has a number of fruit trees. surrounding six white conical bungalows with thatched roofs. Leave a message in Spanish at 750-0375 or fax 750-0373. **Siete Mares**, a restaurant which offers Tico food, burgers, and sandwiches, is nearby.

SIGHTS: Captain Tom, who died of cancer in 1994, was one of Costa Rica's great expatriate characters. Boisterous one-legged Captain Tom arrived in the early 1950s aboard his aging converted sub chaser. At that time, according to Tom, both he and the boat were in "a state of emergency." The remains of his boat can be seen nearby and, by comparison, the Captain was in just dandy shape for quite a few decades thereafter. He would happily talk about how he bought the land for US$30, detailing the adventures he's had since then. He'd tell you how his house was destroyed by an earthquake in 1983, and you could read and sign his visitor's books. As Playa Cacao is the closest swimmable area to Golfito, it was popular with locals who come to eat the Captain's legendary "jungleburgers." Tom was flown to the US, and died the day he was to receive his first chemotherapy treatment. He was buried on his property right by the sea as he requested. His masoleum is covered with white bathroom tiles and is often festooned with flowers.

Playa San Josecito/Casa Orquideas

About half an hour from Golfito by boat (around US$20-35 each way), this botanical garden contains some 50 varieties of fruit trees, 50 types of palms, over 100 species of orchids, and 25 different heliconias. Public tours (US$5 pp, US$20 minimum) are offered from 8:30 AM Sun. to Thurs. Owner Trudy MacAllister says "We offer a hands-on tour where they can see, smell, touch, and taste. and watch the butterflies and birds." A cabin is available for around US$150/wk or US$500/mo. including transport to and from Golfito. You must bring your own food.Solar powered 12-volt electricity, refrigerator, and cooking facilities are provided. For more information leave a message with Bob Hara at 775-0353 or write Apdo. 69, Golfito. You can also reach them via marine band 68.

Dophin Quest

In ths same area is **Dolphin Quest** (☎/fax 775-1742, message: 775-1481). Access is by boat to Playa San Josecito (ask Chico at the *muellecita* — little dock — if Raymondo's book is in town); be sure to bring a flashlight and other necessitities. Rates are around US$20 s, US$30 d for camping; US$30 s or US$45 d for dorm, or US$35 s, US$52.50 d for *cabina* accommodation plus two meals. Conditions are *very* basic. Activities include scuba, snorkeling, fishing, kayaking, hiking, and horseback riding. Write Apdo. 141, Golfito or Box 107, Duncan Mills, CA 95430. In the US phone 707-869-1242 during Sept. and Oct.
www.dolphinquest.com
dolphinquest@email.com

Punta Encanto (Enchanted Point)

This former fishing camp has been newly refurbished and was inaugurated as a 12-room two-storey lodge in Nov. 1992. A generator provides lights and hot water until 9, after which solar cells take over. Waterfalls and trails are on the property. Guided hiking is available, as is volleyball, scuba, fishing, canoeing, and croquet. Boat tours and bay fishing are also possible. Rates are around US$130 d and US$95 s and include meals and RT transport from the airport (if staying for three nights or more). For more information, call 735-5062 or fax 735-5043.

Gulfo Dulce Lodge

The Swiss-run intimate **Gulfo Dulce Lodge** (☎ 383-4839, 735-5062, fax 222-5173, 735-5043; Apdo. 137, 8201 Golfito is near Casa Orquideas and Dolphin Quest. Constructed so as to have a minimal impact on the surrounding environment, its cabins are spacious and attractive. There is a two-night minimum stay, and credit cards are available.

The lodge holds up to 18 in five wooden bungalows with private baths. Facilities include restaurant, small pool, and a variety of excursions; rates run around US$130 s, US$200 d with taxes, meals, boat transfers, and taxes; packages are available.
www.crica.com/golfo.html
aratur@sol.racsa.co.cr

Arco Iris/Rainbow Adventures Lodge

A popular ultra-luxury lodge and nature reserve, **Rainbow Adventures** (☎ 735-5062, fax 735-5043; Apdo. 63, Golfito) is set at Playa Cativo bordering the National Park along the Golfo Dulce. They offer swimming, including a fresh water pool, fishing, snorkeling, kayaking (including night tours on moonlit, phosphorescent evenings), dolphin excursions, birdwatching, library research center, and tours of virgin forest, river and botanical gardens. Rates include transport to and from Golfito, all meals and snacks along with nonalcoholic drinks, beer and wine at meals, snorkel gear, jungle tour, and taxes. There are two attractive cabins as well as a main lodge. Food is basically vegetarian and seafood; meat dishes by request. A variety of trails surround the premises; it's easy to see monkeys, birds and other wildlife.

Sister establishment **Buena Vista Jungle & Beach Lodge** is located just down the beach and offers similar services and amenities. It has a great view and a bit more sea breeze but smaller rooms. Rates are in the US $105-US $175 p.p., p.n. range which includes tax but not service.

All bookings are madein advance. Call 800-565-0722 from the US and Canada, or 503-356-9458, fax 503-690-7735.
www.rainbowcostarica.com
info@rainbowcostarica.com
www.buenavista-costarica.com
info@buenavista-costarica.com

Cabinas Caña Blanca

These two expensive all-wood cabins (☎ 775-0373, fax 750-0373; Apdo. 34, Golfito) are set to the N of Playa Cativo and have small libraries, mosquito nets, dining tables, and modern kitchens with small refrigerators. Airport transfers (three-night minimum) are included. Porches command ocean views. There are hiking trails (look and listen for howlers) as well as snorkeling off the private beach (bring your own equipment). Tours and fishing with light tackle are available, and Peruvian-style meals are available on request. Rates are from around US$180 pp for three nights (including transportation); more expensive packages are available. In the US call 800-462-7424.
rafting@emf.net

South from Golfito (Punta Burica)

The **Punta Burica** area is one of the nation's most remote. It lies due S of Golfito. The most famous tourist establishment here is the nature lodge of Tiskita. A road leads past deforested farmland and then crosses a river via a winch-driven ferry. After the ferry (an experience in itself), it's more cattle farms and then a great view off to the right as you near the ramshackle village of Pavones.

Playa Zancudo

Aptly named after the mosquito, this large beach is becoming increasingly popular during the dry season. However, its very remoteness ensures that it it will be relatively uncrowded year round.

GETTING HERE: It's around US$50 by water taxi. A boat also runs here from the municipal dock on Mon., Wed. and Fri. at around noon or1 PM (about US$2 pp). It leaves Zancudo from Golfito at 6 AM that same day. A bus (three hrs.) may still run here from Golfito during the dry season. Otherwise, you can take the bus to Ciudad Neily and then a bus at 1 PM on to the beach. It's a two-hour drive from Golfito in a four-wheel drive.

ACCOMMODATIONS: The inexpensive/moderate **Cabinas Sol y Mar** (☎776-

0014, 776-0015) has a restaurant with famous fishburgers,a bar, and cottage for rent. The latter is a half-hour walk.
solymar@zancudo.com

Susan and Andrew Robertson's **Cabinas Las Cocos** (message ☎/fax 776-0012) offers accommodation in refurbished banana company homes (around US$42-46 pn, weekly rates available) and also rent a slightly higher priced cabin. **Zancudo Boat Tours** is attached to it. In addition to providing bus service to and from Golfito and surfboard, paddle boat, kayak, and boogieboard rentals, they also will take you all over, but require advance booking.
www.zancudo.com
loscocos@zancudo.com

Roy's **Zancudo Lodge** (☎ 776-0007, 776-0011; Apdo. 41, Playa Zancudo) is basically a fishing lodge.
www.kaosfree.com/zancudo

Another alternative of fisherfolk is **Golfito Sportsfishing (cooper @sol.racsa.co.cr)** and **Big Al's Sportfishing**
bigals@zancudo.com

Also nearby are inexpensive **Restaurant and Cabinas La Vista** which has a small zoo. **Casa Tranquilidad** (☎/fax 775-0449 or fax 775-0373; Apdo. 136, Playa Zancudo) is a bed and breakfast which offers fishing and jungle boat tours. Rates are around US$30s, US$40d. In Canada call 604-525-4403 or fax 604-728-3417.

The **Estero Mar** (☎ 750-0056) is the local hangout and has the only public telephone. Alternatives are **Hotel Pitier, Los Almendros** (which also offers river and ocean sportfishing charters), or reasonably priced **Macondo Italian Restaurant**.

The **Escuela Ecología** (☎ 414-743-7434) offers six-day adventure-oriented ecology courses here.

URL **www.zancudo.com**

Pavones

Surfing is the main reason to come to this legendary surfing spot. An isolated hamlet, Pavones has been embroiled in a controversy which — owing to the intervention of demented US Senator Jesse Helms — may have international implications. The conflict regards a ranch owned by imprisoned drug dealer Danny Fowlie, a US citizen now serving a 30-year sentence there. Middlemen have sold the property, and the US expat owners have confronted squatters who have been living here for more than a decade. No resolution to the conflict is in sight, but Helms has threatened to make the problem an issue, just as he has with similar cases.

In Sept. 1997, Max Dalton a 79-year-old cattle breeder was fatally wounded in a shootout at his ranch. In 1998, US Ambassador Thomas Dodd was alleged to have threatened economic sanctions if Dalton's death were not properly investigated. The remarks were met with alarm by the Costa Rican government. The squatter who shot Dalton was tried and acquitted in 1999. The situation continues to be in flux.

GETTING HERE: Water taxis cost around US$60 RT or you can take the daily bus at 2 PM; it returns at 5. Driving, you should take the Golfito-Río Claro road 10 km before turning towards Conte, another 10 km There's a short ferry ride from Conte across the Río Coto. Allow two hrs. for the trip.

ACCOMMODATION AND FOOD: Very basic to moderate accommodation and food are available. The **Pavón Tico**, Doña María Jiménez's *cabinas*, and the *pulpería*'s rooms (next to the soccer field) are all possibilities as is **Hotel Mauren** which is also near the soccer field.

Perched on a hillside, **Cabinas Vista Dulce** (☎/fax 383-0306; Apdo. 39, Ciudad Neily, Puntarenas) offers panoramic views, horseback tours, fishing, and reasonable prices: US$25 d. Meals are offered. It is run by a Tica-*gringo* couple.

Cabinas La Ponderosa (☎ 775-0131, fax 775-0631) charges US$40 pp, pd including three meals (less without food). Cabins have a/c, fans and baths. A TV lounge/bar supplements the restaurant. In the US, call 407-783-7184 or write them care of the managers' concerned mother Elena at 5281 NE 19th Av., Ft. Lauderdale, FL 33308 or call her at 954-771-9166.

Two km to the S, inexpensive **Bahía Pavones Lodge** is another alternative. Prices include breakfast. Reservations should be made in advance through the Tsunami Surf Shop on Av. Central in Los Yoses. To go back to Zancudo, you can either drive (several hrs. but only in the dry season) or Walter Jiménez, who can be found near the school, will take passengers on charter.

Ecopavones is operated by Cooprena(☎/fax 259-3605, 259-9430) which offers excursions and local flavor. It is at Playa Lagostino and has a lodge, reserve, tours, beaches, fishing, ahd horseback riding. This is a great opportunity to experience local life.
www.agroecoturismo.net
cooprena@sol.racsa.co.cr

Tiskita Lodge

Tiskita, a private 400-acre (162-ha) farm has an extensive 37-acre (15-ha) fruit tree orchard with over 100 varieties of fruit — from guava and durian to starfruit and guanabana. Guests are given a tour and permitted to sample fruit. And of course the presence of these fruit trees ensures superb birdwatching in the area, as well as luring animals from the surrounding primary forest. Horseback riding is also available as are excursions to Corcovado and other trips.

It's necessary to fly or charter a taxi to get here. the lodge is designed for those who require convenience but can do without luxury. If your primary focus in being in Costa Rica is *not* nature, there's no sense in coming here! Rates run from around US$135 s, US$220 d, and US$315 t and include the services of a guide, and three meals. (Other packages are available). Meals are served family-style in the main house which dates from 1979.

Fare is limited in variety but plentiful. Dishes include your basic meat, rice and beans, vegetables, and salad. Breakfast may feature fruit such as fresh mangoes from the garden, cereal, and pancakes. Coffee is always available. Breakfast is around US$7, and lunch and dinner are US$11. Packages are available, some of which provide tie-ins with other lodges in Corcovado and Manuel Antonio. Discounts are available for student groups. The nine sets of simple two- to three-unit stone-and-wood simple cabins (16 in all) with concrete floors, cold-water open-air showers, and verandas (some with hammocks) which are visited by charming human-wary iguanas. Rooms have fans and electricity. There are a wide variety of well maintained trails through primary and secondary forest, a waterfall, lovely bathing pools, and plenty of birds and spider monkeys. Bird cries are every present as is the crash of surf off in the distance. Obtain a map and ask if about any confusing turns if venturing off on your own. A set of stairs leads down to the beach with its rough surf. (Good swimming and snorkeling at low tide.) Be sure to bring everything you need; boots are available. Donated materials for the village school would also be appreciated.

Write Costa Rica Sun Tours, Apdo. 1195, 1250 Escazú or call 233-1511, or fax 233-6890.
www.tiskitalodge.co.cr
tiskita@sol.racsa.co.cr

Casa Punta Banco

Down the road from Tiskita Lodge , this six-bedroom (four double beds and six singles) house has two baths with hot water showers and a fully equipped kitchen, a generator, and a washer and dryer. An extensive tract of primary rainforest surrounds the lodge. Guests will be met at the airport in San José and taken to a bed and breakfast in Moravia; from San José you can fly or drive to Golfito, where you'll meet by the manager who will help you reach the lodge. There's a full-time caretaker on the property who also acts as a guide. Information booklets are also available. Activities while in the area include body surfing (watch for rip tides!), sampling fruits from the orchards, snorkeling, exploring the tide pools, horseback riding, watching nesting sea turtles (in season), and surf fishing. Prices range from US$700 pw for one or two, with US$50 more for each additional person. In the US, ☎ 248-545-890, fax 248-5450536 or write Continental Associates, 202 W Fifth Av., Royal Oak MI 48067. In Costa Rica, contact Warner (Warren) Gallo at Apdo. 5, Golfito; ☎ 775-0666/0924 or fax 750-0087
dsjean@aol.com

OTHER ACCOMMODATION: The village is the place for low-budget accommodation at a number of places; expect to pay around US$5 pp. Horseback riding is also available. Watch for the enormous roosters!

Ciudad Neily/Villa Neily

There's no particular reason to visit this banana and oil palm plantation, but it's a good place to make bus connections as it is 7 km NW of the border with Panama. There are a large number of budget-priced hotels including the **Pensión Familiar** (cheapest), the **Hotel Bulufer**, **Cabinas El Rancho**, **Hotel El Viejero**, **Hotel Nohelia**, **Hotel Central**, and **Hotel Las Vegas**. More expensive are the **Hotel Musuco**, **Cabinas Helga**, **Cabinas Fontana**, and **Cabinas Heyleen**.

You may meet Belgian expatriate Lillian at her **Bar Europa** here or eat at the **Restaurant La Moderna**, the best in town.

FROM NEILY: Running buses to San José (around seven hrs.), the Tracopa terminal here is on the N side of the town's plaza; San Isidro buses also run from here. For Golfito you can catch buses from the stop at the SE corner of the plaza or at the bus terminal in the town's NE end. Buses leave at 7 and 3 for Puerto Jiménez on the Osa Peninsula. For Paso Canoas (Panama), go to this terminal or take a bus from the plaza. **note:** If you want to be guaranteed a seat, it's better to head for the terminal.

> **Finca Cántaros** is set halfway between San Vito and the botanical gardens. It has a children's library set in a renovated antique farmhouse. Funds from the sale of handicrafts here fund the library.

Coto 47

About seven km SW of Neily, this is the closest airport to Panama, and SANSA (☎ 221-9414, 233-0397, 233-3258, fax 255-2176) flies here. The main reason to fly in would be to save time if you are heading for Panama.

Paso Canoas

Again, the main reason to come here is as a stop on the way to Panama. Many Ticos come through here on their way to shopping excursions in Panama and the hotels are often full on weekends and holidays. Stay at the **Hotel Miami**, **Hotel Palace Sur**, **Cabinas Interamericano**, **Hospedaje Hortensia**, or the **Cabinas Los Arcos**. If these are full, head back to Ciudad Neily. Tracopa buses run between here and San José. For more information on travel to Panama, check the "for Panama" section at the end.

Jardín Botánico Wilson (Wilson Botanical Gardens)

Wilson Botanical Gardens were founded by Robert and Catherine Wilson in 1963 with the original intention of establishing a tea plantation. It has evolved into a world-class collection of tropical plants, the most extensive botanical garden in Central America. Its 25 acres (10 ha) of gardens are beautifully landscaped — some areas cultivated in a more European style, others wild — and shaded by palms, oaks, and tree ferns, among many other trees. The gardens are now contiguous to a 590-acre (225-ha) mid-elevation forest reserve.

The reserve and gardens are maintained by the Organization for Tropical Studies which also operates La Selva and the Palo Verde Field Station. The garden maintains over 1,000 genera of plants from some 200 families, one of the world's finest collections of bromeliads and other tropical flora — including orchids, ferns, heliconias, marantas, and palms. The palm collection may be the world's largest, with more than 700 species. There are 278 species of birds in the area. In 1983, UNESCO designated the Garden, along with the forest area (with six km of trails), as part of the Amistad Biosphere Reserve, some 25 km away, which borders the national park of the same name. Gutted by a fire in 1994, the station has been rebuilt.

GETTING HERE: First get to San Vito (see "getting there" under "San Vito" in the following section). After arrival, take another bus or taxi for the last six km. By car, take the Interamerican south past Buenos Aires to the San Vito turnoff on your L, crossing the Río Térraba. From Golfito (to which you can fly), you take the Ciudad Neily bus or drive there, heading S to Ciudad Neily, turning N on Carr. 16, up the steep road to Agua Buena.

PRACTICALITIES: A self-guided nature trail booklet is available. Admission is free on Sun. Half-day visits are around US$5 and full-day visits US$8 (US$16 including lunch). Costa Rican citizens and residents receive discounts on entrance. For day visit reservations (reserve by 10 AM the same day), and for information on group tours (two-day reservation required), call 773-3278, fax 773-3278, or write: Robert and Catherine Wilson Botanical Garden, Apdo. 73, San Vito de Jaba, Coto Brus 8257. For reservations to stay in the dormitory (US$65 and up pp, pd including meals) or the cabins (US$75 pp, room and board; rooms have refrigerators), contact the OTS (☎ 240-6696, fax 240-6783; write

Apdo. 676, 2050 San Pedro).
www.ots.ac.cr
laselva@ns.ots.ac.cr

San Vito de Java

Now home to 37,000 residents, San Vito, was settled by Italian immigrants and was originally dependent on coffee growing. It is set at an elevation of 3,150 ft. (960 m) in the fertile Cotos Brus Valley. San Vito makes a good base for visiting La Amistad International Park or the Wilson Botanical Gardens. Early settlers hoped that they would be on the Interamerican Highway, thus providing access to plantations in Costa Rica and Panama where there was demand for fresh fruit, vegetables, and dairy products.

GETTING HERE: Take *Tracopa's* San Vito bus from C. 2/4, Av. 18, in San José (six hrs., ☎ 221-4214, 773-3410). Another line, *Sáenz y Ureña* (☎ 223-4975) leaves at 7 and 2 from Av. 16/18, C. 13 near Plaza Víquez in San José. *Empresa Alfaro* (☎ 223-8229) also runs from C. 16, Av. 5. Get a *directo* bus if possible. The best time to depart is early, so that you can enjoy the mountain scenery. Numerous buses also run from San Isidro and Golfito (via Ciudad Neily); the very scenic US-built road from Ciudad Neily to San Vito was constructed in 1945 because of its strategic proximity to the Panama Canal.

PRACTICALITIES: Stay in **Hotel Collina Annex**, **Hotel Tropical**, **Hotel Pitier** (☎ 773-3006), or in **Cabinas Las Mirlas** (☎773-3054) which are next to the offices of the Ministerio de Agricultura.

Low-budget/inexpensive **Hotel El Ceibo** (☎ 773-3025) has a restaurant and is in back of the Municipalidad. Its rooms are sunny and attractive and run around US$20 d.

Low-budget **Albergue Firenze** (☎ 773-3206) can be found down the road to Río Terraba which begins to the L from the town's entrance. A bit farther on are low-budget, clean **Cabinas Las Huacas** (☎ 773-3115), an establishment which operates a weekend disco.

Attractive **Paolo's Guest House** (☎ 773-3407) is a two-storey home surrounded by tropical forest. Rates run around US$30 and kitchen use is available.

If you wish to stay near but not in the botanical gardens, **La Cascadas Cabinas and Restaurant** is about 600 m before the gardens on the L hand side coming from San Vito.

For Italian food try the **Mamma Mia Pizzería**, which is in an old house and has low prices, or the **Restaurant Liliana**. Liveliest nightspot is the **Disco Banarara**.

FROM SAN VITO: Buses to San José and San Isidro leave from the *Tracopa* terminal (☎ 773-3410) at the S end of town. From downtown, buses run to Neily; the La Amistad Park towns of Las Mellizas, Las Tablas, and Cotón; and to other local destinations.

Peninsula de Osa and Paraue Nacional Corcovado (Osa Peninsula and Corcovado National Park)

The Osa peninsula is one of Costa Rica's most important natural areas, due to its isolation, biological diversity, and the peninsula's large areas of old growth forest and other undisturbed regions. The bulk of the peninsula is contained in Corcovado National Park. Despite the park, much of the area remains unprotected, and illegal logging is a serious problem here.

Located in the heart of the SW's Golfo Dulce region, it has extensive stretches of mangroves to the N, a large forested plateau on its W flank, and a huge lagoon in the center, which is nearly surrounded by mountains. In addition there are estuaries, wetlands, rocky headlands, rivers, waterfalls, and beaches. Its lowland forest, the area's largest, is the last bastion of indigenous plants and animals in the nation's SW. Surrounded by jolillo palms, 2,471-acre (1,000-ha) Laguna Corcovado, a herbaceous freshwater marsh in the lowlands' center, provides a home for waterfowl, reptiles, and amphibians. The one drawback to all of this is that there are few trails: for the most part you must walk along the beach.

FLORA AND FAUNA: Eight different habitats have been identified, and the park has the nation's greatest wealth and variety of wildlife; there are 13 major ecosystems within the park, and each distinct habitat hosts innumerable species. Forests here are prototypical rainforest: a multitude of species, tall trees with spectacular buttresses, large vines and woody lianas. Areas of high foliage density, such as the Llorana Plateau, contain over 100 tree species per acre. In places, canopy height reaches 180-262 ft. (55-80 m), the highest trees in the nation!

A large number of endemic species call Corcovado home and offer a visual feast of wildlife. In an area only half the size of Yosemite National Park, there are 285 species of birds, 139 species of mammals, 16 species of freshwater fish, and 116 reptiles and amphibians. Corcovado may be the last remaining Costa Rican habitat of the severely endangered harpy eagle. Among the endangered species residing here are squirrel monkeys, jaguars, tapirs, white lipped peccaries, and scarlet macaws.

> For a full account of the fascinating story behind the park's creation read *The Quetzal and the Macaw* by David Rains Wallace.

HISTORY: The concept of turning Corcovado into a national park was put forward in 1970. But the area's remoteness, the creation of other new parks, and the lack of funds prevented its realization. As the decade wore on, more and more families began to settle in the peninsula, hunters were decimating the wildlife (in one instance shooting an entire herd of peccaries just for amusement) and one lumber company, which owned a major section of the future park at that time, cemented a logging partnership agreement with various Japanese companies.

The brutal 1975 murder of Swedish expatriate Olof Wessberg, who was visiting the park in order to investigate its potential as a national park, helped spur President Oduber to start Corcovado. The original 88,956-acre (36,000-ha) park was created in Oct. 1975; 19,113 acres (7,735 ha) consisting of rugged highlands in the peninsula's center were added in 1980, making a total of 108,069 acres (43,735 ha). The park was closed briefly in 1994 when 90 gold panners were peacefully evicted and in 1995 when 150 were ousted.

The forests surrounding Corcovado are being logged at an alarming rate. Environmentalists have been calling for a logging permit ban for the peninsula until an in-depth management study is executed. Legendary Greenpeace ship *The*

A rugged stretch of Corcovado coast.

A beach along the Corcovado park coast.

Rainbow Warrior visited here in 1998 but did not get any satisfactory responses from the government. A Feb. 1999 demostration in the town of Osa led to violence when police tore banners from protesters and dragged some of them off.

GETTING HERE: There are a number of ways to enter both the peninsula and the park, and the way you choose will depend upon your time, finances, and energy.

GOLFITO-RINCÓN-CORCOVADO: Only a madman would take this route, but you'll want to know about it. Inquire in Golfito concerning boats to the small settlement of **Rincón**. If you can get one, it's about a 12-hour hike from there to Rancho Quemado and three additional hours to the Río Drake where you can swim and relax. From there the next town is Drake, and then it's another 90 min. to Agujitas. If you can't get a ride from there with a boat to the park station of San Pedrillo (one hr.), you must walk another 20 km (12 miles). In all of these towns, only the most basic provisions, along with a small selection of fruits, are available.

It takes 2.5 hrs. down the beach to **La Llorona** ("Weeping Woman") which has a 100-ft. (30-m) waterfall cascading onto the beach. Get underneath and experience an intense needle-like shower which varies in intensity from spot to spot. There's a beautiful archlike rock formation along the beach, and you may see hundreds of red fiddler crabs. From the beach there are two indistinct trails: one goes to a waterfall (you must swim across a river and clamber over rocks to get to it) and another (two-three hrs.) goes to a shelter near Laguna Corcovado.

Another alternative is to walk along the beach four hrs. to Sirena.You must wade through three sand flea-infested rivers (Llorona, Corcovado, and Sirena) that can be crossed only at low tide and, as there's no shade, the sun beats down unmercifully. Be sure to check tide tables before departing! You must put your pack on your head, cross the river naked, all the while scratching sand fleas and watching out for the small sharks that reside at river crossings.

GOLFITO-PUERTO JIMÉNEZ-CORCOVADO: This route is described under "from Puerto Jiménez" in the "Puerto Jiménez" section.

BY PLANE: Aeronaves de Costa Rica (☎ 750-0278) offers charter planes that will fly you in to Sirena from Golfito (around US$120/planeload). From San José you can fly with SAETA (☎ 232-1474/9514) for about US$400/planeload.

OTHER ROUTES: Other alternatives are to fly in to Drake Wilderness Camp on the N side of Osa Peninsula, enter via boat from Sierpe and use one of the many lodges at and near Drake Bay as a base for visiting the park (see "Drake Bay" for specifics).

PREPARATIONS: It's better if you can bring your own food as you'll be less of a burden for the park personnel. While a tent is not mandatory, a mosquito net and spray-on insect repellent are. While it's too hot and humid for rain gear, an umbrella is another must, as are rubber boots. Be warned that the chiggers (in the meadows and woods) and sand fleas (on the beaches) are ferocious, so take appropriate precautions! All roads become impassable after a rain; four-wheel-drive vehicles here often use snow chains to get through the mud. If you're planning to fly into the park, you must call the ranger station in advance (☎ 735-5036, fax 735-5011). You can also visit them at their headquarters next to the Banco Nacional in Jiménez and inform them of your arrival date and length of stay. All ranger stations can

One of Corcovado's many lovely waterfalls.

provide accommodation and meals given advance notice — preferably one week.

Puerto Jiménez

This small town is a jumping-off point for Corcovado National Park. Although it was formerly only an overnight pit stop, the growth of the tourism industry has made it a destination in and of itself.

GETTING HERE: *Travelair* (☎ 220-3054, 232-7883 fax 220-0413; information@travelair-costarica.com) flies here from Golfito. (Fly from San José to Golfito and connect). You can also charter a plane (for about US$55) or a water taxi (US$35). There's a bus from Ciudad Neily at 7 and 3 which you can intercept at Chacaritas, also known as Piedras Blancas, on the Interamerican. You can also connect with this bus by taking a *Zona Sur* bus from San José, in which case you should leave as early as possible. From San Isidro de El General, a *bus* (five hrs.) runs here at 5:30 and noon.

DRIVING: By car, you should follow the Interamerican along to Piedras Blancas where you turn R towards Puerto Jiménez, which is another 50 km farther.

PRACTICALITIES: Regrettably, the town is on its way to two-tier pricing for accommodation so be sure you don't get gouged!

Bar, Restaurant, y Cabinas La Carolina.has cabins for rent (around US$6).

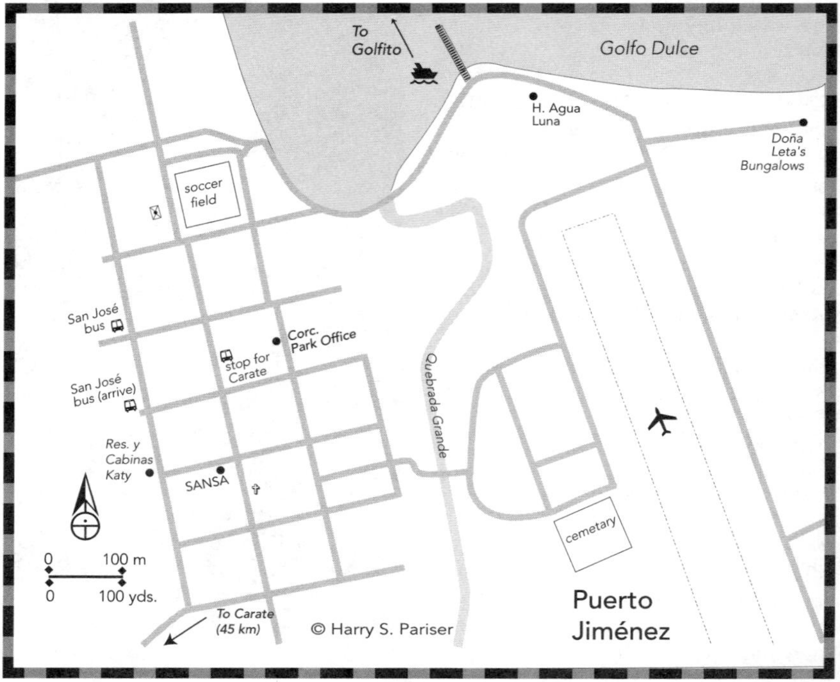

Low-budget **Cabinas Marcelina** (☎ 735-5007, fax 735-5045) has six rooms with bath and fan for around US$30 d.

Cabinas Brisas del Mar (☎ 735-5028, fax 735-5012) has nine low-budget rooms.

Vivero y Jardín Joyosa (near the Texaco station) and **Pensión Quintero** (☎ 735-5087) are also low-budget and can arrange horseback riding and tours.

Cabinas Manglares (☎ 735-5002, fax 735-5121; Apdo. 55-8203, Puerto Jimenez) charges around US$35 d) but not its accommodation standards. You can see scarlet macaws and toucans on the grounds.

Beachfront **Doña Leta's bungalows** (US$35 d; Apdo. 91, Puerto Jiménez) are a set of seven attractive wooden cabinas, restaurant/bar, and offers kayaking, scuba, and jungle treks.

www.hotels.co.cr/donaleta.html
letabell@sol.racsa.co.cr

Opened in 1995, **Cabinas Iguana Iguana** (☎ 735-5158) has seven rooms with private baths in its main building, three more with a shared bath in another building, and six *cabinas*. Rates are around US$15-25 d during the high season. There is a restaurant on the property. Transportation to Corcovado can be arranged.

The **Agua Luna** (☎ 735-5034/5108/5033) is a set of moderate cabins with bar good restaurant, and a/c, bath tubs, TVs, refrigerators, and tours.

El Bambú is a campground around a km to the N of town which offers meals, has guides, and rents tents, bikes, hammocks, horses, and a single car.

Out on the edge of town, **Cabinas Eyelin** (☎ 735-5011) charges around US$10-15 per room; it is a homestay run by a friendly Tico family.

Designed for sportsfisherfolk and adventurers alike, the **Crocodile Bay Lodge** (toll-free ☎ 877-733-5146, fax 707-778-8077) offers fishing and eco-tour packages from US$1,065-4400 depending upon length and number of people.

robin@dnai.com

FOOD: Agua Luna offers seafood and pasta dishes and has a waterfront location.

The local center for services and hanging out is **Soda La Carolina** (☎ 735-5033, fax 735-5073) on the main drag.

Pan Dulce Café and Galeria is on a side street off the main drag. It has dishes as diverse as *gado gado* and veggie burgers as well as great desserts. It also sells the *Tico Times*.

Pizza Rock (☎ 735-5295) serves pizza, salads, and pastas.

Other alternatives include **Comidas Típicas la Campesina** and Restaurant Josette which offers Chinese and seafood dishes.

El Rancho is a good place to have a drink.

Cortel's office is at the corner of the soccer field.

Set next to the Banco Nacional de Costa Rica, the **park office** (☎ 735-5036) is on a street running parallel to the main street. They can give you some information, a permit sheet which you bring with you, and (perhaps) maps.

A **pay phone** is available on the main street.

OUTSIDE TOWN: Cabinas Playa Blanca are less than an hr. to the N of town near La Palma, and there is spartan accommodation where the bus stops in La Palma (the nearest town to Los Patos in the park).

Also to the N is **Albergue Ecoturistico El Tigre** (☎/fax 735-5440, fax 735-5045) which has rooms and meals for around US$35 with baths. Horseback riding and hiking (on the reserve's trails) are available.

In the vicinity, **Ecological Corcovado Guest House** (☎ 775-2422, fax 735-5045) is a bec and breakfast offering spacious rooms and breakfast for around US$25 d.

A bit farther N, the **El Tucán Cabinas and Restaurant** (☎ 775-0522/0033) has low-budget rooms.

La Llanta Picante (☎ 735-5414) is set several km before town on the Río Tigre. It offers bicycle and other tours of its reserve as well as cabins (around US$80 with meals). In the US call/fax 815-235-9307 from 9-9 CST.
spicytire@aol.com

SERVICES: A good place to stop in is at the tourist info center, the **Osa Natural Project** (☎ 735-5062, 735-5169, fax 735-5043, 735-5121); they can hook you up with local lodges and tour operators. **anguilar@sol.racsa.co.cr**

Tobaga Loaciga (☎ 735-5092; marine radio ch. 12) offers tours and fishing trips along the Golfo Dulce.

Everyday Adventure Tours (☎/fax 735-5138; Apdo. 15, Puerto Jimenéz) offers kayaking and hiking trips, tree climbing, fishing, canopy exploration, surfing, diving, and hotel reservations. They are 50 m W of the bus stop.
everyday@sol.racsa.co.cr

Escondido Trex (☎/fax 735-5206) offers kayaking and other single and multi-day trips to the Corcovado and Gulfo Dulce areas. It's located in Soda Carolina.
osatrex@sol.racsa.co.cr

FROM PUERTO JIMÉNEZ: A morning bus (at 5:30), the express bus to San Isidro, and trucks (one hr.) run regularly to the small village of **La Palma**. Here, be sure to visit the Women's Group of La Palma, **ASOFEP** (fax 735-5116), who operate a cafeteria, library, and tourist information center.

You may stay here at low-budget **Cabinas Corcovado** (☎ 775-0433, fax 775-0033) which is set five km from La Palma and 500 m from the entrance to Corcovado, It offers campsites (US$5) and rooms (around US$5 pp); horses are avail(able for US$6 ph. The English-speaking owner is reportedly an excellent guide US$8 ph or US$80 pd).

In La Palma itself, the **El Tucán** offers rooms with private bath for around US$6; there are several other hotels.

From here it's about 12 km (three to four hrs. on foot along a gravel road) to the NE entrance at Los Patos — on the way you must traverse the Río Rincón 19 times. Cars make the trip (one hr.) during the dry season, and you can lease your own vehicle if you wish.

The area around **Los Patos** tends to be slippery and wet. Camping and food can be arranged at the ranger station here (about US$5 for a meal) if arrangements are made in advance. Or you can arrange to stay with **Coopeunioro** (☎ 233-3333, ☎/fax 259-3605, 259-3401), a 13-family cooperative operated by former goldminers. These farmers have 100 ha of forest and aim to expand this to 1,000 ha in order to form a buffer zone around Corcovado. Food and lodging (for up to 12) cost around US$15 pp which includes transport from La Palma.
www.agroecoturismo.net
cooprena@sol.racsa.co.cr

It's then another four to six hrs. (16 km) by trail to **Sirena**. (You may stay and eat at the solar-powered ranger station there but reservations must be made by phone or in person at the ranger station in Puerto Jiménez. They offer lodging in recently constructed dorm rooms; camp in front). They are understaffed and could use volunteers.There are trails, and canoes are available for rental. This would be an ideal spot to spend a few days.

En route there are six km of mountain forest trails and 14 km of hiking through rainforest. You will have to cross a number of streams which can come up to your thighs in the rainy season. (Watch out for poisonous spiders who spin their webs along the trail).

From there, you can proceed to Playa Madrigal (four hrs.) and camp at La Leona, where it's an eight-hr. hike back down to Puerto Jiménez or four to five hrs. (15 km) to Sirena, a trail which must be negotiated at low tide. You'll pass a rusting ship at Punta Chancha.

VIA CARATE: Mini Mercado El Tigre (☎ 735-5075) offers a daily taxi to Carate (departs 6 AM, returns 8:30 AM). Others may be available. Along the way you pass by stretches as deforested as Guanacaste and other stretches which are lush and majestic. Contact Cirilo Espinoza at the *pulpería* next to La Carolina. Taxis can also be chartered through the park office. Once in Carate, it's less than an hour's walk to La Leona ranger station. Don't swim here because of the strong current and the danger from sharks. However, camping near the *pulpería* is fine and popular.

LEAVING THE PENINSULA: After visiting majestic and exhilarating Corcovado, the deforested stretches surrounding it leave one with a sense of loss and depression. A bus runs all the way to San Isidro; from there you can get a bus to San José. Another bus runs to and from Ciudad Neily. There's also a boat (6 AM) and a flight (with Travelair) to Golfito daily.

Lapa Ríos

Remote and luxurious **Lapa Ríos** (Apdo. 100, Puerto Jiménez) is the only Costa Rican rainforest resort of its price and character. While catering to upscale adventurers, it genuinely preserves the surrounding rainforest. A million dollar-plus project, the ridge-perched hotel has one of the most dramatic overlooks in the Osa Peninsula.

HISTORY: Opened in 1993, the hotel was the result of a long-held dream on the part of owners John and Karen Lewis, a musician and lawyer from Minneapolis. The Lewises had served in the Peace Corps in Africa, then hit upon the idea of a reserve that would protect the rainforest while generating an income for themselves. They decided that Costa Rica was the ideal place to start such a venture. The site of Lapa Ríos fulfilled their list of 25 specifications, and construction began in 1990. The Lewises also participated in fund raising and construction of the Carbonera School which serves local school children. The reserve comprises 750 acres of old growth and 250 acres which are being reforested. There's marvelous (but steep) hiking in the reserve, and this is your chance to see pristine old-growth rainforest, some of the most beautiful woods in all of Costa Rica.

PRACTICALITIES: This beautifully designed hotel is constructed of tropical hardwoods, all obtained with permits. A large thatched pavilion, the front part houses the reception and dining area, and its spiral staircase leads up to a catwalk with a 360-degree panorama of the surrounding area. From the patio and swimming pool there's a wonderful view straight across the Gulfo Dulce. The white-walled and thatch-roofed *cabinas*, downhill and spaced out in succession, are next. Inside each of the rooms are two beds with mosquito nets; the windows are covered with netting which keeps out insects while letting in the breeze. The walls use *caña blanca* wood, the desk is made with *almendro* (almond), the roof is of *mangle* (mangrove), and the floor is of *cristobal*. Food is included and good. Dishes are largely continental. Service is impeccable and very formal. Prices run around US$230 d per day including food.

You can contact the office in Puerto Jiménez (☎/fax 735-5130) from Mon. to Fri., 8-5 and Sat. 8-2. The lodge can be reached directly through Coopeserimec, a phone patch service. Call 775-0120.

SERVICES: A beachside *cabaña* is under construction. It's about 15 min. to the beach, which is largely rocky but beautiful. The woods are glorious even if the paths are a bit treacherous and steep in parts. It's easy to see animals such as howlers, the tree buttresses and ephiphytes are impressive and, unlike many other "eco-resorts," you really are in primary forest here.

www.centralamerica.com/cr/hotel/laparios.htm
laparios@sol.racsa.co.cr

Bosque del Cabo

Bosque del Cabo (☎ 735-5206, fax 735-5043; Interlink 528, PO Box 025635, Miami, FL 33152) is a lovely lodge 20 km from Puerto Jiménez. In the ultra-luxury range (including food), this remote 350-acre eco-resort is above Playa Matapolo at Osa's S tip. The entrance is past Lapa Ríos a few km and to the L. Rooms are around US$ 50 or US$100 pp (deluxe) with meals and other amenities included. They have a pool, solar lighting, and a resident guide. Horseback riding with a guide is US$15 pp, pd. As with Lapa Ríos, it should cost you around US$25 to charter a taxi from Puerto Jiménez.

Saving the Osa Rainforest

The **Cecropia Foundation** (☎/fax 735-5532) is a watchdog foundation which is attempting to mobilize a "private forest guard unit which will patrol the zone and be on hand when violations occur." All funds donated go directly to the project.
cecropia@sol.racsa.co.cr

If you book directly and don't come through a travel agency, there's a discount. There's a waterfall and guided horseback tours are available. The owners are looking for physically fit guests who enjoy exploring the area's beaches and trails; box lunches are available. A goal here is to reintroduce scarlet macaws to the wild, but funding (as well as someone to organize the project) is lacking as of yet. There's no electricity, but there is peace and quiet and nature in abundance.

www.bosquedelcabo.com
boscabo@sol.racsa.co.cr

Enroute to Carate

Like Drake Bay and Dominical, this once remote area is developing fast. **Hacienda Bahía Esmeralda** (cell ☎ 381-8521, fax 735-5045, marine band 83) is a luxury-priced three-room guesthouse with three adjacent luxury cottages. It has a freshwater pool, horseback riding, kayaking and is proximate to both rainforest and beach. Cuisine reflects Thai, Mexican, Chinese, French, and Indian influences. Vegan and veggie dishes are on offer. Rates are around US$120 pp, pd including taxes, transportation to and from Puerto Jimenéz (to Matapalo, 18 km).

Encanta la Vida (☎ 735-5062, fax 735-5043) offers horseback riding and fishing; it's around US$150 d.

Casa Bambu Beach House (☎ 263-1650, fax 263-7553) is a home with rooms (around US$70 d) and a yard leading down to a secluded beach
casabambu@juno.com

Nearby **El Tumbo de Las Olas** (fax 735-5045) offers simple cabins (US$50 with breakfast) and pool.

The **Carate Jungle Camp** (☎ 735-5211, fax 735-5049) offers simple rooms with a shared kitchen.

The LookOut Inn (☎ 735-5205) is a three-storey inn with a view; rooms (US$80 d; US$130 with gourmet meals) have painted murals.
www.lookout-inn.com
wendy@lookout-inn.com

Sirena and Vicinity

You may stay and eat at Sirena's ranger station; reservations must be made by phone or in person at the ranger station in Puerto Jiménez. There are foam mattreses but no mosquito nets or sheets; camp in front. Expect to pay US$5 per meal. Be prepared to meet some of the local inhabitants: giant cockroaches, chiggers, and ferocious, insatiable mosquitos. Horses can be hired here, meals are available, and there are laundry facilities. Much of the land around the station is secondary growth, burt one path runs through old growth to the Río Claro.

Ringed by swamps, Laguna Corcovado is accessible only by boat; one path, marked *"Quebrada Camaronero,"* heads towards it. Unless you relish the prospect of being gobbled by sharks, you should avoid swimming in the ocean. The Río Sirena and Río Claro are safe enough as long as you keep out of the crocodiles' jaws.

GETTING HERE: From La Leona, it is a walk of four to five hours (15 km) along a beach and past Punta Salsipuedes to inland trails and then through the jungle until you meet the Río Claro. There you cross and head for Sirena.

FROM SIRENA: It's a 25-km hike (six or seven hrs.) to **San Pedrillo**, the park's NW entrance and ranger station. Fifteen of these are along the beach, seven are via rainforest, and the last three combine jungle and beach. Be sure to travel along the beach at high tide. After about a km on this hike you come to the swiftly flowing **Río Sirena**, which can reach three-four ft. in width during the rainy season (a bit over three ft. in the dry). After this crossing, it's some two hrs. to the **Río Corcovado** which is around two ft. deep at low tide. The **Río Llorna** is a further two hrs. Soon after you come to the **Piedra Arco**, a huge greenery-covered rock arch, the track veers off into the jungle: keep an eye out.

At low tide you can reach **Catarata La Llorona** which cascades beachward; it is the larger of two waterfalls you come to. After a few hrs. on the main trail you come to a beach. From there it's an hr. to the Río San Pedrillo where you can stay and eat. Here, you will find trails and a beautiful waterfall which you can clamber up to and bathe in. It's reached by a path along the river. From here a trail follows the coast six mi.(10 km) to Bahía Drake.

Corcovado Tent Camp

This innovative lodge (☎ 257-0766, 222-0333, fax 257-1665; Apdo. 6941, 1000 San José) is set on the beach about 1.5 km W of Carate at the S entrance to Corcovado. It the brainchild of Costa Rica Expeditions whose founder Michael Kaye has been coming to this area for decades. Not for those who wish to have their every need attended to, it is for those who enjoy simplicity and closeness to nature but want more creature comforts than are found at the ranger station.

ACCOMMODATION AND FOOD: The 10 x 10 ft. white, closely spaced tents have two single beds each. Some are on the beach while others are on a clearing above the kitchen. There are shared baths, electricity (three times daily) for the dining and bar/hammock area, and crystal clear drinking water obtained from the reserve's clear stream. Served buffet-style on two long tables, the food is quite good, especially considering that it must all be brought in by air or boat. Specialties include macadamia pancakes for breakfast, pitchers of fruit juice with meals, and filling entrees of rice, beans, vegetables, salad, and fish or meat. Dietary needs can be catered to upon request. Prices vary according to the package you have, but you can expect to spend around US$60 pp including meals.

GETTING HERE: A 15-min. charter flight from Golfito or a 45-min charter flight from San José brings you here. It's a 30-45 min. walk from the landing strip; your luggage is loaded on a horse-pulled cart.

EXCURSIONS: The beach is at your front door; the sunsets are magnificent, and dinoflagellates eerily illumine the beach at night. It's fun to hike up Quebrada Leona, a small but beautiful small creek. You'll see plenty of crabs, birds, lizards, and perhaps a snake or other wildlife. One of the resident biologists can take you down to the park (US$20 pp plus park admission), and you can hike up the Río Madrigal with him or her. The steep reserve behind the lodge is also well worth visiting, and there's a loop trail. It's easy to see toucans, scarlet macaws, and other birds, and iguanas climb trees and slither across the property. Sunset horseback rides are also available. (You can literally do a lot of birdwatching from your hammock or from your deck, if you have one of the tents perched higher up).

THE CANOPY PLATFORM: This is an interesting way (around US$75 pp) to access the rainforest canopy. From the lodge, it's an easy 1.5 hr. hike up to the beginning of the loop trail where the platform is. Along the way, you're given a guided natural history tour of the area. The 160-ft.-high ajo ("garlic") tree holding the platform is both very sturdy and allows for a superb panoramic view. It took 12 days and eight people to build the platform. Just finding the right tree took a month because it needed to have limbs large enough to support the platform as well as a good view.
www.expeditions.co.cr
costa-rica@expeditions.co.cr

Drake Bay and Vicinity

This placid bay is becoming a popular location as more and more ecotourism lodges open. Sir Francis Drake allegedly set foot here in 1579, thus the name. Regrettably, a road has been constructed. While too primitive for tourism, stretches along the road have already been deforested.

Drake Bay, La Paloma, and Cocalito are all on one side of the river. Aguila de Osa is across the swinging footbridge over the river to the L; Jinetes de Osa is a bit farther; the path to the village is to the R. Marenco is about an hour or so walk away.

GETTING HERE: Although your hotel can arrange transport from San José, you

> "Loggers come in and take enormous amounts of lumber, paying *campesinos* a pittance for it. This is not solving the problem of poverty, and is destroying a valuable resource for *campesinos*."
>
> – Osa Municipality Mayor Juan Carlos Villalobos on logging in the area (1998).
>
> "In the same way that you request the help of the Guardia Civil to repress environmentalists, why don't you also request their help to control the illegal transport of lumber and the unauthorized exploitation of our forests?"
>
> — Congressman Célimo Guido in a 1999 letter to the head of the National Systems of Conservation Areas

can take a bus to Palmar from C. 4, Av. 18 in San José at 5 and 7 AM; ☎ 221-4214. Alternatively, *SANSA* flies to Palmar, as does *Travelair* (☎ 220-3054, 232-7883, fax 220-0413; (information@travelair-costarica.com). From Palmar, you take a bus or charter a taxi to Sierpe, 20 mi.farther.

If you stay at Drake Bay Wilderness Camp you may now travel by air to Drake. You fly via charter to the improved airstrip and then either take a boat straight across or take a jeep ride along a muddy road and then a boat from a shell-covered beach. On the way, you pass several of the mysterious stone spheres which stand in front of a local home. There is a possibility that Travelair may fly here in the future.

From Sierpe, it's a couple of hours downriver and then out to the ocean and Drake Bay. Local dugouts do the route, but they are crowded and occasionally capsize. *Especiales* are faster and available for charter; bargain to get the local rate. Returning, you can generally find a ride with a local.

If you are staying at one of the main lodges, they will ferry you out in one of their boats which are manned by experienced captains. From Drake you will turn into the river where it meets the sea. As your heartrate begins to lower, you travel along the mangrove-lined river. As soon as you spy coconut palms you know you ae getting near the village. Enroute to Palmar, obstacles may include cargo-spraying aircraft and hards of cattle.

Drake Bay Wilderness Camp

Drake Bay Wilderness Camp (☎/fax 770-8012, 380-1942; San José: ☎/fax: 256-7394; Apdo. 98, 8150 Palmar Norte, Osa) was one of the first lodges in the Osa — and the first at its particular location. It is still one of the best in Costa Rica. Owner Herbert married wife Marleny who took him back to her home village. Herb decided the spit of land was a prime location for a fishing camp, and things took off from there! The lodge is set on the flat tip of a narrow peninsula by the Río Agujítas. There are a number of benches and hammocks about and two resident squirrel monkeys provide unforgettable entertainment. (They were pets of some Costa Ricans and have been freed here).

Accommodation is in attractive cabins and large tents (available only during the

> **Visiting the Waterfall**
>
> To get to the Agujitas waterfall, take the road up to the row of houses behind the pulperia in town. Pass some cabinas and continue until you reach a wide fork where you find two tractor-graded roads. One, to the R, heads for Los Planes; the one to the L goes to Bijuagua. Turn L and head 40 m before taking a path to the R where you cross a creek and continue until you get to the Río Agujitas. Walk upriver for around half an hour until you reach the waterfall.

The entrance to Aguila de Osa is a Drake Bay landmark.

dry season). Cabins have reading lights, solar-heated hot water, and slow-moving overhead fans. Food is one of the highlights; fresh baked cinnamon rolls are featured at breakfast, and the dishes are hearty and healthy. This is the sort of place you might want to stay at if you are down-to-earth but still looking for some comfort and want to feel part of a family. Their higher-priced neighbors are a better choice if you want tonier digs with elevated views, but if you are into being cozily comfortable, you should be happy here.

Rates are from around US$50 pp (in tents) and US$70 pp (in cabins) and include meals; children are offered a discount. Also available are scuba, fishing, mountain biking, sea kayaking, bird watching, canoeing, massage, and high-quality guided tours. Charter flights and a wide variety of packages are available.

In addition to the above numbers in the USA call: 1-800-759-4658 -then dial 506-7290 and in Costa Rica call: 224-9090.
www.drakebay.com
hdrake@ticonet.co.cr

Aguila de Osa

Intimate and high quality, **Aguila de Osa** (☎ 296-2190, fax 232-7722; Apdo. 10486-1000, San José; Interlink #898, PO Box 02-5635, Miami, FL 33102) is one of the area's most attractive lodges. Perched on a hillside, its garden setting includes a gourmet restaurant and a pool. It offers sportsfishing (four boats), scuba, birding, and kayaking. It has 14 thatched-roof cabins with verandas. Rates run from around US$220 d on up.
www.centralamerica.com/cr/hotel/aguila aguilacr@sol.racsa.co.cr

Albergue Jinetes de Osa

Albergue Jinetes de Osa (☎ 385-9541; 800-317-0333; fax 303-838-0969) provides bunk bed accommodation, can arrange stays with local families on trips, and has rates which include meals. It is the headquarters of **Costa Rica Adventure Divers**, run by genial dive intructor Greg Chavez. Native Coloradan Greg, together with brother Brian, bought the lodge from a local woman and have made considerable improvements. However, it is still for people who enjoy a simpler style of accommodation. Greg also does the dive tours for some of the other local lodges, and he is a good instructor for first-time snorkelers and divers. He specializes in trips to Caño Island. Rates are around US$50 s. US$100 d; three meals are included. A two-tank dive is US$85; certification and other packages are available.
www.costaricadiving.com
crventur@costaricadiving.com

La Paloma Lodge

La Paloma (☎/fax 239-0954; radio ☎ 239-2801; Apdo. 97-4005, San Antonio de Belen, Heredia) is set atop a hill on the same side as Drake Bay Wilderness Camp. The set of luxury-priced *cabinas* and rooms have great views. They have an open-air restaurant with a great view and friendly, professional management. This offers tours, horseback rides, scuba, kayaking, canoeing, and complimentary use of snorkeling and fishing gear. There's a pool and all rooms offer solar heated hot water as well as ceiling fans. Packages (four nights including transport: around US$600-700) are available.
www.lapalomalodge.com
lapaloma@lapalomalodge.com

Cocalito Lodge

Cocalito (☎ 786-6150, fax 786-6335; 519-782-3978; Apdo. 63, Palmar Norte) is one of the less expensive places to stay. This Canadian-run lodge has a restaurant downstairs and spartan but attractive rooms upstairs. On the Drake Bay side, down from La Palona, it is set on one of the most beautiful spots along the bay — a beach with wonderful sunsets. Generator-supplied electricity is available. In addition to the standard tours offered by everyone, they have sportfishing, a mangrove tour, horseback rides, scuba, and a night at a "jungle inn." Sportfishing is offered. Expect to pay around US$20-35 pp; meal packages are US$30 pp; tax is added to both. CAmping is available for US$5 pp, pd, and is US$10 pp, pd if you use their tent.
www.costarica.net/cocalito
berrybond@aol.com

Other Accommodation

DRAKE VILLAGE ACCOMMODATION: Other, lower-priced accommodations are around the village of Drake which comprises about 250 families. Less expensive are **Casa Mirador** (☎ 227-6914) which is set on a hilltop and **Cabinas Cecilia** (☎ 771-2436) which has two six-bunk bed rooms. The latter offers a variety of trips including an Isla de Caño excursion. The **Cabinas y Restaurant Jade Mar** (☎ 771-2336) has rooms for around US$60.

AGUIJAS: Down the beach from Drake, this small village has basic accommodations offered by Cecilia Steller for about US$18 pp including room and board. Horses with guides are available for around US$25 pd including lunch. Leave messages at 771-3336 or write Apdo. 84, Palmar Norte.

CASA CORCOVADO: This relatively new entry on the Drake scene boasts spacious cabins with large four-poster beds, a thatch-roofed open-air bar, hiking trails through the 170-acre reserve. It has 24-hr. electricity, gourmet meals, and trips. It is accessible only by boat. Rates are around US$177 for the cheapest package. Call 236-3181, fax 256-7409, or write Interlink # 253, PO Box 526770, Miami, FL 33152.
www.casacorcovado.com
corcovado@sol.racsa.co.cr

Delfin Amor Eco Lodge (☎ 394-2632, 283-0122) is a new effort which is part of the multinational Divine Dolphin (which has similar efforts in the Bahamas. They promote the controversial idea that playing with dolphins may help with healing or ameliorating childhood disorders. Rates are US$50 pd including meals; facilities are spartan; packages are available.

www.divine.dolphin.com/delfinamor.htm
info@divine.dolphin.com

JUNGLE AL'S: Al's place (fax 788-8811) will never make it up on the list of "top-ten resorts," and it's not intended to! Al noticed that backpackers coming through were being turned away from the park headquarters because of problems of one sort or another. So he established this "base camp" which is within walking distance of the park and Drake (2.5 hrs.) It's at Playa Rincón, a 2 km sandy beach. He offers horseback riding, diving and fishing charters, and guided tours into the jungle. He charges around US$8 pp, pd for meals all-year-round. The large, shady campground is just steps from the beach, and you can rent a tent here for US$10 pp, pn or pay US$5 pp, pn for your own. If coming from Sierpe, you need to get off at Playa San Josecito and then walk to his place which is 100 m S of the green church building on Playa Rincón.

CAMPANARIO BIOLOGICAL RESERVE: This is a basic lodge (☎ 282-5898, fax 282-8750; Apdo. 56, Santa Ana 2000) without electricity. Six-day, five-night tours are offered.
campinar@sol.racsa.co.cr

Marenco Biological Station

Originally set up to provide a base for biological researchers, Marenco has long been one of the nation's foremost privately-established reserves. It's a homey kind of place as opposed to a snooty eco-resort. Visitors land by boat on the rocky shore and then climb up the concrete pathway on the hill to the office. There's a spacious open-air dining room which offers a tremendous panorama: Cano Island and the facing bay. Sunsets in particular are unforgettable and magnificent!

Screened cabins are attractively designed in line with the functional standard found in the first-generation of Costa Rican eco-tourism lodges: cold-water showers, fans, tables, and beds with mosquito nets. Roofs are thatch with a tin overlay. Rocking chairs on spacious balconies are a definite plus. (An upgrade is in progress).

The staff is friendly and hardworking manager-owner Eduardo Miranda is a delight. Guides are trained biologists who do research in the off season. Meals are served either a la carte or buffet style, and, given the remote location, choices are plentiful.

Marenco distinguishes itself from the competition by its fine collection of hiking trails which pass through primary and secondary forest. It covers 1,250 acres (500 ha). This is a definite plus in the high season because you can avoid the crowded trails in the national park. Grab a walking stick and get an early start. Take your time if you want to see things.

One nice route to take is the steep *La Fila* up to the Giant Forest (take the diversion to see the giant tree), and then the *Bejuco* down to the rainforest and back. Other trails lead to the Río Claro and a hard-to-access waterfall. There's also a nice swimming beach. Optional tours include day visits to Corcovado, Isla de Caño, and the Río Claro. The way to get here is by chartered plane or by land and boat. A wide variety of packages are available. Call 258-1919, fax 255-1346, or write Apdo. 4025, 1000 San José. In the US call 800-278-6223 and in Europe call 1-305-908-4169.
www.marencolodge.com/corcovado
info@marencolodge.com

Formerly "Punta Marenco," **Punta Río Claro National Wildlife Refuge** (☎ 257-

1047, 382-9310, fax 256-4922) is an offshoot of Marenco which is run by one of the Miranda brothers.
www.crdirect.com/marenco
pemide@sol.racsa.co.cr

Río Sierpe Lodge

River Sierpe Lodge (cel ☎ 284-5595, fax 786-6291; in San José: 257-7010, fax 257-7012; PO Box 85, Palmar Norte) is a deep-sea and tidal-basin fishing and nature lodge located in the NE section of the peninsula. Scuba and snorkeling day trips to Isla de Caño and Isla Violin can be arranged, as can fishing, hiking and horseback riding, , birdwatching, kayaking, excursions to Panama, two-day RT cruises to Isla de Coco. Facilities include 17 attractive cabins and a library. Transport is available from Palmar. Arrival at the lodge is by boat. Rates are around US$70 pp including meals and tax but not excursions. Special rates are available for independent travelers, naturalists, and student groups.
escapes@sol.racsa.co.cr

Reserva Biológica Isla de Caño (Caño Island Biological Reserve)

Located 12 mi.(20 km) off the coast, this 480-acre (200-ha) park rises 296 ft. (90 m) above sea level. Most of the 740-acre (300-ha) island is covered by virgin tropical wet forests. It is thought that the island was an indigenous cemetery and, later, a pirate hideaway. Some go so far as to claim that it was the inspiration for Robert Louis Stevenson's *Treasure Island*. Although the tombs have been looted, perfectly fashioned stone spheres remind you of their presence. Its central plateau floods during the rainy season.

Rangers relax at the Caño Island ranger station.

Nearly transparent water surrounds its high cliffs and miniature 100-yard (100-m) beaches. In 1973, the island was rented out to a foreign firm which intended to start a tourist development. The planned wharves and marinas would have devastated the surrounding coral reefs, the largest colony on the Pacific coast. Curiously, the disclosure of plans for a nude beach as part of the development doomed the plans. Still, much of the old growth forest was leveled. In 1976, this island was declared part of Corcovado National Park, and it gained independent status in 1978.

FLORA AND FAUNA: Compared to mainland Corcovado, there is a paucity of species here. There are some 60 species of trees, the most prominent of which is the giant milk tree which provides a drinkable sap. Boa constrictors number among the four species of snakes. A legacy of the pirates, the introduced wild pigs here were exterminated by Sergio Jiménez and his son Tony on behalf of the park service.

GETTING HERE: Unless you have your own boat, a tour or charter is the only way. These can be arranged with virtually any lodge in the vicinity. And on any given day you're more than likely to encounter a group from another lodge sharing the beach.

> ?!? Isla del Caño's name is believed to derive from Costa Rican Spanish slang for "fresh water gutter" because of its many streams.

HIKING: This is the only way to see the aboveground portion of the island. Most of the indigenous relics here have been looted, so the park asks that you not carry daypacks or other bags on the trail. After you get up the hill and along a ways, you begin to comprehend what has been lost through looting and deforestation. There are some splendid old growth trees festooned with epiphytes and some old stone spheres as well as bits of stonework on the ground. It takes about 30 min. to get up the hill to the first junction. The trip to the lighthouse (40 min. each way) is wonderful, but it's steep and somewhat precipitous, so you need permission in advance.

To the L the trail continues for another 20-25 min., where a short trail goes up to a *mirador*; another continues on, then turns off, leading to some spheres and Indian relics. If you continue straight, you'll come to a small waterfall.

Isla del Coco National Park (Parque Nacional Isla del Coco)

Of volcanic origin, Isla del Coco is a steep and rocky island which is blessed with abundant springs and waterfalls. Located about 311 mi.(500 km) off the Pacific coast, the island measures 21 by 13 miles. It may be accessed only at Chatham and Wafer Bays. The island gets 276 in. (7,000 mm) of rainfall per year; its highest point is 2,080-ft. (634-m) Cerro Iglesias. Be careful while visiting here: A tourist mysteriously disappeared in 1989.

By the small stream at smaller, rocky Chatham — named after an 18th C. expeditionary ship— there are a number of rocks inscribed with the names of arriving mariners. Wafer, a few km to the W, is named after a 17th C. actor, physician, and writer who kept company with pirates.

GETTING HERE: The ***Okeanos Aggressor*** (☎ 220-1679, (800) 348-2628, 504-385-

2416, PO Drawer K, Morgan City, LA 70381; www.aggressor.com; divboat@aol.com) and **Ríos Tropicales** (☎ 233-6455, fax 255-4354; Apdo. 472, 1200 San José; www.riostro.com; info@riostro.com) both have very expensive trips. The former is recommended for dive fanatics: that's about all you do on the trip.

Also running dive trips are **Lost World Adventures** (☎ 800-999-0558) and **Escenarios Tropicales** (☎ 224-2555, fax 234-1554)

The **Undersea Hunter** (☎ 800-203-2120) offers live aboard trips as well.
www.underseahunter.com
info@underseahunter.com

The National Park Service might be able to help with chartering. Visiting can be expensive. The government charges for entry, anchoring, and landing a plane. No visit may exceed 12 days.

FLORA AND FAUNA: One might guess that the island gained its name because of an abundance of coconut palms. In reality, however, coconuts are few and far between, with most of the palms belonging to the species *Rooseveltia franklinia* (named after FDR, who visited the island four times). This tree looks like the coconut palm from a distance. Although there are not many animals here, those present are not afraid of man since they have been given no reason to be. To date, over 70 endemic species of plants and 70 types of animals (largely insects) have been identified here. Many cultivated plants have gone wild here, including coffee and the guava and some threaten to supplant some of the native species.

Birds include the frigatebird, the white tern, masked and red-footed boobies, green and blue herons, peregrine falcons, and many others. Three of the seven land birds are endemic, including the Coco island finch, closely related to the species found on the Galapagos. The other two are the cuckoo and Ridgeway's papamoscas. Aside from two small lizards, reptiles and amphibians are entirely absent. Because mammals were not here when the finely-tuned ecosystem evolved, feral pigs and cats wreak havoc. In their search for roots and grubs, pigs dig up the ground, causing trees to topple and soil to erode. The same type of devastation is wrought by goats and deer, though their numbers are smaller. Cats prey on birds and lizards; their only virtue is that they keep down the population of rats, another imported species with no natural enemies.

> ☛ Keep in mind that **trips to Coco** fill up quickly during June, July, and Aug. (the prime months for viewing hammerheads) It is important to pack correctly for a trip to Coco. You must bring save-a-dive kits, signaling devices, extra neoprene, and all personal hygiene items as well as medicine including seasick medication. Just bring a few changes of casual clothes. In winter, you will need to bring waterproof clothing and a six mm wetsuit with hood and gloves.

HISTORY: Legendary Portuguese pirate Benito Bonito and Captain James Thomson and his crew made off with the Peruvian valuables they had contracted to escort, and they are among those who are alleged to have buried treasure here.

Historical happenstance gave Costa Rica sovereignty over the island after it rescued 13 seamen shipwrecked there when a Chilean frigate capsized in 1832. German treasure hunter Augusto Gissler spent 18 years there from 1889 on, searching for treasure unsuccessfully under the cover of a government "agricultural" contract.

A notable incident in island history occurred in 1992 when ships belonging to the militant environmental group Sea Shepherd attacked six Costa Rican fishing boats with paint-filled bullets. They were responding to a tip from a park guard who alleged that the boats were killing dolphins and using the meat for shark bait. The boats denied they were fishing inside the protected park waters.

Shark fins are exported to Japan where they are prized as a delicacy. As a consequence of overfishing, the hammerheads here may be wiped out by the decade's end. Common practice is to slice off the dorsal and pectoral fins, then toss the maimed animals back in the water. Rudderless and unable to swim and therefore to hunt, the sharks starve to death.

In a 1992 development which disturbed environmentalists, the government approved a high-tech search by a US computer magnate for the treasure thought to have been buried by pirate William Thompson. The search was carried out by an ultra-light aircraft equipped with pontoons for sea landing and takeoff. Meanwhile, scuba divers carrying "proton magnetometers" relayed information to a boat stationed offshore.The US$5 million search, they hope, would lead to US$800 million worth of booty. However, at the time of the contract's expiration, the entrepreneurs had come up empty handed. The government announced its intentions to ban further such ventures.

The first ranger station was established here in 1992, and equipment is still inadequate to patrol the 15 km of offshore reserves. Unfortunately, illegal fishing is still common. Friends of Coco Island Foundation is intent on conserving the island and its offshore marine life.

Parque Internacional de la Amistad (La Amistad International Park)

This enormous 479,199-acre (193,929-ha) "friendship" park straddles the upper slopes of the Talamancas, and may someday mesh with a promised twin park in adjoining Panama. Both areas protect invaluable watersheds. The nation's newest park, it has more than doubled the size of the park system. No facilities or services are available and there are very few trails. Elevation within the park ranges from 650 to 11,644 ft. (200-3,459 m).

FLORA AND FAUNA: The park has rainforest, cloud forest, and *páramo* with resident populations of jaguars, tapirs, and pumas. The 400 bird species include quetzals and harpy eagles.

GETTING THERE AND GETTING AROUND: To get here take the bus from San José to San Vito, then on to Las Mellizas. The few trails are all unmarked. Contact the NPS regarding the possibility of hiring a guide and horse. If you have a car, this would be a good day trip from San Vito or San Isidro. Camping is permitted near entrances at Las Mellizas (easiest to access and best for hiking), Aguas Calientes, and at Helechales. Easiest to access, Las Mellizas is best for hiking. To get here take a *San Vito-La Lucha bus* (9:30 AM departure) and walk six km or drive all the way. Trout fishing is possible here with a permit. Horses and guides can also be hired here.

PRACTICALITIES: La Amistad Lodge (☎ 289-7667, fax 289-7858; Apdo. 774, 1000 San José) offers accommodation for around US$60 pp, pn including three meals. They can arrange horses and guides, and you can camp also. Their travel agency, Rainbow Tours, offers a four-day all-inclusive tour for around US$500.

GETTING HERE: A large part of the adventure. The road is reasonably good up until San Vito. Then you move off onto what some might call a gravel road for an hour's boneshaking drive past coffee plantations until you reach the settlement of Las Mellizas. Then you enter the finca itself, passing grove after grove of organic coffee trees until you pull up in front of the main building. In the dry season, an ordinary car can make it up to the Río Coton which is a km from the farm.

The lodge might be best characterized as being Swiss Alpine in design. But the hospitality is pure Tico. The dining room is downstairs and generously proportioned living areas (including a hammock and rocking chairs) are up one level. Some of the rooms are set up a set of stairs and to the back. Rooms are quite comfortable and large with two large beds, excellent lighting, writing desk, and a modern bath with shower stalls.

Food is typical Tico. There are hiking trails near the lodge, but it is better to go with a guide. A country camp is located near virgin forest at Cotoncito.

As a souvenir you might bring home a bottle of organic habanero sauce or jalapeño sauce.

www.laamistad.com
amistad@sol.racsa.co.cr

Monte Amou Lodge (☎/fax 229-3618, call before sending fax; page: 225-2500) adjoins La Amistad International Park and is near Potrero Grande; it has four cabins with three beds each and a main structure with four d rooms with shared baths. Facilities include conference room, birdwatching, and family-style meals.

Other Southern Locales

Palmar Norte/Palmar Sur

This small town, straddling the Río Grande de Terraba, lies 125 km S of San Isidro. Its only attraction is its mysterious *esferas de piedra,* conical stone spheres (see sidebar), which can be found in backyards and other locations. The town is a gateway to Osa and Corcovado. (See "Drake's Bay" under "Corcovado and Osa.")

PRACTICALITIES: Drake Bay lodges may pick you up here and take you to Sierpe to meet your boat.

You can take a bus to Palmar from C. 4, Av. 5/6 in San José with *Tracopa* and *Alfaro* (☎ 221-4214, 223-7685, 222-2666, 222-2051)

SANSA (☎ 221-9414, 233-0397, 233-3258, fax 255-2176) and *Travelair* (☎ 220-3054, 232-7883 fax 220-0413; information@travelair-costarica.com) both fly here.

The **Hotel, Bar, y Restaurant Vista al Cerro** is a new motel-style operation out of the center of town. Rates are around US$10 s, US$13 d.

The **Hacienda Doña Victoria** (☎/fax 786-6269, ☎ 786-7123), set to the S of the airport in Palmar Sur, rents rooms by the fully-equipped house (US$120; hold up to ten) or the room (US$25 s, 45 d). Excursions are offered as is horseback riding.

You may also stay at low-budget **Hotel Xenia** (☎ 786-6129) or the **Casa Amarilla** (☎ 786-6251) which is better; make reservations.

Eat at the **Restaurante Chan Jeng** which is underneath the disco. The nearest outlying accommodation is at **Estero Azul Lodge** (☎ 233-2578, 221-7681, fax 222-0297; Apdo. 1419, 1000 San José), which offers boat trips, fishing, or diving.

Mystery of the Stone Spheres

Conical stone spheres are found in but two locations on the planet: Mexico and Costa Rica. Ranging in size from three inches to about four ft in diameter, they may weigh as much as 15 tons.

Geologists theorize that the stones were formed after a volcano spat magma into the air: landing in a hot-ash-filled valley, the globs cooled slowly until they formed spheres. Others believe that they were formed by hand with stone tools. Golfito resident David Bolland has even theorized that they were shaped by waterfalls tumbling into a man-made pit. The truth is that no one knows how they are formed and why.

The spheres were first "discovered" by US archaeologist Samuel Lothrop in 1948. Similar spheres exist in a remote ravine in the Sierra de Ameca mountain range in west-central Mexico, and Dr. Robert L. Smith of the US Geological Survey has theorized that these spheres were in fact fiery lava flows from some 40 million years ago.

Sierpe

Buses run here from Palmar. This riverside village has a number of places to stay.

Eco-Manglares Lodge (☎ 773-3192, 788-8111) is a set of attractive cabins with decks. Breakfast is included, and the restaurant specializes in Italian cuisine. It has its own boats and offers sea and river excursions. Rates are around US$35 s, US$70 d.

Estero Azul Lodge (☎ 788-8111, fax 788-8251) has wooden cabins with screened porches for around US$65 pp with meals, beer (!), and laundry service.

Hotel Pargo (☎ 788-8111, fax 788-8251) is a two-storey hotel with a/c and fan-equipped rooms (around US$60 d with meals).Two deep-sea fishing boats take guests on tours, fishing, diving, and on island excursions. A catamaran and a canoe are also available as is horseback riding. They will also coordinate reservations and transport to the Drake Bay lodge of your choice. In Canada call or fax 705-286-4859 or write Box 725, Minden, Ontario KOM 2KO.

Veragua River House (☎ 296-3896, 296-5901, ☎/fax 788-8111) is an European-run lodge which features antiques and a library. Rates are around US$100 d with breakfast.

Budget travelers should stay at the **Hotel Margarita**, a large white house in the center.

More upscale is the none-room Canadian-operated **Hotel Pargo Rojo** (☎/fax 788-8032; 705-286-4859 in Canada) which rents rooms with fans and private baths for around US$17 s, US$23 d; a/c is US$5 additional, and refrigerators are available for rent.

For dining, try **Rosita's** or **Restaurante Las Vegas**.

From Sierpe, it's a couple of hours downriver and then out to the ocean and

> Reader R. M. writes "you need a four-wheel-drive to get to Rey Curré. They brought out a pile of their beautiful carved masks and handweaving. lovely stuff. not found later in San José. A proposed dam project will flood them out of their lands. terrible!"

Drake Bay. Local dugouts do the route, but they are crowded and occasionally capsize. *Especiales* are faster and available for charter; bargain to get the local rate. Returning, you can generally find a ride with a local.

Rey Curré

At this village — in the SW Talamancas between Paso Real and Palmar Norte — there's an indigenous craft cooperative. **Fiesta de los Diablos**, the sole remaining Native American festival, takes place every Feb. here. In an allegorical recreation of the struggle between the *Diablitos* (the local Boruca Indians) and a bull (representing the Spaniards), masked *Diablitos* pursue the bull, which is made of burlap topped with a carved wooden head. Local crafts, corn liquor (*chicha*), and *tamales* are for sale.

Boruca

This indigenous village is 11 mi.(18 km) off the Interamerican Highway. During the school year, a bus (two hrs.) leaves for here from Buenos Aires at 1:30. If you walk in, get off at the *entrada* about half an hour by bus after Buenos Aires, and take the two-hr. (eight km) path which branches off of the main road. Lodging can be arranged with a local family if you ask at the *pulpería* or arrange them in advance through **Tur Casa** (☎ 225-1239).

Held on Dec. 8, the local version of **Fiesta de los Negritos** has wildly costumed dancers in blackface. Held in honor of its patron saint, the Virgin of the Immaculate Conception, participants dance to flute and drum accompaniment in time to the *sarocla*, a frame with a horse's head.

WEAVING: Boruca women are famous for their weaving. Dyes are produced from leaves, bark, and even a mollusk. Products include placemats, blouses, rugs, bags, and table runners.

MUSEUM: An **Eco Museo** has exhibits are labeled in Spanish.

TOURS: University professor and anthropologist Mildred Periera (☎ 253-9935, 253-3127) leads tours to the area every few months. This is a great way to visit.

> ?!? Costa Rica's Panamerican Highway is part of the same stretch that connects Alaska with Tierra del Fuego. It was built during the Second World War with the financial and engineering assistance of the US because a land connection between the US and the Panama Canal was considered to be vital security reasons.

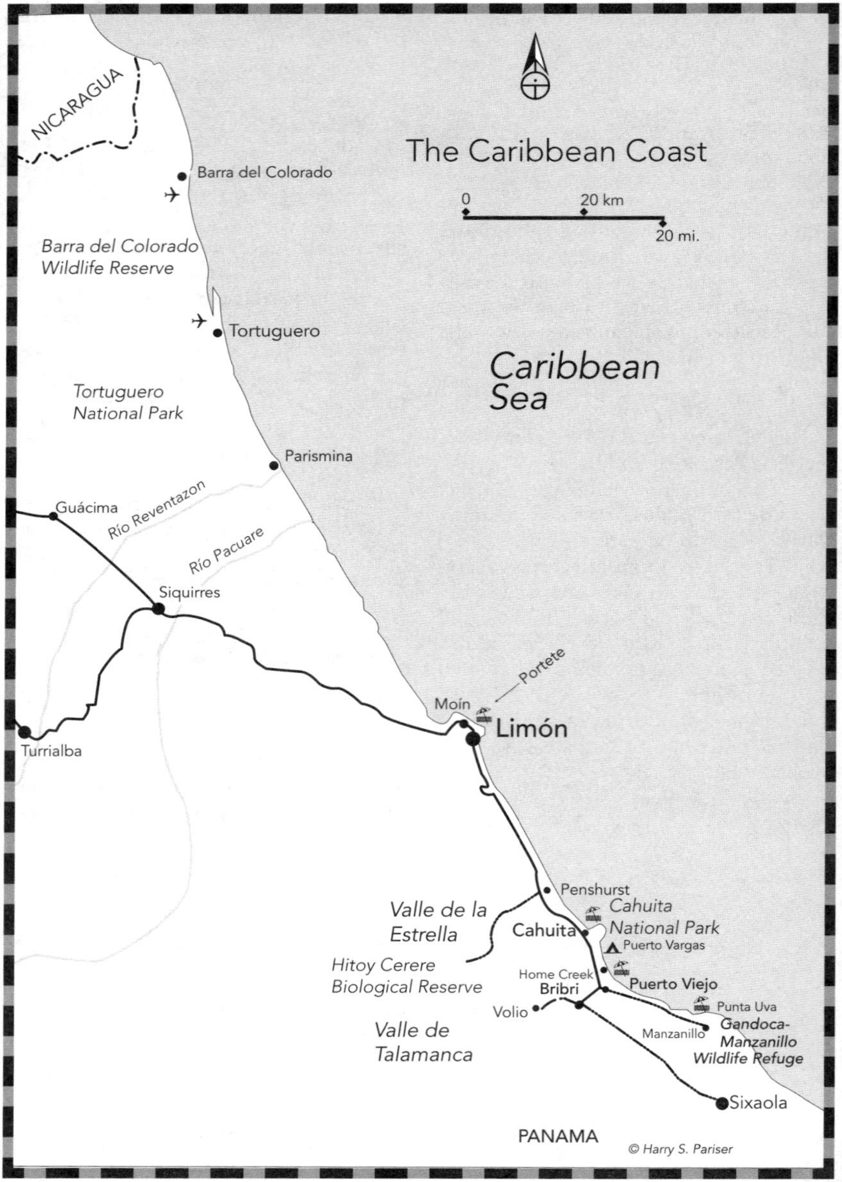
The Caribbean Coast
0
20 km
20 mi.
NICARAGUA
Barra del Colorado
Barra del Colorado Wildlife Reserve
Tortuguero
Tortuguero National Park
Caribbean Sea
Parismina
Guácima
Río Reventazon
Río Pacuare
Siquirres
Portete
Moín
Limón
Turrialba
Penshurst
Valle de la Estrella
Cahuita
Cahuita National Park
Puerto Vargas
Hitoy Cerere Biological Reserve
Home Creek
Bribri
Puerto Viejo
Volio
Punta Uva
Valle de Talamanca
Manzanillo
Gandoca-Manzanillo Wildlife Refuge
Sixaola
PANAMA
© Harry S. Pariser

The Caribbean Coast

The nation's Caribbean side is the "banana frontier," an area covering nearly 20% of the nation's land mass. Of its more than 170,000 inhabitants, today less than 25% of the population are of African American heritage. However, you'll still hear the distinctive dialect of the colorful local English all along this coast. A common greeting is "Whoppen," What's happening," and "all right" or "OK" is substituted for *adios*. Fortunately for the visitor, the area's touristic potential remains virtually untapped, and mile-after-mile of pristine palm tree-lined beaches line the coast.

EXPLORING: Anytime is a good time to visit this area, but the best time to visit the beaches to the S is Sept. and Oct. There's really only one main road: it runs across to Limón and then down the coast to Sixaola. Bus service is good. The major tourist spots here are Cahuita and Puerto Viejo.

In addition to the coral reef offshore at Cahuita, parks on this coast include the internationally renowned Tortuguero, Barra del Colorado Wildlife Refuge, Hitoy-Cerere Reserve to the S, and far to the S the Gandoca-Manzanillo Wildlife Refuge. Tortuguero, Barra del Colorado, and Caño Negro (to the W of Tortuguero) are set to be linked with similar wildife refuges in Nicaragua under the SI-A-PAZ agreement. However, deforestation by banana plantations and cattle farms is swiftly dealing a death blow to the plan's probability of institution in any effective form.

Refugio Nacional Barra del Colorado (Barra del Colorado Nat'l Wildlife Refuge)

The Caribbean coast's waterway system terminates at 227,332-acre (92,000-ha) Barra del Colorado National Resrve Although Barra del Colorado was once a prosperous lumber center and cargo depot, timber depletion has led to its demise. Today, sports fishing is the big business in town.

Much of the W portion of the reserve remains unexplored, but infrared satellite photos show that illegal logging is proceeding in this area at an alarming rate. As with Tortuguero, rainfall here is in excess of 250 in. (6,250 mm) per month.

The flora, fauna, and local cultural milieu resemble Tortuguero's. Waterways are lined with raffia and *manicaria* palms, *cativo*, bloodwood, and wild tamarind. There are over 240 species of birds. Hundreds of thousands of bright yellow alemanda butterflies cover the trees during the winter months.

GETTING HERE: It may be possible to get back and forth between Tortuguero and Barra del Colorado via infrequent coconut barges which sometimes take passengers, or you can charter a boat, which is very expensive. From Barra Colorado village (pop. 900) the Río San Juan goes up to the Sarapiquí which leads to the small town of Puerto Viejo. From there a rough road leads down to San José. You may also drive from Guápiles through Cariari N to Puerto Lindo (or take a bus leaving at 2 PM). From there it is 20 min. to Barra by boat (leaves at 6 PM, departs at 4:45 AM).

BY AIR: *SANSA* (☎ 221-9414, 233-0397/3258, fax 255-2176) flies as does *Travelair* (☎ 220-3054, 232-7883 fax 220-0413; information@travelair-costarica.com).

BY THE RIVER: Another way to get here is the Río Colorado Lodge's **trip up the Río Sarapiquí from Puerto Viejo**. An unusual adventure, this tour runs from Puerto Viejo up the Río Sarapiquí to the Río Colorado Lodge and then back to San José. First, you are bused from your hotel to the dock at Río Frio. Along the way, you stop for breakfast, pass waterfalls, and get to see a lot of beautfiul countryside. After boarding the *Colorado Queen*, you cruise up the dark green Sarapiquí; swallows fly low over the water. Blue plastic bags strewn across roots by the bank are discards from the banana plantation, disturbing reminders of the industry's ill effects. You might see birds such as blue heron, dairy cows grazing by the banks, epiphyte-laden trees, riverside homes, women washing clothes, and children bathing. The river widens and becomes shallower, passing by a largely deforested stretch. You might spot horses, a canoe with multicolored diagonal stripes, banks lined with fields of wild cane, and communities such as Arbolitas. Sadly, there is no virgin jungle (primary tropical forest) along this stretch. You must pass through Nicaragua briefly before returning to Costa Rica.

The wide river continues as you swing R onto the Río Colorado. The narrow San Juan del Norte continues on to Greytown (San Juan del Norte) but you need a canoe to pass.

You pass by an enormous *ceiba* tree as you head up the Caño Bravo, one of two passageways the more jungly of the two although still largely secondary forest. Howler monkeys swing through the trees above. The river is dazzlingly green on both sides, with thatched huts and coconut palms dotted here and there. A while later, Barra del Colorado comes into sight, and you pull up at the lodge. The middle of the river contains sandbars, and the other portion of the village lies across the wide river.

Priced at around US$200, the tour may be reversed on occasion in which case the route will vary and during green sea turtle nesting season (July, Aug., Sept.), a special excursion will be made to see turtles nest. For more information and booking call 1-800-243-9777 in the US.

Oasis Tours (☎ 766-6108, 766-6260, cell. ☎: 380-9493) offers a similar trip from Puerto Viejo de Sarapiquí for around US$75 pp OW. A two-day, one-night tour is priced at around US$150.

ORIENTATION: Barra is a very small village. An asphalted airstrip cuts down its middle, and a soccer field is next to it. While the Río Colorado Lodge has access to the village directly, Silver King is cut off. Tarponland is right near the Río Colorado Lodge. The place to go here is definitely the amazingly long and wild beach. To the R you can see the island of Uvita off the coast of Limón.

ACCOMMODATION/FISHING LODGES: This area is famous for the giant tarpon (sábalo) which have secured the area its reputation worldwide. All are very expensive, and packages are available.

Founded by Archie Fields, **Río Colorado Lodge** (☎ 232-8610/4063 in San José; 800-243-9777 in the US; Apdo. 10560, 1000 San José) offers simple cabins with Jacuzzi and satellite TV. The only lodge set right near the Colorado's river

mouth, it offers good fishing year round. Comfortable rooms feature private baths, hot showers; three buffet meals are served. In the evening, guitarists from the neighboring village often drop by to strum a few numbers. There's also a small zoo as well as a quiet lagoon perfect for swimming. The Río Colorado Lodge is no longer the plushest lodge available, but the others can't compete with its tons of atmosphere. Rooms are comfortable but not lavish with fan, twin beds, and hot water shower. Dinner features fish and another main course along with vegetables, corn bread, and desserts such as flan. Breakfast is served on the front patio, and you order a la carte from a selection including omelettes. Packages run from six days, five nights (around US$1,300) to eight days, seven nights (around US$1,950).
www.sportsmanweb.com
tarpon@sol.racsa.co.cr
tarpon4u@mindspring.com

Opened in 1993, **Silver King Lodge** offers very comfortable facilities which are a bit upscale compared to the others in the area. They have 19-ft. Carolina skiffs, canoes and kayaks, and other boats, a good restaurant, a giant Jacuzzi, and video/book library. They also cater to naturalists who would like to avoid comparatively crowded Tortuguero. *Outside* has cited it as "one of the top 50 lodges for outside recreational activities in the world." In Costa Rica call 381-01403 or fax 381-0849. In the US call 800-611-1649 or 813-942-7959 or write Aerocasillas, Dept. 1597, Box 025216, Miami, FL 33102.
www.silverkinglodge.com
slvrkng@sol.racsa.co.cr

The other lodges are across the river.

With housing in A-frames, **Isla de Pesca** (☎ 223-4560 or 21-6673 in San José, fax 255-2533; Apdo. 8-4390, 1000 San José)

Canoes are the traditional way to get around the canals which stretch north from Limón .

is another major fishing lodge. In the US call 800-245-8420, 305-539-1630/1631, fax 305-539-1123 or write Costa Sol International, 1717 N Bayshore Dr., Ste. 3333, Miami, FL 33132. They also have a tropical river safari up the Corobicí.

Casa Mar Fishing Lodge (☎/fax 221-8661; PO Drawer 787, Islamorada, FL 33036) has 12 rooms and offers three-day packages for around US$1,000. In the US call (800) 327-2880 or (305) 664-4615.

A half-hr. boat trip upriver, the **Delta Wildlife Lodge** (☎ 253-7816, fax 233-9357) offers hiking, swimming, boat trips, and turtle watching. Three-day packages run around US$250 pp.

Samay Lagoon Lodge (☎ 284-7047, fax 383-6370 ; Apdo. 12767-1000, San José) is a German endeavor, an ecologically designed luxury 22-room ho☎ It offers canoe tours, fishing, and evening turtle watching tours Rates are around US$200 for a three-day, two-night tour. Canoe rental is free of charge to guests.
www.samay.com
info@samay.com

Upriver in Nicaragua, **The Río Indio lodge** (☎ 289-8401, 231-4299, fax 289-0009 ; Apdo. 850-1250, Escazú) is a new lodge which combines fishing with "eco" activities. It has a restaurant, pool. spa, kayaking, horseback riding, a recreated indigenous village, a remote tent camp, and cottages in the jungle. It is intended to prove that "eco-tourism projects, when combined with educationn and research, can create strong, sustainable local economies as well as protect the ecosystem." It should be open in 2000.
www.bluwing.com
bluewing @sol.racsa.co.cr

FOOD AND SERVICES: In the village, minimal facilities are available aside from those mentioned above. Painted a brilliant raspberry and white, **Soda Naomi** is one of the only places where you can make a phone call, buy food, watch TV, and (sometimes) eat. **Pulpería Cecí** has bread and a few other things as does **Pulpería Ricardo Fernandez**. **Soda La Fiesta** has light food and drink; a red-and-white sleigh-on-snow tapestry graces its wall.

The Rain Goddess

One of the most unusual ways to get around Costa Rica's Barra del Colorado area is on the *Rain Goddess* (☎ 231-4299, fax 231-3816; Apdo. 850-1250, Escazú), a 65-ft.-long by 18-ft.-wide houseboat. The idea of the boat is the creation of Dr. Alfredo Lopez, an MD born in Costa Rica but partially raised in California. Dr. Lopez, a licensed retired physician, also uses the houseboat to give free medical care to the indigent locals on both sides of the border. His belief is that tourism must have local benefits. He hires local hunters to guide tourists intent on photographing animals in the hope that they will come to learn the value of preserving wildlife. The boat has six staterooms with bath. Fully carpeted and a/c, it has a gourmet seafood restaurant, cellular phone, and TV/VCR. The boat is designed for fishermen who want to go where few have fished before as well as for nature tourists. Each trip takes a minimum of six and a maximum of 12, and a trip is three days or longer. Boarding is at Barra del Colorado; you either fly or boat in. Rates are around US$600 pp for three days and two nights of a nature tour or US$1,600 for five days and three nights including three days of fishing. In the US, call 800-308-3394.
bluewing@sol.racsa.co.cr

OTHER ACCOMMODATION: Set in Isla Brava within the refuge, **Finca La Cecilia** is a five-bedroom thatched-roof lodge. You can hike around the island or take boat trips. Set in Caño Zapote on the road to Puerto Lindo, **Panatanal** offers accommodation for up to six. Boat rides, hiking, and horseback riding are offered. Room and board are around US$25 pp, pd. For more information contact the Asociacíon de Microempresarios Turisticos de Pococí (ASOMEP; ☎ 767-7010/7245).

Parque Nacional Tortuguero (Tortuguero National Park)

The area known as Tortuguero, "region of turtles," is on the NE side of the country N of Limón. These flatlands (Las Llanuras de Tortuguero) were formed over millions of years as sediment washed down river systems and was trapped and stabliized by vegetation such as the raffia palms. One of the nation's most popular parks (around 30,000 visitors per year), its waterways are excellent places to see wildlife. A tropical wet forest life zone, the average annual rainfall here exceeds 197 in. (5,000 mm). While June and July are among the rainiest months, Aug. and Sept. have less rainfall than other months. The 11 habitats range from herbaceous marsh communities to high rainforest. The small village of Tortuguero is the only settlement.

FLORA AND FAUNA: Despite the rampant deforestation surrounding it, Tortuguero remains an area that fulfills the Westerner's expectation of a tropical jungle. There are over 2,000 plant species including 400 species of trees. The coconuts found here are introduced relics from the days when plantations flourished in the area. Seagrapes dominate the coastal dunes.

Of the 16 endangered mammals in Costa Rica, 13 are found in or near the park. One of them, the elusive manatee, is also found but rarely spotted.

?!¿ Considered to be a living fossil because it resembles similar species which lived during the upper Cretaceaous 90 million years ago, the **gar** (*Attratosteus tropicus*) has a body covered with bony or plaque-like scales. Ranging in length between four and seven ft. (1.25 and 2 m), its long, narrow snout supports strong jaws lined with crocodile-like teeth. Often it lies motionless, as if suspended in the water. Because of its tasty, bone-free flesh and practice of laying its eggs in shallow water, the fish is endangered. There are some 55 other fish species as well.

Although the area to the W of the park has been ecologically devastated through logging and hunting, jaguars, three-toed sloths, and river otters populate the portion E of the Sierpe hills.

The 37 species of amphibians and 52 species of reptiles include four species of sea turtles (green, loggerhead, leatherback and hawksbill), the crocodile, the *caimán*, and poison dart, tranparent glass, and smoky frogs.

The 406 species of birds include the green macaw, violaceous trogon, Montezuma oropendola, Central American curassow, the keel billed toucan, the greenback heron, and the yellowtailed oriole.

HISTORY: The Caribbean's largest nesting area for the green sea turtle, Tortuguero originally gained fame as a hunting ground. The first settlers were closely related to the Maya. The area's first Spanish settlement was at San Juan de la Cruz some 25 mi. to the N. In the mid-1700s, cacao plantations were established at Matina, 25 mi. to the S. Native Americans and Afro-Caribbeans worked the plantations but repeated raids by the Zambos-Miskitos forced their abandonment by 1848.

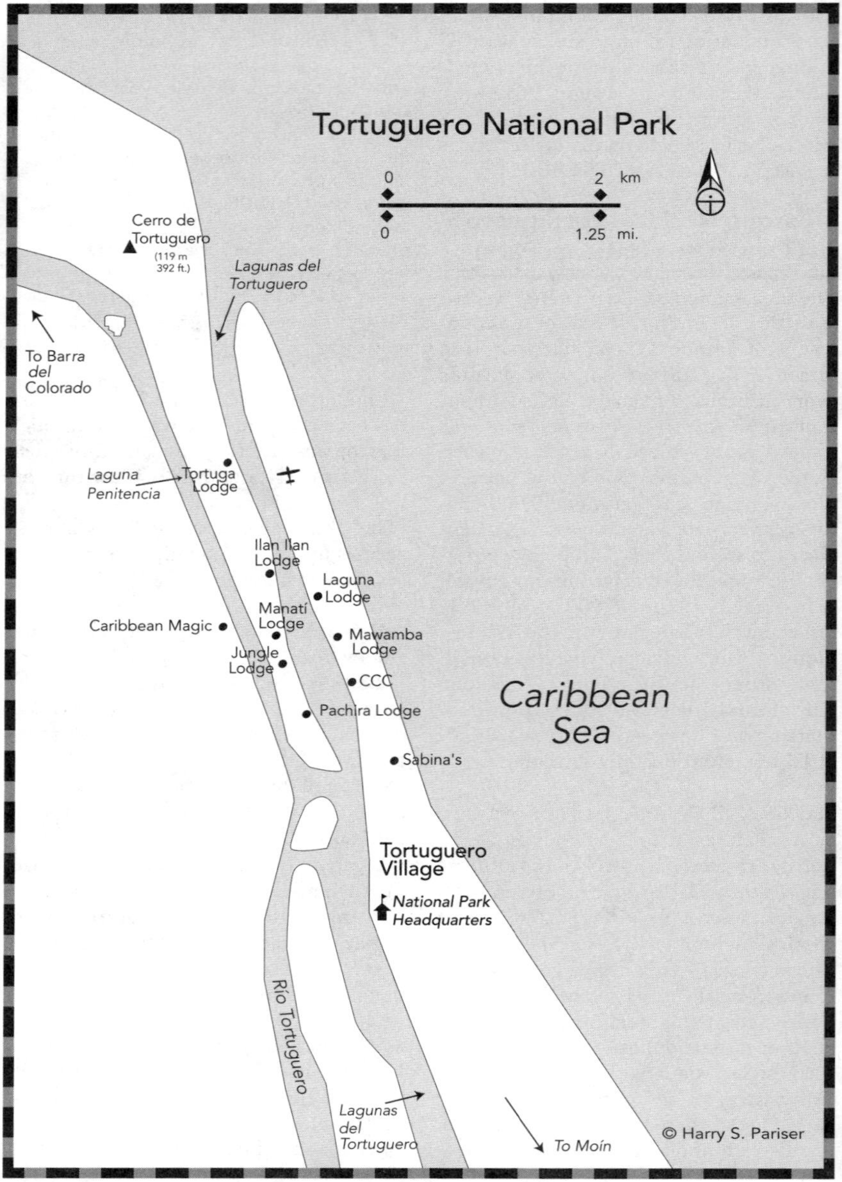
Tortuguero National Park
0
2 km
0
1.25 mi.
Cerro de Tortuguero
(119 m 392 ft.)
Lagunas del Tortuguero
To Barra del Colorado
Laguna Penitencia
Tortuga Lodge
Ilan Ilan Lodge
Laguna Lodge
Manatí Lodge
Caribbean Magic
Mawamba Lodge
Jungle Lodge
CCC
Pachira Lodge
Caribbean Sea
Sabina's
Tortuguero Village
National Park Headquarters
Río Tortuguero
Lagunas del Tortuguero
To Moín
© Harry S. Pariser

By the 1700s, Tortuguero was famous for turtle meat, oil, and shells. In 1912, an 18-ton vessel ironically named the *Vanguard* began running loads of turtles between Limón and Tortuguero. A turtle turner, known as a *velador*, was assigned to each mile of the 22-mile beach. His task was to turn turtles on their backs and tie a log to their flippers; they were then floated out to sea and collected offshore.

Beginning in the 1940s, a series of sawmills transformed the local economy before each went out of business. When the last closed in 1972, the village's population declined to around 100. Tortuguero's rise to prominence in the public eye resulted from Archie Carr's study of sea turtles in the 1950s. In 1959, responding to the threat posed by poachers, logging, and stray dogs, Carr and Costa Rican scientists and conservationists formed the Caribbean Conservation Corps (CCC), the first nongovernmental conservation organization (NGO) to be established in the Caribbean.

Although a 1963 executive decree gave protection on paper by establishing a turtle reserve, the establishment of the national park (also by executive decree) in 1970, provided the power to deter poaching. Canals were constructed during the early 1970s, and the first public phone was connected in 1972. In 1975 the reserve was expanded to nearly 50,000 acres (19,700 ha) including 15 mi. (24 km) of nesting beach. The effort was dealt a setback after the Legislative Assembly voted in 1979 to reduce offshore turtle hunting limits from 12 to three miles.

Although the 12-mi. limit was maintained in park waters, the reduction meant that the *barricada* of turtles would have to swim through enemy waters to reach safe haven. An international letter-writing campaign resulted in a presidential veto of the bill. In 1982, the first electric generator began running in the village. The area had begun to catch up with the times.

The Fundación Neotrópica won an important court victory in 1997 when it regained possession of land purchased with funds from a Dutch group. The 16,800-acre (16,800-ha) tract had been claimed by the Triangle Development company who maintianed that the foundation had deserted the land because it had not developed it. The court ruling recognized "ecological possession," inactivity with the intent to preserve, a new legal concept.

Until recently, Tortuguero has remained the only one of the larger parks which has not been enlarged since its creation. Although numerous studies since the 1970s had recommended that the park be enlarged from 19,700 ha to 80,000 ha, no action had been taken. In 1992 the decision to add 10,000 ha to the park (which will be purchased in the future) was announced, with the intention of joining it to Barra del Colorado to form a megapark. This expansion is critical to increase the probability of survival of the jaguar and white-lipped peccary populations. Donations are needed to cover the US$1,000-per-acre cost. Send them to CCC, Box 2866, Gainesville, FL

If you are going to be staying in Tortuguero National Park for more than a night, be sure to get a multiple-day pass: US$10 buys you three days woth of entries.

The Caribbean Conservation Corp's fine quarterly newsletter, *Velador*, will keep you informed of developments in the park. Join as an individual for US$35 or as a family for US$50. Write Box 2866, Gainesville, FL 32602. To join by phone call 800-678-7853. Visa/MasterCard accepted.

www.cccturtle.org
ccc@cccturtle.org

32602 or you can contribute to the Fundación Neotropica.

ENVIRONMENTAL PROBLEMS: As with all of the parks, a number of environment-related controversies have emerged. Great controversy has been aroused by the plan to build a road to Tortuguero village. The town's Development Council has spearheaded the "No to the Highway" group which maintains that a road would have a devastating effect on the community. Some business owners, municipal government officials and outside investors want the road, and a March 1999 incident pitted locals in favor of the road against the federal government when approximately a hundred of them attempted to fill in a ditch excavated by the Environment Ministry in order to keep vehicles from entering the park via the illegal road.

Another danger to the park has been posed by the banana plantations. More than 74,000 acres (30,000 ha) on its borders have been converted to banana plantations, resulting in the loss of some 14 billion rainforest plants and trees. On June 9, 1992, Costa Rican authorities accused the British multinational Geest Caribbean of violating the 1969 Forestry Law. Allegedly, the company cleared 400 ha of primary and secondary forests in the Siquirres and Pococi areas. Millions of dollars have been spent in clearing terrain, including illegally cutting trees along river banks a practice which contributes to soil erosion and results in waterway sedimentation. Some of the territory involved adjoins the park, and the habitats of sloths, green macaws, and monkeys were destroyed in the process. Company officials claim that they were granted permits by local forestry officials and cleared no forest. There have already been a number of mysterious fish kills in the area in recent years which environmentalists blame on agrochemicals. The fish population has declined, and leatherback turtles have mistaken the blue plastic bags (presumably) for jellyfish and choked to death. In addition, Park Director Eduardo Chamorro has recommened that locals not eat fish from the canals because of the pollution.

A positive development is the biodigester, a donation from JAPDEVA, which is used for which is used for converting organic waste into fertilizer and usable methane gas and as a centre for recycling. This was the result of an ex-ICE engineer who approached them with the idea. A great example of how one person can make and important difference to a community!

As of Jan. 2000 only electric-powered boats are allowed to be in certain areas of the park.

ORIENTATION: Commonly known as **Los Canales**, 99 mi. (160 km) of inland waterways flow up the NE coast to Tortuguero and then on to Barra Colorado where these eight rivers merge into a series of lagoons. Utilizing the already existing natural channels, canals were dug during the 1970s to connect them, thus providing a natural waterway in a region where no highway would be feasible. Extending from the transport center of Moín to the N of Puerto Limón, every type of craft from dugout canoes and fishing boats to tour boats ply these waters.

The first village, 32 km upriver, is Parismina. Then, you come to the park office, the village of Tortuguero (spread out on a narrow peninsula; it has the Tropical Lodge, the Cabinas Tortuguero, the beachside Mawamba, and the Cabinas Miss Junie). The Pachira is across the river from the village, and the Jungle Lodge is further up, followed by the Ilan-Ilan, the Manatí, and Tortuga Lodge. The Mawamba Lodge (beachside) leads to the Laguna Lodge and then the airstrip and the John H. Phipps Biological Field Station (known as the CCC). The waterway indirectly leads on to Barra del Colorado.

GETTING THERE/TOURS: Tour boats are the way to go if your schedule is inflexible, and they will stop for wildlife photos. With the demise of the government boat, there's no way to go by boat save to charter your own which is a relatively expensive option; unless you have a group, it might be cheaper to fly both ways. Many tour companies travel the canals, and all offer a variety of schedules. Packages run from US$155 to US$400 depending upon the lodge and length of stay at the lodge.

Costa Rican Expeditions (☎ 257-0766, 222-0333, fax 257-1665; costa-rica@expeditions.co.cr; www.expeditions.co.cr) will either fly or boat you in to their Tortuga Lodge. (You will receive a banana along with a cartoon).

Limón's **Hotel Matama** (☎ 758-1123) also offers boat trips as far as Parismina where you overnight.

The Mawamba (☎ 223-2421, fax 222-4932) will take you slowly upriver to their **Mawamba Lodge**, owned by textile magnate Mauricio Dada. A bonus is that you can walk between the village and the lodge.

Agencia Mitur/Tortuguero Jungle Adventures (☎ 255-2031, 255-2262, fax 255-1946) has trips aboard their *Colorado Prince*; you stay at the Ilan-Ilan Ho☎ Their office is on 5 Paseo de Colón, 10 m W of the Hospital de Niños. (There have been some complaints received about their operation).

"La Jungla" S. A. (☎ 758-2843, 234-1297) also has launches and tours. One of the least expensive companies, **Cotur** (☎ 233-0155/6579/0133/0226, fax 233-0778; cotour@sol.racsa.co.cr) buses you to Moín where you board either the *Miss Caribe* or the *Miss America* to the Jungle Lodge, located a km N of Tortuguero village across the river.

Caño Palma Biological Station

An exciting river excursion from Tortuguero is to the Canadian-run **Estación Bíologica Caño Palma** which covers 100 acres (200 ha) of tropical lowland forest. It's eight km to the N along the Caño Palma canal inside the boundaries of the Colorado National Wildlife Reserve. This field station was founded by zoologist Marilyn Cole of the Canadian Organization for Tropical Education and Rainforest Conservation (COTERC). The station aims to preserve the area, inform the public, and conduct research. Toward this end, it gives slide lectures on the rainforest and its preservation to schoolchildren in Toronto.

The surrounding area holds and abundance of wildlife including jaguars, margays, three species of monkeys, green parrots, toucans, anteaters, sloths, tapirs, river otters, and other species. Studies carried out here include research on migratory birds and on the behavioral patterns of howler monkeys.

Visits are US$2 pp. After a brief introduction, you will be taken on a brief guided tour of one of the trails. Volunteers are welcome; they must be over 21 and be able to contribute financially towards their stay. The organization is currently running a campaign to purchase land adjacent to the station. Dubbed "Save An Acre," it involves purchasing a quarter-acre for US$35 or a full acre for US$125; all funds donated will be used for purchasing the land and not for administrative costs. For more information call 381-4114. In Canada call 905-831-88096, fax 905-837-8118, or write COTERC, Box 335, Pickering, Ontario LIV 2R6.

www.interhop.net/~coterc

coterc@interhop.net

Daryl Loth is an expatriate Canadian who has lived in the Tortuguero community for five years and has had a hand in several of the sustainable development projects in the area. He runs a 'not for profit' information center located in the center of town in front of the Catholic Church. He can put people interested in staying in a local hotel or touring the canals in touch with the independent businesses and guides. He also offers **ecologically friendly tours** in a boat with a low emission four-stroke motor and a super silent electric motor. Daryl also rents **kayaks** (around US$10 for a morning), the proceeds from which go towards purchasing educational materials for the new high school.
safari@sol.racsa.co.cr

Affiliated with Río Colorado Lodge in Barra Colorado, **Adventure Tours** (☎ 232-4063) offers a number of packages including a trip up to the Nicaraguan border. (See trip description in the "Puerto Viejo de la Sarapiquí section").

Laguna Lodge (☎ 255-3740) will also take you up.

Piloted by local ecology experts Fran and Modesto Watson, the ***Francesca*** (☎/fax 226-0986) will take you on a trip for around US$170-185 pp including meals, accommodation, (in high season) overland transport, and overland transport and the entrance fee for the National Park. Turtle watching is included.
members.tripod.com/~FrancescaTours
fvwatson@sol.racsa.co.cr

Jungle Tom (☎ 385-2266, fax 225-8268) will take you on a one-day tour to Tortuguero for around US$75; a one-night option costs US$160 and includes five meals and three tours. You stay in a small lodge in Parismina.

If you wish to visit the canals and come back the same day, Limón's **Laura Tropical Tours** (☎ 758-2410) will accommodate you. The US$65 fee includes lunch.

Tortuguaro Safaris (☎ 392-3201; PO Box 025216, Miami, FL) also offers trips and environmentally friendly tourswith Daryl Loth, a resident Canadian naturalist. He can also tell you how to get to Tortuguero inexpensively via the boat that is accessible by bus from the village of Cariari.
safari@sol.racsa.co.cr

Caño Blanco Marina (☎ 259-8216) offer mass-market oriented day trips to Tortuguero for around US$90 pp. Their bus departs daily from the front of the Gran Hotel Costa Rica in San José. They also offer transport-only.
www.pndsrl.com/tucantico/index.html
toucanti@sol.racsa.co.cr

ON YOUR OWN: The *Gran Delta*, the government-run launch, is no longer running. Although you will still have to pay around US$50 pp RT (US$25 OW), doing it on your own has clear cost advantages over going on a tour. However, you have to have time and to be flexible in your standards. **Alfred Brown** (☎ 758-0824) and **Modesto and Fran Watson** (☎ 226-0896; see above) both take passengers.

Another alternative is to go to the dock at Moín at around 8 AM and see what's available. In the village ask Albert next to the Pancana Restaurant concerning return trips. Transport (around US$10 OW) is also available at the Geest banana plantations near Cariari from which you can get transport to San José. Priority is given to village residents. To get here, take a 9 AM Bus from from the Limon bus terminal in San Jose to Cariari. After arriving at 11, take the noon *La Geest Casa Verde* bus to the terminal where the bus meets the boat. Call the *pulpería* at 710-6716 for more

The ideal way to experience the wonder of this park is to rent a **dugout canoe** (*cacuyo*) from a Tortuguero villager (make sure that yours has a plastic bailer). A guide will accompany you for about US$10 pd. Park it beside a bank, and take in the thousands of sounds that emerge. For those accustomed to the deafening noise of the city, it is wondrous to discover these other sounds of a nature that exists and functions quite apart from the will or regulation of humanity.

The best times to go are very early in the morning (when the lodge boats are not present but the animals are) and late in the afternoon. The advantage of a smaller boat is that you can maneuver in right close to shore.

information and confirmation (very important).

BY AIR: *Travelair* (☎ 220-3054, 232-7883 fax 220-0413; information@travelair-costarica.com) flies here. You can also fly into Tortuguero with Costa Rica Expeditions in a smaller plane for around US$90 OW; they land at the airport near near the former CCC research station As you depart from Pavas airport, you pass over the suburbs of San José and across the majestic, generally cloud-shrouded mountainous expanse of Braulio Carrillo National Park — tropical greenery at its most splendid. As if it were deliberately conducting an ecology lesson along its flight route, the plane next passes over humongous banana plantations and by stretches of deforested land before the canals and beaches of Tortuguero come into view just before the plane touches down.

DEPARTING FROM MOÍN: The only hotel here, the Hostal Moín, has been converted into a full time brothel. Two *típico* restaurants are here. Ask permission to visit the compound of JAPDEVA, the government agency in charge of the area's economic development, where you can observe river port operations underway. Here, you can see the waterway. Just N from Moín is an ICT-run park and farther N, at **Playa Barra de Matina**, is a refuge for nesting sea turtles. vegetation. Passing yellow highway signs denoting the kilometers to nearby villages at intersections, you steam upriver, the wildlife-filled greenery reflected on either side. Along the river, you might see howler or spider monkeys, caymans, turtles, white egrets, great blue herons, night herons, toucans, blue green kingfishers, a sleeping sloth snuggling on a branch overhead, floating water hyacinths, or mud turtles jumping and splashing in the water. If you stop for a moment you can hear the intense hum of insects contrasting with the surf pounding off in the distance.

If you wish, you may stop at the **Jalova Ranger Station** which will involve paying the admission fee (US$6). You may then go on the new nature trail or visit the Visitors' Center. After the ranger station, the canal widens and everything save nature vanishes.

LODGES: Most of the lodges here can take you fishing upriver; for fishing lodges on this coast see Barra del Colorado above. One of the nicest places to stay and eat here is Costa Rica Expedition's **Tortuga Lodge** (☎ 222-0333, 527-0766, fax 257-1665; Apdo. 6941, San José 1000; Dept. 235, Box 025216, Miami, FL 33102-5216; costa-rica@expeditions.co.cr www.expeditions.co.cr). The lodge gives you everything you might wish for while still being in the heart of the jungle. Three hearty meals are served daily, and the family-style meals include things like granola as part of the breakfast, and vegetables, rice, beans, fish or fowl or meat, and soup or salad for lunch and dinner. The trail behind the lodge has a large number of poison dart frogs, and you may see other flora and fauna as well. In the front of the lodge, fishing and fruit bats fly over the docks at night while marine toads are found on the ground. Every type of excursion from fishing to turtle walks is offered. An unusual feature of the lodge is that none of the doors have locks because there have never been any problems with theft.

Package rates are around US$350 for two days, one night, and US$800 for three-days, two nights. This includes meals and OW transport by bus and boat with the return by plane.

There's no charge for depositing you on the other side of the river where the beach and the turtle research station are. From there, it's a long but pleasant hike down along the black sand beach to the village of Tortuguero. On the way, you walk by an open air museum showing the multiple ways plastic has been put to use in modern society. Free admission. If you head in from the coast, there's a trail (good birdwatching) which leads to Mawamba. The mosquitoes will be overjoyed to see you, and giant silky golden web spiders line the path as well.

www.expeditions.co.cr
costarica@expeditions.co.cr

The Hotel Ilán-Ilán (☎ 255-2031/2262, fax 255-1946; Apdo. 91, 1150 San José) is downriver from the Tortuga Lodge and on the same side. They charge around US$225 for a three-day package.

One of the newest lodges, the **El Manatí Ecological Lodge** (☎/fax 383-0330) offers simple cabins with fan and private bath for around US$17.50 pp including a large breakfast; dinner is US$7. This is a good lower-end budget alternative. Friendly owners Fernando Figuls and Lilia Montejo de Figuls have set up the **Save the Manatee Foundation of Costa Rica**. Refugees from the urban sprawl of San José, they had the idea of making a new life for themselves in someplace pristine. They started living in a tent and have built the place up. They can help you with reasonable (around US$40 pp) RT accommodation from Moin. It is across from the Laguna Lodge.

Also on this side of the river, the **Jungle Lodge** (☎ 233-0155/6579/0133, fax 233-0778; 800-815-5019; 305-267-6644) is run by Cotur which also has trips (around US$250 for a three-day package).
cotour@sol.racsa.co.cr

Within walking distance of the village, the 36-room **Mawamba** (☎ 223-2421, fax 255-4039) has similar rates and a swimming pool. A library and conference center is under construction. Guided forest hike and four-hr. boat ride are included in rates.
www.crica.com/hotels/mawamba.htm
mawamba@sol.racsa.co.cr

Situated in the same general area, the **Laguna Lodge** (☎/fax 225-3740; Apdo. 7, 3180 San José) offers a three day/two night tour. Rooms have baths and ceiling fans, basic but hearty meals are served family-style, there is a pool, and a vari-

?!? The **manatee** is a distant relative of the elephant. A team of biologists at the U of Melbourne have studied the kidneys of embryonic African elephants and have found nephrostones – tiny funnel-shaped ducts found only in aquatic vertebrates, thus linking them to the manatees. Theory has it that the elephant's trunk may once have served as a snorkel!

The **Pachira Lodge** (☎ 256-7080, fax 223-1119, pager: 225-2500; Apdo. 1818, 1002 San José) offers three-day, two-night packages. This is one of the newer lodges, and its highly attractive rooms reflect that. The walkways are torchlit at night, and meals are served buffet-style in an attractive dining room. They have good guides and attentive staff; there is a small gift shop, bar, and pool room. There is occasional live music. It is, however, not intimate.
paccira@sol.racsa.co.cr

VILLAGE ACCOMODATION: If you're on a tight budget, you'll wish to stay in the village, populated by a mix of African-Americans, white Ticos, and the descendants of Miskito Indians. The peaceful environs are bordered on one side by pounding surf and rustling palms while its other side is lined with houses facing the canal. Dogs sleep in the sun, and chickens cluck about.

One disadvantage of staying here is that there's no backup generator. You all sweat together when it breaks down. The other disadvantage is that you can be relaxing and all of a sudden a group of 30 tourists will appear in your peripheral vision and march right through, video cameras in hand.

An alternative for budget travelers, **Sabina's Cabanas** (around US$5, more expensive with private bath) are clean and pleasant. The only problem with the place is that Sabina is not known as being the friendliest of souls.

Similarly priced but probably superior, the **Meryscar** is 200 m S of the information booth. Low budget **Cabinas Brisas del Mar** and **Cabinas Tortuguero** are others.

On the outskirts of town, **Cabinas Miss Junie** (☎ 710-0523) offers rooms for around US$35 d; it has a good restaurant.

On the mainland all by itself, **Boca del Río** (☎ 385-4676, 800-226-9896) has simple tent cabins for an affordable US$5 pp! Bring your own tent and save US$2 pp. They also provide one room for US$30.

You can also stay upriver at **Cabinas Tatané** (☎ 222-2175, fax 223-1609 for package tour info) whose owner (Marco Zamora) will come and get you in his boat. He can also guide you to turtles.

Meals here in the village are around US$4-US$5 for what you get in similar surroundings and quality for US$2 in San José. Eat at **Tio Leo's** restaurant, **Comidas Miss Junie**, the **Meryscar**, **Sabina's**, **The Vine** (sandwiches and pizzas) or the **Pacana Restaurante** which entertains with natural history videos at night. You can also try the **Abastecedor Riversan**.

If you're staying in town, the best things to do are to hang your hammock and relax, hike the visitor's trail behind the ranger's station (good wildlife viewing opportunities), and rent a boat or canoe to see the wildlife (around US$1.50-4 ph (guide often included in rates; considerably cheaper than going with the lodges and may be preferable). Many things in town are comparatively expensive, and some things are unobtainable; bring everything you need with you from San José or from home.

> ☛ The **Reserva Pacuare**, a leatherback turtle reserve on the Caribbean coast, needs volunteers (US$100 pw donation). You will be asked to walk the beaches at night to deter poachers, tag turtles, and move nests. They also have a beach house for rent; this could be a great experience for the adventurous. Contact Carlos or Maggie Fernández (% 233-0451, 233-0508, 391-9975, 383-1064 fax 221-2820).
> **leatherback@yahoo.com**

GETTING AROUND: Locals give day tours of the canals and hiking trails for very reasonable prices. You can ask anyone you meet because they are probably related to one of the guides or ask at the information centre located across from the Catholic church."

During turtle season the licensed guides obtain permission at the park's information kiosk to take their clients to the beach. This is a good place to find a turtle guide between 4-6 PM.

A two-hr. tour with a licensed bilingual guide can be had for US$10 pp.(maximum 10 people per guide, and lodges charge around US$15-25 pp.

Small-scale tour opertators Fran and Modesto Watson recommend hooking up with **Pamfilo** in the village. He's a knowlegeable ex-manatee hunter turned tour guide.

NIGHT TOURS: Studies are on to determine the effects of these tours on the park's life. Criticism has been leveled at the tours because the huge beams used disturb the animals.

HIKING: A hike up 390-ft. (119-m) **Cerro Tortuguero**, the park's highest point and the area's highest peak, affords an overview of the canal system. Local legend maintains that a turtle-shaped magnetic rock inside a cave on this mountain attracts the ferromagnetic crystals within the turtles' brains. One story has it that the rock revolves, drawing the turtles in, and then returns to its original position. Some locals raised a stink when gravel was removed from the mountain to pave the airstrip, maintaining that the mountain would be altered and the turtles would not return!

A nice walk is along the beach down to or from the village of Tortuguero and on to the frequently waterlogged *El Gavilán* nature trail (or the new self-guiding trail) which runs in back of the park headquarters. (Payment of park entrance fee is required).

INFORMATION AND SHOPPING: In the village you may visit the **Landon C. Clay Frick Natural History Visitor Center** (US$1 admission) which features full-color displays as well as information about the area's sea turtles. A video is also shown, and there is a gift shop which helps fund programs here. It's open daily from 10-noon and from 2-5:30.

One of the best places to get information and recommendations is at **The Jungle Shop** (☎ 710-6716), a store run by Elvin (an experienced fishing guide) and Antoinette Gutiérrez, which is across from the The Vine Coffee Shop.

GREEN TURTLE RESEARCH STATION: Organized in 1959 by Dr. Archie Carr, the Caribbean Conservation Corporation operates two permanent field research facilities: one is in the Bahamas and the other is this station. Acquired in 1963, the original was built in the 1940s as temporary quarters for land surveyors with the United Fruit Company. The John H. Phipps Biological Field Station opened in Aug. 1995.

VOLUNTEERING: The Caribbean Conservation Corp offers one- and two-week packages for volunteers here. For more information, see "volunteering" in the "Introduction."

EGGLAYING: Largest of the sea turtles, leatherbacks nest on the beach primarily in March and April and hatch from May through June; they are also occasionally found through to the commencement of the green turtle nesting season in July. Continuing on from July to Sept., thousands of green sea turtle females lay annually in Tortuguero, the largest such colony in the Americas. Solitary and rarely encountered, the hawksbill also nests here from July to Sept. The first recorded observation of egglaying was by the Dutch in 1592. Turtles lay eggs at night.

You are required to go with a guide. Flashlight and camera flash use are *prohibited* because you may frighten a mother arriving to nest, sending her lumbering back towards the water. After searching for a spot which the high tide will not reach, the mother turtle becomes totally involved in digging the nest, shoveling out the round nest with her paddle-shaped hind legs.

Crouching over the nest, which may reach 164 in. (50 cm) in depth, she expels an average of 100 eggs together with a lubricating fluid. After covering the nest with sand, she returns to the sea. During the two hour or so procedure, she heaves constant sighs and her eyes tear, presumably to clear her eyes of sand. Facing the world's greatest obstacle course, the hatchlings race to the sea two months later. Very few survive to breeding age some 30 years later. Those females that do will return to nest on the same beach.

No turtle tagged here has been found nesting on any other beach, and genetic tests suggest that green turtles only nest on the beach where they were born. For further information about sea turtles consult the Caribbean Conservation Corp's superbly informative brochure *Tortuguero's Sea Turtles.*

Tortuguero's Top Ten

These are the top ten questions asked by visitors to the John H. Phipps Biological Field Station at Tortuguero.

10. "What kind of animal is a poacher?"
9. "Where are the white sandy beaches?"
8. "I'm just using my flashlight to find drift-seeds." (The same local also asked: "What's the best way to get past the guards down the beach?")
7. "Is this a male or a female turtle?
6. "How do I get out of this place?"
5. "Do the turtles *like* to be tagged?"
4. "Do you tag them in the ears?"
3. "If I can't take a picture then what's the point?"
2. "Is this species extinct?"
1. "Do the turtles find the holes or do they have to dig them?"

Courtesy of David Godfrey (1996)

FROM TORTUGUERO: Many lodges can transport you up to Barra del Colorado at a cost. You can also charter a boat (also very expensive) or get a ride on a passing coconut barge. Besides flying back, you can take the canal route which may be part of your tour. Because the canal to Moín became silted up after the April 1991 earthquake in combination with the changing land use patterns, many boats use a route down to El Carmen, a banana plantation near Siquirres.

If you pass through this seemingly endless plantation, you'll note the different colored ribbons securing the plastic bags to the plants. These indicate different stages of maturity and range from yellow, blue and green to red, which indicates a mature plant.

Stop at the processing center to see the group of workers who sort, spray, and pack the bananas dipping their hands directly into fungicide-imbued water. The first quality (for export), second quality (for internal consumption), and third quality (for cattle feed or baby food) are separated, with the rejects being thrown in an overhead rack. The best bananas are placed on trays and fumigated with hand sprayers, labeled, and then thrown into boxes for export.

Parismina

The small village of Parismina is best known as a center for sports fishing.

On the edge of the village of Parismina, **Parismina Fishing Lodge** (☎ 222-6055, 288-2446, 236-0348, fax 222-1760, 236-1718) features rooms in wooden cottages. They also have a "wild monkey nature tour" and tours of the Tortuguero canals. They have been highly recommended by readers. Expect to spend around US$1,500 pp for a three-day fishing package.

The **Río Parismina Lodge** (☎ 229-7597, fax 798-0918, 800-338-5688) offeriing fishing packages. They have a pool, Jacuzzi, restaurant, and rooms with fans.

Caribbean Expedition Lodge (☎/fax 323-8118) is set at the Parismina's mouth and has six spacious cabins; packages are available.

The Jungle Tarpon Lodge (☎ 907-262-4515) offers seven-day, six-night tarpon fishing (and ecotourism) packages.
greatalaska@greatalaska.com

Parismina Tarpon Rancho (☎ 257-3553, fax 222-1760, 800-862-1003) offers both fishing and eco-tourist adventures.

Parismina Lodge (☎ 768-8636) offers spartan rooms as part of a three-day US$165 pp package.

Chito's Lodge (☎ 768-8636) has a pool. Rates are around US$90 pp, pd with transfers.

> "We will do whatever it takes to prevent the Central Americanization of our country." — trade unionist Albino Vargas, 1997.

Limón

Hot and humid **Limón** (pop. 65,000) was the first town to be successfully established in the nation's tropical lowlands. Originally founded with the intention of rivaling Puntarenas as a coffee export port, it ended up instead devoted mainly to banana export.

Founded in the 1880s in an unpopulated swampy area facing the Atlantic 104 mi.(168 km) from San José, Limón grew to 7,000 by 1927. In its golden age, it rivaled San José as a commercial center where North Americans, Jamaicans, Cubans, Panamaneans, Britons, Germans, and Chinese lived and traded. The nation's very first "company" town, Limón fell victim to its own slavish dependence on the banana. Despite the banana's reappearance in the 1950s, Limón never recovered after the industry's initial slump.

An earthquake on April 22, 1991 hit the town hard. Frustration with slow response on the part of the government led protesters to block the streets with rickety trucks on May 18, 1992. The protests, which lasted four days, were quelled with tear gas and 90 were arrested. Although the head of the Rural Guard alleged that the protesters were "drug addicts and criminals," the protests did spur government action. The five-day 1993 "Operation Rasta" failed to arrest any drug dealers or seize any contraband. An internal investigation a month later revealed the reason: some security officials were in cahoots with traffickers and had tipped them off!

Today, Limón is a small, sweaty town with atmosphere galore. Although it has substantially recovered from the earthquake, problems remain.

Street scene, Limón

GETTING HERE: Buses for Limón (approx. three hrs.) depart on the half-hr. from 5 AM-7PM from the Gran Terminal del Caribe (☎ 256-4248; C. Central near Av. 11). Try to board a direct bus.

warning *Buy tickets in advance if traveling on a weekend or holiday.*

BY CAR: Open since 1987, the Guápiles Highway, a toll road, has shortened driving time from San José to 165 km (102 miles) or 2 1/4 hrs. A tunnel runs under Barva and through Parque Nacional Braulio Carrillo to Guápiles, then on to Limón.

GETTING AROUND: Limón is laid out similarly to San José except that there is no segregation of odd and even streets, there are no street signs, and no locals are aware of the numbering system. Distances are usually given in terms of how many meters it is from the market, park, or small radio station. One positive feature amidst all of this confusion is that many residents speak English — or at least "Jamaica-talk" English.

The main street is Av. 2 ("Market Street"), which extends E from the train station to Vargas Park near the waterfront. Av. 3, 4, and on up, run parallel and to the N. Calle 1 runs N-S along Vargas Park. Higher numbered *calles* run along parallel to the W. To get to Moín from here, take a public bus which runs past Portete en route. Taxis wait at the S side of the *mercado* starting in the wee hours of the morning.

SIGHTS: There's not much to see in Limón proper. Other than the bars, the best place to hang out is in **Parque Vargas**. Ask any sloth! Mainly preoccupied with the fine arts of sleeping and tummyscratching, they occasionally descend to defecate or sip water from the fountains.

Across from the park is the cream-colored, stuccoed **Alcaldía** (city hall). Containing historical material relevant to the area, the **Ethnohistorical Museum** is theoretically open Tues.-Sat. 10-5.

Also here, situated on Av. 2, C. 3/4, the **market** is a lively place to visit.

Off the town's coast is the small island of **Uvita** where Columbus anchored during his first voyage.

The **Asociación China** has a Chinese shrine, with a map showing Chinese routes of emigration all over the world; vicious mahjong games — alive with the lyrically loud snap of slammed pieces — take place here at night.

NEARBY BEACHES: Four km N of town, the small beach of **Playa Bonita** (safe swimming only on the N end) is followed by a rocky overlook at **Portete**, where local fishermen ply their trade. You can watch

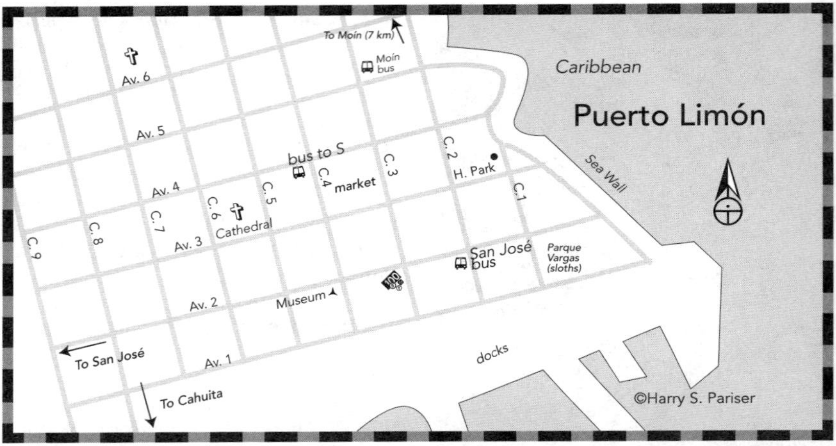

lobster traps being prepared and may even buy fish and lobster from these fishermen. Note the dugout canoes here stored under a bamboo-fashioned stand along the shore. Two bar-restaurants are here.

The 31-acre (12.5-ha) **Parque Cariari**, set between Bonita and Portete, has paths with toucans, parrots, sloths, iguanas, basilisks, and innumerable butterflies. A place to avoid swimming is at Playa Cieneguita, located just S of town, which is reported to be the most polluted in the nation.

ACCOMMODATIONS: The town is someplace you will need to spend the night in as opposed to use as a base. Spartan but inexpensive **Hotel Acón** (☎ 758-1010, fax 758-2924; Apdo. 528, Limón) has a/c, disco, and a communal TV; it's centrally located.

Hotel Teté (☎ 758-11122, fax 758-0707) is set in the market's NW corner and is serviceable. It's around US$20 d.

Aged but still charming, inexpensive (around US$20-40 d depending on the room) **Hotel Park** (☎ 758-3476) is at Av. 3, C. 1/2. Around the same price are the **Internacional** (☎ 758-0662) at C. 3, Av. 5, and a/c **Hotel Miami** (☎ /fax 758-0490; Apdo. 2800, 7300, Limón) at Av. 2, C. 4/5.

LOW-BUDGET ACCOMMODATION: As it's so hot, you'll probably want to have a room with a fan.The **Hotel Palace** (☎ 758-0419) is across from the Instituto Nacional de Seguros. The **Hotel Cariari** (☎ 758-1395) is next door.

Also try around the market (Av. 2, C. 3/4) for the cheapest places, most of which are noisy. These include the **Hotel Oriental** (☎ 758-0117), **Hotel Lincoln** (☎ 758-0074, Av. 5, C. 2/3), **Pensión Los Angeles** (Av. 7, C. 6/7), **Pensión Costa Rica** (1.5 blocks E of the Parque Vargas), **Pensión El Sauce**, **Paraiso** (C. 5, Av. 5/6), rat infested **Pensión Dorita** (Av. 4, C. 3/4), the **Balmoral**, the **Fung**, the **Linda Vista**, and the **Caballo Blanco**.

OUTSIDE OF TOWN: The more deluxe hotels are all near Portete to the N. Located a few km to the N, inexpensive **Hotel Las Olas** (☎ 758-1414; Apdo. 701, Limón) has fans or a/c, swimming pools, restaurant, satellite TV, and sauna.

Inexpensive **Hotel Matama** (☎ 758-1123, fax 758-4499) is near Playa Bonita and has a restaurant and pool.

Across the road, **Apartotel Cocorí** (☎/fax 758-2930, 257-4674, 255-3702) which offers rooms for around US$40 d if you reserve directly. It has a reasonable restaurant, a pool, and tours to Tortuguero which leave daily. Nearby, bed and breakfast **Casa de Bamboo** (☎ 758-1653) charges around US$45 d.

The **Albergue Turístico** (☎ 798-3090) is near the Cocorí and is secure, clean, and good value at around US$30 for rooms with fan or a/c.

Featuring round thatched bungalows with a/c, restaurant, car rental, and pools, expensive (US$65 d) **Hotel Maribú Caribe** (☎ 758-4010, 758-4543, fax 758-3541; Apdo. 623, 7300 Limón) is one km closer to Limón.

The **Jardín Tropical Azul** (☎ 253-5424) offers a/c cabins for around US$60 d with breakfast which have phone and TV. Facilities include pools, tennis, basketball court, and restaurant.

FOOD: Shrimp and lobster are slightly less expensive than elsewhere around here. Try the a/c dining room of the **Hotel Acón** or, two km to the N, the **Hotel Las Olas.**

La Antillita serves good food and sometimes has live music.

Soda La Estrella, set 100 m W from the NW corner of the market, offers cheap *casados*.

The seedy exterior of **Restaurante Doña Toda**, set on the market's E side, masks a clean interior, and it is good value. Be sure to let them know what you think about having sea turtle on the menu!

For Chinese food try the **Cien Kung**, across from the Texaco station at the Palacio Encantador.

Inside the Internacional (C. 3, Av. 5) is the **Turkeski**. The **La Fuente** is at C. 3, Av. 3/4.

Also try the **American Bar** (C. 1, Av. 2 opposite Vargas Park) which has seafood and beef. The **Soda Gemini** nearby has a good buffet and cakes. **Rasa's** serves international food. Also try the **Apollo Once**, around the corner from the Baptist Church.

Soda Mares serves fine fruit drinks and seafood. **Café Verde** on Av. 3, C. 19/21 near the former train station and the bus stop for San José, offers expresso, capuccino, sandwiches, German pastries, Italian pasta dishes, and salads, as well as Tico breakfasts.

Market food (Av. 2, C. 3/4) is the cheapest around.

Heading along the seawall up to Moín, you first come to the seafood-oriented **Arrecife**, then **Springfield** which serves typical local food for about US$5/meal. Next is the **Manchester**, the deluxe **El Zapote**, and then the **Soda Encato**. The **Kimbandu** is a pricey but attractively located Caribbean-cuisine restaurant at Playa Bonita.

SERVICES: Two blocks N of the market's E corner, the **Helenik Souvenir Shop and Tourist Information Center** (☎ 758-2086) offers laundry service and tour connections.

The **Farmacia Buenos Aires** (☎ 798-4430) is open Mon. to Sat. 7-7. It's 25 m E of the Banco Nacional.

ENTERTAINMENT: Hookers and sailors frequent some of the bars. Opening onto the street, the American Bar (C. 1, Av. 2 opposite Vargas Park) is a live wire. The **Mark 15** disco is across from the Anglican Church. Also try the **Springfield** on the N outskirts or visit the **Johnny Dixon Bar** at Playa Bonita.

Limón's Carnival

Centering around the date of Oct. 12 (the former Columbus Day now known as the Día de las Culturas), Limón's *carnaval* features calypso and reggae, parades, and dancing in the streets. It had its origins in 1949 when Alfred King, returning from Panama, brought the idea back with him. The celebration has its locus around the market where there are gambling and food stalls. typically, events take place from Tues. to Sun. with bullfights, clown parade, horse races, art exhibits, bathing suit parade, volleyball contests, fireworks, and other events including an eight-hour concert featuring an international selection of bands.

The stretch from Escuela General Tomas Guardia to the Black Star Line building in the town center becomes an "alcohol-free zone" with craft and food stands. It features art exhibitions and a daily calypso contest. A shuttle also runs to Uvita where there're stands as well as music. (If planning to attend, be sure to book a hotel room way in advance. The *Tico Times* generally prints a schedule of events).

The **Atlantic Cinema** shows films.

warning: *Be careful walking around Limón at night!*

EVENTS AND FESTIVALS: The main event is ***carnaval*** (see box). The Limón area celebrates **May Day** with cricket matches, picnics, quadrille dances, and domino matches.

A **surfing championship** takes place annually at Playa Bonita situated to the N of town.

FROM LIMÓN: Alas, there is no longer any train service. The bus to Playa Bonita, Portete, and Moín leaves hourly from C. 4, Av. 4 in front of Radio Casino in Limón. As there's no bus station, tickets are sold in offices by the bus stops.

In addition to San José (daily 5 AM-7:30 PM), buses also run S through Cahuita and Puerto Viejo (5, 8, 10, 1, 4) to Bribri and Sixaola bordering Panama. There's also a direct (via Cahuita and Puerto Viejo) bus to Manzanillo which leaves at 6 and 2:30. Buy tickets the day before (or at least several hours in advance to avoid the rush) and arrive early to secure a seat. If going to the Black Beach area of Cahuita (hotels you should get off at La Union stop on the main highway and walk the one km in.

> Sit on the L after Limón to get the best views. Along the way you pass stands offering *pipas* (drinking coconuts) as well as soberingly vast stretches of banana plantations.

Heading South from Limón

Río Bananito Lodge

Closest adventure lodge to Limón, the **Río Bananito Lodge** (☎/fax 253-8818, fax 224-2640) is set out of the way in the mountains; to get here, you must cross four rivers; transport is offered from Bananito the event that you do not have a four-wheel-drive vehicle. It has seven cabins on stilts with views. Activities include rappelling down a waterfall, horseback riding, and hiking. Rates are around US$135 d with three meals. No credit cards.
www.netins.net/showcase/costarica
conselva@sol.racsa.co.cr

Aviarios del Caribe (Aviary of the Caribbean)

Aviary of the Caribbean is a small bed and breakfast and wildlife sanctuary established by Luis and Judy Arroyo, a Tico and *norteamericano* couple who met in Alaska. It is one of the last bas-tions in the area against the encroaching banana plantations.It is set 30 km S of Limón and 10 km N of Cahuita, and the road signs make it obvious.

Boat tours (around US$25 pp) are offered from 6:30 to 3. You will see some of the 247 species of birds that have been identified so far, along with other creatures such as *caimáns*, monkeys, and river otters. There are poison dart and other frogs on display which are captured and then returned to the wild after a few days. The caged birds on display were donated and/or born in captivity so they cannot survive in the wild. You may have the chance to meet Buttercup, the couple's pet baby sloth. Its mother was killed on the road. There are several other less amicable two-toed sloths: one hangs out on the couch in the living room watching TV! The rooms are spacious and priced moderately (at around US$60 d), with breakfast included. For more information/reservations fax 758-4459 or write Apdo. 569, 7300 Limón.

Orquídeas Mundo
(Piedmont Restaurant)

This nursery, restaurant, and campground is run by Pierre Dubois (381-1076; Apdo. 575, Limón 7300) , a former botanist at Montreal's Botanical Gardens. He is here to pursue a lifelong dream of hybridizing rare SE Asian orchids. Dubois gives guided tours (US$5 pp), one of which surveys his nursery and another which traverses nearby trails where insects, birds, and ornamentals abound. His restaurant, open daily 6 AM-10 PM, serves inexpensive "Cordon Bleu Tropical" dishes. To get here cross the Río Estrella bridge and then turn R at the sign which says Penhurst. The Dubois family lives 600 m down the road on the R.

www.greencoast.com/orchid

Reserva Biológica Hitoy Cerere
(Hitoy Cerere Biological Reserve)

The isolated 22,620-acre (9,154-ha) reserve, Hitoy Cerere Reserve is set between the heavily cultivated Estrella and Telirre river valleys. Its steep peaks, which include Bobócara (2,618 ft., 798 m) and Bitácara (3,363 ft., 1,025 m), have served to isolate it even from the three surrounding Indian settlements. Its rugged topography is what saved it from development.

> ?! The name **Hitoy Cerere** stems from the combination of two Native American names applied to two rivers in the area: *Hitoy* means "woolly" in the sense of mossy or covered with vegetation, and *Cerere* means clear waters.

FLORA AND FAUNA: Rising to heights of 100 ft. (30 m) or more, the reserve's lofty trees include the wild cashew, the Santa María, balsa, and calyptrogyne or "dovetail" tree. There are also a large number of medicinal plants and trees within the reserve as well as over 200 species of orchids. More than 118 in. (3,000 mm) of rain fall annually, and the average temperature is between 72.5° and 77°F (22.5°-25°C). Wildlife found here include three species of opossum, pizotes, sloths, anteaters, agoutis, pacas, racoons, margays, kinkajous, otters, jaguars, tapirs, white-faced and howler monkeys. The 115 species of birds include the cayenne squirrel cuckoo and the blue-headed parrot.

PRACTICALITIES: It's accessible by four-wheel-drive vehicle. You can get taxi service from Finca 16 in the Estrella Valley Standard Fruit Co. Banana Plantation which, in turn, can be reached by the Valle de la Estrella bus from

The Talamanca Region

Talamanca is Costa Rica's southeastern frontier region.. Virtually inaccessible until the late 1970s, Talamanca remains the nation's poorest yet greenest section. Shaped like a triangle, this densely forested region remained untouched until the end of the 19th C. Its name derives from the Miskito Indian word *Talamalka*, which means "place of blood," referring to the end of a hunt.

Most of the resident indigenous peoples did not make this their original home. After the Bribri, Guatuso, and Cabécar tribes burned down several missions and killed priests, they were forcibly resettled here and in Guanacaste. The three indigenous peoples' reserves in the area are the Talamanca Bribri, Talamanca Cabécar, and KékoLdi.

Today, the region still retains considerable charm. You can still hear such Jamaican-style phrases as "*How you keeping*?" and "*How de morning*?" The region is a relaxing melting pot of Native American, African-American, and Spanish culture.

Formerly *the place* to come for those who want to rough it, a/c resorts with swimming pools have been steadily moving in. Tourism as a monoculture has replaced *cacao*, driven out by a virus mysteriously introduced at the same time as the banana plantations were attempting to buy up land in the area.

Although the impact of tourism has caused a shift away from traditional life for the largely African-American coastal dwellers, the Bribri and Cabécar peoples still maintain many of their customs and ancient beliefs side by side with their jeans and radios.

Although the tribes theoretically control what happens within their own borders, Oceana Minera, a Canadian mining multinational, was granted a permit in 1993 to prospect for copper and gold within the reserve. The tribal leaders are protesting the invasion along with attempts by the legislature to make it easier to gain access to mineral and petroleum concessions on native reserves in the Talamanca region.

Largely owing to longstanding prejudice, the area still remains neglected by the government. The ICT's idea of doing something beneficial for visitors is to put up large and garish blue signs indicating "hotel," "*cabiña,*" and "restaurant" right in front of hotels, *cabiñas*, and restaurants. Only the freeway and the Howard Johnsons are lacking! Meanwhile, the roads are terrible, sewage systems and running water are nonexistent, and potentially dangerous beaches with undertow remain unmarked.

Limón. By car, head W from Penhurst. In order to reserve meals and lodging, call 233-5473 about a week beforehand. Camping is permitted. While there are no formal trails, you can follow the ones used by the rangers and the Indians who reside around the reserve's perimeter.

WATERFALLS: From the ranger station, head R and cross the river and continue upstream until you find the falls and swimming hole; a second, less impressive set are around a half hour upstream. They're found just off from the turnoff to the small creeek to the L which is around a km away.

Cahuita National Park (Parque Nacional Cahuita)

Cahuita — a relaxed and somnolent village of about 3,000— is located by the entrance to to Cahuita National Park, one of the nation's most popular attractions. Originally known as "The Bluff," its name was changed to Cahuita — a Spanish language transliteration of two Miskito Indian words, *cawi* (a small tree traditionally used to make dugout canoes) and *ta* (a point of land) — by a 1915 presidential decree. In recent years — following the completion of a road and the establishment of the national park— tourism in the town has grown at a phenomenal pace.

Much of the popularity stems from its verdancy (in comparison to the aridity of the Pacific coast), its easy accessiblity, and the pleasant onshore breeze here. So far, however, the town retains its character and shows no signs of being transformed. Do note that theft is on the rise here (in tandem with the crack problem) so take appropriate precautions.

FLORA, FAUNA, AND THE REEF: While the most famed life is underwater, there's plenty to see on the ground as well. Thousands of coconut trees line the beaches, and it's easy to see monkeys as you walk along.

The 593-acre (240-ha) reef is outlined by the seaward waves which break against it. It generally is less than three feet deep near the coast and in places where live coral grow, though up to 21 ft. (seven m) deep in the several channels. There are 34 species of coral, over 100 of seaweed, and 500 species of fish. The water is clearest from Feb. to April. There are also two old shipwrecks, complete with cannons.

ENVIRONMENTAL PROBLEMS: Sadly, the reef has been dying because of production practices on the banana plantations. Trees are cut along river banks and replaced with banana plants, which allow the soil to float downstream, and chemicals flow freely into irrigation canals, which run into rivers. The combination of sedimentation with agrochemicals has suffocated some 60% of the reef. The fish supply is also decreasing owing to the fact that the larger fish were drawn in to feast on the smaller ones, which have now been killed off. In July 1990, in a bizarre incident, an estimated half-million fish were discovered floating belly-up in the Río Matina, apparent victims of phorate, a chemical employed on the plantations. Government officials blamed the poisoning on fishermen! Results of the government lab tests and investigation remain sealed.

GETTING HERE: Buses for Cahuita (approx. four hrs.) depart at 10, 1:30, and 4 from the Gran Terminal del Caribe (☎ 256-4248; C. Central near Av. 11).

Direct buses to Sixaola (bypassing Limón) leave from at 6 and 3:30, passing both park entrances. (Sixaola is about 25 min. farther down the road.)

From Limón, buses (one hr.) leave from Av. 4, C. 3/4 at 5, 8, 10, 1, 4, and 6. If you get a 7 AM bus from San José, there should be no problem meeting the 10 AM bus out of Limón.

Sit on the L after Limón to get the best views. Along the way you pass stands offering *pipas* (drinking coconuts) as well as soberingly vast stretches of banana plantations.

ORIENTATION: Cahuita's wide sand-topped gravel streets have *cabinas* and restaurants interspersed at intervals. The bus stop is next to the miniature "park" and across from Salon Vaz, the most popular bar.

One side of the wide gravel main street leads to Hotel Cahuita and the park entrance. The Black Beach is in the other direction. The road heading towards the water leads to Cabinas Palmer and then around the corner and down to the L, to Surfside and then on to Edith's.

The road to the Black Beach follows Miss Edith's past the Guardia Civil and continues on down with sandy stretches punctuated by coral outcrops. This is a beautiful road to either walk or cycle. On the way, you pass blooming hibiscus, birds, palms, giant green iguanas — their finned backs undulating like a pack of cards being shuffled — while the pounding surf is off to the R.

HISTORY: Cahuita's name comes from the indigenous words *kawe* (mahogany) and *ta* (point). Up until recent decades, it remained a remote, sleepy village. These days tourism, in the form of mom-and-pop enterprises is an important feature of the local economy.

Created in 1970, **Cahuita National Park** includes 2,636 acres (1,067 ha) of land and the 1,483 acres (600 ha) of coral reefs which are located 1,640 ft. (500 m) offshore. Only 20% of the local farmers were reimbursed as promised after the park's creation. Problems here include runoff of silt from banana plantations, which is killing the reef, and poaching of turtle eggs and iguanas, which is decimating local populations.

Perhaps the combined effect of years of poor attitude and insensitivity on the part of the national government caused the community to react as they did when René Castro, the Minister of Natural Resources, unilaterally acted to raise park fees for foreigners to an atronomical US$15 pd on Sept. 1 1994. In early Sept.

A footpath in Cahuita National Park. A trail stretches along the coast from the village to the ranger stztion at Puerto Vargas.

1994, townspeople took over the park entrances in order to prevent the new edict from being enforced. In addition, Cahuita Tours owner Tony Mora filed a motion before the Supreme Court seeking an injunction against the park fees.

In response to the takeover, the ministry published a quarter-page ad in *La Nación* advising visitors against visiting the park. Minister Castro maintained that Cahuita "is a zone where the tourists who go experiment with attitudes we do not want in our country. Those types of visitors (read low budget backpackers), unfortunately for them, will have to find themselves another country." To this date, the park remains in local hands with the National Park Service in control of only the Puerto Vargas sector.

VISITING THE NATIONAL PARK: Cross a bridge down past Hotel Cahuita to enter the park. Several picnic tables are near the entrance where you should give a contribution toward park maintenance.

The sandy beach stretches out in the distance as far as the eye can see. Both the beach and the nature trail to its rear come to a halt in front of a river which must be crossed. Along the way the trail is alive with bright blue morpho (birdwing) butterflies, land crabs, birds and, at times, monkeys.

If you're planning on continuing, you'll need a good pair of shoes or windsurfing sandals. Soon, you'll reach a shallow stream, the Río Perezoso, colored red from the tannic acid released by decomposed vegetation. The water all along this stretch is smooth and translucent because the surf is breaking on the reef way offshore.

ACCOMMODATION: Although no longer a backpacker's rustic paradise, much of the accommodation here remains fairly inexpensive (around US$10 pp or less depending upon numbers and location). Having benefiting from a project funded by the California Cooperative Federation and the National Union of the Development of Cooperatives, *cabinas* have proliferated and have become a veritable mom-and-pop industry. Most of the more imaginative ones are operated by the local Italian, Swiss, and German population. The rest of the bunch all incorporate an identical concrete box design and are set in rows.

If you're coming on a tight budget, it's better to travel in a group, which reduces the cost considerably. Some hotels have one price for foreigners and a secret lower price for locals. Much of the town's lodging is listed in this section, but there are still others if these are full. There's plenty of digs available so you should look around first and bargain if you're planning on staying for a while. New places are opening all the time, so don't confine yourself to the ones listed here!

Taking the first diagonal R before you get into town and heading down the road brings you to inexpensive **Cabinas Coriosos** which is just around the corner from Restaurante Típico.

Delapidated but atmospheric inexpensive **Hotel Cahuita** (☎ .750-0201) is conveniently located next to the park entrance. It has a restaurant. Their *cabinas* with fans and bath are dark. Next door, low-budget/inexpensive **Cabinas Sol y Mar** (☎ 750-0237) has rooms with private baths; the upstairs ones have balconies. Across the street from these two, **Cabinas Vaz** (☎ 750-0218) is also in the low-budget/inexpensive range and is owned by the same strongman that operates the bar up the street. Low-budget **Cabinas Rhode Island** are set behind them.

The German-owned four-rm. **Alby Lodge** (☎/fax 755-0031; Apdo. 840, Limón) charges around US$30-40 for two to four for its attractive rooms. It is to the R and down a path before the park entrance.

Tips From Joelle (www.Cahuita.com)

"You might want to know that Cahuita covers the streets with white beach sand now. Really romantic! Salon Vaz is no longer Salon Vaz, but rather Coco Bar although the locals are just getting used to the name, and just as often say 'Salon Vaz.' No sign though."

"There is a little used public message board at the boutique (mine) next to Cabinas Cawa in case one needs a contact point when meeting up with someone."

"It is most advantageous when one is trying to leave to wait at the Vaz/Coco's bus stop at the park where there is shade and benches, and take whichever bus comes first. I often take the *directo* to Limón and then *directo* to San José because if I let one get by, the next may be full."

"In Limon, a taxi from the Cahuita stop to the San Jose stop (about four blocks) costs a dollar if you are heavliy loaded with baggage."

"People need to know not to swim with kids at the park entrance, there is just too much current sometimes. The farther in you walk the safer it is. The river mouth is ideal."

"AIDS: The pristine state of rural areas in Costa Rica is misleading. People should take extreme caution if they are going to fool around. People should double bag it."

"In Cahuita we have had running water around the clock since 1996, and they finally built a clinic! We have a wonderful caring bilingual young doctor."

"The best medicine in the whole wide world for mosquito bites, sunburn, rashes, or even as a sunblock is Calergin, which you can buy at any CR pharmacy, Bottle or tube. It has calamine, a 'caine to numb itch or pain, an antihistamine, and zinc oxide. I swear if you out it on a new mosquito bite it goes away! I don't travel without it. Great stuff."

"One of the best places to eat Afro Caribe dishes is right on the porch of one of the bars downtown with Miss Maudie. (She feuds periodically and switches between the main two) She speaks English and her physique testifies to the tastiness of her own cooking! Don't eat the turtle. While it may be okay for the locals it's WRONG for us."

"While natural Citronella is used as a mosquito repellent, it attracts bees."

"The road can be great if you get there in the first six months after they redo it (every two years)!"

One of the superior places to stay, **Cabinas Palmer** (☎ 750-0243) charges in the low-budget range for its room in the house and a bit more for its facing set of *cabinas*. It's down from Salon Vaz, on the way to the beach. Low-budget/inexpensive **Cabinas Jenny** (☎ 750-0256) is just down the road by the water and has hammocks.

Low-budget/inexpensive **Cabinas Brisas del Mar** (☎ 750-0267) is across from the school and near the ocean.

Another really very nice place to stay is low-budget/inexpensive **Surf Side Cabinas** (☎ 750-0246, 750-0203) down to the L behind the school; accommodation ranges from single (US$5 to quad. (US$20).

Inexpensive **Cabinas Tito** (ext.750-0286) is near the Rural Guard.

Inexpensive **Cabinas Colibri** (ext.750-0263) offers rooms with private baths, hammocks, and kitchens.

The **Pastry Shop**, next door, has one *cabina*. Others in this area include inexpensive **Cabinas Sulila**, and **Cabinas Smith**.

warning The problem with virtually all centrally located digs is that you have to endure the pulsations from Salon Vaz until the wee hours every single night.

Those who need quiet to sleep should position themselves farther out.

BLACK BEACH ACCOMMODATION: Out of range of the pulsating nightly riddims pouring out from Salon Vaz, the Black Beach area has a wide range of hostelries. More will definitely have opened by the time you arrive.

Clean and hospitable **Cabinas Arrecifes** (☎/fax 755-008) is 100 m E and 25 m S from the police station. It offers an outdoor restaurant, and 10 rooms for around US$10 s, US$20 d, and US$25 t. Bike rental is available, and credit cards are accepted.

Near the ball field and about a km from town, inexpensive-moderate thatched-roof **Cabinas Atlántida** (☎ 755-0115, fax 750-0213) has fans and offers breakfast. The Spanish management is friendly and helpful, and the cabins are attractive and well built. Each unit has a bath with hot shower, and there is a sitting area in front of each. They have a great pool and a restaurant for guests. Rates are around US$55 d, US$65 t, US$75 quad.

www.atlantida.co.cr
atlantis@sol.racsa.co.cr

Set nearby and to the rear, **Colibri Paradise** (☎ 755-0055) is a sort of four bungalows which charge around US$30-40 depending upon the number of peope. Each has a full kitchen. English, French, and Spanish are spoken.

Offering three quiet bungalows with private baths and fans, Spanish-style **El Encanto Bed and Breakfast** (☎/fax 755-0113; Apdo. 1234, Limón) is set amidst gardens and has a patio restaurant. Rates run around US$29 s, US$39 d, and US$ 49 t. with breakfast. Owners Michael and Karen Russell are very friendly, and this is a great place to stay.

The **Taller de Artesanias** (Letty's) has low-budget rooms. Italian-run with two-storey, stone and wood structures, inexpensive **Cabinas Black Beach** (☎ 750-0251), hold up to four. Next door, **Jardín Rocallo** (Apdol 152, Limón) charges US$30 for rooms (longer-term discount) with a kitchen and refrigerator.

Advertising for surfers, Soda Ciancla offers low-budget and spartan *cabinas* called **Cabinas El Ancla**.

To its rear, attractive and inexpensive **Apartamiento Iguana** (☎ 755-0005, fax 755-0054) consists of two small houses for rent with kitchens for around US$50 per night. Rooms are around US$15 d.

Hotel Jaguar (ext.750-0238, ☎ 226-3775, fax 226-4693; Apdo. 7046, 1000 San José) offers large rooms with queen-sized beds and attached bath with hot shower. There are no fans, but the ceilings are high, air circulation is good, and the rooms cool down just fine at night. It has a restaurant with innovative cuisine; breakfast is included in the price. Dietary preferences will be catered to; their vegetarian dishes are also well prepared. Rooms are around US$30 s and US$55 d.

jaguar@sol.racsa.co.cr

Way up at the end of the road, low-budget/inexpensive **Cabinas Algebra** (☎ 776-0057) offers one *cabina* for up to three without kitchen and a second for four with kitchen. One night is free if you stay for a week.

Swiss-owned and managed **Chalet Hibiscus** (Apdo. 943, Limón) has two houses (each accommodates four to six) facing a coral rock beach which rent for around US$100 per night; two more with a pool in front (US$80) are across the road. Less expensive *cabinas* (US$45) are also available. They have a small gift shop.

The **Magellan Inn** (☎/fax 755-0035; Apdo. 1234, Limón) is a highly attractive

set of cabinas which have a pool, restaurant, and bar; it is at Playa Viquez, and rates are around US$60 d (US$70 t) including continental breakfast and tax. Its gourmet restaurant **Casa Creole** is next door. If you have a car or don't mind the long walk (or short bike ride) to town, this would be a good place to stay.
www.web-span.com/tropinet/magellan1.html
borgato@sol.racsa.co.cr

Tropicana (☎/fax 755-0059) is across from the beach and offers rooms on the second floor for around US$35 with tax and breakfast; use of bikes is included.
borgato@sol.racsa.co.cr

Run by a local, **Ruby's** consists of five low-budget units. Just down the road towards the beach from the La Union bus stop are inexpensive 12-unit **Cabinas Arco Iris**, small and low-budget **Cabinas Margarita** (☎ 750-0205) — which has fish painted on the outside — inexpensive closely set **Cabinas Viviene**, and **Vishnu** (☎ 755-0263).

Run by Italians from Bologna and set next to the Jaguar, **Bungalow Malú** (☎ 755-0006) offers three low-budget/inexpensive and very attractive *cabinas* which contain two single beds and one queen as well as a refrigerator. There are two fans in each room and hot water. You can cook at their *ranchito*.

Next down to the R, you will find **Casa Suecia**. A house for rent is also on the R. Five-room relaxing **Cabinas Piscina Natural** (US$15 d) is also in the area. It has a saltwater pool, hammocks, and gardens.

RETREATS: Samasati Retreat Center (☎ 224-1870, fax 224-5032) is for New Age readers of this book. Yoga, dolphin interaction, visiting a local shaman, bodywork, and other activities are offered. They have a reserve.
www.samsati.com

CAMPING: If you're game to camp, the only formal campgrounds are at the other park entrance at Puerto Vargas. Showers, toilets, and water are available; watch your things. You must pay a fee.

FOOD: Depending upon where you're staying, you may find yourself spending more per meal than per night. Most of the food is higher priced than that found in similar establishments in San José, but without a corresponding increase in quality. Many of the restaurants have near-identical menus and prices, offering Italian food, sandwiches, and other dishes popular with tourists.

Miss Edith's is still one the least expensive and best places to dine. She offers some vegetarian specialties. Be prepared for a long wait.

Offering seafood, Chinese-run **Vista del Mar** is near the park and offers the best value in town. Several others are across the street. A friendly lady sells baked goods and drinks at the park entrance.

Cha Cha Cha, next to Cahuita Tours, is the best in-town choice for gourmet food at reasonable prices.

Sol y Mar and **Cabinas Vaz** both have restaurants, as does **Cabinas Surfside**. Near Cabinas Vaz, the **Defi** has seafood, pizza, and veggie goodies. Screened in and attractive, **El Típico** is up the road and off to the L.

Out down the road, **Cabinas Black Beach** has a restaurant. **Brigitte** has an inexpensive restaurant which serves a number of vegetarian dishes. On a side road, **Restaurante Vishnu** offers yogurt and other healthy food. **Bananas** is the name of Cabinas Algebra's attractive porch-top restaurant which serves up local cuisine.

Still farther on, popular **Margaritaville**, a Canadian-owned organic food restaurant, is open for dinner. A meal is about US$5 and includes fresh baked bread.

Even farther out (next to the Magellan at 2.5 km), the **Casa Creole** (☎ 755-0104) is a gourmet French Caribbean restaurant. Expect to spend US$15-20 pp for dinner.

On the road from Black Beach to the main road is **Cafeteria Vishnu**. Offering pasta, crepes, and pizza, **Pizzeria El Cactus** is across the road.

There are a number of stores and *pulperías* including **Super Vaz** which is 100 m N of the main entrance to town.

> ***URL*** **www.cahuita.com** *A delightful portrait by Joelle, a frequent visitor.*

SERVICES: Cahuita Tours (☎ 750-0232, fax 775-0082) changes travelers checks, offers tours (glass bottomed boat and numerous others: US$200 pp) and rents snorkeling equipment and bicycles. It is owned and managed by local notable Tony Mora. There is a pay phone right by its counters, and they will receive and send faxes for you.

Mairena Cruz operates **Snorkeling Tours** (☎ 755-0089) which is 250 m E from the entrance to La Unión. They offer bird-watching and snorkeling (US$20 pp).

José McCloud (☎/fax. 755-0071) is a local tour guide who offers jungle hiking. His office is next to Godfrey's public phone. **dltacb@sol.racsa.co.cr**

Roberto Tours (☎ 755-0117, 755-0092) is set 100 m to the S of the bus stop. Tortuguero, fishing, snorkeling (US$14 pp), horseback riding, and other trips. The rent bikes and snorkeling gear.

Turistica Cahuita (☎ 755-0071) offers Tortuguero trips; bicycle, surfboard, and snorkeling gear rentals, and the usual other excursions. They are 50 m N from Cahuita Park.

There's a **book exchange** near Brigitte's in Black Beach.

Others include **Walter Cunningham** (ext 750-0229) and **Carlos Mairena** (ext.750-0288).

At Black Beach, **Brigitte** (Apdo. 1152, Limón) rents horses and offers tours.Feel free to use **Cliff's tennis courts** which are next to the Hotel Margaritaville on the Black Beach road. Cliff may even take you on for a game.

Along the Black Beach road, **Tienda de Artesanía** sells local crafts including jewelry. Vendors sell Guatemalan goods near the park entrance.

ENTERTAINMENT: The local hot spot is **Salon Vaz**, a typical bar with a large "disco" in back and lots of cool Rastaphonians hanging out. **Bar Hannia** nearby plays reggae as well. The **Defi** has reggae on weekends.

FROM CAHUITA: The boarding spot is right by the park and across from the Salon Vaz. The following times may change, so double-check them.

Buses to Limón run at 6:30, 10:15, 12;15, 1:30, and 5.

Buses from Puerto Viejo pass through at approximately 7, 8, 10, 11:15, 2, 4, and 5, but these may be full so it may be better to take a bus up to Limón and then on to San José. Or you might spend a day in Puerto Viejo and catch the 4 or 5 PM bus from there to San José.

Buses for Limón leave at 6:30, 9, noon, 3, 4:30, and 6.

> ***i*** **Cahuita Tours** offers a full-color brochure which has a map as well as hotel and restaurant listings.

Puerto Viejo de Talamanca

This "Old Harbor," surrounds a small bay with still waters and beautiful black sand beaches. Winding around the coast, the road unveils its beauty at every turn as you approach. Children play in front of the crashing surf. The capsized The town area is relatively compact, but hotels, many of which are "waiting for the walk-in," now stretch down the coast nearly as far as Manzanillo village. barge at the village entrance once was used to carry black sand for export.

The town's lifestyle gives new meaning to the term "laid back." Although this is fast changing in the wake of megabucks development, the inhabitants here still retain an attitude of innocence towards foreigners no longer found in places such as Jamaica.

> ***URL*** **www.greencoast.com** *A fine guide to alternative Talalamanca.*

GETTING HERE: Direct buses (four hrs. and 195 km, ☎ 221-0524) from San José depart at 6, 1:30, and 3:30; these run via Cahuita all the way to Bri Bri, and on to Sixaola on the Panamanian border. To arrange a ride into Puerto Viejo from El Cruce (the crossroads) where this bus leaves you, telephone 758-3844 or 758-0854 two days in advance. Otherwise it's a couple of km walk into town unless you stay at the outlying lodges.

A direct bus leaves from the same stop in San José at 3:30. Buses from San José to Puerto Limón leave hourly from the NE corner of Parque Nacional (2.5 hrs). From there, buses to Sixaola which enter Puerto Viejo (1.5 hrs) depart at 5, 10, 1, and 4. From Limón you can also take a

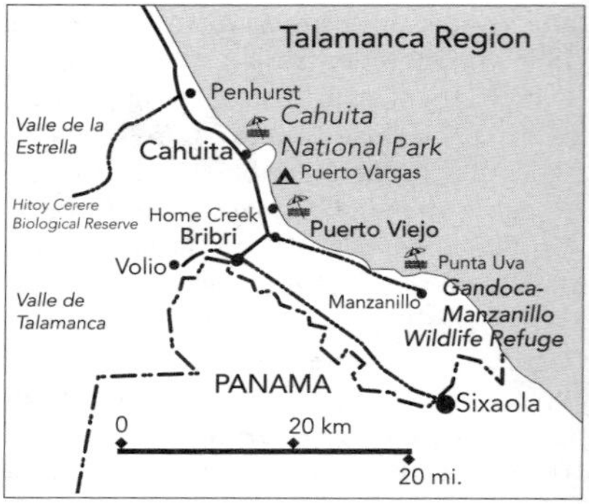

bus directly to Manzanillo; it leaves at 6 and 2. From La Cruce on the road is unpaved. Plans are to pave it, which could easily swamp the village with a flood of tourists.

SIGHTS: There really has not been much in the way of visitor-oriented attractions until recently. And nature still remains the main attraction. One place definitely worth visiting is friendly Finca La Isla Botanical Gardens (☎/fax 750-0046) offer tours and has rooms for US$8 pp.
www.greencoast.com
jarbot@sol.racsa.co.cr

ACCOMMODATIONS: The number of **Puerto Viejo**'s hotels have grown along with its popularity. New hotels here have been sprouting up rapidly. While the area is fast becoming overdeveloped and increasingly upscale, good values can still be found. However, you have to count on spending around US$8 pp, up from US$3 just a few years back. Be aware that the area packs out around Christmas and Easter as well as on certain high season weekends.

Way out in the outback, **Nairy Awary** (☎ 380-9082, fax c/o Francesco Rosini: 718-6047; c/o Cortel Battan 7251) is somewhere past the village of San Miguel in Talamanca. Facilities include horseback riding and lessons, mountain bike rental, indigenous contact program, waterfall, hiking, archaeological sites, and a four-rm lodge. Rates are around US$25 pp, pn with board; trades are available.

A 49-acre (20-ha) private reserve with nature trails, **Nature Lodge Chimuri** (message: ☎/fax 750-0119) has Bribri-style cabins set 1,500 ft. (500 m) from the beach. It has three two-person cabins for around US$23 and one four-person cabin for US$33. Horseback rides, night walks (US$12 pp), visits to its butterfly farm, and camping trips to the Indian reservation are also available. Bikes and rubber boots can be rented by visitors. For more infomation contact Cabinas Chimuri, Puerto Viejo de Limón, Talamanca.
atecmail@sol.racsa.co.cr

Low-budget **Cabinas Black Sands** has limited facilities but is spectacularly located on the beach. The new owners have preserved it intact. A communal kitchen is available. There is also a separately-owned *cabiña* for rent here.
www.green coast.com
bsands@sol.racsa.co.cr

The **Chimuri Beach Cottages** (☎/fax 750-0119) rent attractive units for US$150/week or US$250/mo. It is run by the owners and former managers of Cabinas Chimuri.
atecmail@sol.racsa.co.cr

Farther down the road towards Limón are **Cabinas Azulilla** (☎ 228-6748) which has two rooms (US$30) with private bath and shared kitchen. Rentals for the entire property is available as are weekly rates. Low-budget and spartan **Cabinas BW** are nearby.

On the way to town around the curve, moderate **Cabinas Playa Negra** (☎ 556-1132) has one nine-person unit with kitchen, TV, and private bath and two

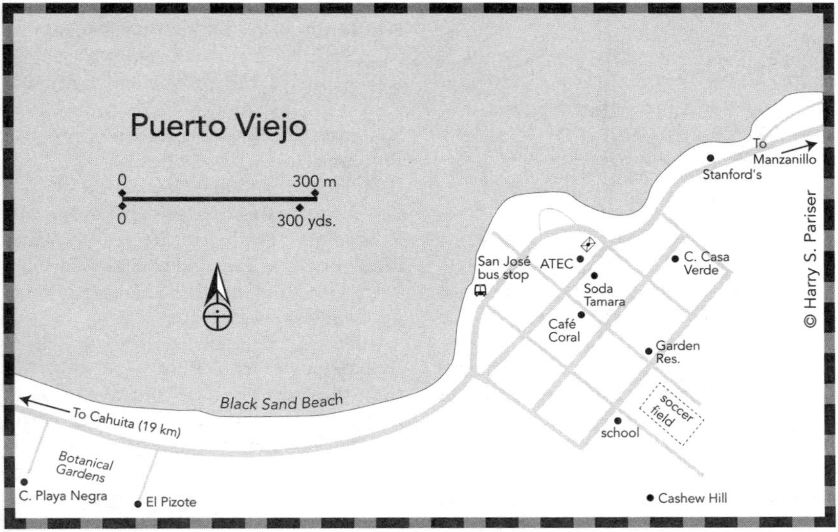

Seeing the Real Talamanca

With headquarters across from Soda Tamara in the town center, **ATEC**, the Association of Ecotorism and Conservation of Talamanca, is an exciting recent development on the local scene. The organization's goals are to promote ecological tourism and environmental education for the local population and for visitors. In most of Costa Rica, the situation is one of eco-exploitation rather than "ecotourism." Most guides are paid only a pittance compared to what tourists who take the tours pay. ATEC tours are limited to six participants and afford you the opportunity to see how Costa Ricans really live. These tours can be difficult so make sure you choose one that suits your needs. In the Cahuita area, snorkeling, a bird walk, farm walks, and others are offered. In Puerto Viejo walks are offered around farms and to the Kekoldi Indian Reserve. Snorkeling and camping can be arranged at Punta Mona. Three trips are also conducted in the Manzanillo-Gandoca Reserve, with a Gandoca/ANAI overnight hike which includes a visit to an experimental fruit farm and may allow you to spot a nesting sea turtle (for more information on ANAI, see "volunteering" in the Practicalities section). Prices run from about US$12.50 for a half-day trip to US$70 for a three-night trip (not including food and lodging). A half-day of birding is US$12.50, and a snorkeling trip is around US$17. For information write ATEC: ☎/fax 750-0191, 750-0188; Puerto Viejo
atecmail@sol.racsa.co.cr

four-person units with kitchen and private bath. They have a *soda* which serves fresh fish.

Closer in to town, **Mr. O'Conner** has one room with private bath and fan for a low-budget rate (three persons maximum).

Casa Maximo B&B (☎ 750-0021) charges around US$20 d; rooms have shared bath.

One of the best places to stay in town, Swiss-run **Cabinas Casa Verde** (☎750-0015, fax 750-0047; René Kessler, Apdo. 1114, Limón) charges around US$18 s and US$30d.

The **Hotel Maritza** (☎/fax 798-1844) charges inexpensive prices for its new set of *cabinas* behind the hotel; the rooms above the hotel are among the cheapest in town.

Cabinas Ritz and **Hotel Puerto Viejo** are towards the bottom of the low-budget scale.

More expensive are **Cabinas Manuel León** (☎ 758-0854), **Cabinas Anselmo** (only one unit), **Cabinas Stanford** (fans), **Cabinas Támara**, and **Cabinas Recife**.

Cabinas Frederico has two units (six persons maximum) for US$15 with private bath and stove.

Cabinas Zoyla has four units at US$5 (two person maximum) with private bath.

Cabinas Grant (Bello Horizonte) which has 11 rooms (US$20 s, US$30 d) and two cabinas; for information and reservations, call 758-2845 in Limón. Rates include breakfast at its restaurant.

Another alternative is the inexpensive **Pensión Agaricia** which serves breakfast to guests. Near it are **Cabinas Rico Rico** which are higher priced and feature a communal kitchen.

Cabinas Las Brisas stand next to the Pulpería Violeta.

Low-budget **Cabinas Jacaranda** (☎ 750-0069) are next to the Garden Restaurant. Rooms are simple but attractivly decorated. Prices are around US$15 d without bath, US$ 20 d and US$ 25 t with bath.
atecmail@sol.racsa.co.cr

Inexpensive **Hotel Pura Vida** is across from the soccer field. About five min. on foot from the soccer field and into the woods (look for the sign near the goalpost), the low-budget (around US$4 pp) **Kiskadee** — run by a delightful retired *nortemaericano* woman — offers attractive dorm-style rooms. The kitchen here is available for around 50 cents pd extra. It's great for birdwatching.

Up another route from the soccer field, **Cashew Jungle Lodging** offers a dorm room in the basement of a fantastic house for a slightly higher rate as well as *cabinas* . It's just isolated enough from town to be perfect.

The **Cabinas La Salsa Brava** are on the beach and low-budget. Low-budget **Cabinas Garibaldi** are nearby.

UPSCALE ACCOMMODATIONS: New Yorker Eddie Ryan has four attractive cabins for around US$50 d. Breakfast, tours, and horseback rentals are also offered. Contact him at Cabinas Maritza (☎ 798-1844).

The most expensive and most deluxe place to stay near town is definitely **El Pizote** (☎ 221-0986, fax 255-1527, 750-0088) which is set back from the Black Beach as you approach town. It's named after the mischievous coatis who once inhabited a cage to one side near the entrance. The bungalows and cabins are behind the main lodge. Rates run from around US$50 d to US$74 s or d for the bungalows, which have private baths. Food is extra.

www.hotels.co.cr/pizote.html
pizotelg@sol.racsa.co.cr

FOOD: If you're planning on doing your own cooking, don't miss the once-weekly vegetable truck which pulls in across from the Támara on Wed. afternoons. Other food is available at the vegetable store. Food prices have skyrocketed here in recent years, which is one reason why you don't see many locals eating out.

One of the most popular places, **Soda Támara** has a nice patio in the back. They're open 6:30-9 and closed on Tues. Another great place to eat is the **El Parquecito**, which has popular fish *casados* as well as lobster. Owner Earl here offers fishing charters. **Soda Marley** is juxtaposed with Cabinas Támara.

Amimodo, near the beach, serves Italian and seafood specialties.

Near the soccer field and very popular, The **Garden Restaurant** serves Creole, Caribbean, and Asian food. Dishes range from jungle passion salad to a range of vegetarian and seafood dishes. **Stanford's** has a balcony overlooking the sea. They have vegetarian dishes as well as fish dinners.

Soda Coral has a large breakfast menu and serves pizza most afternoons during tourist season.

Other places to try include **Salsa de Talamanca**, **Bambú**, the **Red Stripe Café**, the **Mexitico Restaurant** (at the Hotel Puerto Viejo) and the **Restaurant Maritza**.

FAMILY COOKING: Out in Manzanillo, Miss Marva Miss Alfonsina, Miss Edith, and Doña Cipriana will prepare homecooked meals if notified in advance.

BAKED GOODS: Miss Dolly, Miss Sam, and Miss Daisy sell traditional treats. Miss Sam also sometimes has food but "this isn't a restaurant." Mateo sells whole wheat bread at his home near the soccer field.

ENTERTAINMENT: In tourist season the large disco below **Stanford's** has live music as does **Bambú**, just to the S past the dump. Stanford's gets packed out and incredibly humid. It can be more like visiting a sauna than a disco.

During the day, you can also watch surfers. However, keep in mind that the waters here are not for beginners. A 29-year-old US citizen drowned here in 1994 while surfing.

SERVICES: Most of the locations of services and activities listed here can be found on the map in town — that is if it hasn't gotten ripped off again! Make **phone calls** from Hotel Maritza and Pulpería Manuel León. The nearest **banking** service is in Bribri. A Ministry of Health clinic there is open Mon. to Fri. from 7-4. In Puerto Viejo, Dr. Rosa León sees patients from 5:30-8 PM and on an emergency basis.

To **rent bicycles** contact the Soda Bela, Aldo Figueroa, Jacobo Brent at Cabinas Kaya, Petra at El Escape Caribeño, and René and Priscilla in Punta Uva.

For **horseback riding**, contact Mauricio Salazar (☎/fax 750-0119) and Antonio at "Tropical Paradise." Earl Brown can arrange **snorkeling** and **ocean fishing** expeditions. Lica at Hotel Puerto Viejo repairs **surf boards**. There is no bank here; you can change traveler's checks at Stanford's.

Contact **Al Rankin's Tours** (☎ 798-1556) for tours or ATEC (see sidebar).

FROM PUERTO VIEJO: A direct bus (more expensive than changing in Limón) departs for San José daily at about 7. The bus to Limón leaves Mon to Sat. at 6, 11, and 4 and on Sun. at 6 and 4. From Manzanillo you can take a bus directly to Limón; it leaves at 9 and 4:30. If you can get to the crossroads (*cruce*), the express bus from Sixaola to San José passes by at around 6:30, 9:30, 11:30 and 4. The bus to Bribri leaves at 6:30, 11:30, 2:30, and 5:30, returning at 12 and 3:30.

Vicinity of Puerto Viejo de Talamanca

Punta Cocles

Undeveloped just a few years ago, the long stretch to Manzanillo is rapidly becoming overdeveloped and environmentally degraded in the process. The development since 1990 has been phenomenal. The Cocles Beach now has a lifeguard-manned watchtower as well as signs to indicate the unsafe places.

If you want to stay here and have a car, the best procedure is to drive around and check to see what's new (indubitably a lot), and what looks like good value in line with your standards. There are a number of restaurants (including **Soda Elena**, **Selvyn's** (reasonable), and **Soda Naturales**. About the only truly low-budget accommodations are modest rooms (US$4 pp) across from the **El Duende Feliz**, an Italian bistro with good pastas, salads, and other dishes.

Bungalows Escape Caribeño (☎/fax 750-0103) is just 400 m from El Bambú. A two-person unit is around US$40 and a four-person unit is US$50. Both have private bath and fan.

La Isla (☎/fax 750-0109) is set near the beach with five rooms (around US$40 d); it commands great views of Isla Cocles. **cgw@erols.com**

Cabinas El Tesoro (☎ 750-0128) offers rooms (around US$30 d) and cabinas (around 40-50; sleep five). Facilities include freee fax an free coffee. **academy@sol.racsa.co.cr**

Inexpensive **Tio Lio's Resorts** are just past the bridges to the R.

Luxurious **Hotel Punta Cocles** (☎ 234-0306, fax 234-0014) offers pool, a/c, and kitchens. It was a "Best Western" franchise at press time.

Built by Canadian multimillionaire "environmentalist" Maurice Strong, the **Villas del Caribe** (☎ 233-2200, fax 221-2801), ultra-luxury apartments housing from two to five persons, look out over the beach. These units have been the subject of controversy because they were constructed on Indian land.

Hotel Kashá (☎ 288-2563, 257-4911, fax 222-2213) has large, attractive rooms (around US$65) Jacuzzi, gardens, and a restaurant, the **Reef Café**.

Low-budget to inexpensive, **Selvin's Cabinas** are next to the restaurant (closed Mon.) of the same name. They are near the great beach and are good value (US$8) for backpackers.

Walaba (☎ 224-7972/6364) has a large lodge which holds 15 as well as a set of cabinas which hold four to six.

Cabinas Katty has two inexpensive four-person units with private bath.

Moderately priced **Cabinas DASA** at Playa Chiquita has four units ranging from low-budget to inexpensive. For information and current rates contact Elizabeth at 220-4089 or Rosa María at 236-2631.

Maracú (☎ 225-6215) has one house with kitchen.

German-managed 10-rm. **Playa Chiquita** Lodge (☎ 750-0062, 223-7479, fax 223-7479) is yet another expensive hotel which has paths down to the beach. Rates for its spacious rooms are around US$40 d, US$50 t with full breakfast.
infoweb.co.cr/bissinger
wolfbiss @sol.racsa.co.cr

A set of three bungalows with fans and a gourmet restaurant, **Kasha** (☎ 288-2563, fax 222-2213) is also at this beach. Rates are around US$60 d.

Also along this stretch is **Yaré** (☎/fax 750-0106), a set of colorful cabinas (around US$35) which are equipped with kitchenettes and a good restaurant.

La Casa de Papito (fax: 750-0080 has four bungalows (with porches and hammocks) for around US$50;

Villa Paraiso (fax 798-4244) has eight cabins with baths and decks. There's also a movie lounge, and boogie boards and bikes are available for rent. Its **Paloma Café** serves dishes ranging from vegetarian lasagna to rice pilaf to cheesecake.

Opened in 1997, the 18-rm. **Casa Camarona** (☎ 224-3050, fax 222-6184) lodge has a restaurant and rents kayaks and bicycles. Facilities are handicapped accessible. Rates are around US$35 s, US$ 50 d plus tax.
camarona@ticonet.co.cr

The French-run **Shawandha** (☎ 750-0018, fax. 750-0037), near Manzanillo, has a gourmet restaurant. The attractive 12 thatched-roof units each rent for around US$80 d with breakfast. A lot of work went into their design, and this is a special place to visit.

Punta Uva

From Puerto Viejo, the road continues to Manzanillo, 12 km to the S. A scarcely populated area, it is also still one of the nation's most beautiful. This beach is third in line, after Playas Pirikiri (famed for its "beach break") and Chiquita, in the series running to the S from the village. Offshore are 650-ft. (200-m) coral reefs. Although the Punta Uva area is part of the Gandoca-Manzanillo Reserve, unfortunately there are no funds for buying out these tracts, and there is no enforcement of regulations.

One of the most heinous examples of unscrupulous developers using "ecotourism" to devastate the environment is found at the Hotel Las Palmas. Czech developer Jan Kalina began construction of a US$3 million hotel in Jan. 1989 without obtaining the proper permits first. Permission was granted on June 17, 1990 but Kalina flaunted the rules requiring that development within the reserve must be both sustainable and not damage the surrounding environment. He has been accused of filling in marshlands to construct a road, using coral material as landfill, cutting and burning forest, and excavating and dredging land in the area to build a canal. Unfortunately, the hotel opened, and has now been divided into two: the **Palm Beach Resort** and the **Hotel Suerre Caribbean Beach.**

If you are looking for an alternative, low-budget **Angela's Cabinas** are near **Bustamante's Restaurant here**.

Ranchito serves tropical fruit drinks and other specialties in a garden settiing.

ALMONDS AND CORALS TENT CAMP: The very special **Almonds and Corals Tent Camp** (☎ 272-2024, 272-4175, fax 272-2220, beeper: 296-2626, cellular: 385-7776; Apdo. 681, 2300 Costa Rica) is near the reserve. Set a kilometer or so before Manzanillo and a few hundred m back from the main road, the lodge has 12 tent-cottages. The winner of a 1997 ecotourism award, it is the child of Aurola Gamez and her husband Odio who is a practicing physician.

Each unit consists of a large roofed cottage with screening, like a large screened porch on stilts. Although the other units are relatively close, nature is all around. You will be awakened in the wee hours of the morning by the cries of howler monkeys, and a night hike reveals an abundance of nocturnal activity. The cottages have hammocks (a brilliant addition) cold water showers and toilets, and large canvas tents which house two single beds with reading lights and tables. The two beds have no frame on facing edges so they may be combined. There are an abundance of electric outlets (power is 24 hours), and floor fans are available.

You are literally inside a littoral forest which contributes to the ambiance. The forest's seductive mystique is greatly enhanced by wooden walkways, illuminated nightly by kerosene torches. These boardwalks connect the rooms with the lovely beach and thatched dining and activities pavilions. Guided hikes of Manzanillo reserve are available Edward Wallen, an employee, generally comes along and shares his insightful knowledge of medicinal plants.

This would be an ideal place to relax for a few days, kayak, swim, and snorkel. A rental car would enable you to explore the surrounding area. Food is tasty, and special diets can be catered to. Meals are generally buffet.

RT, two-night packages are available for around US$300 pp including tax. This includes six meals, a snorkeling tour by boat, and one guided hike. Rates are otherwise around US$40 s, US$60 d, US$70 t in the low season and US$50 s, US$70 d, US$75 t in the winter.
www.geoexpediciones.com
almonds@sol.racsa.co.cr.

Outcrop, Manzanillo Reserve

Manzanillo and Refugio Gandoca-Manzanillo

Gandoca-Manzanillo is a mixed–management reserve, meaning that its goal is not only preserving resources but also sustaining them through their active use by the community in the pursuit of economic development. Sadly, this covenant has been continually violated— by loggers illegally operating inside and outside the reserve and by unscrupulous developers, who ignore regulations and bribe officials. Nevertheless, the portion of the reserve from Manzanillo village onwards remains relatively pristine and one of the most spectacularly beautiful places in Costa Rica, if not the world.

FLORA AND FAUNA: The reserve is the only area containing mangrove swamps along the Caribbean Coast; there's also *cativo* forest, a 741–acre (300 ha) estuary, two *jolillo* swamps, and coral reefs. Some of the mammals residing here include the tapir, manatee, margay, sloth, paca, and ocelot. Birds include the falcon, hawk, pelican, chestnut–mandibled toucan, and five species of parrots. Of 358 species of birds sighted, 40% are rarely seen in neighboring Panama. Crocodiles and *caimán* are also found.

PRACTICALITIES/TOURS: Boat rides, snorkeling and trips to Playa Gandoca can be arranged through the ATEC office in Puerto Viejo and through Almonds and Corals (see below). There's a public telephone at the *pulpéria* in Gandoca. In Manzanillo, the low–budget **Cabinas Maxi** has five units alongside a bar, disco, and *pulpería*.

GETTING THERE, GETTING AROUND, AND HIKING: The Limón–Manzanillo will likely find that you can't return for another ten years! Further info is under "extending your visa" in the Introduction.

FOR PANAMA: The situation in Panama has been deteriorating for some years now, and it is not as safe as Costa Rica to visit. Check the embassy in Centro Colón to see if you need a visa (☎ 225–0667; open 8–noon) for Panama before departing. A 30–day tourist card for Canadians and US citizens can be obtained from Copa (☎ 223–7033, 221–5596; C. 1, Av. 5) in San José. You will need to show a RT ticket of some sort to enter the country. Flights are available, and Alas Ciricanas (☎ 255-4266) has flights from San José to downtown Panama City.

BY BUS: *Ticabus* (☎ 221–9229/8954), Calle 9, Av. 4, runs to Panama City for about US$20. It departs daily at 10 PM and arrives in Panama City at 5 PM. Departing daily at 7:30 AM and noon and arriving at 4:30 and 9 PM respectively, *Tracopa bus* (☎ 221–4214, 223–7685), Av. 18, C. 4, runs to David, Panama for around US$9. From here you can take another bus on to *Panama City* hourly (7 hrs.) or an *express* at noon and midnight (5.5 hrs). *Auto Transportes Upala* (☎ 247–0051; C. 16, Av. 3/5) and *Auto Transportes Mepe* (☎ 221–0524; Av. 11, C. Central/1) run to Changuinola. Other alternatives are to fly directly (around US$130), fly *SANSA* (☎ 221–9414, 323–0397,233–3258, fax 255–2176) to Coto 47 (US$25 OW) from Mon. to Sat. and then take a taxi to Paso Canoas on the border where you can catch a bus into Panama, or travel overland to David and then fly to Panama City; the Paso Canoas border closes here from 12–2 daily.

FROM THE CARIBBEAN COAST: The town of Sixaola (La Puente) becomes **Guabito** in Panama. The border is theoretically open daily from 7–1 and 1–5, but it may be closed from 11-2. From here, minibuses run the 16 km to Changuinola where you find the first bank, and a hotel.

From here you can fly to David or travel on by train (daily) or bus to the run-down banana port of **Almirante** which has hotels and boats (US$2, 35 min.) to **Bocas del Toro**, a set of offshore islands where you can find still-pristine Caribbean waters and lifestyle. (Flights are also available from San José).

Stay at inexpensive and tremendously atmospheric **Hotel Bahía** (☎ 757-9626), at **Hotel Thomas** (☎ 757-9248), or at one of the low-budget *pensiones*. Diving is available. From Almirante you must take another boat to **Chiriquí Grande** (another small town with hotels) which connects by road to David. From David, you can visit the cool town of **Boquete** which lies about 20 km to the E; stay at **Pensión Virginia**, **Pensión Marilos**, or **Hotel Panamonte**. This town fills up for its flower festival which is held annually in Jan. In short, it's much easier and faster to go via Paso Canoas, but this route is more adventurous.

INFORMATION: The best current information on travel conditions in the country can be found in *Mexico and Central America Handbook*; public libraries generally have a current edition.

TOURS: Contact **Centro de Aventuras** (☎ 507-27-6746/8946, fax 27-6477; Box 6-4197 El Dorado, Panama, Republic of Panama). They offer various birdwatching, snorkeling, and expedition tours.

FOR NICARAGUA: A visa is no longer required for US citizens, but you must change US$60 at the border. Canadians do require a visa. Call the Nicaraguan Embassy in La California at 233–8747 to check on the latest requirements. If flying, expect to pay around US$100 OW. Most companies don't want their rental cars visiting Nicaragua.

> If you're planning to cruise through Costa Rica and head on to S America, a **vehicular ferry service** runs three times a week between Cristóbal in Panamá and Cartagena, Columbia. This eliminates the need to ship your vehicle to S America. For more information, call Rodrigo Gómez or Harry Evetts in Panamá at 507-64-5564 or 64-5699.

Spanish Vocabulary

Days of the Week

domingo	Sunday
lunes	Monday
martes	Tuesday
miercoles	Wednesday
jueves	Thursday
viernes	Friday
sabado	Saturday

Months of the Year

enero	January
febrero	February
marzo	March
abril	April
mayo	May
junio	June
julio	July
agosto	August
septiembre	September
octubre	October
noviembre	November
diciembre	December

Numbers

uno	one
dos	two
tres	three
cuatro	four
cinco	five
seis	six
siete	seven
ocho	eight
nueve	enine
diez	ten
once	eleven
doce	twelve
trece	thirteen
catorce	fourteen
quince	fifteen
dieciseis	sixteen
diecisiete	seventeen
dieciocho	eighteen
diecinueve	nineteen
veinte	twenty
veintiuno	twenty one
veintidos	twenty two
treinta	thirty
cuarenta	forty
cincuenta	fifty
sesenta	sixty
setenta	seventy
ochenta	eighty
noventa	ninety
cien	one hundred
cento uno	one hundred one
doscientos	two hundred
quinientos	five hundred
mil	one thousand
mil uno	one thousand one
dos mil	two thousand
un million	one million
mil milliones	one billion
primero	first
segundo	second
tercero	third
cuarto	fourth
quinto	fifth
sexto	sixth
septimo	seventh
octavo	eighth
noveno	ninth
decimo	tenth
undecimo	eleventh
duodecimo	twelfth
ultimo	last

Conversation

¿Como esta usted?	How are you?
Bien, gracias, y usted?	Well, thanks, and you?
Buenas dias.	Good morning.
Buenas tardes.	Good afternoon.
Buenas noches.	Good evening/ night.
Hasta la vista.	See you again.
Hasta luego.	So long.
¡Buen suerte!	Good luck!
Adios.	Goodbye.
Mucho gusto de conocerle.	Glad to meet you.
Felicidades.	Congratulations.
Muchas felicidades.	Happy birthday.

Feliz Navidad.	MerryChristmas.
Feliz Año Nuevo.	Happy NewYear.
Gracias.	Thank you.
Por favor.	Please.
De nada/con mucho gusto.	You're welcome.
Perdoneme.	Pardon me.
¿Como se llama esto?	What do you call this?
Lo siento.	I'm sorry.
Permitame.	Permit me.
Quisiera...	I would like...
Adelante.	Come in.
Permitame presentarle...	May I introduce...
¿Como se llamo usted?	What is your name?
Me llamo...	My name is...
No se.	I don't know.
Tengo sed.	I am thirsty.
Tengo hambre.	I am hungry.
Soy norteamericano/a	I am an American.
¿Donde puedo encontrar...	Where can I find...?
¿Que es esto?	What is this?
¿Habla usted ingles?	Do you speak English?
Hablo/entiendo un poco español.	I speak/understand a little Spanish
¿Hay alguien aqui que hable ingles?	Is there anyone here who speaks English?
Le entiendo.	I understand you.
No entiendo.	I don't understand.
Hable mas despacio por favor.	Please speak more slowly.
Repita por favor.	Please repeat.

Telling Time

¿Que hora es?	What time is it?
Son las...	It's...
...cinco.	five o'clock.
...ocho y diez.	ten past eight.
...seis y cuaro.	...quarter past six.
...cinco y media.	....half past five.
...siete y menos cinco.	....five of seven.
.antes de ayer	day before yest.
a noche.	yesterday eve.
esta mañana.	this morning.
a mediodia.	at noon.
en la noche.	in the evening.
de noche.	at night.
a medianoche.	at midnight.
mañana.	tomorrow.
en la mañana.	tomorrow AM.
en la noche.	tomorrow PM.
pasado mañana.	dayaftertomorrow

Directions

¿En que direccion queda...?	In which direction is...?
Llevemea... por favor.	Take me to... please.
Lleva me alla... porfavor.	Take me there please..
¿Que lugar es este?	What place is this?
¿Donde queda el pueblo?	Where is the town?
¿Cual es el mejor camino? para...?	Which is the best road to...? from?
De vuelta a la derecha.	Turn to the R.
De vuelta a la isquierda.	Turn to the L.
Sigaderecho.	Go this way.
En esta direccion.	In this direction.
¿A que distancia estamos de...?	How far is it to...?
¿Es este el camino a...?	Is this the road to...?
¿Es....cerca?	Is it......near?
....lejos?	...far?
....norte?	...north?
....sur?	...south?
....este?	...east?
....oeste?	...west?
Indique me por favor.	Please point.
Hagame favor de decirme.	Please direct me to..
donde esta...	Where is
....el telephono?	...the telephone?
...el excusado?	...the bathroom?
...el correo?	...the post office?
...el banco?	..the bank?
...la comisaria..	..the police stn?

Accommodations

`Estoy buscando un hotel....	I am looking for a hotel that's...
...bueno	....good.
....barato	....cheap.
...cercano	....nearby.
...limpio	....clean.
¿Dónde hay hotel, pensión, hospedaje?	Where is a hotel, pensión, hospedaje?
Hay habitaciones libres?	Do you have rooms available?
¿Dónde están	Where are the
...los baños?	bathrooms?
...los servicios?	toilets?
Quisiera un...	I would like a....
....cuarto sencillo	....single room.
....cuarto con baño	....room with a bath.
....cuarto doble	....double room.
¿Puedoverlo?	May I see it?
¿Cuanto cuesta?	What's the cost?
¡Es demasiado caro!	It's too expensive!

Language Study Notes

Glossary

a la tica – in the Costa Rican fashion

apartotels – an apartment hotel which has rooms with kitchen facilities. These are often suites and, in adddition to daily, usually have weekly as well as monthly rates.

buttress – You'll often hear this term used in reference to rainforest trees. Although most roots are invariably a combination here are three main varieties: often looping or undulating from side to side, serpentine buttresses extend some distance from the tree. Flying buttresses are of the stilt-root type. Resembling giant wedges, plank buttresses are the most spectacular of the three.

bocas – Costa Rican term for late afternoon hors d'oeuvres

bombetas – Tico fireworks whose explosivesounds may rouse you from sleep.

cabina, cabinas – literally cabin or cabins, these are sometimes similar to motels and sometimes identical with apartment hotels

cafetaleros – the wealthy coffee growers who have commanded a dominant economic and political influence.

cantina – small local bar

cantone – counties, administrative district of a province

carretera – a route or highway

colón – the currency of the country; divided into 100 centimes.

distritos – districts, subdivisions of a canton

hospedaje – an inexpensive hotel usually run by a family

iglesia – church

jefe politico – district political chief who is appointed by the president

marimba – a xylophone constructed with gourds traditionally found in many Latin American and African nations.

medieria – a type of land tenure in which the landlord supplies everything except labor

mirador – a scenic lookout point

mesa – polling place

municipalidad – municipal council

Nica, Nicas – Nickname for Nicaraguans

pensión – an inexpensive hotel

precarista – a squatter on agricultural land so named for his "precarious" position.

pulpería – general store

punta guanacasteco – the national dance, performed with marimba and guitar accompaniment.

sendero – a hiking trail

soda –small bar or snack joint

Tico, Ticos – The nickname commonly applied to the Costa Rican people.

tugurios – Urban slums, generally constructed on hills or areas subject to flooding. They are the locus of ills such as environmental contamination, ill health, prostitution, crime, and broken families.

turno – town festival

Booklist

Travel and Description

Finchley, Alan. *Costa Rica: An Alternative for Americans* (New Brunswick, NJ, 1975

Nelson, Harold D. *Costa Rica: A Country Study* . Washington, D.C.: American University, 1983.

Ras, Barbara. *Costa Rica: A Traveller's Literary Companion*. San Francisco, CA: Whereabouts Press, 1994. *A diverse collection of 26 stories.*

Villafranca, Richard. *Costa Rica: Gem of American Republics*. New York, 1976.

Flora and Fauna

Allen, Dorothy. *The Rainforest of Gulfo Dulce.* Sanford, CA: Sanford Press, 1977.

Allen, P.H. *The Rain Forests of Golfo Dulce*. Gainesville: University of FL Press, 1956.

Boza, Mario A. and Rolando Mendoza. *The National Parks of Costa Rica*. Madrid: Industrias Graficas Alvi, S. A., 1981.

Boza, Mario A. *Costa Rica National Parks* . Madrid: Infaco, S. A., 1988.

Hall, Carolyn. *Costa Rica, a geographical interpretation in historical perspective.* Boulder, CO: Westview Press, 1985. *Possibly the best ecological guide to any nation ever.*

Carr, Archie F. *The Windward Road.* Tallahassee, FL: University Presses of Florida, 1955.

de Vries, Phillip J. *Butterflies of Costa Rica*. Princeton, NJ: Princeton University Press, 1987.

Forsyth, Adrian. *Journey through a Tropical Jungle*. Toronto: Greely de Pencier Books, 1988.

Janzen, Daniel H., ed. *Costa Rica National History*. Chicago: University of Chicago Press, 1983. *An excellent guide to a selection of flora and fauna.*

Skutch, Alexander F. A. *A Naturalist in Costa Rica*. Gainesville, FL: University of Florida Press, 1971.

Stiles, Gary and Alexander Skutch. *A Guide to the Birds of Costa Rica*. Ithaca, NY: Cornell University Press, 1989. *This suberb 477-page guide lists not only everything you might want to know about the nation's birds (including description, mating calls, habits, and range) but also illustrates them in beautiful color plates. As an added bonus, descriptions of numerous avian habitats and locations of some birding localities are included.*

> ***URL***
>
> **birds.cornell.edu/LNS/CommercialProductns/csamerica/crbirdsong.htm**
> sells a variety of great CDs of animal and bird cries in the rainforest.

Politics and Economics

Ameringer, Charles D. *Don Pepe: A Political Biography of José Figueres of Costa Rica* : Albuquerque, 1978

Ameringer, Charles D.. *Democracy in Costa Ric* : New York, 1982

Bell, John P. *Crisis in Costa Rica: The 1948 Revolution* University of Texas Press: Austin TX, 1971.

Denton, *Charles F. Patterns of Costa Rican Politics.* Allyn and Bacon: Boston, 1971.

Edelman, Marc and Joanne Kenen. *The Costa Rica Reader*. New York: Grove

Weidenfield, 1989. *An excellent introduction covering everything from cooperatives to* contras.

English, Burt H. *Liberacion Nacional in Costa Rica.* Gainsville, FL, 1971.

Herrick, Bruce and Barclay Hudson. *Urban Poverty and Economic Development: A Case Study of Costa* Rica. NY, NY, 1980.

Interbook, Inc. Rural Development in Costa Rica. NY, NY 1978.

Jones, *Chester Lloyd, Costa Rica and Civilization in the Caribbean.* Russell & Russell: New York, 1967. This rather dry account written by a University of Wisconsin economics and political science professor was first published in 1935.

Rolbein, Seth. *Nobel Costa Rica.* New York: St. Martin's Press, 1989. A first-hand account of Costa Rican politics and its press during the late 1980s.

Saunders, John. *Rural Electrification & Development: Social and Economic Development in Costa Rica and Colombia.* Boulder, CO, 1978

Seligson, Mitchell A. *Peasants of Costa Rica and the Rise of Agrarian Capitalism.* Madison, Wi, 1980

Sociology and Anthropology

Biesanz, John and Mary. *Costa Rican Life.* Westport, Ct: Greenwoood Press, Inc., 1979. A portrait of sleepy Costa Rican life as it was during the laid back 1940s.

Biesanz, Richard and Karen Zumbris Biesanz and Mavis Hiltunen Biesanz. *The Costa Ricans.* Prospect Heights, IL: Waveland, 1987 (updated edition).

Art

Jones, Juile, (ed.), Michael Kan and Michael J. Snarkis. *Between Continents/Between Seas: Pre-Columbian Art of Costa Rica.* Detriot: Abrams/Detroit Institute of the Arts, 1981.

Index

Q

R

S

T

My Costa Rican Diary

My Costa Rican Diary

My Costa Rican Diary

My Costa Rican Diary